Applied Mathematics for Technical Students

Applied Mathematics
for
Technical Students

By

MURLAN S. CORRINGTON, M.Sc.

Radio Engineer, Advanced Development Section,
RCA Victor Division of the Radio Corporation
of America
Camden, New Jersey

REVISED EDITION

PUBLISHED BY HARPER & ROW, PUBLISHERS
New York, Evanston, and London

Contents

Preface to the First Edition

This textbook was written as part of a program of the Rochester Athenaeum and Mechanics Institute for developing teaching materials of a practical nature which are closely related to the actual requirements of various jobs in industry. A careful study was made of the skills, knowledge, and attitudes essential in modern industry to determine what parts of mathematics are of greatest importance. This book is a combination of theory and application and was written for trade schools, factory training courses, or pre-engineering studies; any mechanic or engineer can use it for home study or reference. It begins with a review of arithmetic that does not assume much previous training. Much of the material was used for several years in classes for freshmen and was revised from time to time to make it more understandable.

This is not just another mathematics book, but one which should appeal to thoughtful and progressive teachers. Arithmetic, algebra, logarithms, and trigonometry have been included in one volume, yet it is advanced enough for a thorough course. Either a long or a short course can be given by proper selection of the material. Emphasis has been placed on solving problems by clear thinking, not by blind substitution in formulas.

It should never be necessary to tell any student that a course of mathematical study is a necessary evil; the need for it should be made obvious by requiring him to solve actual practical problems written in the same form that they occur in practice.

The problems have been carefully selected to illustrate the various mathematical principles. They vary greatly in difficulty. Some are easy and can be solved by students with a limited mathematical background, but others are difficult enough to encourage the best students to do far more than the average even though they may have had some preliminary training in the same subject matter.

Although many engineering problems involve cubic or higher-degree equations, or other equations which cannot be solved in terms of elementary functions, no attempt has been made to teach such methods here since they are beyond the scope of this book.

Many of the problems are presented as mechanical drawings, dimensioned and labeled according to present engineering standards. Various types of drawings are used since no one style is adequate for all problems, and all are used in practice. Considerable emphasis has been placed on numerical computation and methods of checking because most engineering problems require reliable numerical answers. Much practice is necessary to develop accuracy and speed in such calculations and there is often a wide gap between the theory and the actual numerical calculation. Special tables have been included to aid in solving the problems; most of them are given to five decimal places since that is the accuracy required in many applications.

The old-fashioned puzzle problems of algebra have been eliminated; they usually do not deal with practical conditions. Instead, the geometrical and physical applications of algebra have been stressed. Elaborate methods of factoring are omitted since very few expressions that actually occur in practice can be factored. Development of proficiency in algebra should be a means to an end, not an end in itself.

A section on natural logarithms has been included, as well as a short set of tables, because they are frequently met in applied mathematical problems. Graphs have been introduced as a natural help to gain clearness and concreteness and to interpret some of the mathematical solutions. The applications of radian measure have been stressed since they are useful in finding arc length, areas, etc. Methods for interpolating to seconds are given for use with the five-place tables.

Answers have been given to alternate problems, so the instructor can assign problems with or without answers as he desires.

The author will be grateful to receive any corrections in the text or answers.

M. S. C.

Camden, N. J.
February, 1943

Preface to the Revised Edition

The revision of the text material for the revised edition of this book has given the author an opportunity to add several sections that are helpful in teaching a thorough course in applied mathematics. The first chapter on arithmetic has been extended by adding a discussion of simplified methods for extracting square and cube roots. Parts of the chapter have been revised to clarify the presentation and some of the problems have been changed.

The chapter on geometry is completely new and includes the essential propositions required for the solution of practical problems. Chapter VII, on graphic methods, is also new and methods are presented for solving higher-degree and transcendental equations. The applications of log, semi-log and polar graph paper are also discussed, since such graphic methods are used regularly in the solution of practical problems.

The chapter on trigonometry has been extended to include a method for solving right triangles without tables, and additional formulas are given for finding the diameter of a circle circumscribed about a triangle. Many new problems have been added at the end to illustrate the various techniques for solving equations and to serve as a review of the entire course.

A few errors have been corrected in the examples, and many of the tables and answers have been rechecked to insure accuracy.

Murlan S. Corrington

Haddonfield, N. J.
October 1, 1951

Applied Mathematics for Technical Students

In physical science a first essential step in the direction of learning any subject is to find principles of numerical reckoning and practicable methods for measuring some quality connected with it. I often say that when you can measure what you are speaking about and express it in numbers you know something about it; but when you cannot measure it, when you cannot express it in numbers, your knowledge is of a meagre and unsatisfactory kind: it may be the beginning of knowledge, but you have scarcely, in your thoughts, advanced to the stage of science, whatever the matter may be.

LORD KELVIN

CHAPTER I

Arithmetic with Applications

THE BEST ENGINEER IS THE ONE WHO ALWAYS USES THE shortest and easiest method in doing a job. His work shows system throughout and he checks the work as closely as the data permit. He uses his common sense, and looks at the answer to see whether it is logical. He uses tables, slide rules and handbooks to make the computations easy, clear and accurate. It is always possible to go back and check any step and see if all the factors have been considered. The important steps only are shown, the scratch work being done on other paper.

The form in which the engineer states a problem and lays out his solution is just as important as the correct answer. This is more than a question of neatness; it is a matter of adhering to standard practices and eliminating trivial details that obscure the important facts.

In engineering work calculations must be checked. The checker's time is valuable, and good form in working out problems aids the checker, for mistakes show up clearly. The original calculator who follows a good form can often catch his own mistakes in a quick review.

Avoid crowding. A crowded paper is difficult to read and check. Leave a space between problems. Erase neatly. Marking over figures and scratching out are sure signs of careless work.

Suggestions

1. Plan the arrangement of the work before starting.
2. Draw a neat figure to scale.
3. State the given and the required parts and write the formulas which are to be used, solving each one for the unknown part.

4. Write out the form for the problem.
5. Fill in the numerical parts from the tables or by computation. *Be sure to copy the given numbers correctly.*
6. If possible, never use calculated results in finding the other unknowns. Use an equation which involves only the parts given in the problem. Then if you make a mistake you will not carry it through the rest of the problem.
7. Be sure that the units are all alike. If some lengths are given in feet and others in inches change them all to the same units. Label the calculations and *always put the proper units* (pound-inches, feet, cubic inches, etc.) *after each answer.* The units are just as important as the numerical part of the answer.
8. Do not omit any important calculation that shows a step in the solution of the problem.
9. *Do not clutter up the solution with a lot of long divisions and multiplications and other elementary arithmetic. Use a separate sheet of paper for these and save time by using a slide rule wherever possible.*
10. Never use a dot as a sign of multiplication.

Accuracy

All the computations should be carried out to the same accuracy as the data given in the problem. The purpose of the answer should be considered. Thus in calculating the length of a rafter it would be foolish to carry it to 0.0001 inch, but certain gear problems require this accuracy. In most engineering calculations, the result is accurate enough if the first three or four significant figures are correct. This is approximately the accuracy that is obtained by the use of the common 10-inch slide rule.

General Definitions

Several general definitions in arithmetic should be reviewed before starting the solution of problems. Some of the most important are given here.

An **integer** is a whole number. *Examples:* 2, 3, 7, 15.

A **prime number** is a number that can be divided by no other numbers than itself and 1. *Examples:* 1, 2, 3, 5, 7, 13.

An **even number** is a number exactly divisible by 2. *Examples:* 2, 4, 6, 18, 38.

An **odd number** is a number not exactly divisible by 2. *Examples:* 1, 3, 9, 27, 49.

The **minuend** is a number from which another is to be subtracted. The **subtrahend** is the number to be subtracted. The **remainder** is the result of the subtraction.

The **multiplicand** is a number to be multiplied by another. The **multiplier** is the number by which it is multiplied. The **product** is the result of the multiplication.

The **dividend** is a number to be divided by another. The **divisor** is the number by which it is divided, and the **quotient** is the result of the division.

A **common divisor** or **common factor** of two or more numbers is a number by which each can be exactly divided. If this common factor is the largest one that will exactly divide each of the numbers, it is termed the **greatest common divisor.**

A **multiple** of any number is a number such that the original number will be contained in it a whole number of times. The smallest number that will exactly contain each of several numbers is called the **least common multiple.**

The **reciprocal** of a number is 1 divided by that number. *Example:* The reciprocal of 5 is $\frac{1}{5}$. The reciprocal of 13 is $\frac{1}{13}$.

Addition, Subtraction, Multiplication and Division in Combinations

It is assumed that the student has had sufficient mathematical training and practice to make unnecessary a detailed explanation of the fundamental operations of arithmetic: addition, subtraction, multiplication and division.

Most problems in arithmetic are combinations of the various fundamental processes rather than problems involving only one of these processes. In the solution of such problems the relative importance of signs must be taken into consideration. The following rules are very important and should be memorized:

Rules

1. *A series of additions can be taken in any order.* Thus $7 + 4 + 8 + 2 = 21$ when added in any order.
2. *A series of subtractions must be taken in the order given.* Thus $100 - 25 - 18 = 57$. But this cannot be written as $25 - 100 - 18$ and give 57.
3. *A series of multiplications can be taken in any order.* Thus $4(5)(6) = 120$ or $5(6)(4) = 120$.
4. *A series of divisions must be taken in the order given.* Thus $625 \div 25 \div 5 = 5$; but if it is written as $25 \div 625 \div 5$, there is an entirely different answer, $\frac{1}{125}$.

    In practice it is desirable to use fractions and parentheses to avoid any possible confusion as to the operation meant. Thus, the last equation should be written:

$$\frac{625}{25(5)} = 5$$

This is especially important when the problem involves the four operations of addition, subtraction, multiplication and division. Thus, $100 + 50 \div 2 \times 5 - 6$ should be written $100 + \dfrac{50}{2(5)} - 6$.

5. When the expression is unusually complicated, parentheses ( ), brackets [ ] and braces { } are used to enclose the different parts of the problem. These marks are always used in pairs, in the above order, as needed. When they are used, *the operations inside the parentheses or brackets are to be performed first. Each result is then multiplied by any number directly in front of the corresponding parenthesis or bracket, if there is no plus or minus sign between the number and the parenthesis, before any other operations are performed.* Combinations such as (( )) should be avoided; use [( )] instead.

Example: $12 + 2\{5[3 - 7(8 - 4) + 2(6)] + 3[2 + 11(6 - 1)]\} = ?$

The value of the first bracket is

$$3 - 28 + 12 = -13$$

The second bracket equals
$$2 + 55 = 57$$
The value of the quantity inside the braces is
$$5(-13) + 3(57) = 106$$
The final result is
$$12 + 2(106) = 224$$

Cancellation

In solving problems, a form like the following often occurs:

$$\frac{25(32)(81)(13)}{5(96)(13)(9)}$$

This can be solved by doing all the multiplications in the numerator, then all the multiplications in the denominator, and lastly dividing the products obtained to secure the final result. This process is usually long and complicated and can be largely eliminated by the use of a method called cancellation.

$$\frac{\overset{5\ \ 1\ \ \overset{3}{\cancel{9}}\ \ 1}{\cancel{25}(\cancel{32})\,(\cancel{81})\,(\cancel{13})}}{\underset{1\ \ \cancel{3}\ \ 1\ \ 1}{\cancel{5}(\cancel{96})(\cancel{13})(\cancel{9})}} = \frac{15}{1} = 15$$

It will be seen from the above example that much of the work can be eliminated by first doing all the cancellations that are possible.

The 5 goes into 25 five times. The 5 is crossed out or canceled and the figure 1 placed underneath. Likewise 25 is crossed out and the figure 5 placed above it.

In like manner, 32 goes into 96 three times, and the 9 at the right in the denominator goes into the 81 of the numerator nine times.

In turn the 3 obtained by dividing 96 by 32 goes into the 9 above the 81 three times.

The 13 goes into 13 once.

Finally, all the figures left above the line are multiplied together and all the figures left below the line are multiplied together and the result is written as shown.

It should be noted that this method can be used only if the numbers in the numerator and denominator are multiplied; it cannot be used if there are also addition and subtraction.

If addition and subtraction are involved as well as multiplication, the operations in the numerator are completed first, the operations in the denominator next, and the final result is written as a fraction.

Example: $\dfrac{25(6) + 8 - 3}{15(2) + 4 - 5} = \dfrac{155}{29}$

The numerator is first simplified:

$$25(6) + 8 - 3 = 150 + 8 - 3 = 155$$

The denominator is equal to:

$$15(2) + 4 - 5 = 30 + 4 - 5 = 29$$

The fraction should be reduced if possible.

Methods for Simplifying Computations

It is often convenient to have methods for further shortening these processes, and a few of them will now be presented to show the possibilities in this direction. Many other methods for reducing the labor of computation can be developed by the student.

In the problems involving division, the following short-cuts are frequently used to advantage.

1. A number is exactly divisible by 2 if the right-hand digit is zero or a figure divisible by 2.
2. A number is exactly divisible by 3 if the sum of its digits is divisible by 3.
3. A number is exactly divisible by 4 if the number represented by the last two digits on the right is divisible by 4, or if the original number itself ends in two zeros.
4. A number is exactly divisible by 5 if the last figure on the right is zero or 5.
5. A number can be divided exactly by 6 if it is an even number and if the sum of its digits is divisible by 3.
6. A number is exactly divisible by 8 if the number represented by the last three digits is divisible by 8.

7. A number can be exactly divided by 9 if the sum of its digits is divisible by 9.

8. Any number ending in zero can be exactly divided by 10.

9. To divide by 250, multiply by 4 and divide by 1000. This gives the correct result since

$$\frac{4}{1000} = \frac{1}{250}$$

Various methods can be used to shorten the process of multiplication.

1. To multiply by 125, it is only necessary to multiply by 1000 and divide by 8 since

$$\frac{1000}{8} = 125$$

2. To multiply by 250, multiply by 1000 and divide by 4 since

$$\frac{1000}{4} = 250$$

3. To multiply by 9, multiply the number by 10 and subtract the original number.

These methods are by no means all that can be developed; they are presented here simply as illustrations of what can be done along this line.

EXERCISE 1.1

Perform the indicated operations in the following problems:

1. $65 - 21 + 34(3)$

2. $117 - 8(4) + 25 \div 6$

3. $\dfrac{225}{9(7)} - 35 + 36$

4. $\dfrac{81}{3(9 - 6)} + 11(8 - 6)$

5. $\dfrac{360(150)(264)(280)}{88(72)(30)(140)}$

6. $\dfrac{360(66)(75)(70)}{30(35)(22)(36)}$

7. $\dfrac{143(64)(37)(54)(1127)(17)}{111(96)(117)(6762)(153)}$

8. $\dfrac{67(68)(69)(70)}{2(3)(4)(5)}$

9. $\dfrac{14(76) - 256(6) - 375}{9(51) - 809(2) + 256(5)}$

10. $\dfrac{32 + 6(7) - 4(4) + 334}{94(2) - 7(18) + 9(4)}$

11. $\dfrac{512(3) + 625(6) - 28(38)}{17(54) + 64(40) - 3236}$

12. $\dfrac{16(22)(24)(7)}{88(7)(9)(24)}$

13. $\dfrac{288(864)(999)}{48(135)(66)}$

14. If 107 washers weigh 1 lb, how many boxes of 6 dozen each can be filled from a keg containing 50 lb?

15. If it takes 9 men 23 eight-hour days to do a piece of work, how many hours will it take 17 men to do it at the same rate?

16. A brass casting weighs 27 oz. When milled and drilled it weighs $23\frac{1}{2}$ oz. If the casting costs 45 cents per lb and the scrap sells for 19 cents per lb, find the cost of the metal in the finished piece.

17. If the feed of a drill is $\frac{1}{110}$ in. per revolution, how long will it take to drill a hole $3\frac{11}{32}$ in. deep if the drill makes 600 rpm?

18. If a copper wire weighs 9.74 lb per thousand ft, find the weight of $387\frac{1}{4}$ miles and the cost at 38 cents per lb.

19. A stone slab 5 ft long, 3 ft wide, and $7\frac{1}{2}$ in. thick weighs 1640 lb. What is the weight of a similar slab 6 ft long, 2 ft wide, and 17 in. thick?

20. If steel weighs 0.28 lb per cu in., find the cost of a 24 × 48-in. sheet 0.040 in. thick, at 13 cents per lb.

21. Find the cost of plastering the walls and ceiling of a room 18 ft long, 14 ft wide, and 8 ft high, at $2.50 per sq yd. Allow 100 sq ft for openings and baseboard.

22. An 8-in.-diameter grinding wheel runs at 1800 rpm with a 6-in. drive pulley. How fast will it run with a 5-in. pulley?

23. The teeth of a saw move 2800 ft per min. If the saw has 128 teeth $\frac{3}{8}$ in. apart, find the revolutions per minute of the saw.

24. A barrel of cement contains 4 cu ft, and will make 0.694 cu yd of concrete if four parts gravel, two parts sand, one part cement and 30 gallons of water are used. How much does the mixture shrink on mixing? Where does the rest go? One gal = 231 cu in.

25. The tensile strength of nickel steel is 90,000 lb per sq in. of cross section. What pull will a square bar stand if it is $\frac{5}{8}$ in. on a side?

26. If it costs $889,875 per year to buy coal for a power plant, how many tons of coal per day, on the average, will be consumed if the coal costs $8.60 per ton? Assume 365 days per year.

27. If it takes 21 min to set up a blanking press and 47 min to blank 1000 pieces, how much will the labor cost on a run of 50,000 pieces, if the base rate for setups is $1.60 per hour and for blanking $1.40 per hour? What is the cost for 1000 pieces if 5 per cent are defective?

COMMON FRACTIONS

An indicated division such as $\frac{2 \cdot 5}{5}$ is called a fraction. A fraction is made up of two parts, the number above the line or **numerator,** and the number below the line or **denominator.** In general a fraction is understood to mean a division which does not result in a whole number as a quotient. Thus $\frac{6}{7}$, $\frac{4}{5}$, $\frac{1}{8}$ are examples of the type of fractions most commonly met in practice.

A fraction having a numerator smaller than the denominator is called a **proper fraction** and one with a numerator equal to or larger than the denominator is called an **improper fraction.**

When a division does not result in a whole number quotient but part of the dividend is left over, the resulting expression, consisting of a whole number and a fraction, is called a **mixed number.** Thus $\frac{15628}{25} = 625\frac{3}{25}$. The result $625\frac{3}{25}$ is called a mixed number and means $625 + \frac{3}{25}$. It is read six hundred twenty-five and three twenty-fifths.

To change the mixed number back to the fractional form, multiply the whole number, 625, by the denominator, 25; then add 3 and put this result over the 25. Thus

$$625(25) + 3 = 15628$$

and the fraction is $\frac{15628}{25}$.

Least Common Denominator

The least common denominator of two or more fractions is the smallest number that can be exactly divided by each of the denominators. Thus the least common denominator of $\frac{1}{2}$ and $\frac{3}{4}$ is 4, because 4 is the smallest number that will exactly contain both 2 and 4. The least common denominator of $\frac{1}{2}$, $\frac{3}{4}$ and $\frac{2}{3}$ is 12, because 12 is the smallest number that will exactly contain 2, 4 and 3.

It is frequently desirable to change a fraction so its denominator is a different, larger number, but the value of the fraction must not change. This can be done by multiplying both the numerator and denominator by the same number, the number being properly chosen to give the required denominator. The value of this new fraction is exactly the same as that of the old, but the new one has a different numerator and a different denominator, and it is not in its lowest terms.

Example: Change $\frac{1}{2}$ to a fraction with 6 as the denominator.

If the 2 is multiplied by 3, the product is 6. Therefore the numerator and denominator of the fraction should each be multiplied by three.

$$\frac{1}{2} = \frac{1(3)}{2(3)} = \frac{3}{6}$$

In the same way

$$\frac{1}{3} = \frac{2}{6} = \frac{4}{12} = \frac{20}{60}, \text{ etc.}$$

and

$$\frac{1}{4} = \frac{2}{8} = \frac{4}{16} = \frac{6}{24}, \text{ etc.}$$

also

$$\frac{1}{5} = \frac{2}{10} = \frac{4}{20} = \frac{5}{25}, \text{ etc.}$$

Sometimes it is difficult to determine the least common denominator at sight. In such cases, the denominators of the fractions for which the least common denominator is required should be factored into prime numbers. *To obtain the least common denominator, each different factor occurring in the denominators should be taken the greatest number of times it appears in any one denominator, and the product of these different factors found.*

Example: Find the least common denominator of $\frac{1}{32}$, $\frac{1}{40}$ and $\frac{1}{48}$.

Each of the three numbers 32, 40 and 48 should be factored into prime numbers.

$$32 = 2(2)(2)(2)(2)$$
$$40 = 2(2)(2)(5)$$
$$48 = 2(2)(2)(2)(3)$$

The lowest common denominator

$$\text{L.C.D.} = 2(2)(2)(2)(2)(5)(3) = 480$$

Two appears five times as a factor in 32; 5 appears once in 40; and 3 appears once in 48. The lowest common denominator becomes $2(2)(2)(2)(2)(5)(3) = 480$, since each factor must be taken the maximum number of times it occurs in any one denominator.

The fractions can now be changed so that each has the lowest common denominator.

$$\frac{1}{32} = \frac{1(15)}{32(15)} = \frac{15}{480}$$

$$\frac{1}{40} = \frac{1(12)}{40(12)} = \frac{12}{480}$$

and $$\frac{1}{48} = \frac{1(10)}{48(10)} = \frac{10}{480}$$

Addition and Subtraction of Fractions

In order to add or subtract fractions, they should all be changed so that they have the lowest common denominator. They can then be added by adding the numerators and dividing the sum by the common denominator; or one can be subtracted from another by subtracting the numerators and dividing by the common denominator.

Example 1: Add $\frac{1}{2}$ and $\frac{4}{5}$.

The lowest common denominator is 10.

$$\tfrac{1}{2} + \tfrac{4}{5} = \tfrac{5}{10} + \tfrac{8}{10} = \tfrac{13}{10} = 1\tfrac{3}{10}$$

Example 2: Add $\frac{1}{4}$, $\frac{1}{3}$ and $\frac{5}{6}$.

The lowest common denominator is 60.

$$\tfrac{1}{4} + \tfrac{1}{3} + \tfrac{5}{6} = \tfrac{15}{60} + \tfrac{12}{60} + \tfrac{50}{60} = \tfrac{77}{60} = 1\tfrac{17}{60}$$

Example 3: Subtract $\frac{1}{4}$ from $\frac{1}{2}$.

Change the two fractions so that they have a common denominator, and subtract.

$$\tfrac{1}{2} - \tfrac{1}{4} = \tfrac{2}{4} - \tfrac{1}{4} = \tfrac{1}{4}$$

Example 4: Subtract $\frac{5}{8}$ from $\frac{6}{7}$.

$$\frac{6}{7} - \frac{5}{8} = \frac{48}{56} - \frac{35}{56} = \frac{48 - 35}{56} = \frac{13}{56}$$

Multiplication of Fractions

To multiply a fraction by a whole number, multiply the numerator by the number and divide the product by the denominator. Reduce the result to lowest terms.

Example: Multiply $\frac{2}{3}$ by 6.

$$\tfrac{2}{3}(6) = \tfrac{12}{3} = 4$$

To multiply any number of fractions together, multiply all the numerators together, multiply all the denominators together, and write the result as a fraction with numerator equal to the product of all the numerators and denominator equal to the product of all the denominators. The resulting fraction should be reduced to lowest terms.

Example: Multiply $\frac{1}{8}$ by $\frac{4}{5}$ by $\frac{7}{15}$.

$$\frac{1}{8} \times \frac{4}{5} \times \frac{7}{15} = \frac{1(4)(7)}{8(5)(15)} = \frac{28}{600} = \frac{7}{150}$$

The $\frac{28}{600}$ was reduced to its lowest terms by dividing both the numerator and denominator by 4, giving $\frac{7}{150}$.

This example can also be solved by cancellation.

$$\frac{1}{8} \times \frac{4}{5} \times \frac{7}{15} = \frac{1(\overset{1}{\cancel{4}})(7)}{\underset{2}{\cancel{8}}(5)(15)} = \frac{7}{2(5)(15)} = \frac{7}{150}$$

Division of Fractions

To divide a fraction by a whole number means to divide it into a number of equal parts, the number of parts being equal to the number by which the fraction was divided. If $\frac{1}{2}$ is divided by 5, each part must equal $\frac{1}{10}$ because $\frac{1}{10}$ multiplied by 5 gives $\frac{1}{2}$. This result can be obtained by multiplying $\frac{1}{2}$ by the reciprocal of 5, or $\frac{1}{5}$.

Example: Divide $\frac{1}{3}$ by 6.

$$\frac{1}{3} \div 6 = \frac{1}{3}(\frac{1}{6}) = \frac{1}{18}$$

To divide a whole number, or a fraction, by a fraction, invert the fractional divisor by interchanging the numerator and denominator and then multiply by this inverted form.

Example: Divide $\frac{4}{5}$ by $\frac{2}{3}$.

$$\frac{\frac{4}{5}}{\frac{2}{3}} = \frac{4}{5} \times \frac{3}{2} = \frac{12}{10} = \frac{6}{5} = 1\frac{1}{5}$$

Problems Involving Addition, Subtraction, Multiplication and Division

It is seldom that problems involve only addition, or subtraction, or multiplication, or division. More often they involve two or more of these operations, and they must be solved by combining the different forms illustrated previously.

In order to solve such combination problems, it is only necessary to keep in mind that, of the fundamental operations, multiplication and division should be performed before addition and subtraction unless brackets or parentheses are inserted. Brackets or parentheses inserted around some portion of the work indicate that that portion should be done first.

Example: Solve the following problem:

$$\frac{\frac{5}{18} + \left\{ \left(\frac{21}{16} \times \frac{32}{64} \right) \div \frac{3}{4} \right\} - \frac{1}{9}}{\left\{ \left(\frac{2}{3} + \frac{5}{8} \right) \times \frac{40}{56} \right\} \div \left(\frac{8}{11} - \frac{16}{33} \right)}$$

First simplify the numerator:

$$\frac{21}{\cancel{16}_{1}} \times \frac{\cancel{32}^{\,\cancel{2}^{1}}}{\cancel{64}_{32}} = \frac{21}{32}$$

$$\frac{21}{32} \div \frac{3}{4} = \frac{\cancel{21}^{7}}{\cancel{32}_{8}} \times \frac{\cancel{4}^{1}}{\cancel{3}_{1}} = \frac{7}{8}$$

$$\frac{5}{18} + \frac{7}{8} - \frac{1}{9} = \frac{20}{72} + \frac{63}{72} - \frac{8}{72} = \frac{20 + 63 - 8}{72} = \frac{75}{72} = \frac{25}{24}$$

The numerator, simplified, is $\frac{25}{24}$.

Next simplify the denominator:

$$\frac{2}{3} + \frac{5}{8} = \frac{16}{24} + \frac{15}{24} = \frac{31}{24}$$

$$\frac{31}{\cancel{24}_{3}} \times \frac{\cancel{40}^{5}}{56} = \frac{155}{168}$$

$$\frac{8}{11} - \frac{16}{33} = \frac{24}{33} - \frac{16}{33} = \frac{8}{33}$$

The denominator is given by

$$\frac{155}{168} \div \frac{8}{33} = \frac{155}{\cancel{168}_{56}} \times \frac{\cancel{33}^{11}}{8} = \frac{1705}{448}$$

Now the whole expression, simplified, is $\dfrac{\frac{25}{24}}{\frac{1705}{448}}$ and it becomes

$$\frac{25}{24} \div \frac{1705}{448} = \frac{\overset{5}{\cancel{25}}}{\underset{3}{\cancel{24}}} \times \frac{\overset{56}{\cancel{448}}}{\underset{341}{\cancel{1705}}} = \frac{280}{1023}$$

EXERCISE 1.2

1. Find the length of the bolt shown.

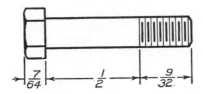

2. Find the distance x.

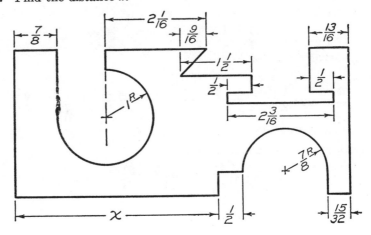

3. Supply the missing dimension if the total length is $3\frac{5}{16}$ in.

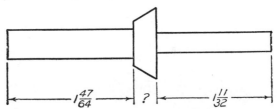

4. Find the diameter of the taper at the center.

5. How many screws $\frac{11}{64}$ in. long can be cut from a brass rod 12 ft long if $\frac{1}{8}$ in. is wasted at each cut?

6. A lathe has a feed of $\frac{3}{128}$ in. per revolution. If the speed is 120 rpm, how many seconds will it take to turn a rod 15 in. long?

7. A rod $1\frac{7}{8}$ in. in diameter is to be turned down in a lathe. If one cut of $\frac{1}{64}$ in. is made, and another of 0.002 in., what is the final diameter?

8. How many washers $\frac{3}{4}$ in. in diameter can be made from a 1-in. strip of steel 6 ft long, allowing $\frac{1}{8}$ in. scrap between blanks?

9. Three pipes open from a tank. Two empty out of the tank and one empties into the tank. The first can empty the tank in 6 hr, and the second in 4 hr. The third can fill it in 3 hr. How long will it take to empty the tank? *Hint:* Figure how much each one can do in one hour.

Solve the following complex fractions:

10. $\dfrac{\frac{2}{3}\left(\frac{4}{13}\right) + \frac{15}{39}}{\left(\frac{5}{6} - \frac{1}{4}\right)\left(\frac{6}{13}\right)}$

11. $\dfrac{\dfrac{1 + \frac{1}{2}}{2} + \dfrac{1}{4}}{\dfrac{2 + \frac{1}{4}}{4 + \frac{1}{2}} + \dfrac{1}{2}}$

12. $\dfrac{\left(\frac{3}{4}\right)\left(\frac{17}{18}\right)\left(\frac{8}{3}\right) - \frac{1}{4} + \frac{3}{8}}{\left(\frac{9}{17}\right)\left(\frac{14}{42}\right)\left(\frac{3}{2}\right) - \frac{1}{2} + \frac{6}{7}}$

13. $\dfrac{\left(\frac{9}{13} \div \frac{3}{26}\right) \div \left(\frac{3}{4} \times \frac{3}{8}\right)}{\frac{17}{19} \times \frac{1}{2} - \frac{5}{19} + \frac{3}{4}}$

14. $\dfrac{\dfrac{\frac{7}{8} + \left(\frac{1}{3} \times \frac{4}{5}\right) - \frac{1}{6}}{\frac{1}{5} + \frac{3}{4} - \frac{5}{6} \div 1\frac{2}{6}}}{\dfrac{\frac{5}{6} \div \left(\frac{1}{3} \times \frac{4}{9} \times \frac{11}{18}\right)}{\frac{1}{2} \div \left(\frac{3}{5} \times \frac{5}{9}\right) - \frac{1}{4}}}$

15. Solve the following continued fraction:

$$2 + \cfrac{1}{2 + \cfrac{1}{2 + \cfrac{1}{2 + \cfrac{1}{2 + \cfrac{1}{2 + \frac{1}{2}}}}}}$$

These fractions are frequently encountered in problems in compound gearing. *Hint:* Start at the bottom and work toward the top.

16. Reduce the following fractions to their lowest terms:

$$\frac{43758}{1684683} \qquad \frac{168399}{85239}$$

17. Which is larger,

$$\frac{23}{49} \text{ or } \frac{11}{23}; \ \frac{17}{37} \text{ or } \frac{33}{77}; \ \frac{47}{87} \text{ or } \frac{29}{54}?$$

18. A steel rod $\frac{7}{16}$ in. in diameter was cut into five pieces of lengths $2\frac{1}{16}$, $3\frac{5}{8}$, $8\frac{11}{64}$, $5\frac{23}{32}$ and $1\frac{3}{4}$ in. What was the length of the rod before cutting if $\frac{3}{32}$ in. was wasted in each cut?

19. The outside diameter of a pipe is $3\frac{7}{8}$ in. If the pipe is $\frac{7}{64}$ in. thick, find the inside diameter.

20. A round shaft should be $1\frac{5}{64}$ in. in diameter and the micrometer reads 1.087 in. How deep a cut should be made on a lathe to bring it down to the correct size?

21. A round shaft should be $1\frac{9}{64}$ in. and measures 1.144 in. How much is it oversize?

22. Two steel pins of diameter $\frac{7}{8}$ in. and $\frac{11}{16}$ in. are spaced $3\frac{13}{64}$ in. center to center. Find the outside distance across them.

23. How many prints can be made on a sheet of print paper 30×36 in. if the negative size is $2\frac{1}{4} \times 3\frac{1}{4}$ in., the border is $\frac{1}{8}$ in., and $\frac{1}{16}$ in. all around is required for trimming?

24. A camera lens mount is 23 mm long. During manufacture, the mount is made from a $1\frac{5}{16}$-in. diameter brass rod and $\frac{1}{8}$ in. is required to cut off the stock between mounts. Brass weighs 0.30 lb per cu in., and sells for $0.40 per lb. Find the material cost per mount. 1 in. = 2.54 cm.

DECIMAL FRACTIONS

Fractions having 10 or any multiple of 10 for a denominator are termed **decimal fractions.** Thus

$$\frac{9}{10}, \quad \frac{17}{100}, \quad \frac{25}{1000}$$

are decimal fractions.

Decimal Point

The writing of such fractions is simplified by omitting the denominator and indicating the denominator by placing a dot (.) called a **decimal point** in the numerator so that there are as many places to the right of this decimal point as there are zeros in the denominator. Thus

$$\tfrac{9}{10} = 0.9 \qquad \tfrac{25}{1000} = 0.025$$
$$\tfrac{17}{100} = 0.17$$

Note in the one illustration that a zero was placed at the left of the 25 in order to give enough places to show three zeros in the denominator. When there is no whole number to the left of the decimal point, a zero should always be written as shown.

From the above explanation it can readily be seen that the location of the decimal point has a great deal of meaning. For each place the decimal point is moved to the right, the decimal fraction is multiplied by 10; and for each place the decimal point is moved toward the left, the decimal fraction is divided by 10. For example, 1.78 becomes 17.8 when the point is moved one place toward the right and 0.178 when it is moved one place toward the left.

Addition and Subtraction of Decimals

Write the numbers so that the decimal points are under each other, and then proceed as in any addition or subtraction of whole numbers. Add zeros to the right if necessary to give enough decimal places.

Example 1: Add 1.78, 1.907, 3.8, 5.0056.

```
 1.7800
 1.9070
 3.8000
 5.0056
12.4926
```

To check the work, add the columns starting from the top, and then repeat, starting from the bottom.

Example 2: Subtract 4.368 from 7.1592.

```
  7.1592
- 4.3680
  2.7912
```

To check, add the remainder to the subtrahend; this should give the minuend. This should be done automatically whenever two numbers are subtracted.

Multiplication of Decimals

Multiply the numbers together just as you do any two whole numbers and put the decimal point as many places from the right in the answer as the sum of the places at the right of the decimal points in the two numbers multiplied.

Example: Multiply 26.14 by 5.22.

$$
\begin{array}{r}
2\,6.1\,4 \\
5.2\,2 \\
\hline
5\,2\,2\,8 \\
5\,2\,2\,8 \\
1\,3\,0\,7\,0 \\
\hline
1\,3\,6.4\,5\,0\,8
\end{array}
$$

As a check for decimal point, estimate the answer roughly. Thus, in the above example, 26.14(5.22) is approximately 25(5) or about 125. Thus the answer is 136.4, and not 13.64 or 1364.

Checking Computations by the Excess of Nines

The excess of nines is, by definition, the remainder of a number which has been divided by 9. Thus 61 divided by 9 gives 6 with a remainder of 7. Therefore the excess of nines in 61 is 7.

The excess of nines can also be found by adding all the digits and taking the excess of the sum. Obviously this is much simpler than dividing each number by 9 to find the excess.

Example 1: Find the excess of nines in 28,365.

The sum of the digits is

$$2 + 8 + 3 + 6 + 5 = 24$$

with an excess of 6. The excess, 6, can be obtained by adding the 2 and the 4 of the sum. Thus to find the excess of nines in a number, add the digits and keep adding until finally only one number is left.

Since the excess of nines is wanted, and not the actual sum of the digits, the work can be simplified by not including any groups of numbers which total 9. Thus for 369,781 the sum of the digits is $3 + 6 + 9 + 7 + 8 + 1 = 34$, giving an excess of 7. This can be simplified by canceling all the numbers which add to 9 before adding the digits. Thus $(6 + 3)$, (9) and $(8 + 1)$ can be neglected in the addition, leaving 7 as the excess of nines.

Example 2: Multiply 394.37 by 54.327 and check by the excess of nines.

The excess of nines of the multiplicand times the excess of nines of the multiplier should equal the excess of nines of the product. The rows can also be checked in the same way.

$$
\begin{array}{l}
3\ 9\ 4.3\ 7 \longrightarrow \text{excess} = 8 \quad 8(3) = 24 \\
\underline{\ \ 5\ 4.3\ 2\ 7} \longrightarrow \text{excess} = 3 \qquad \text{excess} = 6 \\
\overline{2\ 7\ 6\ 0\ 5\ 9} \longrightarrow \text{excess} = 2 \\
\quad 7\ 8\ 8\ 7\ 4 \\
\ \ 1\ 1\ 8\ 3\ 1\ 1 \\
\ 1\ 5\ 7\ 7\ 4\ 8 \\
\underline{1\ 9\ 7\ 1\ 8\ 5} \\
\overline{2\ 1\ 4\ 2\ 4.9\ 3\ 8\ 9\ 9} \longrightarrow \text{excess} = 6
\end{array}
$$

Thus, the first row was formed by multiplying the multiplicand by 7. Since $7(8) = 56$, or an excess of 2, the excess of nines of the first row must also be 2. The other rows can be checked similarly.

Division of Decimals

To divide one decimal by another, perform the division just as you do for whole numbers and point off as many places in the quotient as the number of decimal places in the dividend minus the number of places in the divisor.

Example 1: Divide 67.255 by 2.5.

$$
\begin{array}{r}
26.902 \\
2.5\overline{)67.2550} \\
\underline{50} \\
172 \\
\underline{150} \\
225 \\
\underline{225} \\
50 \\
\underline{50}
\end{array}
$$

As a rough check for the decimal point, $67.255 \div 2.5$ is approximately $60 \div 2$ or 30. Thus the quotient is 26.902 and not 2.69 or 269.0.

Example 2: Divide 175,607 by 547 and check the result by the excess of nines.

To check division by the excess of nines, *the excess of nines of the divisor times the excess of nines of the quotient plus the excess of nines of the remainder equals the excess of nines of the dividend.*

$$
\begin{array}{r}
321 \longrightarrow \text{excess} = 6 \\
\text{excess} = 7 \longleftarrow 547\overline{)175607} \longrightarrow \text{excess} = 8 \\
\underline{1641} \\
1150 \\
\underline{1094} \\
567 \\
\underline{547} \\
20 \longrightarrow \text{excess} = 2
\end{array}
$$

Thus $7(6) + 2 = 44$ with an excess of 8, which checks the division.

Changing a Common Fraction to a Decimal

Place a decimal point at the right of the numerator of the common fraction and add enough zeros after the decimal point so that the numerator can be divided by the denominator. Then perform this division and place the decimal point in the result so that there are as many places at the right of the decimal point as there were zeros added to the numerator.

Example: Change $\frac{5}{8}$ and $\frac{3}{4}$ to decimals.

$$\frac{5}{8} = \frac{5.000}{8} = 0.625$$

$$\frac{3}{4} = \frac{3.00}{4} = 0.75$$

Changing a Decimal to a Common Fraction

In place of the decimal point, put a denominator of 1 followed by as many zeros as there are decimal places in the original number. Then reduce to lowest terms or to a mixed number.

Example: Change 1.67 and 0.875 to common fractions.

$$1.67 = \tfrac{167}{100} = 1\tfrac{67}{100}$$
$$0.875 = \tfrac{875}{1000} = \tfrac{7}{8}$$

Decimal Equivalents of Common Fractions

$\frac{1}{64} = 0.015625$ $\frac{33}{64} = 0.515625$

$\frac{1}{32} = \frac{2}{64} = 0.03125$ $\frac{17}{32} = \frac{34}{64} = 0.53125$

$\frac{3}{64} = 0.046875$ $\frac{35}{64} = 0.546875$

$\frac{1}{16} = \frac{2}{32} = \frac{4}{64} = 0.0625$ $\frac{9}{16} = \frac{18}{32} = \frac{36}{64} = 0.5625$

$\frac{5}{64} = 0.078125$ $\frac{37}{64} = 0.578125$

$\frac{3}{32} = \frac{6}{64} = 0.09375$ $\frac{19}{32} = \frac{38}{64} = 0.59375$

$\frac{7}{64} = 0.109375$ $\frac{39}{64} = 0.609375$

$\frac{1}{8} = \frac{4}{32} = \frac{8}{64} = 0.125$ $\frac{5}{8} = \frac{20}{32} = \frac{40}{64} = 0.625$

$\frac{9}{64} = 0.140625$ $\frac{41}{64} = 0.640625$

$\frac{5}{32} = \frac{10}{64} = 0.15625$ $\frac{21}{32} = \frac{42}{64} = 0.65625$

$\frac{11}{64} = 0.171875$ $\frac{43}{64} = 0.671875$

$\frac{3}{16} = \frac{6}{32} = \frac{12}{64} = 0.1875$ $\frac{11}{16} = \frac{22}{32} = \frac{44}{64} = 0.6875$

$\frac{13}{64} = 0.203125$ $\frac{45}{64} = 0.703125$

$\frac{7}{32} = \frac{14}{64} = 0.21875$ $\frac{23}{32} = \frac{46}{64} = 0.71875$

$\frac{15}{64} = 0.234375$ $\frac{47}{64} = 0.734375$

$\frac{1}{4} = \frac{8}{32} = \frac{16}{64} = 0.25$ $\frac{3}{4} = \frac{24}{32} = \frac{48}{64} = 0.75$

$\frac{17}{64} = 0.265625$ $\frac{49}{64} = 0.765625$

$\frac{9}{32} = \frac{18}{64} = 0.28125$ $\frac{25}{32} = \frac{50}{64} = 0.78125$

$\frac{19}{64} = 0.296875$ $\frac{51}{64} = 0.796875$

$\frac{5}{16} = \frac{10}{32} = \frac{20}{64} = 0.3125$ $\frac{13}{16} = \frac{26}{32} = \frac{52}{64} = 0.8125$

$\frac{21}{64} = 0.328125$ $\frac{53}{64} = 0.828125$

$\frac{11}{32} = \frac{22}{64} = 0.34375$ $\frac{27}{32} = \frac{54}{64} = 0.84375$

$\frac{23}{64} = 0.359375$ $\frac{55}{64} = 0.859375$

$\frac{3}{8} = \frac{12}{32} = \frac{24}{64} = 0.375$ $\frac{7}{8} = \frac{28}{32} = \frac{56}{64} = 0.875$

$\frac{25}{64} = 0.390625$ $\frac{57}{64} = 0.890625$

$\frac{13}{32} = \frac{26}{64} = 0.40625$ $\frac{29}{32} = \frac{58}{64} = 0.90625$

$\frac{27}{64} = 0.421875$ $\frac{59}{64} = 0.921875$

$\frac{7}{16} = \frac{14}{32} = \frac{28}{64} = 0.4375$ $\frac{15}{16} = \frac{30}{32} = \frac{60}{64} = 0.9375$

$\frac{29}{64} = 0.453125$ $\frac{61}{64} = 0.953125$

$\frac{15}{32} = \frac{30}{64} = 0.46875$ $\frac{31}{32} = \frac{62}{64} = 0.96875$

$\frac{31}{64} = 0.484375$ $\frac{63}{64} = 0.984375$

$\frac{1}{2} = \frac{16}{32} = \frac{32}{64} = 0.50$ $1 = \frac{32}{32} = \frac{64}{64} = 1.0000$

EXERCISE 1.3

1. Add 1.7854, 20.436, 502.71, 0.708 and 114.00.

2. Add 2.8165, 22.29, 34.1002, 1.0079 and 0.0041.

3. Add 1.73, $\frac{1}{8}$, 97.83, $\frac{3}{16}$, 273.01, 174, $\frac{17}{64}$ and $\frac{1384}{173(64)}$.

4. Add $\frac{3}{16}$, 2.178, $\frac{53}{64}$, $\frac{17}{32}$, 22.0175, 23.0991.

5. Change to common fractions: 0.95, 1.384, 0.083333$\frac{1}{3}$, and 0.0666$\frac{2}{3}$. *Hint:* $0.066\frac{2}{3} = 0.066 + \frac{0.002}{3}$.

6. Multiply, and check by excess of nines.
   75.1(8.62)
   1.051(110.02)
   90.89(17.003)

7. Multiply, and check by excess of nines.
   29.17(3.025)
   1.056(22.995)
   0.00411(0.01733)

8. Divide, and check by excess of nines.
   23.146 by 16.3
   228.3732 by 13.2
   1930.7 by 26.43
   0.000399 by 0.0054

9. Divide, and check by excess of nines.
   78.542 by 25.3
   2.7182846 by 1.9825
   0.043612 by 5.5
   456.7 by 0.00781

10. Change $\frac{37}{93}$ and $\frac{16}{21}$ to decimal fractions.

PERCENTAGE

Two per cent of a number means two hundredths of the number; 5 per cent means five hundredths. Per cent means by the hundred, so 100% of a number means $\frac{100}{100}$ of the number or the whole number, where % is a sign used to mean per cent. Thus to change to per cent, move the decimal point two places to the right; 0.526 is 52.6%.

In order to change a fraction such as $\frac{3}{5}$ to per cent, it is necessary only to change it to a fraction having 100 as the denominator. Thus,

$$\frac{3}{5} = \frac{60}{100} = 60\%$$

However, the above should not be confused with $\frac{3}{5}$ of 1%. This does not mean $\frac{3}{5}$, or 60%, but rather $\frac{3}{5}$ of 1%, which is the same as $\frac{3}{5}$ of $\frac{1}{100}$ or $\frac{3}{500} = 0.006$.

So $\frac{3}{5} = 60\% = 0.60$

but $\frac{3}{5}$ of $1\% = 0.006$

Three types of problems are commonly encountered when dealing with percentages. They will be illustrated by examples.

Example 1: Find $12\frac{1}{2}\%$ of 240.

In this case 240 is called the **base**, $12\frac{1}{2}\%$ is called the **rate**, and the result is called the **percentage**.

$$12\frac{1}{2}\% = 0.125$$

and $0.125(240) = 30$

so 30 is $12\frac{1}{2}\%$ of 240

Example 2: 15 is what per cent of 75?

In this case, 75 is the base, 15 is the percentage, and the result will be the rate. The problem means: 15 is how many hundredths of 75?

$$\frac{15}{75} = \frac{1}{5} = 0.20 = 20\%$$

so 15 is 20% of 75

Example 3: 24 is 75% of what number?

In this case, 24 is the percentage of the whole number, 75% is the rate, and the result will be the base.

$$24 = 75\% \text{ of number}$$
$$\frac{24}{75} = 0.32 = 1\% \text{ of number}$$
$$100(0.32) = 32 = 100\% \text{ of number}$$

Percentage Error

The constants of engineering used for practical calculations are often derived from measurements or observed readings, and thus are subject to errors. To obtain an accurate figure, a number of measurements or observations are made under various conditions, and the average result is taken.

The average can be found by adding all the results and dividing the sum by the number of observations. This average is taken as the correct figure. The error of any particular observation is the difference between it and the calculated average. This error is often expressed in per cent.

Example: In measuring the width of a metal strip with calipers, the following readings were taken: 2.37 in., 2.39 in., 2.30 in., 2.37 in., 2.36 in. Find the average width and the percentage error in the largest reading.

The sum of the readings is

$$2.37 + 2.39 + 2.36 + 2.37 + 2.36 = 11.85 \text{ in.}$$
$$11.85 \div 5 = 2.370 \text{ in.} = \text{average}$$
$$2.39 - 2.370 = 0.02 = \text{error in largest reading}$$
$$\frac{0.02}{2.370} = 0.0084 = 0.84\% \text{ error}$$

EXERCISE 1.4

1. Find 15% of 625; $22\frac{1}{2}$% of 1.426; $62\frac{1}{2}$% of 0.6785; 45% of 5827.56.

2. 24 is what per cent of 74?
   2 is what per cent of 9?
   17 is what per cent of 11?
   756 is what per cent of 1452?
   89 is what per cent of 35?

3. 25 is $62\frac{1}{2}$ per cent of what number?
   617 is 70 per cent of what number?
   0.782 is 75 per cent of what number?
   0.045 is $12\frac{1}{2}$ per cent of what number?
   1.72 is $87\frac{1}{2}$ per cent of what number?

4. A student working in a factory makes 85 cents per hour for 35 hours per week. He receives a raise of 15%. How many dollars a week will he receive?

5. A statement for $367.48 allows 2% discount for cash. How much will have to be paid?

6. A house and lot cost $15,000. If taxes, repairs and other expenses amount to $840 per year, what rent must the owner receive in order to clear 6% on his investment?

7. A manufacturer sells to a wholesaler at a profit of 20%; the wholesaler to the retailer at a 25% gain; and the retailer to the consumer at a gain of 60%. If the consumer paid $14.40, find the cost to the manufacturer.

8. An article is listed at $375 with discounts of 25% and 15%. How will the 25% discount be changed to offset an increase of 5% in the initial cost?

9. In making a certain casting, 6 lb $4\frac{1}{2}$ oz of brass were used at 42.3 cents per lb. The milling took 7 min at $1.40 per hr; the drilling 16 sec at $1.60 per hr; the lathe work $2\frac{1}{2}$ min at $1.72 per hr; and the finishing $3\frac{1}{4}$ min at $1.10 per hr. Inspection and packing cost $1.80 per thousand. If the office expense is 40% on cost and the profit is 60% on the total cost, find the manufacturer's selling price.

10. The U. S. Navy specifications for valve bronze are:

Copper	87.00%	Lead	1.00%
Tin	7.00%	Zinc	4.94%
Iron	0.06%		

Find the amount of tin, iron, lead and zinc to be mixed with 19 lb of copper, and the weight of the mixture.

11. Common yellow brass is made of 61.6% copper, 2.9% lead, 0.2% tin and the rest zinc by weight. How many pounds of zinc must be added to 198 lb of copper in making brass?

12. A series of readings of a shaft diameter was: 1.078 in., 1.080 in., 1.077 in., 1.079 in., 1.075 in. and 1.081 in. Find the average diameter and the percentage error in the smallest reading.

RATIO AND PROPORTION

Ratio

The relation of one quantity to another can be expressed in any one of several ways. One convenient way to express the relationship is by means of a **ratio**. *The ratio of one number to another is the quotient of the first divided by the second, either implied or actually divided.*

Thus the ratio of $4 to $2 can be written as $\dfrac{\$4}{\$2}$, which is an implied division, or as 2, which is the result of performing the division. It can also be written $4 : $2, which is read $4 *is to* $2.

The two numbers used in a ratio are called the **terms** of the ratio. The first number is called the **antecedent** and is the dividend or numerator; the second number is called the **consequent** and is the divisor or denominator. Since a ratio is an indicated division, the rules relating to fractions apply to a ratio. The ratio $2 : $4 is the **inverse ratio** of $4 : $2.

From the idea of a ratio, it is apparent that a ratio can be stated between two quantities only when the quantities are alike. That is, a ratio cannot be stated between two unlike quantities such as dollars and gallons.

Example: In reading the speed of a motor, a wheel with a rubber rim is used on a tachometer and this wheel is placed against the circumference of a pulley on the motor shaft. The reading of the tachometer is 7200 rpm. The diameter of the wheel on the tachometer is

1 in., and the diameter of the pulley is 4 in. What is the actual speed of the motor?

The ratio of the diameters is 1 : 4 and the speed varies inversely as the ratio of the diameters. Thus

$$\frac{\text{Speed of motor}}{\text{Speed of tachometer}} = \frac{1}{4}$$

The speed of the motor is $\frac{1}{4}$ of the speed of the tachometer, since the diameter of the pulley on the shaft of the motor is 4 times that of the wheel on the tachometer. Therefore

$$\text{Speed of motor} = \tfrac{1}{4}(7200) = 1800 \text{ rpm}$$

Proportion

A **proportion** is a statement of equality between two ratios. Thus $4 : $2 and $8 : $4 are each ratios and since they are equal in value they can be combined into a proportion,

$$\$4 : \$2 = \$8 : \$4$$

It is not necessary that the two ratios refer to the same quantities. Thus $4 : $2 = 2 men : 1 man is just as much a proportion as the first one.

The first and last terms of any proportion are called the **extremes.** The second and third terms are called the **means.**

The following relationships will be found to be true for any proportion:

1. *The product of the means is equal to the product of the extremes.*
2. *The product of the extremes divided by one mean gives the other mean.*
3. *The product of the means divided by one extreme gives the other extreme.*

Two quantities can be in **direct proportion** or in **inverse proportion.** If one quantity increases at the same time that the second increases, or if both decrease together, they vary directly.

Suppose that a pipe runs water at 5 gal per min. If the length of time the water runs is increased, the amount of water increases; twice as much time will give twice as much water. The proportion could be written

$$\frac{W_1}{W_2} = \frac{T_1}{T_2}$$

where W_1 is the amount of water flowing in time T_1 and W_2 is the amount of water flowing in time T_2. Note that the proportion is direct; the first amount of water is to the second amount of water as the first time is to the second time.

It often happens that two quantities are in **inverse proportion,** that is, as one *increases* the other *decreases*. If 20 men can do a certain amount of work in 25 days, it will take 35 men less time to do the same work if they all work at the previous rate. As the number of men *increases*, the time required *decreases*. This gives an inverse proportion. The proportion can be written

$$\frac{M_1}{M_2} = \frac{T_2}{T_1}$$

where M_1 is the first number of men, M_2 is the second number of men, T_1 is the first time required to do the work, and T_2 is the second time required. Note that in this case the second ratio is inverted, as compared to the preceding one, which was a direct proportion.

If the numerical values are substituted in this equation:

$$\frac{20}{35} = \frac{T_2}{25}$$
$$35\ T_2 = 20(25)$$
$$T_2 = 14\tfrac{2}{7} \text{ days}$$

It takes $14\tfrac{2}{7}$ days for the second group of men to do the work.

The proportion is always direct or inverse. If it is always set up in the way shown, it will be easy to complete the solution.

EXERCISE 1.5

1. If it takes 10 men 25 days to do a piece of work, how long will it take 15 men to do the same work?
2. Eight men in 25 days of 6 hr each can unload 1000 cu yd of gravel. How many men will be required to unload it in 10 days, working 9 hr per day?
3. A certain tank is filled with liquid by means of a measure holding exactly 190 cu in. If the measure must be used 125 times to fill the tank, what is the capacity of the tank in cu ft?
4. A $\tfrac{3}{4}$-in. bolt weighs 0.631 lb. How many bolts are there in a 250-lb box?

5. Find the revolutions per minute of a pulley 18 in. in diameter if it is driven by a crossed belt from a 22-in. pulley that makes 76 rpm.

6. If 25 men in 14 days of 8 hr each can dig a ditch 110 rods long, 12 ft wide and 7 ft deep, how many 6-hr days will it take 30 men to dig a ditch 750 rods long, 4 ft wide, and 9 ft deep if they work at the same rate?

7. A man drives to town at 30 mph and drives home at 20 mph. Find his average speed.

8. A bearing alloy is $\frac{31}{41}$ copper, $\frac{7}{41}$ tin and $\frac{3}{41}$ zinc. How many pounds of each in 548 lb of the metal?

POWERS AND ROOTS

Powers and Exponents

When a number is multiplied by itself it is said to be *squared*, or raised to the second power. If it is multiplied by itself three times, it is *cubed*, or raised to the third power.

Instead of writing $2(2)(2) = 8$, it can be written $2^3 = 8$. The number 3, written to the right and a little above the 2, is called an **exponent** and shows how many times 2 is multiplied by itself. Thus 8^7 means to multiply 8 by itself 7 times.

In engineering, powers of 10 are often used. Thus, since $100,000,000 = 10^8$, a number such as $375,600,000$ can be written as 3.756×10^8.

By the use of negative exponents, the powers of 10 can be put in the denominator. Thus

$$10^{-1} = \frac{1}{10}$$

$$10^{-2} = \frac{1}{10(10)} = \frac{1}{100}$$

and

$$10^{-4} = \frac{1}{10(10)(10)(10)} = \frac{1}{10,000}$$

When numbers expressed with powers of 10 are multiplied, the exponents of 10 are added. Thus

$$(7 \times 10^6)(8 \times 10^9) = 56 \times 10^{15}$$
$$(4 \times 10^5)(3 \times 10^{-2}) = 12 \times 10^3$$

Roots

A root of a number is found by the inverse process of finding a power. Thus, if 4 is divided into two equal factors 2×2, one of these equal factors is called the square root of 4. If 27 is divided into the three equal factors $3 \times 3 \times 3$, one of these three equal factors is called the cube root of 27.

The **square root** of a number is one of the two equal factors into which it can be divided.

The **cube root** of a number is one of the three equal factors into which it can be divided.

The **fourth root** of a number is one of the four equal factors into which it can be divided.

A root of a number is indicated by a sign $\sqrt{}$ called a radical sign. If a small figure is placed in the opening at the front of the sign, it indicates which root is to be taken. If this figure is omitted, the second or square root is understood. Thus,

$$\sqrt{49} = 7, \text{ the square root of 49}$$
$$\sqrt[3]{125} = 5, \text{ the cube root of 125}$$
$$\sqrt[4]{16} = 2, \text{ the fourth root of 16}$$

Square Root

It is often necessary to find the square root of a number; hence a method for doing this will now be presented. First the square root of a number that is a perfect square will be found, and then a number that is not a perfect square will be taken. Note that a perfect square is a number whose square root comes out even, whereas the square root of a number not a perfect square is a continued decimal.

Example 1: Find $\sqrt{390625}$.

First, starting at the decimal point and proceeding to the left, divide the number into periods with two figures in a period, as indicated by marks placed between the 2 and the 6 and between the 0 and the 9. This divides the number into three periods, 39'06'25, and indicates that the root will contain three figures ahead of the decimal point.

Now find the largest perfect square that is contained in the first period. This is 36, and should be placed directly under the 39.

Its square root is 6, which should be placed as the first figure in the root just above the 39. Now subtract the 36 from the 39, leaving a remainder of 3, and bring down the next period, 06, at the right of the 3, giving the result 306.

As a trial divisor of the 306, multiply the first figure of the root, 6, by 2 and place this result, 12, at the left of the 306. Then find how many times this 12 is contained in 30, not 306. This gives 2, which is the second figure of the root and is placed at the right of the first figure of the root. The 2 is also put at the right of the trial divisor, 12, making a complete divisor of 122. This complete divisor multiplied by the 2 which was just found gives 244, which in turn is subtracted from the 306, giving a remainder of 62.

Now bring down the next period of the original number beside this second remainder; this gives the number 6225. Multiplying the part of the root already found, 62, by 2, gives a trial divisor of 124. Divide 622, not 6225, by this, and take the result 5 as the third figure of the root. Put this 5 at the right of the trial divisor, 124, giving 1245 as the true divisor. This 1245 multiplied by the third figure 5, which was just found for the root, gives 6225, which is written under the remainder 6225. As the subtraction of 6225 from 6225 gives no remainder and since there are no more periods in the original number, the square root process is complete. Thus the square root of 390625 is 625.

$$
\begin{array}{ll}
\begin{array}{r}
6\ \ 2\ \ 5 \\[-2pt]
\overline{\sqrt{39'06'25}} \\
36 \\
\hline
122)\overline{306} \\
244 \\
\hline
1245)\overline{6225} \\
6225 \\
\hline
\end{array}
&
\begin{array}{r}
\text{Check}\qquad 625 \\
625 \\
\hline
3125 \\
1250 \\
3750 \\
\hline
390625 \\
\end{array}
\end{array}
$$

Example 2: Find $\sqrt{1050.624}$.

This square root is found in exactly the same manner as the first example. Starting at the decimal point, proceed in each direction to divide the number into periods of two figures each.

The largest perfect square contained in the first period at the left is 9 and the square root of this is 3. This 3 is placed above for the first figure of the root and the 9 is placed under the period 10 and subtracted, leaving 1. Then the next period is brought down beside the 1, giving 150. The trial divisor is twice 3 or 6, which is contained in 15 two times. The second figure of the root is 2 and it is also placed with the trial divisor 6, making a complete divisor of 62. This multiplied by 2 is 124 and subtraction from 150 gives 26. The next period, 62, being brought down gives 2662 as a remainder. The trial divisor is twice 32 or 64, which is contained in 266 four times, giving 4 as the third figure of the root. This is put with the trial divisor 64, giving 644 for the complete divisor and four times 644 is 2576, which subtracted from 2662 leaves 86.

Now the next period, 40, is brought down beside the 86, giving 8640; and the next trial divisor is twice 324 or 648, which is contained in 864 once. This gives the next figure in the root, 1. Bringing this figure, 1, down into the divisor makes the complete divisor 6481. Multiplying the complete divisor by 1 gives 6481, which is subtracted from 8640 leaving 2159. When the final two ciphers are brought down, the new dividend is 215900. Now 3241 of the root gives 6482 as the trial divisor, which is contained in 21590 three times. This gives 3 as the last figure in the root and makes the complete divisor 64823. Multiplication of 64823 by 3 gives 194469, which subtracted from 215900 leaves 21431 as a remainder. Thus the square root of 1050.624, to three decimal places, is 32.413 with a remainder of 0.021431.

It should be noted that the decimal point in the root is placed in accordance with the number of periods in the original figure. Since there are two periods to the left of the decimal point in the original number, there must be two numbers to the left of the decimal point in the root.

$$
\begin{array}{ll}
\phantom{\sqrt{}}3 \ \ 2. \ 4 \ \ 1 \ \ 3 \ ^{+} \\
\sqrt{10'50.62'40'00} \\
\phantom{\sqrt{}}9 \\
62)\overline{150} \\
124 \\
644)\overline{2662} \\
2576 \\
6481)\ \overline{8640} \\
6481 \\
64823)\overline{215900} \\
194469 \\
\overline{21431} \ \ \text{Remainder}
\end{array}
\qquad
\begin{array}{l}
\text{Check} \qquad
\begin{array}{r}
3\,2.4\ 1\ 3 \\
3\,2.4\ 1\ 3 \\
\hline
9\,7\,2\,3\,9 \\
3\,2\,4\,1\,3 \\
\hline
1\,2\,9\,6\,5\,2 \\
6\,4\,8\,2\,6 \\
9\,7\,2\,3\,9 \\
\hline
1\,0\,5\,0.6\,0\,2\,5\,6\,9 \\
2\,1\,4\,3\,1 \\
\hline
1\,0\,5\,0.6\,2\,4\,0\,0\,0
\end{array}
\end{array}
$$

Checking Square Root by the Excess of Nines

The excess of nines of the root squared, plus the excess of nines of the remainder, equals the excess of nines of the radicand. Thus $4^2 + 2 = 18$, having an excess of 0. This checks with the excess of nines of the radicand.

$$3 \quad 2. \; 4 \quad 1 \quad 3 \; ^+ \longrightarrow \text{excess} = 4$$
$$\sqrt{10'50.62'40'00} \quad \longrightarrow \text{excess} = 0$$

```
         3  2. 4  1  3 +  ──➤ excess = 4
 √10'50.62'40'00          ──➤ excess = 0
   9
  62)150
     124
    644)2662
        2576
       6481) 8640
             6481
         64823)215900
               194469
                21431 ──➤ excess = 2
```

Simplified Method of Extracting Square Roots

The method of extracting square roots which is described in the preceding sections is the conventional one taught in most schools. With modern calculating machines, the method is not used because it is too complicated and difficult. The preferred method is as follows:

1. Make an estimate of the square root. This can be done by looking in the tables in the back of the book.
2. Divide the number by the estimate.
3. Average the quotient obtained and the original estimate. This will be an improved approximation of the desired root.
4. Divide the original number by the improved approximation.
5. Average the new quotient and the improved approximation to obtain the next approximation.
6. Repeat steps 4 and 5 if necessary to obtain extreme accuracy.

Example: Find the square root of 1285.6.

From the tables of powers in the back of the book, the first estimate is 35.8.

$$\frac{1285.6}{35.8} = 35.9106$$

The first improved estimate is

$$\tfrac{1}{2}(35.8 + 35.9106) = 35.8553.$$

This approximation can be improved by the same method.

$$\frac{1285.6}{35.8553} = 35.855\ 229\ 213\ 0$$

The second improved approximation is

$\frac{1}{2}(35.8553 + 35.855\ 229\ 213\ 0) = 35.855\ 264\ 606\ 5$

which is correct within 0.3 unit in the last significant figure.

This method is much simpler than the procedure described in the preceding section. The division is especially easy to do on a computing machine. An important advantage is that the number of correct significant figures is doubled each time the approximation is improved. The first estimate was correct to one half of the third significant figure. The error of the first improved estimate was less than four tenths of the sixth significant figure, and the second approximation was correct within 0.3 unit in the twelfth significant figure.

Another important advantage of this system is that it is "self-healing." If an error is made at any step of the process it merely slows down the convergence; the correct result will be obtained if the process is continued.

Simplified Method of Extracting Cube Roots

The method of extracting cube roots is similar to that for square roots. The steps are:

1. Make an estimate of the cube root. This can be done by looking in the tables in the back of the book.
2. Divide the number by the square of the first estimate.
3. Add the quotient obtained to twice the original estimate, and divide the sum by 3. This is an improved approximation of the root.
4. Repeat steps 2 and 3 if necessary to obtain extreme accuracy.

Example: Find the cube root of 238.56.

From the tables, the first estimate is 6.20 and $6.20^2 = 38.4400$.

$$\frac{238.56}{38.4400} = 6.20604$$

$\frac{1}{3}(6.20 + 6.20 + 6.20604) = 6.20201$

The next approximation is

$$\frac{238.56}{(6.20201)^2} = 6.202\ 013\ 422\ 49$$

$$\tfrac{1}{3}(6.20201 + 6.20201 + 6.202\ 013\ 422\ 49) = 6.202\ 011\ 140\ 8$$

which is correct within 0.3 unit in the eleventh significant figure.

This method of extracting the cube root of a number has the same advantages as that for the square root. The number of significant figures is doubled each time the approximation is improved, and any errors made will be corrected by successive steps.

Square Root Applications

In engineering, the most useful application of square root is to find the third side of a right triangle when the other two sides are known.

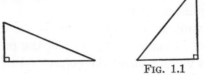

Fig. 1.1

The three triangles in Fig. 1.1 are all right triangles since each one has a right angle, or 90° angle. The side opposite the right angle is always the **hypotenuse,** and the other two sides are the **altitude** and **base,** as shown by Fig. 1.2. The Pythagorean theorem of geometry states that *the square of the hypotenuse equals the sum of the squares of the other two sides.* Thus, in Fig. 1.3

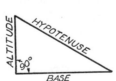

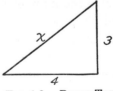

FIG. 1.2.—PARTS OF A RIGHT TRIANGLE. FIG. 1.3.—RIGHT TRIANGLE.

$$(\text{Base})^2 = 4^2 = 16$$
$$(\text{Altitude})^2 = 3^2 = \underline{9}$$
$$(\text{Hypotenuse})^2 = 25$$
$$\text{Hypotenuse} = \sqrt{25} = 5$$

If the altitude is a, the base b, and the hypotenuse c, then

$$a^2 + b^2 = c^2$$

so
$$c = \sqrt{a^2 + b^2}$$

If the hypotenuse and altitude are given, then

$$b^2 = c^2 - a^2$$

and
$$b = \sqrt{c^2 - a^2}$$

Also, to find the altitude,

$$a = \sqrt{c^2 - b^2}$$

Example: The hypotenuse of a right triangle is $11\frac{1}{2}$ in. and the altitude is $7\frac{3}{4}$ in. Find the base.

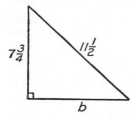

Given $\begin{cases} a = 7\frac{3}{4} \text{ in.} \\ c = 11\frac{1}{2} \text{ in.} \end{cases}$ Find: $b = 8.49$ in.

FORMULA

$$b = \sqrt{c^2 - a^2}$$

COMPUTATION

$$\begin{aligned} c &= 11.5 & c^2 &= 132.2500 \\ a &= 7.75 & a^2 &= \underline{60.0625} \\ & & b^2 &= 72.1875 \end{aligned}$$

$$b = \sqrt{72.1875} = 8.49 \text{ in.}$$

EXERCISE 1.6

1. The altitude of a right triangle is 1.3 ft and the base is 1.2 ft. Find the hypotenuse.

2. The hypotenuse of a triangle is 3 ft $9\frac{3}{4}$ in., and the base is 2 ft $10\frac{1}{8}$ in. Find the altitude.

3. Find the distance between opposite corners of a room 14 ft 6 in. long and 12 ft 8 in. wide.

4. Find the distance between holes, center to center, in the sketch shown.

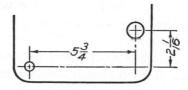

5. Find the length along the center line of the piece shown.

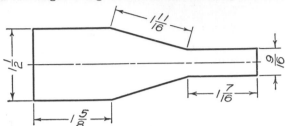

6. If a stairway has a rise of $7\frac{1}{2}$ in. and a tread of 10 in., and the second floor is 10 ft $7\frac{1}{2}$ in. higher than the first floor, find the length of the stair stringer.

7. A roof has a rise of 4 ft in a run of 7 ft. Find the length of a rafter, allowing 14 in. for overhang, if the house is 28 ft wide.

8. The expression $V = \sqrt{2\,gh}$ gives the velocity V in ft per sec a body will have after falling from a height h. Find the value for V for a body that has fallen 350 ft. Use $g = 32.2$.

9. Find the 4th root of 104.8576. *Hint:* Take the square root twice.

10. Find the 4th root of 0.00000625. *Hint:* Same as for Problem 9.

11. A guy wire is attached to the top of a construction tower 82 ft high, and is anchored 175 ft from the base. How long is the guy wire?

12. In order to look well, a panel door on a milling machine should be so proportioned that its diagonal is twice its width. If its width is $7\frac{3}{8}$ in., what should be its length?

13. Find the diagonal of the following photographic plates:

$$3\tfrac{1}{4} \times 4\tfrac{1}{4} \text{ in.} \qquad 6\tfrac{1}{2} \times 8\tfrac{1}{2} \text{ in.}$$
$$3\tfrac{1}{4} \times 5\tfrac{1}{2} \text{ in.}$$

WEIGHTS AND MEASURES

English System

It is important that the student acquaint himself early in his study of mathematics with the two systems of weights and measures in common use. These two are the English system and the metric system. The former is in everyday use in the United States, but the latter is used in Europe, in the laboratory, and in most scientific work.

The English system has no common factor running through the entire system. This makes it difficult to obtain a clear picture of it. This combined with the fact that commerce between nations makes it advisable to have a uniform system of weights and measures has brought the metric system into use.

Metric System

The metric system has a common factor, 10, that runs through it and as a result it is much simpler and easier to use than the English system. Some of the more common terms of the metric system are:

meter — unit of length
liter — unit of volume
gram — unit of weight
milli — meaning one-thousandth of
centi — meaning one-hundredth of
kilo — meaning one thousand times

Thus there are 100 centimeters in a meter, 1000 milligrams in a gram and 1000 grams in a kilogram.

UNITED STATES WEIGHTS AND MEASURES

Measures of weight

7000 grains = 1 pound (avoirdupois lb)
16 ounces (avoirdupois oz) = 1 pound (avoirdupois lb)
100 pounds = 1 hundredweight
2000 pounds = 1 ton (short ton)
2240 pounds = 1 long ton

Measures of length

12 inches (in.) = 1 foot (ft)
3 feet = 1 yard (yd)
$5\frac{1}{2}$ yards = 1 rod
$16\frac{1}{2}$ feet = 1 rod
320 rods = 1 mile
5280 feet = 1 mile

Measures of area

144 square inches (sq in.) = 1 square foot (sq ft)
9 square feet = 1 square yard (sq yd)
30.25 square yards = 1 square rod (sq rod)
160 square rods = 1 acre = 43,560 sq ft
640 acres = 1 square mile (sq mi)

Measures of volume

$$1728 \text{ cubic inches (cu in.)} = 1 \text{ cubic foot (cu ft)}$$
$$27 \text{ cubic feet} = 1 \text{ cubic yard (cu yd)}$$

Liquid measure

$$1 \text{ fluid ounce} = 0.0625 \text{ liquid pint}$$
$$4 \text{ gills} = 1 \text{ pint}$$
$$2 \text{ pints} = 1 \text{ quart (qt)}$$
$$4 \text{ quarts} = 1 \text{ gallon (gal)}$$
$$31\tfrac{1}{2} \text{ gallons} = 1 \text{ barrel (bbl)}$$
$$231 \text{ cubic inches} = 1 \text{ gallon}$$

Dry measure

$$2 \text{ pints} = 1 \text{ quart (qt)}$$
$$8 \text{ quarts} = 1 \text{ peck (pk)}$$
$$4 \text{ pecks} = 1 \text{ bushel (bu)}$$
$$2150.42 \text{ cubic inches} = 1 \text{ bushel}$$

Time measure

$$60 \text{ seconds (sec)} = 1 \text{ minute (min)}$$
$$60 \text{ minutes} = 1 \text{ hour (hr)}$$
$$24 \text{ hours} = 1 \text{ day}$$
$$365 \text{ days} = 1 \text{ common year (yr)}$$
$$366 \text{ days} = 1 \text{ leap year}$$

CONVERSION TABLES

Measures of length

$$1 \text{ inch} = 2.54 \text{ centimeters}$$
$$1 \text{ foot} = 30.48 \text{ centimeters}$$
$$1 \text{ meter} = 39.37 \text{ inches}$$
$$1 \text{ mile} = 1.609347 \text{ kilometers}$$

Measures of area

$$1 \text{ square inch} = 6.4516 \text{ square centimeters}$$
$$1 \text{ square meter} = 10.7639 \text{ square feet}$$
$$= 1.1960 \text{ square yards}$$

Measures of volume

$$1 \text{ cubic inch} = 16.3872 \text{ cubic centimeters}$$
$$1 \text{ cubic centimeter} = 0.0610234 \text{ cubic inches}$$
$$1 \text{ cubic foot} = 28.316 \text{ liters}$$
$$1 \text{ pint (liquid)} = 473.17 \text{ cubic centimeters}$$
$$1 \text{ liter} = 0.26418 \text{ gallon}$$
$$= 1.000027 \text{ cubic decimeters}$$

Measures of weight

$$1 \text{ gram} = 980.6 \text{ dynes}$$
$$1 \text{ ounce avoirdupois} = 28.350 \text{ grams}$$
$$1 \text{ kilogram} = 2.204622 \text{ pounds avoirdupois}$$
$$1 \text{ pound avoirdupois} = 453.592 \text{ grams}$$

Formulas

In practical problems, the student will often find that he has an expression containing letters which he has to replace with numbers, and then solve the expression for a letter whose value is not given. Such expressions are called formulas and are a valuable aid to the engineer. But the student should not become so impressed with the importance of these formulas that he cannot do without them. It would be far better for him, in such a case, to forget that such formulas ever existed and solve his problem by his own reasoning powers. He will be surprised at the end to find that he has actually used the formula for that particular case without knowing it. In other words, a formula is nothing but a short concise way of stating a truth that has been developed through logical reasoning.

In many formulas, the first letter of a word is used for the symbol of the word. Thus in the expression

$$HP = \frac{PLAN}{33,000}$$

used in connection with the steam engine,

HP stands for horsepower
P = effective steam pressure in pounds per square inch
L = length of piston stroke in feet
A = area of piston in square inches
N = number of strokes per minute

Example: In the above expression, find the horsepower if $P = 50$ lb per sq in., $L = 2\frac{1}{2}$ ft, $A = 200$ sq in., and $N = 75$ strokes per minute.

$$HP = \frac{PLAN}{33,000} = \frac{50(2.5)(200)(75)}{33,000} = 56.8$$

Density and Specific Gravity

Density and specific gravity are terms used in connection with the weights of bodies. **Density** is understood to be the mass of a body per unit volume and is generally given in pounds per cubic foot in the English system and in grams per cubic centimeter in the metric system. **Specific gravity** is the term used for the ratio of the densities of two materials or bodies, and thus it is an abstract number since it is a ratio.

Generally, for convenience, water is selected as the standard by which to state the specific gravity of other substances, particularly solids and liquids. The specific gravities of gases are usually stated in terms of air or hydrogen.

The specific gravity of a substance is found by determining the weight of a certain volume of it and dividing this weight by the weight of an equal volume of water.

The standard taken is the weight of a cubic foot of water, which is approximately 62.4 pounds. If W stands for the weight of the substance per cubic foot and sg for its specific gravity, the relationship

$$sg = \frac{W}{62.4}$$

results from the definition of specific gravity. This can be generalized to give

$$sg = \frac{W}{S}$$

where W equals the weight of unit volume of the substance and S is the weight of unit volume of the standard.

Example 1: What is the specific gravity of a slate panel if 1 cu ft weighs 175 lb?

$$sg = \frac{W}{62.4} = \frac{175}{62.4} = 2.80$$

Example 2: What is the specific gravity of a substance, 45 cu in. of which weigh 5 lb?

Since there are 1728 cu in. in 1 cu ft, 1 cu ft of the substance will weigh

$$\frac{5}{45}(1728) = \frac{1728}{9} = 192 \text{ lb}$$

Then

$$sg = \frac{W}{62.4} = \frac{192}{62.4} = 3.08$$

Practical Computation

In practical engineering work, much use is made of tables and formulas. Thus there are tables of squares and cubes of numbers, of roots, reciprocals, areas of circles, and many others. Many geometric forms have formulas for computing areas and other essential parts. These formulas greatly reduce the labor of making computations. To use them, it is only necessary to select the formula that gives the unknown part in terms of the known parts, and substitute the values. There is a series of tables in the back of the book, and some charts with formulas follow these examples.

Example 1: Find the area of an equilateral triangle with side 2 in. From the chart,

$$A = 0.43301 \ s^2$$
$$= 0.43301(2)^2 = 1.732 \text{ sq in.}$$

Example 2: Find the total surface area of a cylinder 6 ft in diameter and 8 ft high. From the chart,

$$A = 2 \pi r(r + h)$$
$$= 2(3.1416)(3)(3 + 8) = 207.35 \text{ sq ft}$$

WEIGHTS OF DIFFERENT MATERIALS

Material	Lb per cu ft	Lb per cu in.
Aluminum	165	0.0955
Brass	524	0.3032
Brick	112	0.0648
Bronze	552	0.3195
Cement	194	0.1123
Concrete	137	0.0793
Copper	556	0.3218
Gasoline	43.7	0.0253
Gravel	109	0.0631
Ice	56	0.0324
Iron, cast	449	0.2600
Iron, wrought	490	0.2834
Lead	709	0.4105
Nickel	537	0.3108
Nitric acid	94	0.0544
Sand, dry	100	0.0579
Silver	657	0.3802
Steel	490	0.2833
Sulphuric acid	115	0.0664
Tin	455	0.2632
Water	62.4	0.0361
Wood, white pine	31.2	0.018
Wood, cherry	43.7	0.025
Zinc, cast	428	0.2476
Zinc, rolled	446	0.2581

CONSTANTS FOR COMPUTATION

SQUARE	EQUILATERAL TRIANGLE

SQUARE

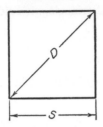

$A = \text{area} = s^2 = \frac{1}{2} D^2$

$D = 1.4142\, s = 1.4142\sqrt{A}$

$s = 0.70711\, D = \sqrt{A}$

EQUILATERAL TRIANGLE

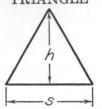

$A = \text{area} = 0.43301\, s^2$

$\qquad = 0.57735\, h^2$

$h = 0.86603\, s$

$s = 1.1547\, h$

RECTANGLE

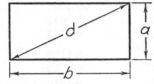

$A = \text{area} = ab$

$\qquad = a\sqrt{d^2 - a^2} = b\sqrt{d^2 - b^2}$

$a = \sqrt{d^2 - b^2} = \dfrac{A}{b}$

$b = \sqrt{d^2 - a^2} = \dfrac{A}{a}$

RIGHT–ANGLE TRIANGLE

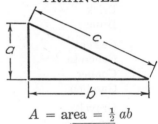

$A = \text{area} = \frac{1}{2}\, ab$

$a = \sqrt{c^2 - b^2}$

$b = \sqrt{c^2 - a^2}$

$c = \sqrt{a^2 + b^2}$

TRIANGLE

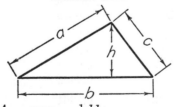

$A = \text{area} = \frac{1}{2}\, bh$

$A = \sqrt{s(s - a)(s - b)(s - c)}$

where

$s = \frac{1}{2}(a + b + c)$

TRAPEZOID

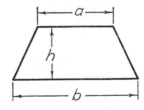

$A = \text{area} = \frac{1}{2}(a + b)h$

CONSTANTS FOR COMPUTATION

CIRCLE

A = area = πr^2 = 3.1416 r^2
C = circumference = $2\,\pi r$
r = 0.56419 $\sqrt{A}$
d = 1.12838 $\sqrt{A}$

FILLET

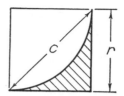

A = area
$\quad = r^2 - \frac{1}{4}\,\pi r^2$
$\quad = 0.2146\,r^2$
$\quad = 0.1073\,c^2$

ANNULUS

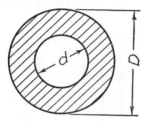

Area = $\frac{\pi}{4}(D^2 - d^2)$

ELLIPSE

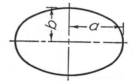

Area = πab
Perimeter = $\pi\sqrt{2(a^2 + b^2)}$
$\quad$ approximately

HEXAGON

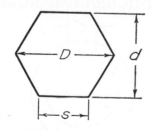

d = 0.86603 D = 1.73205 s
D = 1.1547 d = ? s
A = 0.64952 D^2 = 0.86603 d^2
$\quad = 2.5981\,s^2$

OCTAGON

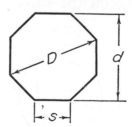

d = 0.92388 D = 2.4142 s
D = 1.0824 d = 2.6131 s
A = 0.82842 d^2 = 0.70711 D^2
$\quad = 4.8284\,s^2$

CONSTANTS FOR COMPUTATION

SPHERE

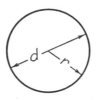

$V = \frac{4}{3}\pi r^3 = \frac{1}{6}\pi d^3 = 4.1888\, r^3$
$A = \text{area} = 4\pi r^2 = \pi d^2$
$\quad = 12.5664\, r^2$

CYLINDER

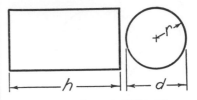

$V = \pi r^2 h = 0.7854\, d^2 h$
$s = \text{curved surface}$
$\quad = 2\pi rh = \pi dh$
$A = \text{total area}$
$\quad = 2\pi r(r + h)$

SQUARE PRISM

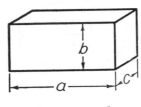

Volume $= abc$

FRUSTUM OF CONE

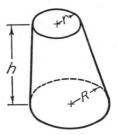

Volume $= \frac{1}{3}\pi h(R^2 + Rr + r^2)$

TORUS OR RING

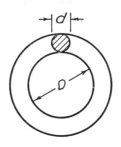

Volume $= \frac{1}{4}\pi^2 d^2(D + d)$

SEMICIRCULAR RING

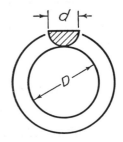

Volume $= \frac{1}{8}\pi d^2(\pi D + \pi d - \frac{4}{3}d)$
$\quad = 1.2337\, d^2 D$
$\quad + 0.71010\, d^3$

EXERCISE 1.7

1. Find the length of a $\frac{7}{8}$-in. wrought-iron rod weighing 18 lb 5 oz.

2. What must be the opening between the jaws of an end wrench made to fit a hexagonal nut 2 in. across corners? Express to the nearest $\frac{1}{16}$ in.

3. If gasoline costs $0.21 per gal, find the cost of filling a gas tank 1 ft in diameter and 4 ft long if it has 3 gal in it to start with, and the pump will pump only by gallons.

4. A sharp V thread with the cross section of an equilateral triangle is cut on a shaft. Find the depth, if the pitch is $\frac{1}{8}$ in.

5. Which is larger, 17 in. or 43 cm?

6. Find the difference in cubic inches in the volume of a milliliter and a centimeter cube.

    Note: At a general industrial conference held under the auspices of the American Standards Association on October 21, 1932, unanimous approval was given to the suggested change in the inch-centimeter conversion factor to 1 inch = 2.54 centimeters. This replaces the former factor of 1 inch = 2.540005 centimeters. The volume of the liter was not changed.

7. Steel weighs 490 lb per cu ft. How many grams per cc is this?

8. How many kilometers per hour is 74 ft per sec?

9. A wooden pattern weighs $11\frac{1}{8}$ oz. Find the weight of the brass casting if the pattern was made of cherry.

10. Find the weight of a cast-iron ball 10 in. in diameter.

11. Test the accuracy of the old saying, "A pint's a pound the world around," for water.

12. To what diameter should a rod be turned before milling a hexagon of 1.25-in. side on the end of it?

13. A can holds 1 pt and is 4 in. high. Find the length of a label for it, allowing $\frac{3}{16}$ in. for pasting.

14. A gasoline tank is in a horizontal position in the ground and is 20 ft long by 6 ft in diameter. Find the number of gallons of gasoline in it when it is half full.

15. What does a pressure of 14.7 lb per sq in. represent in grams per sq cm?

16. A skater made a mile in 3 min $23\frac{2}{5}$ sec. This represents what time for 1500 meters?

17. A pond $\frac{1}{2}$ acre in area is frozen over. If the specific gravity of ice is 0.92 and the ice is 4 in. thick, what is the weight of the ice in the pond in tons?

18. The tire of a car is 8.00 × 15. Find the number of revolutions the wheel makes in 2 miles.

19. If the gear ratio of a car is 11 to 39 and the tire diameter is 28 in., how many rpm does the motor make at 60 mph?

20. What is the weight of 17 gal of water?

21. One square mile is how many square kilometers?

22. One square yard is how many square meters?

23. How many miles in 87 km?

24. How many cubic meters in 3 cu yd?

25. Find the area of a brass fillet of radius $\frac{9}{16}$ in., and the weight per foot.

26. A steel fillet has a radius of $2\frac{7}{8}$ in. Find the weight per foot and the area.

27. What is the weight of a $\frac{3}{16}$-in. round steel rod per running inch?

28. Find the weight of a $\frac{5}{8}$-in. square brass bar per ft.

29. How many cubic yards of concrete in the culvert shown, if it is 165 ft long?

30. Find the number of square inches in the plate shown.

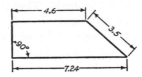

31. Find the area of the part shown, in square feet.

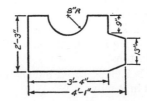

32. Find the area of the gasket shown, in square inches.

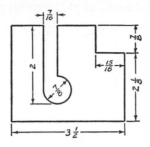

33. Find the shaded area. The circles are evenly spaced.

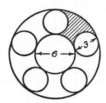

34. The scaffolding on a certain construction job is as shown. Find the length of each member.

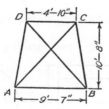

35. By accident a flat was cut on a circular disk, as shown. If this flat is turned off in a lathe using the old center, what will be the new diameter?

36. It is desired to round off the corner of a $\frac{3}{8}$-in. steel plate for 2 in as shown. Find the weight of the metal removed.

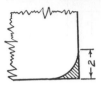

37. Find the weight of the angle plate shown.

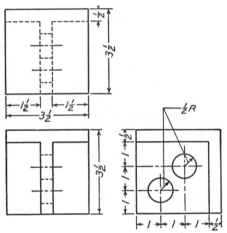

ANGLE PLATE. MATERIAL — C. I.

38. Find the weight of the brass bushing shown.

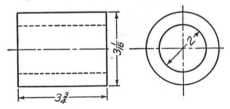

39. Find the number of hexagonal-head steel bolts, as per sketch in a 100-lb keg. Neglect threads and rounded corners.

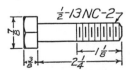

40. Find the weight of 68 brackets as shown, and the cost at 12 cents per pound.

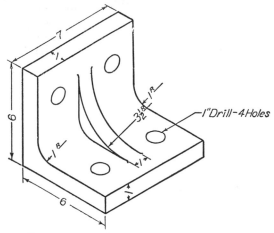

BRACKET. MATERIAL — C. I.

41. Find the volume and weight of the pouring block shown.

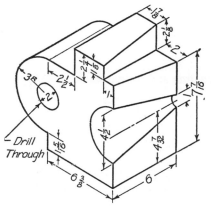

POURING BLOCK. MATERIAL — BRONZE.

Hint: Divide the missing upper-right corner into a rectangular parallelepiped, two wedges, and a pyramid.

42. Find the volume and weight of the ring shown.

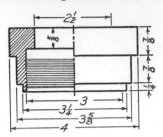

RETAINING RING. 4″ DIAMETER BRASS.

43. Find the volume of the core block shown.

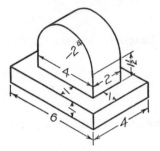

CORE BLOCK.

44. Find the volume and weight of the bracket shown.

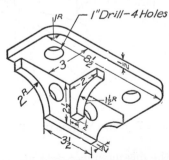

UPPER BRACKET. MATERIAL — C. I.

45. Find the volume and weight of the cold rolled steel plug gage shown.

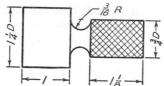

PLUG GAGE.   MATERIAL — C. R. S.

46. Find the cost of covering the roof shown with patent roofing at \$7.75 per square, of 100 sq ft.

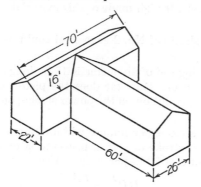

47. Find the number of cubic feet of concrete in the column shown.

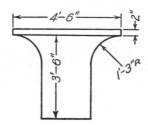

Hint: Subtract one half the volume of a semicircular ring from the volume of a hollow cylinder 4 ft 6 in. in diameter and 1 ft 3 in. thick.

48. Find the weight of a steel sheet 0.072 in. thick, 6 ft long, 18 in. wide at one end and 15 in. wide at the other. The edges of the plate are straight lines.

49. A cast-iron weight is found to be 0.24 lb short weight. How deep a $\frac{3}{4}$-in. hole must be drilled and filled with lead to make it just right?

50. Find the largest square shaft that can be cut from a 1-in. rod.

51. A single-acting pump has a cylinder diameter of 8 in. and a stroke of 12 in. If it makes 45 strokes per minute, find the gallons pumped per hour.

52. A 6-cylinder car has 28-in. tires and a gear ratio of 39 to 11. Find the number of explosions in driving 20,000 miles.

53. The wheel of a car with 29-in. tires makes 540 rpm. What is the speed of the car?

54. No. 2 gage sheet steel is 0.266 in. thick. Find the weight of a 100-gal barrel 4 ft high made of this material. Assume straight sides.

55. How many sheets of No. 2 gage steel could be packed in a box 1 ft deep?

56. The connecting rod of an engine is 18 in. long and the throw of the crank is 6 in. How far does the piston move during the first quarter revolution on the power stroke; on the compression stroke?

57. How many strokes per minute will a 60-hp steam engine have with a piston stroke of 2 ft, a piston area of 150 sq in., and a steam pressure of 50 lb per sq in.? Use

$$HP = \frac{PLAN}{33,000}$$

CHAPTER II

Fundamentals of Algebra

SYMBOLS ARE OFTEN USED IN ARITHMETIC FOR VARIOUS quantities in order to save time and effort. The area of a circle is given by the equation $A = \pi R^2$, where A is the area and R is the radius. The area of circles could be expressed in tables of values giving the area for each corresponding diameter. This would be useful if the tables were always available, but they would not show clearly how the area varies with the radius and they could not be easily memorized. The formula is much better because it expresses the area of all circles; anyone can learn it and from it calculate the area even if the tables were not available.

In algebra the same signs and symbols are used as in arithmetic, but algebra is a continuation of the process. More extensive and general methods are developed which make it possible to solve a whole class of problems at once and which reduce much of the work to routine. Formulas can be worked out for finding the answers to complicated problems quickly and with a minimum of effort.

In arithmetic there are several kinds of definite quantities. There is the ordinary number, such as 5, and there is the number of things, such as 5 inches, 4 machines, 10 bolts, or other units. The next step is to include fractions, such as $1\frac{2}{3}$ and 1.752; these may also be combined with definite units. These examples are called **commensurate numbers** because they can be expressed exactly by whole numbers and fractions. Many other numbers which are used in arithmetic cannot be expressed exactly. One of these is π, used in the above equation for the area of a circle. This will never come out even, in decimal form; it is 3.14159 $\cdots$. The dots at the end mean that it can be worked out to as many decimal places as may be necessary.

The square roots of many numbers also give endless decimals. The square root of 2, $\sqrt{2} = 1.4142 \cdots$, or 3, $\sqrt{3} = 1.732 \cdots$, are examples. These are all called **incommensurate numbers** because they cannot be expressed exactly in terms of the given units.

In the equation for the area of a circle, $A = \pi R^2$, R represents the radius not of any particular circle but of any circle. If a numerical value is substituted for R, then the resulting expression applies only to one particular circle. Likewise, the area of a rectangle is $A = LW$, where L is the length and W is the width. These are all general numbers, and are usually represented by letters. General numbers or letters are used in algebra instead of the numerical quantities of arithmetic. The letters are a means for representing the unknown values until a definite answer to a particular problem is needed.

In arithmetic, numerical equations were used such as $12 + 3 - 7 = 8$. In algebra letters and numbers, such as $a + 2b - 3c = d$, are used. Sometimes letters are multiplied together, as in $axyz$.

Definitions

Several definitions are important to the study of algebra.

A **term** is a part of an algebraic expression not separated by a plus or minus sign. Thus in $x - 3ay + 2z$, there are three terms, namely, x, $3ay$ and $2z$. An **algebraic term** is a term containing only algebraic symbols. The **degree of a term** is the sum of the exponents of its literal factors, i.e., the number of literal factors with unit exponents that can be found in it. For example, x^2 is of the second degree, xyz^2 is of the fourth degree, etc.

A **coefficient** is generally taken as the numerical part of a term, and is usually written before the literal part, like 2 in $2x$ or in $2(x + y)$. In general, it is the product of all the factors of a term except a certain one (or a certain set) of which the product is said to be the coefficient. For example, in $2axyz$, $2axy$ is the coefficient of z, $2ayz$ is the coefficient of x, etc. If no numerical part is expressed, 1 is understood.

An **exponent** is a positive integer at the right and above a letter or quantity indicating that the letter or quantity is to be taken as a factor as many times as there are units in this integer. For example, $3^2 = 3(3)$ and $x^3 = x(x)(x)$. If no exponent is shown, 1 is understood; thus $x = x^1$. Until the laws of exponents are discussed at length, any letter used as an exponent must be assumed to be a positive integer.

A **monomial** is an algebraic expression consisting of one term, such as $2\,xy$ or $-15\,abx$. A **multinomial** is an algebraic expression of two or more terms, such as $3\,xy - \dfrac{x}{y} + az^2$. A **binomial** is a multinomial of two terms, such as $2\,x + 5\,y$ or $2 - (a + b)$. A **trinomial** is a multinomial of three terms, such as $x^2 - 3\,x + 2$.

A **polynomial** is a special case of a multinomial. It is a *rational, integral* expression. An expression is rational and integral in certain letters if these letters are involved only in the operations of addition, subtraction and multiplication. To be rational, the letters must not be involved in the extraction of roots, and to be integral excludes division of these letters. Thus $2\,x^2 - 3\,xy + 4\,y^2$ is a polynomial in x and y, $3\,x^2 + \dfrac{x}{y} + \sqrt{x}$ is not a polynomial, since it is neither rational nor integral.

The **degree of a polynomial** is the highest degree of any of its terms. Thus in the polynomial $x^2y^2 - 3\,xyz^3 + yz$ the terms are of degree 4, 5 and 2; hence the degree of the polynomial is 5.

Positive and Negative Numbers

In arithmetic rules were given for the subtraction of numbers. These worked properly until one tried to subtract one number from a smaller one, such as $5 - 8 = ?$ In order to make such operations possible, negative numbers were developed. These numbers are preceded by a $-$ sign, and the ordinary or positive numbers are preceded by a $+$ sign. Thus $+5$ is the ordinary 5 and -5 is a negative 5.

To illustrate the operation of this system, the number system is represented by the numbered line in Fig. 2.1. A point is arbitrarily chosen as zero and equal spaces are marked off to the right and left of it. These are numbered consecutively $+1$, $+2$, $+3 \cdots$ to the right and $-1, -2, -3 \cdots$ to the left. Thus the sign of a number indicates the direction.

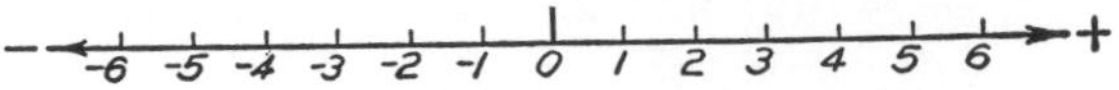

FIG. 2.1.—POSITIVE AND NEGATIVE NUMBERS.

The number $+6$ means not only six units, but also that they are to be counted to the right. Likewise -4 means to count four units to the left. To solve the problem $5 - 8 = ?$ with Fig. 2.1, start out at $+5$ and count to the left eight units. The answer is -3.

Addition

The use of negative numbers gives the addition and subtraction of numbers a much wider range. Addition of a negative number thus decreases the sum. If a negative number added to a positive number decreases the sum, a negative number subtracted from a positive number should increase the sum. The following rules for addition are derived from this.

Rules

1. *When adding two algebraic numbers with like signs, find the sum and prefix the common sign.*
2. *If the signs are unlike, find the difference of the two numbers and prefix the sign of the numerically larger number.*
3. *If there are more than two terms with both $+$ and $-$ signs, find the sum of all the $+$ terms and the sum of all the $-$ terms, and use Rule 2.*

The following additions illustrate the rules.

Example 1:

$$
\begin{array}{cccc}
+4 & +4 & +3 & +9\,x \\
+3 & -2 & -6 & +12\,x \\
\hline
+7 & +2 & -3 & +21\,x
\end{array}
$$

$$
\begin{array}{cc}
+9\,ab & +11 \\
-11\,ab & +6 \\
\hline
-2\,ab & -4 \\
\end{array}
$$

$$+17 - 4 = +13 \quad \text{(Rule 3)}$$

$$
\begin{array}{c}
+3\,ab \\
-5\,ab \\
+8\,ab \\
\hline
+6\,ab \quad \text{(Rule 3)}
\end{array}
$$

Similar algebraic terms can be added in order; the sum of any number of similar terms is the same regardless of how the terms may be grouped. Dissimilar terms cannot be added directly, but the addition can be indicated by a sign between them.

Example 2:

$$7\,a + 5\,a = 12\,a$$
But $$15\,b + 16\,c = 15\,b + 16\,c$$

These cannot be added to give a single term; the operation can only be indicated.

$$2\,a - 5\,c + a = 3\,a - 5\,c$$

Two of the terms can be added.

Example 3: Add the following terms: $6\,x,\ -5\,x,\ \frac{2}{3}\,x,\ -\frac{1}{3}\,x.$

$$6\,x - 5\,x + \tfrac{2}{3}\,x - \tfrac{1}{3}\,x = x + \tfrac{1}{3}\,x = \tfrac{4}{3}\,x$$

Since the terms are all like, the coefficients can be added.

Example 4: Add the following expressions:

$$4\,a - 2\,b + 6\,c;\ \ 7\,a - 2\,c;\ \ -a + b;\ \ -2\,a - 3\,b - 5\,c + d.$$

First, for convenience, write all similar terms in the same column, and then find the algebraic sum of each column.

$$
\begin{array}{l}
4\,a - 2\,b + 6\,c \\
7\,a \qquad\quad - 2\,c \\
-\ \ a + \ b \\
-\,2\,a - 3\,b - 5\,c + d \\
\hline
+\,8\,a - 4\,b - \ \ c + d
\end{array}
$$

Subtraction

Subtraction is the inverse of addition. When both signs are + or both are −, the process is the same as in arithmetic. It is no longer necessary that the minuend be larger than the subtrahend, and either or both can be negative. Subtraction can be considered as the addition of a term with the sign changed. *To subtract one term from another, change the sign of the subtrahend mentally and add.* Polynomials are subtracted term by term. The like terms should be placed in columns and subtracted.

Example: Subtract the following terms:

$$\begin{array}{r} + 12\,x \\ + \ 5\,x \\ \hline + \ 7\,x \end{array} \qquad \begin{array}{r} + 12\,x \\ - \ 5\,x \\ \hline + 17\,x \end{array} \qquad \begin{array}{r} - 15\,y \\ - \ 5\,y \\ \hline - 10\,y \end{array} \qquad \begin{array}{r} - 15\,y \\ + \ 5\,y \\ \hline - 20\,y \end{array}$$

$$\begin{array}{r} + 3\,ax^2 - 16\,y^2 - 3\,z \\ - 5\,ax^2 + \ 4\,y^2 - 8\,z \\ \hline + 8\,ax^2 - 20\,y^2 + 5\,z \end{array} \qquad \begin{array}{r} 20\,ab \\ - 11\,cd \\ \hline 20\,ab + 11\,cd \end{array}$$

Parentheses

It is often necessary to group terms and consider a whole group, or several groups, as a single term. This grouping is indicated by parentheses ( ), brackets [ ], or braces { }. The + or − sign in front of the group applies to each term in the group. This gives the following rules for the removal of parentheses or brackets:

Rules

1. *If parentheses (or brackets) are preceded by a + sign, the parentheses can be removed without changing the signs of the terms inside the parentheses.*
2. *If parentheses (or brackets) are preceded by a − sign, the parentheses can be removed if the sign of each term inside the parentheses is changed.*

Example 1: Remove the parentheses.

$$5\,x + (3\,y - 4\,z) = 5\,x + 3\,y - 4\,z$$
$$5\,x - (3\,y - 4\,z) = 5\,x - 3\,y + 4\,z$$

Sometimes there are several groups in one problem. In this case, remove the inner parentheses first, then the next outer ones, and so on, applying the above rules each time.

Example 2: Remove the parentheses, brackets and braces, and simplify.

$$10\,x - [a - \{6\,b + (2\,a - b) - 3\,b\} + 2\,x]$$
$$= 10\,x - [a - \{6\,b + 2\,a - b - 3\,b\} + 2\,x]$$
$$= 10\,x - [a - 6\,b - 2\,a + b + 3\,b + 2\,x]$$
$$= 10\,x - a + 6\,b + 2\,a - b - 3\,b - 2\,x$$
$$= 8\,x + a + 2\,b$$

EXERCISE 2.1

Find the sum in each of the following problems:

1. $15\,a - 3\,b + 6\,c;\; -7\,a + 7\,b - 4\,d;\; 10\,d - 2\,b + 3\,a;$
$7\,c - 4\,a + 7\,b + 15\,c;\; 10\,c + 5\,a + 2\,c$

2. $7\,x - 4\,y + 2\,z;\; -3\,x + 5\,z - 6\,y;\; 10\,z + 5\,x - 3\,y;$
$9\,y + 14\,x + 15\,z - 12\,y$

3. $-15\,a - 12\,b + 3\,d;\; 6\,a + 6\,b - 12\,c;\; 2\,a + 15\,b - 6\,d + 4\,c;$
$7\,d + 3\,a - 4\,d - 6\,b;\; 12\,c + 16\,b - 14\,d + 13\,c$

4. $10\,x - 4\,y + 6\,z;\; -10\,z + 4\,x + 5\,y;\; 7\,y + 2\,x - 6\,z;$
$8\,z + 5\,x + 3\,z - 4\,y;\; -7\,z - 3\,x - 8\,y - 5\,x$

5. $17\,y^2 - 14\,z - 12\,x^3;\; 18\,x^3 + 12\,z - 19\,y^2;$
$25\,z + 16\,y^2 - 14\,x^3;\; 21\,x^3 - 23\,y^2 + 15\,z$

6. $7\,x^{\frac{1}{2}} + 4\,y^{\frac{1}{2}} - z;\; 5\,z - 6\,y^{\frac{1}{2}} - 5\,x^{\frac{1}{2}};\; 15\,y^{\frac{1}{2}} - 2\,x^{\frac{1}{2}} - 6\,z;$
$10\,y^{\frac{1}{2}} - 11\,z - 9\,x^{\frac{1}{2}}$

7. $9\,a^{\frac{3}{2}} - 10\,b^{\frac{3}{2}} + 6\,c^{\frac{3}{2}};\; 15\,b^{\frac{3}{2}} - c^{\frac{3}{2}} + a^{\frac{3}{2}};\; 21\,c^{\frac{3}{2}} - 5\,a^{\frac{3}{2}} - 20\,b^{\frac{3}{2}};$
$25\,a^{\frac{3}{2}} - 16\,c^{\frac{3}{2}} - 12\,b^{\frac{3}{2}}$

8. $12\,a + 7\,b + 6\,c - d;\; 2\,d - 3\,b + 5\,c - 4\,a;$
$3\,c + 2\,b - 6\,a + 4\,d;\; -4\,b + 9\,a - 3\,c + 6\,d;$
$-5\,d - 5\,c + 6\,b + 3\,a$

Simplify each of the following:

9. $a - b - (c + d)$

10. $m + (2\,m - n) - (3\,n - m) + n$

11. $2\,xy + 4\,y^2 - (x^2 + xy - y^2)$

12. $a - (c - d - b) + (b - c) - (c + d)$

13. $6\,x - [2\,a - \{3\,b + (2\,b - a) - b\} + 3\,x]$

14. $4\,m - [2\,p + 4\,m - (n - m) + 2 - (5\,p - 2\,n + 6\,m)]$

15. $15\,a - [\{6 - 2\,b - (5\,b + 2\,c)\} + b - 5 - (4\,a - 7\,b + 6)]$

16. $x^4 - \{[x^3 - (x - 1)] - [x^4 - (1 - x) + x^3] - x^4 + 6\}$

17. $a - (b + c) - [a - \{b + c - (c + a - b) + (b - a) + (c - a)\}]$

18. $ac - \{6 - x - (b - c + ac - x)\} + [b - (x - c + 6)]$

19. $1 - x - \{1 - [x - (1 - x) - (x + 2)] - [(1 - x) - (x - 1)]\}$

Multiplication

In algebra, the same principles of multiplication hold as in arithmetic, and the same notation is used. The number to be multiplied is the multiplicand; the number by which the multiplicand is multiplied is the multiplier; and the result is the product.

The sign of multiplication is usually the parentheses enclosing the factors. Sometimes a dot (·) is placed between the factors, but here care is needed because it is easily confused with the decimal point. Since the multiplication sign of arithmetic ($\times$) is easily confused with an x, it should not be used in algebra. The best way is always to use parentheses. When two unlike letters like x and y are multiplied, the result is written xy with no sign between.

The process of multiplication is similar to that in arithmetic. Set the numbers down in the same way as in arithmetic and follow the usual procedure.

Example:

$$
\begin{array}{ll}
\begin{array}{r} 2 \text{ ft } 3 \text{ in.} \\ 2 \\ \hline 4 \text{ ft } 6 \text{ in.} \end{array} &
\begin{array}{r} 2\,a + 3\,b \\ 2 \\ \hline 4\,a + 6\,b \end{array}
\end{array}
$$

Each term is multiplied in turn by the multiplier.

If a rectangle is a in. wide and b in. long, the area is (a in.) (b in.) $= ab$ sq in. If a square is a in. on a side, the area is (a in.)(a in.) $= a^2$ sq in.

Consider the product $a^2(a^3)$. If this is written out completely it becomes $a(a) \cdot (a)(a)(a) = a^5$. The exponent of the product is obtained by adding the exponents of the factors. If a^n is one factor, then

$$a^n(a) = a^{n+1}$$

and the general rule may be stated as

$$a^n(a^m) = a^{n+m}$$

This is true for all values of m and n.

By this rule

$$(3\,a^2)(5\,a^3) = 3(a)(a)(5)(a)(a)(a) = 15\,a^5$$

and $\qquad (2\,a^2b)(3\,ab^3) = 6\,a^3b^4.$

Rules for Multiplication

1. *The coefficient of the product is equal to the product of the coefficients of the terms multiplied.*
2. *Each letter in each term in the product will have an exponent equal to the sum of the exponents of that letter in all the terms.*

Example: $4\ ab^2(6\ a^3b)(3\ b^4)$

Coefficients	$4(6)(3) = 72$
Exponent of a	$1 + 3 + 0 = 4$
Exponent of b	$2 + 1 + 4 = 7$
Answer	$72\ a^4b^7$

When the exponent is 1, it is not shown. Thus $a^1 = a$. This must be remembered in adding the exponents. If the letter does not appear in the term, the exponent is zero. The third term could have been written $(3\ a^0b^4)$.

Rules for Signs

1. *If each of two terms has the same sign, either positive or negative, the sign of the product is positive.*
2. *If two terms have unlike signs, one positive and one negative, the sign of the product is negative.*
3. *In the product of several terms, an even number of minus signs makes the sign of the product positive; an odd number of minus signs makes the sign of the product negative.*

Examples:

$$(-6\ a)(-3\ b) = +18\ ab \qquad \text{Rule 1}$$
$$(-3\ ab)(4\ bc^2) = -12\ ab^2c^2 \qquad \text{Rule 2}$$
$$(2\ ab)(-3\ a^2c)(-5\ b^2c) = +30\ a^3b^3c^2 \qquad \text{Rule 3}$$

Multiplication of Multinomials

When two multinomials are to be multiplied, write them one below the other. Multiply each term of the multiplicand by the first term of the multiplier. Put down these terms in a row. Next multiply the multiplicand by the second term of the multiplier. Write these terms in a second row. Arrange the terms in the second row that are like those in the first row in columns. Carry out the multiplication for each term of the multiplier. Add the columns to obtain the product.

Example 1: Multiply $(c + d)(c + d)$.

$$
\begin{array}{l}
c\ + d \\
\underline{c\ + d} \\
c^2\ +\quad cd \qquad \text{Multiply by } c \\
\underline{\quad+\quad cd + d^2} \quad \text{Multiply by } d \\
c^2 + 2\ cd + d^2
\end{array}
$$

Example 2: Multiply $a^2 + 2\,ab - 3\,b^2$ by $ab - b^2$.
This is more difficult but is done in the same way.

$$\begin{array}{l} a^2 \;+ 2\,ab \;- 3\,b^2 \\ ab \;- b^2 \\ \hline a^3b + 2\,a^2b^2 - 3\,ab^3 \\ \quad - \quad a^2b^2 - 2\,ab^3 + 3\,b^4 \\ \hline a^3b + \quad a^2b^2 - 5\,ab^3 + 3\,b^4 \end{array}$$

Sometimes some of the columns may add up to zero. In this case, the terms in those columns do not appear in the product.

Example 3: Multiply $a^3 - a^2b + ab^2 - b^3$ by $a + b$.

$$\begin{array}{l} a^3 - a^2b + ab^2 - b^3 \\ a + b \\ \hline a^4 - a^3b + a^2b^2 - ab^3 \\ \quad + a^3b - a^2b^2 + ab^3 \;- b^4 \\ \hline a^4 \qquad\qquad\qquad\qquad\quad - b^4 \end{array}$$

EXERCISE 2.2

Multiply the following:

1. $4\,a(3\,b)(2\,c)$
2. $-3\,a(-2\,b)(-d)(-3\,c)$
3. $-2\,a(-4\,b)(-6\,c)$
4. $6\,a(7\,b)$
5. $-5\,a(-6\,b)$
6. $-4\,a(3\,b)$
7. $(b + c)(b - c)$
8. $(a - 5)(a + 5)$
9. $(ac + 6)(ac - 6)$
10. $(3\,a^2 + 2\,b^2)(3\,a^2 - 2\,b^2)$
11. $(a + b - c)(a - b + c)$
12. $(x - 6\,y + 4\,z)(2\,x + 3\,y + 2\,z)$
13. $(5\,x + 3)(2\,x - 4)$
14. $(10\,x + 5)(6\,x + 4)$
15. $(6\,a^2 + 1)(a^2 - 7)$
16. $(a - 5)(a - 2)$
17. $(a^2b^2 + 6\,c)(5\,a^2b^2 - 3\,c)$

18. $(a + b + c)(a + b - c)$

19. $(x + y + z)(x - y - z)$

20. $(x^4 - m^2 + 1)(x^4 + m^2 + 1)$

21. $(y^2 + 3x - 2)(y^2 - 3x + 2)$

22. $[(a + b) + (x + y)][(a + b) - (x + y)]$

23. $(a^2 + ab + b^2)(a^2 - ab + b^2)$

24. $(2a + 3b - 4c)(2a + 3b + 4c)$

25. $(y^2 + 2y - 1)(y^2 - 2y + 1)$

26. Find the area.

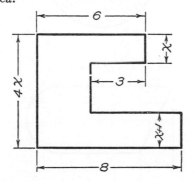

27. Find the area.

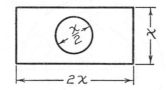

28. Find the area.

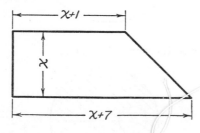

29.   Find the area of the annulus.

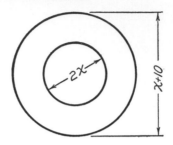

30.   Find the volume of the torus.

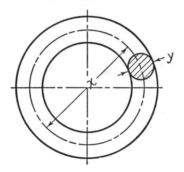

31.   Find the area of the shaded surface.

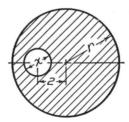

32.   Find the area.

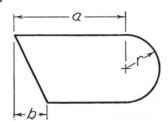

33. Find the area.

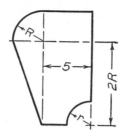

34. Find the area.

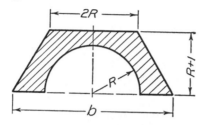

35. Find the volume of the solid shown.

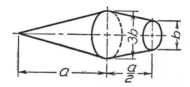

DIVISION OF MONOMIALS

In algebra as in arithmetic, division is the inverse of multiplication. In multiplication, two numbers are given and the product is required. In division one of the numbers and the product are given and the other number is required. The **dividend** is the number to be divided; the **divisor** is the number by which the division is made; and the **quotient** is the result.

From the principles of multiplication, the following quotients are obtained.

$$(+ x)(+ y) = + xy \quad \text{so} \quad (+ xy) \div (+ y) = + x$$
$$(- x)(+ y) = - xy \quad \text{so} \quad (- xy) \div (+ y) = - x$$
$$(+ x)(- y) = - xy \quad \text{so} \quad (- xy) \div (- y) = + x$$
$$(- x)(- y) = + xy \quad \text{so} \quad (+ xy) \div (- y) = - x$$

When the signs are like, the sign of the quotient is plus; when they are unlike, the quotient is negative.

Also $$\frac{8\,x^5}{4\,x^2} = \frac{\overset{2}{\cancel{8}}(x)(x)(x)(\cancel{x})(\cancel{x})}{\cancel{4}(\cancel{x})(\cancel{x})} = 2\,x^{5-2} = 2\,x^3$$

and $$\frac{15\,a^2b^3c}{3\,ab^3c^2} = \frac{5\,a}{c} = 5\,ac^{-1}$$

To see what happened to the b term in the last example, note that

$$\frac{b^3}{b^3} = b^{3-3} = b^0$$

but $$\frac{b^3}{b^3} = 1$$

so $$b^0 = 1$$

and the b does not appear in the result.

The exponent of c is $1 - 2 = -1$. c^{-1} is the same as $\frac{1}{c}$. This may be generalized to

$$b^m \div b^n = b^{m-n}$$

Rules for Division of Monomials by Monomials

1. *The sign of the quotient is plus when the dividend and divisor have like signs and minus when they have unlike signs.*
2. *The coefficient of the quotient is equal to the numerical coefficient of the dividend divided by the numerical coefficient of the divisor.*
3. *The exponent of each of the literal factors of the quotient equals the exponent of the dividend minus the exponent of the divisor having the same base.*
4. *Any number, except zero, to the zero power equals 1.*

Sometimes the letters in the dividend are not the same as the letters in the divisor. In this case, the division cannot actually be performed but is merely indicated. Thus, $\frac{3\,ab}{cd}$ cannot be divided; it is left in that form. Sometimes part of the division can be performed: $\frac{a^2bc}{bd} = \frac{a^2c}{d}$.

Negative Exponents

Thus far the negative exponent has not been defined, since the definition of an exponent was limited to positive integers. To take a as a factor -3 times has no meaning as yet. The definition should be stated so that the law of exponents still applies. If $a^n(a^m) = a^{m+n}$, $a^n(a^{-n}) = a^{n-n} = a^0 = 1$, then $a^{-n} = \dfrac{1}{a^n}$. This will make the law $a^n \div a^m = a^{n-m}$ true when n and m are any positive integers. Thus $2^{-3} = \dfrac{1}{2^3} = \dfrac{1}{8}$ and $a^3(a^{-4}) = a^{-1}$.

Division of a Polynomial by a Monomial

When a polynomial is the dividend and a monomial the divisor, divide each term of the polynomial by the monomial.

Example 1: Divide $ax + cx$ by x.

$$\frac{ax + cx}{x} = a + c$$

Example 2: Divide $8\,xy^2 + 14\,xyz^2 - 3\,x^2y$ by $2\,xy$.

$$\frac{8\,xy^2 + 14\,xyz^2 - 3\,x^2y}{2\,xy} = 4\,y + 7\,z^2 - 1.5\,x$$

Division of Polynomials

When two polynomials are to be divided, the operation is like long division.

Example 1: Divide $a^2 - 5\,ab + 4\,b^2$ by $a - 4\,b$.

$$
\begin{array}{ll}
a^2 - 5\,ab + 4\,b^2 & \underline{a - 4\,b} \\
\underline{a^2 - 4\,ab} & a - b \quad \textbf{Answer} \\
\quad -\ ab + 4\,b^2 & \\
\quad \underline{-\ ab + 4\,b^2} &
\end{array}
$$

First rearrange the terms of both dividend and divisor, if necessary, so that the exponents of one of the common literal factors are in descending order. Next, divide the first term (a^2) of the dividend by the first term (a) of the divisor and write the quotient (a) as the first term of the result. Multiply each term of the divisor by this term and set the result down under the dividend. Subtracting gives $-ab + 4\,b^2$. This is the new dividend. Divide $-ab$ by a and you get $-b$. Write this down as the second term of the result. Multiplying the divisor by this gives $- ab + 4 b^2$. When this is subtracted, the remainder is zero, and the division is complete.

The division can be checked by multiplying $(a - 4 b)$ by $(a - b)$ to give $a^2 - 5 ab + 4 b^2$.

It often happens that the division does not come out even but leaves a remainder. In this case, the remainder is put over the divisor and the resulting fraction is considered part of the answer.

Example 2: Divide $a^3 + 2 a^2 - 3 a + 6$ by $a - 2$.

$$
\begin{array}{r|l}
a^3 + 2 a^2 - 3 a + 6 & a - 2 \\
a^3 - 2 a^2 & \\ \cline{1-1}
\quad 4 a^2 - 3 a & a^2 + 4 a + 5 + \dfrac{16}{a - 2} \\
\quad 4 a^2 - 8 a & \\ \cline{1-1}
\qquad 5 a + 6 & \\
\qquad 5 a - 10 & \\ \cline{1-1}
\qquad\qquad 16 &
\end{array}
$$

To prove the result, multiply the quotient by the divisor; this should give the dividend.

$$
\begin{array}{r}
a^2 + 4 a + 5 \\
a - 2 \\ \hline
a^3 + 4 a^2 + 5 a \\
- 2 a^2 - 8 a - 10 \\ \hline
a^3 + 2 a^2 - 3 a - 10 \\
+ 16 \\ \hline
a^3 + 2 a^2 - 3 a + 6
\end{array}
$$

Add the remainder

Example 3: Divide $x^4 + 1$ by $x + 1$.

$$
\begin{array}{r|l}
x^4 \qquad\qquad + 1 & x + 1 \\
x^4 + x^3 & \\ \cline{1-1}
\quad - x^3 & x^3 - x^2 + x - 1 + \dfrac{2}{x + 1} \\
\quad - x^3 - x^2 & \\ \cline{1-1}
\qquad x^2 & \\
\qquad x^2 + x & \\ \cline{1-1}
\qquad\quad - x + 1 & \\
\qquad\quad - x - 1 & \\ \cline{1-1}
\qquad\qquad + 2 &
\end{array}
$$

There is no x^3 term in the dividend, so the x^3 in the first product is subtracted from zero, giving $- x^3$. The x^2 and x terms are subtracted in the same way. The $+ 1$ in the dividend is not brought down until it is needed.

EXERCISE 2.3

Perform the following indicated divisions:

1. $y^2 + y - 20$ by $y + 5$
2. $x^2 - 18 - 3x$ by $x - 6$
3. $81 + x^4 + 9x^2$ by $x^2 - 3x + 9$
4. $x^4 + 4x^2 + 16$ by $4 + x^2 + 2x$
5. $x^8 + x^6 + x^4 + x^2 + 3x - 1$ by $x + 1$
6. $25y^5 - y^3 - 8y - 2y^2$ by $5y^2 - 4y$
7. $2x^4 - 5x^3y + 6x^2y^2 - 4xy^3 + y^4$ by $x^2 - xy + y^2$
8. $x^4 + 1$ by $x - 1$
9. $y^4 - 3y^3 + y^2 + 2y - 1$ by $y^2 - y - 2$
10. $x^6 + y^6$ by $x + y$
11. $x^6 - y^6$ by $x - y$
12. $x^6 + 5x^5 - x^3 + 2x + 4$ by $x - 1$
13. 1 by $1 - x$ to five terms
14. $x^6 - 64$ by $x - 2$
15. $x^6 + 38x + 12$ by $x + 2$
16. $x^6 + 27x^2 - 9x - 10$ by $5 - 3x + x^2$
17. $x^5 - 19x - 6$ by $x + 2$
18. $x^5 + 243$ by $x + 3$
19. $x^4 + 7x - x^3 - 10x^2 + 15$ by $x^2 - 2x - 3$
20. $60y^2 - 62y^3 - 36y + 30y^4 + 8$ by $5y - 2$
21. $28y^4 - 2 - 6y + 6y^2 + 6y^3$ by $2y + 2 + 2y^2$
22. $x^4 - 625$ by $5 + x$
23. $6y - 29y^3 - 8y^2 + 4 + 21y^4$ by $3y - 2$
24. $y^7 - y^3 - 10y - 36 - 2y^5$ by $y - 2$
25. $25x^2 + 3x^4 - 20x^3 - 6 + 16x$ by $2 - 8x + 3x^2$
26. $16 - 8y - 27y^2 + 7y^3 + 2y^4$ by $y^2 - 4 + 5y$
27. $6y^4 + 4 - 18y + 30y^2 - 23y^3$ by $2 - 5y + 2y^2$
28. $32y^3 - 4 - 16y^2 - 25y + 24y^4$ by $6y^2 - 4 - y$
29. $b^3 - 2b^2d + 4bd^2 - bx^2 - 4d^2x + 2dx^2$ by $b - x$
30. $x^{2n} + 30 + 11x^n$ by $x^n + 6$

FACTORING

The multiplication of certain binomials gives type forms. Some of these occur with great regularity in mathematics and need special consideration. It is often important to be able to discover the original two factors when the product is given. Six types that are especially common will be considered.

Type I $$ax + ay + az = a(x + y + z)$$

Here a is a common monomial factor because it occurs in each term. It can be put outside the parentheses as shown. This common factor can be more than one letter and is not necessarily to the first power.

Example 1: Factor $2\ ab^2xy + 6\ abx^2y^2 - 16\ ab^3x^2y$.
The common factor is $2\ abxy$ and the factors are

$$2\ abxy(b + 3\ xy - 8\ b^2x)$$

The first factor contains all that is common to all the terms, and the second is the quotient found by dividing the multinomial by the monomial factor.

Example 2: Factor $ax + bx + ay + by$.
x is the common factor of the first two terms and y is the common factor of the last two, so

$$x(a + b) + y(a + b) = (x + y)(a + b)$$

Since the two terms are like, the coefficients can be added as shown.

Type II $$a^2 + 2\ ab + b^2 = (a + b)(a + b)$$

This result is easily obtained by multiplying the two factors.

$$
\begin{array}{l}
a\ + b \\
a\ + b \\
\hline
a^2 + ab \\
\quad\quad ab + b^2 \\
\hline
a^2 + 2\ ab + b^2
\end{array}
$$

Rule: *The square of the sum of two quantities is equal to the square of the first plus twice the product of the first and second plus the square of the second.*

This product is usually indicated as $(a + b)^2$. A common error made by students is writing $(a + b)^2 = a^2 + b^2$. In Fig. 2.2 $(a + b)^2$ is the total area of the large square, and is seen to equal $a^2 + b^2 + ab + ab$. The above error is caused by omitting the two rectangles, each of area ab. The letters need not be a and b; any others can be used. Thus

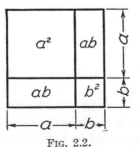

FIG. 2.2.

$$(x + y)^2 = x^2 + 2\ xy + y^2.$$

Type III $a^2 - 2\,ab + b^2 = (a - b)(a - b)$

This result is similar to that in Type II, except that the sign of the middle term is minus. It can be verified by multiplication as before.

$$
\begin{array}{l}
a \; - \; b \\
\underline{a \; - \; b} \\
a^2 - \;\; ab \\
\underline{\;\; - \;\; ab + b^2} \\
a^2 - 2\,ab + b^2
\end{array}
$$

Rule: *The square of the difference of two quantities is equal to the square of the first minus twice the product of the first and second plus the square of the second.*

For example $a^2 - 6\,ay + 9\,y^2 = (a - 3\,y)^2$. Here b stands for $3\,y$.

Type IV $a^2 - b^2 = (a + b)(a - b)$

This result is important and can be obtained by multiplication. The ab terms have opposite signs and cancel.

$$
\begin{array}{l}
a \; + \; b \\
\underline{a \; - \; b} \\
a^2 + ab \\
\underline{\;\; - \; ab - b^2} \\
a^2 \qquad - b^2
\end{array}
$$

Rule: *The product of the sum and difference of two quantities is the square of the first minus the square of the second.*

Thus $x^2 - 25\,y^2 = (x - 5\,y)(x + 5\,y)$, since x^2 and $25\,y^2$ are both perfect squares.

Type V $x^2 + ax + b$

This is a more difficult type to factor. It is first necessary to find two factors of b whose sum is a. If these two factors are c and d, so that $c + d = a$, the two factors of the expression are $(x + c)$ and $(x + d)$.

Example 1: Factor $x^2 + 5\,x + 6$.

The two factors of 6 which add up to 5 are 2 and 3; hence the factors are $(x + 2)(x + 3)$.

Example 2: Factor $x^2 - 9\,x - 36$.

The two factors of -36 whose sum is -9 are -12 and $+3$. This gives the result

$$x^2 - 9\,x - 36 = (x - 12)(x + 3).$$

Since the sign of the last term is negative, the two factors of -36 must have opposite signs.

Example 3: Factor $3 x^2 - 72 xy + 429 y^2$.

First remove the common factor; this gives

$$3(x^2 - 24 xy + 143 y^2)$$

The factors of $143 y^2$ are $11 y$ and $13 y$. Since the second term is negative and the last term is positive, the signs of the $11 y$ and $13 y$ must be alike and both must be negative. Thus

$$3 x^2 - 72 xy + 429 y^2 = 3(x - 11 y)(x - 13 y)$$

Type VI $\qquad\qquad ax^2 + bx + c$

The method used to factor $x^2 + ax + b$ can be extended to apply here. Factors of both the ax^2 term and the third term must be found and a trial process used to determine what factors will be used to obtain the proper middle term.

Example: Factor $15 x^2 + 28 x + 12$.

The factors of $15 x^2$ are $\qquad 15 x$ and $\qquad x$
or $\quad 5 x$ and $\quad 3 x$
The factors of 12 are $\quad + 4 \quad$ and $+ 3$
or $+ 6 \quad$ and $+ 2$
or $+ 12 \quad$ and $+ 1$

Arranging these factors together in all possible combinations gives:

1. $(15 x + 4)(x + 3)$ 7. $(5 x + 4)(3 x + 3)$
2. $(15 x + 3)(x + 4)$ 8. $(5 x + 3)(3 x + 4)$
3. $(15 x + 6)(x + 2)$ 9. $(5 x + 6)(3 x + 2)$
4. $(15 x + 2)(x + 6)$ 10. $(5 x + 2)(3 x + 6)$
5. $(15 x + 12)(x + 1)$ 11. $(5 x + 12)(3 x + 1)$
6. $(15 x + 1)(x + 12)$ 12. $(5 x + 1)(3 x + 12)$

A study of these combinations will show that only No. 9 will give the proper middle term, $28 x$; therefore

$$15 x^2 + 28 x + 12 = (5 x + 6)(3 x + 2)$$

EXERCISE 2.4

Factor the following:

1. $12 a^2xy - 24 ax^2y^2 + 18 a^3x^2y$
2. $3 x^5y - 15 x^3y^2 + 5 x^2y^3$
3. $x^{10} + x^9 - x^8 + x^7 - x^6$
4. $25 a^2bx^3 + 35 a^3b^2x^4 - 45 a^2b^2x^5$
5. $3 a^3b^3 + 6 a^2b^2 + 3 ab$ 7. $x^3 - x^2 - 2 x + 2$
6. $ax - ay + bx - by$ 8. $12 x^3 - 8 xy - 3 x^4 + 2 x^2y$

9. $ay - a - by + b - cy + c$
10. $16\,bx + 12\,by - 8\,ax - 6\,ay$
11. $x^2 + 8\,x + 16$
12. $5\,x^2 - 30\,x + 45$
13. $9\,x^2y^2 + 6\,xy + 1$
14. $16\,x^4 + 26\,x^2 + 9$
15. $9(a + b)^2 + 24(a + b) + 16$
16. $25\,x^4 + 10\,x^2y^2 + y^4$
17. $x^4 - 49$
18. $1 - 625\,x^4$
19. $x^2 - a^2$
20. $144\,x^2 - 400\,y^2$
21. $(2\,a - 3\,b)^2 - (3\,x + y)^2$
22. $25\,x^2 - (6\,x + y)^2$
23. $x^{2a} - y^{2b}$
24. $9\,c^2 - (b - c)^2$
25. $x^2 + 11\,x + 30$
26. $x^2 + 10\,ax - 24\,a^2$
27. $27 - 6\,x - x^2$
28. $x^6 + 14\,ax^3 + 24\,a^2$

29. $x^4 - 16\,b^3x^2 - 36\,b^6$
30. $x^{10} + 9\,x^5y + 18\,y^2$
31. $x^4 + x^2b^2 - 110\,b^4$
32. $5\,x^4 + 100\,x^2y^2 + 480\,y^4$
33. $3\,a^2 + 24\,a - 384$
34. $2\,ax + a^2 - 63\,x^2$
35. $9\,a^2 - 42\,a + 40$
36. $9\,x^2 - 10\,x - 16$
37. $3\,b^2 - 10\,ab + 3\,a^2$
38. $16\,b^2 + 50\,b - 21$
39. $15\,a^2 + 17\,a - 4$
40. $27\,x^2 - 3\,x - 14$
41. $21\,x^2 - x - 10$
42. $36\,a^2 - 48\,a - 20$
43. $9\,x^6 + 43\,x^3 - 10$
44. $16\,x^4 + 20\,x^2 - 66$
45. $a^2b - b^3$
46. $3\,any + 2\,an - 3\,bmy - 2\,bm$
47. $bx^2 - 10\,bx - 39\,b$
48. $a^2 - 3\,ab + 4\,ac - 12\,bc$

49. $a^2 + 9\,b^2 + 25\,c^2 - 6\,ab - 10\,ac + 30\,bc$
50. $m^2n^2 + n^2x^2 + x^2y^2 - 2\,mn^2x + 2\,mnxy - 2\,nx^2y$

FRACTIONS

Fractions which occur in algebra are similar to those in arithmetic. The terms numerator and denominator have the same meanings, and the same operations can be performed as in arithmetic.

The sign that is written in front of the dividing line of a fraction is the sign of the fraction, and refers to the fraction as a whole and not to either the numerator or the denominator. The numerator and denominator also each have a sign.

In the fraction $-\dfrac{-2\,a}{8\,b}$ the sign of the fraction is minus, the sign of the numerator is also minus, and the sign of the denominator is plus. In accordance with the rules for multiplication and division, any two of the three signs can be changed without changing the value of the fraction.   Thus

$$-\frac{-2\,a}{3\,b} = -\frac{+2\,a}{-3\,b} = +\frac{-2\,a}{-3\,b} = +\frac{+2\,a}{+3\,b}$$

If just one sign is changed, the value of the fraction is reversed in sign.

Rules

1. *The sign of the fraction is not altered if the signs of both numerator and denominator are changed.*
2. *The sign of the fraction must be changed if the sign of either numerator or denominator, but not both, is changed.*

It is important to remember that if the numerator or denominator is a multinomial, the sign of each term should be changed, not just the first one.   Thus

$$-\frac{x}{a-b} = +\frac{x}{-(a-b)} = \frac{x}{-a+b} = \frac{x}{b-a}$$

A common error is to change the sign of part of the numerator or denominator.   Thus

$$-\frac{x}{a-b} \neq \frac{x}{a+b}$$

and

$$\frac{x-y}{a-b} \neq \frac{x+y}{a+b}$$

The sign $\neq$ means "is *not* equal to."

In case the numerator or denominator is in factored form, change the sign of one factor, not all of them.   Thus

$$-\frac{(a-b)(a-2\,b)}{x+y} = \frac{(-a+b)(a-2\,b)}{x+y}$$

The sign of the first factor only was changed.

Operations with Fractions

Rule: *If both the numerator and denominator of a fraction are multiplied or divided by the same quantity, the value of the fraction is not changed.*

Thus

$$\frac{x}{y} = \frac{ax}{ay}$$

The numerator and denominator can often be factored and the common factors canceled.

Example 1: Reduce $\dfrac{x^2 - y^2}{x^2 + 2\,xy + y^2}$ to its lowest terms.

$$\frac{x^2 - y^2}{x^2 + 2\,xy + y^2} = \frac{\cancel{(x + y)}(x - y)}{\cancel{(x + y)}(x + y)} = \frac{x - y}{x + y}$$

Example 2: Change $\dfrac{x + y}{x - y}$ to a fraction with denominator equal to $x^2 - y^2$.

The denominator must be multiplied by $x + y$ to give $x^2 - y^2$. To keep the value of the fraction the same, both numerator and denominator are multiplied by the same factor.

$$\frac{x + y}{x - y} = \frac{(x + y)(x + y)}{(x - y)(x + y)} = \frac{x^2 + 2\,xy + y^2}{x^2 - y^2}$$

Example 3: Reduce $\dfrac{(x - 3)(x^2 - 5\,x + 4)}{x^2 - 4\,x + 3}$ to its lowest terms.

$$\frac{(x - 3)(x^2 - 5\,x + 4)}{x^2 - 4\,x + 3} = \frac{\cancel{(x - 3)}(x - 4)\cancel{(x - 1)}}{\cancel{(x - 3)}\cancel{(x - 1)}} = x - 4$$

Example 4: Reduce $\dfrac{abx - aby}{y^2 - x^2}$ to its lowest terms.

$$\frac{abx - aby}{y^2 - x^2} = \frac{ab\overset{-1}{\cancel{(x - y)}}}{\cancel{(y - x)}(y + x)} = -\frac{ab}{x + y}$$

Since $x - y = (-1)(y - x)$, $(y - x)$ in the denominator cancels into $(x - y)$ of the numerator and gives -1.

A common error is to cancel a factor of the denominator into only a part of the numerator. Thus

$$\frac{(a + b)(a - b) + 2\,a}{a - b} \neq \frac{(a + b)\cancel{(a - b)} + 2\,a}{\cancel{a - b}}$$

Addition of Fractions

The addition of algebraic fractions is almost the same as the corresponding operation in arithmetic. The first step is to reduce them all to a common denominator. If a series of fractions all have the same denominator, the sum is equal to the algebraic sum of the numerators divided by the common denominator.

Example 1: Change $\dfrac{a}{5}$ and $\dfrac{x}{3\,y}$ to fractions with a lowest common denominator.

The lowest common denominator is $15\,y$. So

$$\frac{a}{5} = \frac{(a)(3\,y)}{5(3\,y)} = \frac{3\,ay}{15\,y}$$

and

$$\frac{x}{3\,y} = \frac{(x)(5)}{(3\,y)(5)} = \frac{5\,x}{15\,y}$$

Example 2: Change $\dfrac{2\,a}{a+b}$ and $\dfrac{a+b}{a-b}$ to fractions having a lowest common denominator.

The lowest common denominator is $(a+b)(a-b)$. Hence

$$\frac{2\,a}{a+b} = \frac{2\,a(a-b)}{(a+b)(a-b)} = \frac{2\,a^2 - 2\,ab}{a^2 - b^2}$$

and

$$\frac{a+b}{a-b} = \frac{(a+b)(a+b)}{(a-b)(a+b)} = \frac{a^2 + 2\,ab + b^2}{a^2 - b^2}$$

Example 3: Add $\dfrac{2\,x}{3}$, $\dfrac{7\,x}{5}$ and $\dfrac{9\,y}{10}$.

$$\frac{2\,x}{3} + \frac{7\,x}{5} + \frac{9\,y}{10} = \frac{20\,x}{30} + \frac{42\,x}{30} + \frac{27\,y}{30} = \frac{62\,x + 27\,y}{30}$$

Example 4: Simplify $\dfrac{7\,a}{a+b} - \dfrac{3\,b}{a-b} + \dfrac{6\,ab}{a^2 - b^2}$.

$$\frac{7\,a}{a+b} - \frac{3\,b}{a-b} + \frac{6\,ab}{a^2 - b^2} = \frac{7\,a(a-b)}{a^2 - b^2} - \frac{3\,b(a+b)}{a^2 - b^2} + \frac{6\,ab}{a^2 - b^2}$$

$$= \frac{7\,a^2 - 7\,ab}{a^2 - b^2} - \frac{3\,ab + 3\,b^2}{a^2 - b^2} + \frac{6\,ab}{a^2 - b^2}$$

$$= \frac{7\,a^2 - 7\,ab - 3\,ab - 3\,b^2 + 6\,ab}{a^2 - b^2}$$

$$= \frac{7\,a^2 - 4\,ab - 3\,b^2}{a^2 - b^2}$$

$$= \frac{(7\,a + 3\,b)(a - b)}{(a+b)(a-b)} = \frac{7\,a + 3\,b}{a+b}$$

Multiplication and Division of Fractions

These operations are almost the same for algebraic fractions as for fractions in arithmetic. The product of two or more fractions is equal to the product of the numerators divided by the product of the denominators. Any common factors in the numerator and denominator should be canceled.

Example 1: Multiply $\dfrac{2\,a}{3\,bx}$ by $\dfrac{x^2y}{4}$.

$$\left(\frac{2\,a}{3\,bx}\right)\left(\frac{x^2y}{4}\right) = \frac{\overset{x}{\cancel{2}}\,a\cancel{x}^{2}y}{\underset{6}{\cancel{12}\,b\cancel{x}}} = \frac{axy}{6\,b}$$

Example 2: Multiply $\dfrac{x^2 + 2\,xy + y^2}{x - y}$ by $\dfrac{x^2 - 2\,xy + y^2}{x + y}$.

$$\left(\frac{x^2 + 2\,xy + y^2}{x - y}\right)\left(\frac{x^2 - 2\,xy + y^2}{x + y}\right) = \frac{(x + y)\cancel{(x + y)}\cancel{(x - y)}(x - y)}{\cancel{(x - y)}\cancel{(x + y)}}$$
$$= (x + y)(x - y) = x^2 - y^2$$

To divide two fractions, multiply the first by the reciprocal of the second. This is done by inverting the second and multiplying by the first. As in multiplication, any common factors in the numerator and denominator should be canceled.

Example 3: Divide $\dfrac{x^2 - 9}{x^2 - 1}$ by $\dfrac{x + 3}{x + 1}$.

$$\frac{x^2 - 9}{x^2 - 1} \div \frac{x + 3}{x + 1} = \left(\frac{x^2 - 9}{x^2 - 1}\right)\left(\frac{x + 1}{x + 3}\right)$$
$$= \frac{\cancel{(x + 3)}(x - 3)\cancel{(x + 1)}}{(x - 1)\cancel{(x + 1)}\cancel{(x + 3)}} = \frac{x - 3}{x - 1}$$

Example 4: Divide $\dfrac{x^2 - x - 6}{x^2 - 25}$ by $\dfrac{x^2 + x - 12}{x^2 - x - 20}$.

$$\frac{x^2 - x - 6}{x^2 - 25} \div \frac{x^2 + x - 12}{x^2 - x - 20} = \left(\frac{x^2 - x - 6}{x^2 - 25}\right)\left(\frac{x^2 - x - 20}{x^2 + x - 12}\right)$$
$$= \frac{\cancel{(x - 3)}(x + 2)\cancel{(x - 5)}\cancel{(x + 4)}}{\cancel{(x - 5)}(x + 5)\cancel{(x + 4)}\cancel{(x - 3)}} = \frac{x + 2}{x + 5}$$

EXERCISE 2.5

Reduce to lowest terms:

1. $\dfrac{36\,a^2bx^3y}{16\,ab^2xy}$

2. $\dfrac{6\,xy^2z^5}{18\,x^2y^2z^2}$

3. $-\dfrac{-\,r^2st^3}{9\,rs}$

4. $-\dfrac{x^2 - y^2}{y - x}$

5. $\dfrac{8\,x^3 - 18\,xy^2}{6\,y - 4\,x}$

Simplify the following:

6. $\dfrac{1 - 2x}{4x^2 - 1}$

9. $\dfrac{4x - 3}{x} - \dfrac{1 - x}{2x - 1} + \dfrac{5x^2 + 1}{x - 2x^2}$

7. $\dfrac{a^2b - ab}{1 - a^2}$

10. $\dfrac{x^2 + 7x - 30}{x^2 - 7x + 12}$

8. $\dfrac{x}{x - y} + \dfrac{y}{x + y} + \dfrac{x^2 + y^2}{y^2 + x^2}$

11. $\dfrac{20x^3 + 20x^2y + 5xy^2}{60x^5 - 15x^3y^2}$

12. $\left(\dfrac{-a - b}{b - a}\right)\left(\dfrac{a^2 - b^2}{(a + b)^2}\right)$

13. $\left\{\dfrac{5(3 - x)}{-2(x + 1)}\right\}\left\{\dfrac{4(x + 1)(x + 2)}{15(x - 3)}\right\}$

14. $\left(\dfrac{a + b}{xy}\right) \div \left(\dfrac{a^2 - b^2}{x^2y}\right)$

15. $\left(6x - 1 - \dfrac{1}{x}\right) \div \left(\dfrac{2x - 1}{3x}\right)$

16. $\left(\dfrac{a + b}{a} - \dfrac{a + b}{b}\right) \div \left(\dfrac{1}{a} - \dfrac{1}{b}\right)$

17. $\left\{\dfrac{12c^3b}{5(c^3 - b^3)}\right\}\left\{\dfrac{35(c^2 + bc + b^2)}{14c^2b^2}\right\}$

18. $\dfrac{1}{2} + \dfrac{b}{a - b} + \dfrac{2a^2}{b^2 - a^2} + \dfrac{-a}{a + b}$

19. $\left\{\dfrac{3t^2 - 2t - 1}{2t^2 + t - 1}\right\}\left\{\dfrac{2t^2 + 5t - 3}{3t^2 + 7t + 2}\right\}\left\{\dfrac{4t^2 + 10t + 4}{4t^2 - 2t - 2}\right\}$

20. $\left\{\dfrac{x^2 + 9xy + 18y^2}{x^2 - 9xy + 20y^2}\right\} \div \left\{\dfrac{x^2 + 6xy + 9y^2}{xy^2 - 4y^3}\right\}$

21. $\dfrac{a^2 + 2a - 15}{a^2 - 5a + 6} - \dfrac{5a - 4}{2 - a}$

22. $\left(x - 1 + \dfrac{6}{x - 6}\right) \div \left(x - 2 + \dfrac{3}{x - 6}\right)$

EXPONENTS

An exponent has already been defined as a positive integer at the right and above a letter or quantity indicating that the letter or quantity is to be taken as a factor as many times as there are units in this integer. Thus $x^3 = x(x)(x)$.

The law of multiplication for integral exponents was shown to be

$$a^n(a^m) = a^{n+m}$$

It was also shown that *any quantity except zero raised to the zero power is equal to 1,* since

$$\frac{b^n}{b^n} = b^{n-n} = b^0 = 1$$

and also that

$$a^{-n} = \frac{1}{a^n}$$

The law of division for integral exponents was given as

$$b^m \div b^n = b^{m-n}$$

The next law of integral exponents states that *a quantity is raised to a power by multiplying the exponents by the power.*

$$(a^m)^n = a^{mn}$$

Proof:
$$(a^m)^n = (a^m)(a^m) \cdots n \text{ times}$$
$$= a^{m+m+ \cdots}$$
$$= a^{mn}$$

Another law of integral exponents states that *the power of a product is equal to the product of the factors, each raised to the power indicated by the exponent.*

$$(ab)^n = a^n b^n$$

Proof: Since $(ab)^n = (ab)(ab) \cdots n$ times, the order of multiplication can be arranged in a group of n a's and n b's. Thus

$$(ab)^n = \{(a)(a) \cdots n \text{ times}\}\{(b)(b) \cdots n \text{ times}\} = a^n b^n$$

The next law of integral exponents states that *the power of a quotient is equal to the quotient of the quantities, each raised to the power indicated by the exponent.*

$$\left(\frac{a}{b}\right)^n = \frac{a^n}{b^n}$$

Proof: $\left(\dfrac{a}{b}\right)\left(\dfrac{a}{b}\right) \cdots n \text{ times} = \dfrac{a(a) \cdots n \text{ times}}{b(b) \cdots n \text{ times}} = \dfrac{a^n}{b^n}$

It can be shown that these laws hold when the exponents are positive or negative integers or zero.

Thus far fractional exponents have not been defined. Thus $5^{\frac{2}{3}}$ has no meaning as yet, and therefore we are free to define it to suit ourselves. For this definition to be most useful, the preceding laws of exponents should apply to it. Since $(a^m)^n = a^{mn}$,

$$(a^{\frac{3}{5}})^5 \qquad \text{should equal} \qquad a^3$$

and $$(a^{\frac{1}{3}})^3 \qquad \text{should equal} \qquad a$$

A **fractional exponent** is defined as a fraction at the right and above a quantity, the denominator denoting a principle root of the quantity and the numerator a power of this root. By this definition, $8^{\frac{2}{3}} = \sqrt[3]{8^2} = \sqrt[3]{64} = 4$, and $3^{\frac{1}{3}} = \sqrt[3]{3} = 1.442 \cdots$.

Imaginary and Complex Numbers

It is not possible to extract the square root of a negative number and obtain a result which can be expressed as a real number, because no real number, when squared, can give a negative result. The square of every real number is either zero or positive.

A new class of numbers will be defined. The

$$\sqrt{-1}$$

is the **imaginary unit** and is denoted by i, so

$$i = \sqrt{-1}$$

The square root of a negative number can now be taken. Thus

$$\sqrt{-9} = \sqrt{9(-1)} = \sqrt{9}\sqrt{-1} = 3i$$

and

$$\sqrt{-12} = \sqrt{12(-1)} = \sqrt{4}\sqrt{3}\sqrt{-1} = 2\sqrt{3}i$$

An important point to notice is that

$$\sqrt{-1}\sqrt{-1} = -1 \quad \text{and not} \quad +1,$$

since if the square root of a number is squared, the result should be the original number. Evidently $\sqrt{-1}$ when squared should not give $+1$ because that is not the original number. Thus

$$i^2 = -1$$
$$i^3 = i^2(i) = -i$$
$$i^4 = +1, \text{ etc.}$$

The expression $a + ib$, where a and b are real numbers, is called a **complex number**. It is the sum of the **real part** a and the **imaginary part** ib. A real number is therefore a special case of complex numbers, where $b = 0$. If $a = 0$ and $b \neq 0$, the resulting number ib is a **pure imaginary number**.

Restrictions in the Use of Fractional Exponents

It is necessary to apply some restrictions in the use of fractional exponents if all the laws are to apply in all cases. Thus $a^{\frac{1}{n}}$ denotes the real nth root of a if there is only one, and the positive one if there are two. The law $a^{\frac{1}{n}}b^{\frac{1}{n}} = (ab)^{\frac{1}{n}}$ does not hold if a and b are both negative and n is even. Thus, if $a = -2$, $b = -3$ and $n = 2$,

$$(-2)^{\frac{1}{2}}(-3)^{\frac{1}{2}} = -\sqrt{6}$$

instead of $+\sqrt{6}$ as indicated by the formula.

This is easier to understand if the results are expressed in terms of the imaginary unit i. Thus

$$(-2)^{\frac{1}{2}}(-3)^{\frac{1}{2}} = \sqrt{2}\,i\sqrt{3}\,i = \sqrt{6}\,i^2 = -\sqrt{6}$$

Likewise

$$(-1)^{\frac{1}{2}}(-1)^{\frac{1}{2}} = i(i) = i^2 = -1$$

If the product had been taken as

$$[(-1)(-1)]^{\frac{1}{2}} = (+1)^{\frac{1}{2}} = +1$$

the result would have been wrong.

Always combine and simplify fractional exponents before working with them. Only one case remains, $(-a)^{\frac{m}{n}}$, where m and n are not both even. In this case it does not matter in which order they are applied.

The law $\left(\dfrac{a}{b}\right)^{\frac{1}{n}} = \dfrac{a^{\frac{1}{n}}}{b^{\frac{1}{n}}}$ does not hold when n is even, a is positive and b is negative. Thus $\left(\dfrac{9}{-4}\right)^{\frac{1}{2}} = \dfrac{3}{2}\sqrt{-1}$. The formula would give $\dfrac{\sqrt{9}}{\sqrt{-4}} = \dfrac{3}{2\sqrt{-1}} = -\dfrac{3}{2}\sqrt{-1}$. The signs are opposite.

An error which is common is to set $2\,x^{-1} = \dfrac{1}{2\,x}$. The 2 does not have -1 as an exponent and should not be placed in the denominator. The correct result is $2\,x^{-1} = \dfrac{2}{x}$. If the other result were intended, the equation would have been stated $(2\,x)^{-1} = \dfrac{1}{2\,x}$.

RADICALS

The algebra of fractional exponents is commonly expressed in a different form by using radicals. The **radical sign** is the same symbol $\sqrt{}$ that is used in arithmetic and it has the same meaning. By the definition of a fractional exponent, $a^{\frac{1}{n}} = \sqrt[n]{a}$ since $a^{\frac{1}{n}}$ was defined as the real nth root of a. The number n which is written above the radical is called the *index* of the radical. Ordinarily the index is omitted when it is 2, meaning the square root.

$\sqrt{3}$ is read "the square root of three"

$\sqrt[3]{x}$ is read "the cube root of x"

$\sqrt[5]{y^2}$ is read "the fifth root of y^2"

$\sqrt[n]{x + y}$ is read "the nth root of $x + y$"

The laws of fractional exponents can also be written with radicals. Thus

$$a^{\frac{1}{n}}b^{\frac{1}{n}} = (ab)^{\frac{1}{n}}$$

can be written

$$\sqrt[n]{a}\sqrt[n]{b} = \sqrt[n]{ab}$$

For example, $\sqrt{a}\sqrt{b} = \sqrt{ab}$ and $\sqrt{m}\sqrt{m^3} = \sqrt{m^4}$

The law

$$\left(\frac{a}{b}\right)^{\frac{1}{n}} = \frac{a^{\frac{1}{n}}}{b^{\frac{1}{n}}}$$

can be written

$$\sqrt[n]{\frac{a}{b}} = \frac{\sqrt[n]{a}}{\sqrt[n]{b}}$$

The quantity $a^{\frac{m}{n}}$ was defined as the nth root of a^m, and in radical form becomes

$$a^{\frac{m}{n}} = \sqrt[n]{a^m}$$

For example, $a^{\frac{2}{3}} = \sqrt[3]{a^2}$, and $b^{\frac{3}{2}} = \sqrt{b^3}$

Since $(a^{\frac{1}{n}})^m = a^{\frac{m}{n}}$, a radical is raised to a power by raising the quantity under the radical sign to that power. Thus

$$(\sqrt[n]{a})^m = \sqrt[n]{a^m}$$

For example,

$$(\sqrt{3})^3 = \sqrt{3^3} = \sqrt{27}, \quad \text{and} \quad (\sqrt{x^3})^3 = \sqrt{x^9}$$

Simplification of Radicals

In order to simplify radicals it is easier to express them in certain standard forms. For example,

$$\sqrt{12} = \sqrt{4(3)} = \sqrt{4}\sqrt{3} = 2\sqrt{3}$$

Here the square root of one factor of 12 was taken, thus reducing the quantity under the radical to the lowest value.

At first sight $\sqrt{18}$ and $\sqrt{50}$ do not appear to be similar. If they were to be added, the square root of each one would first be extracted and the results added. However, by first simplifying each one the work is reduced.

$$\sqrt{18} = \sqrt{9(2)} = 3\sqrt{2}$$
$$\sqrt{50} = \sqrt{25(2)} = 5\sqrt{2}$$

The sum is seen to be $8\sqrt{2}$. They can be added directly because the two radicals are now alike.

Likewise $\sqrt{\frac{2}{3}}$ can be calculated directly, but it is better to simplify it first. If $\sqrt{2}$ and $\sqrt{3}$ were each calculated and the results divided, a long computation would be involved because both would be long decimals and it is not easy to divide by a number with so many figures. It would be easier if the denominator were a simple integer. Therefore the fraction is changed so that the denominator is a perfect square.

$$\sqrt{\frac{2}{3}} = \sqrt{\frac{6}{9}} = \frac{\sqrt{6}}{\sqrt{9}} = \frac{1}{3}\sqrt{6}$$

This is the standard form of the radical, and it is easier to calculate its value.

A radical is in the simplest form when:

1. The quantity under the radical is as small, or to as small a power, as possible.
2. No fraction occurs under the radical and no radical occurs in the denominator.
3. All operations indicated have been carried out.
4. All similar radicals have been combined.

Example 1: Simplify $\sqrt{48}$.

$$\sqrt{48} = \sqrt{16(3)} = 4\sqrt{3}$$

Example 2: Add $\sqrt{12}$, $2\sqrt{48}$ and $\sqrt{147}$.

$$\sqrt{12} = \sqrt{4(3)} = 2\sqrt{3}$$
$$2\sqrt{48} = 2\sqrt{16(3)} = 8\sqrt{3}$$
$$\sqrt{147} = \sqrt{49(3)} = 7\sqrt{3}$$
$$\text{Total} = 17\sqrt{3}$$

Example 3: Simplify $\sqrt[3]{16\,x^5y^4}$.

$$\sqrt[3]{16\,x^5y^4} = \sqrt[3]{8\,x^3y^3(2\,x^2y)} = 2\,xy\sqrt[3]{2\,x^2y}$$

Example 4: Simplify $\sqrt{\dfrac{28\,ab^2}{3\,c}}$.

$$\sqrt{\frac{28\,ab^2}{3\,c}} = \sqrt{\frac{4\,b^2(7\,a)(3\,c)}{9\,c^2}} = \frac{2\,b}{3\,c}\sqrt{21\,ac}$$

Example 5: Simplify $\sqrt{\dfrac{x-y}{x+y}}$.

$$\sqrt{\frac{x-y}{x+y}} = \sqrt{\frac{(x-y)(x+y)}{(x+y)^2}} = \frac{\sqrt{x^2-y^2}}{x+y}$$

Example 6: Simplify $\sqrt[3]{7\,x^{-3}y^{-4}}$.

$$\sqrt[3]{7\,x^{-3}y^{-4}} = \sqrt[3]{\frac{7}{x^3y^4}} = \sqrt[3]{\frac{7\,y^2}{x^3y^6}} = \frac{\sqrt[3]{7\,y^2}}{xy^2}$$

Example 7: Simplify $\sqrt[3]{-54}$.

$$\sqrt[3]{-54} = \sqrt[3]{-27(2)} = -3\sqrt[3]{2}$$

Example 8: Simplify $\sqrt{4\,xyz} - \sqrt[4]{x^2y^2z^2} + \sqrt[6]{64\,x^3y^3z^3}$.

$$\sqrt{4\,xyz} = 2\,x^{\frac{1}{2}}y^{\frac{1}{2}}z^{\frac{1}{2}}$$

$$-\sqrt[4]{x^2y^2z^2} = -\,x^{\frac{2}{4}}y^{\frac{2}{4}}z^{\frac{2}{4}} = -\,x^{\frac{1}{2}}y^{\frac{1}{2}}z^{\frac{1}{2}}$$

$$\sqrt[6]{64\,x^3y^3z^3} = 2\,x^{\frac{3}{6}}y^{\frac{3}{6}}z^{\frac{3}{6}} = 2\,x^{\frac{1}{2}}y^{\frac{1}{2}}z^{\frac{1}{2}}$$

$$\text{Total} = 3\,x^{\frac{1}{2}}y^{\frac{1}{2}}z^{\frac{1}{2}}$$

$$= 3\sqrt{xyz}$$

EXERCISE 2.6

Simplify:

1. $2^{\frac{1}{3}}(2^{\frac{2}{3}})$

2. $a^{\frac{1}{2}}(a^{\frac{3}{2}})$

3. $r^{\frac{3}{2}}(r^{-\frac{3}{2}})$

4. $\dfrac{a^0b^{\frac{2}{3}}}{b^{\frac{1}{3}}}$

5. $(8^{\frac{2}{3}})^2$

6. $\sqrt{27}$

7. $\sqrt{50}$

8. $\sqrt[3]{256}$

9. $\sqrt[3]{\frac{1}{16}}$

10. $\sqrt[3]{125(x+y)^4}$

11. $\sqrt{18\,a - 9}$

12. $\sqrt{27(x+y)(x-y)^5}$

13. $\sqrt{32\,a^2 - 16\,a}$

14. $\sqrt[4]{a^6b^4(x+y)}$

15. $\sqrt{18(x-y)^3a^4}$

16. $\sqrt{\dfrac{147\,b^2}{3\,x^2}}$

17. $\sqrt[n]{\dfrac{6\,a^{3n}}{y^n}}$

18. $\sqrt[n]{\dfrac{2^n x^{n+m}}{x^{mn}}}$

Write with fractional exponents:

19. $\sqrt[3]{-0.108}$

20. $\sqrt{a^3bc}$

21. $\sqrt[5]{a^3y^6x^7}$

22. $\sqrt[7]{a^2b^4c^6}$

23. $\sqrt{27\,x^4 - 9\,x^3y^2}$

Simplify:

24. $\sqrt{18} + \sqrt{98} + \sqrt{128}$

25. $(a-b)\sqrt{\dfrac{1}{a-b}}$

26. $\sqrt{27} + 2\sqrt{48} \quad 3\sqrt{75}$

27. $\sqrt{2} - \dfrac{1}{\sqrt{2}}$

28. $\sqrt{24} - \sqrt{\frac{2}{3}}$

29. $\sqrt{\dfrac{x}{y}} - \sqrt{\dfrac{y}{x}}$

30. $\sqrt{a^3 - a^2b} - \sqrt{ab^2 - b^3} - \sqrt{(a+b)(a^2 - b^2)}$

31. $\sqrt[6]{9\, x^4 y^2}$

32. $\sqrt{2} + \sqrt[4]{4} - 3\sqrt[8]{16}$

33. $\sqrt{\dfrac{x+y}{x^2-y^2}}$

34. $\sqrt{\dfrac{x-y}{x+y}} - \sqrt{\dfrac{x+y}{x-y}}$

35. $\sqrt{\frac{2}{3}}\,\sqrt{\frac{3}{4}}$

36. $\sqrt{5}\sqrt{20}$

37. $\sqrt{18}\sqrt{21}$

Divide:

38. $\sqrt{28} - \sqrt{63}$ by $\sqrt{14}$

39. $\sqrt{45}$ by $\sqrt{5}$

40. $\sqrt{xy}$ by $\sqrt{\dfrac{x}{y}}$

41. $x + x^{\frac{1}{2}}y^{\frac{1}{2}} + y$ by $x^{\frac{1}{2}} - x^{\frac{1}{4}}y^{\frac{1}{4}} + y^{\frac{1}{2}}$

Simplify:

42. $(3\sqrt{5}-2\sqrt{3})(3\sqrt{5}+2\sqrt{3})$

43. $(3x + x\sqrt{3})(3x - x\sqrt{3})$

44. $\{\sqrt{x+1}\sqrt{x-1}\}^2$

45. $(2a^{\frac{2}{3}} - 3a^{\frac{1}{3}} + a^{-\frac{1}{3}} - 4)(3a^{\frac{4}{3}} - 2a^{\frac{2}{3}} + a)$

46. $(2\sqrt[5]{x^4})^2$

47. $\sqrt{(a^2 + a^{-2})^2 - 4}$

48. $(3\sqrt{2} - \sqrt{18})^2$

49. $\left[\left(x^{\frac{1}{a+b}}\right)^{a-\frac{b^2}{a}}\right]^{\frac{a}{a-b}}$

50. $\left(\dfrac{x^{a+b}}{x^b}\right)^a\left(\dfrac{x^{b-a}}{x^b}\right)^{a-b}$

Linear Equations and Formulas

The algebraic quantities which have been used in the preceding sections were nearly all abstract quantities. The letters were used to illustrate the fundamental operations of algebra which are performed in solving practical problems. Many formulas for solving problems can be derived by algebra by writing equations relating the unknown quantity to the known quantities. These equations are then solved for the unknown quantity.

To solve an equation involves finding all the values for the unknown that will make the equation true. These values are called the roots of the equation. For this purpose certain assumptions are made which are considered to be obvious truths; they are called axioms.

Axioms

1. *If equal quantities are added to equal quantities, the sums are equal.*

2. *If equal quantities are subtracted from equal quantities, the remainders are equal.*

3. *If equal quantities are multiplied by equal quantities, the products are equal.*

4. *If equal quantities are divided by equal quantities, not zero, the quotients are equal.*

A study of these axioms shows that the operations of addition, subtraction, multiplication and division can be done on one side of an equation if they are also performed on the other side. Thus one can

1. Add the same quantity to both sides of an equation.
2. Subtract the same quantity from both sides of an equation.
3. Multiply both sides of an equation by the same quantity.
4. Divide both sides of an equation by the same quantity.

Example 1: Add 8 to both sides of the equation $x + y = 7$.

$$x + y = 7$$
$$x + y + 8 = 7 + 8 = 15$$

Example 2: Subtract b from both sides of the equation $x + b + y = 2\,a$.

$$x + b + y = 2\,a$$
$$x + b + y - b = 2\,a - b$$
$$x + y = 2\,a - b$$

Example 3: Multiply the equation $\dfrac{a + b}{3} = \dfrac{b}{5}$ by 15.

$$15\left(\frac{a + b}{3}\right) = 15\left(\frac{b}{5}\right)$$

Simplify
$$5(a + b) = 3\,b$$

Example 4: Add $2\,a$ to both sides of the equation $x - 2\,a = 3\,a$.

$$x - 2\,a = 3\,a$$
$$x - 2\,a + 2\,a = 3\,a + 2\,a$$
$$x - 5\,a$$

Transposition

In Example 2 the b was moved from one side of the equation to the other by subtracting b from both sides. When this is done the sign of the term changes. Likewise in Example 4 $- 2\,a$ was moved to the other side by changing it to $+ 2\,a$.

This process is called *transposition* and is important in algebra. To solve an equation, all the terms containing the unknown are transposed to the left side and all the others to the right side. Both sides are next simplified and then divided by the coefficient of the unknown to obtain the solution.

Rules

1. *Transpose all terms containing the unknown to the left side of the equation and all other terms to the right. When transposing a term from one side to the other always change its sign.*
2. *Collect the terms on each side.*
3. *Divide each side of the equation by the coefficient of the unknown.*

Example 1: Solve the equation $45\,x - 15 = 20\,x + 35$ for x.

$$45\,x - 15 = 20\,x + 35$$

Transpose	$45\,x - 20\,x = 35 + 15$	Rule 1
Collect terms	$25\,x = 50$	Rule 2
	$x = 2$	Rule 3

Example 2: Solve for x.

$$7\,x - (2\,x + 5) + (4\,x + 3) = 2\,x + (5\,x - 6) + 12$$
$$7\,x - 2\,x - 5 + 4\,x + 3 = 2\,x + 5\,x - 6 + 12$$
$$7\,x - 2\,x + 4\,x - 2\,x - 5\,x = -6 + 12 + 5 - 3$$
$$2\,x = 8$$
$$x = 4$$

Example 3: Solve for x.

$$3.8\,x - (7.3 - 2.1\,x) = 3(0.1\,x - 2.9).$$
$$3.8\,x - 7.3 + 2.1\,x = 0.3\,x - 8.7$$
$$3.8\,x + 2.1\,x - 0.3\,x = -8.7 + 7.3$$
$$5.6\,x = -1.4$$
$$x = -0.25$$

Equations Containing Fractions

Algebraic equations often contain fractions which must be eliminated before solving the equations. This process is sometimes called **clearing of fractions**. This is done by multiplying each side of the equation by the lowest common multiple of the denominators. The unknown terms then are transposed

to the left side and all others to the right and the resulting
equation is solved for the unknown.

Example 1: Solve the equation $\dfrac{x-6}{3} = 3 - \dfrac{x}{2}$ for x.

$$\frac{x-6}{3} = 3 - \frac{x}{2}$$

Multiply by the lowest common multiple of the denominators,
which is 6.

$$2(x-6) = 3(6) - 3x$$
$$2x - 12 = 18 - 3x$$

Transpose $\qquad 2x + 3x = 18 + 12$

Collect terms $\qquad\quad 5x = 30$
$$x = 6$$

Example 2: Solve the equation $\dfrac{7y}{6} - \dfrac{5}{3} = \dfrac{3y}{5} - \dfrac{1}{4}$ for y.

Clear of fractions by multiplying by 60.

$$70y - 100 = 36y - 15$$
$$34y = 85$$
$$y = 2.5$$

Example 3: Solve the equation $\dfrac{6x+7}{15} - \dfrac{2x+6}{7x+23} = \dfrac{2x+1}{5}$ for x.

The lowest common denominator is $15(7x+23)$.

$$(7x+23)(6x+7) - 15(2x+6) = 3(7x+23)(2x+1)$$
$$42x^2 + 187x + 161 - 30x - 90 = 42x^2 + 159x + 69$$
$$-2x = -2$$
$$x = 1$$

Check: $\qquad\qquad \dfrac{6+7}{15} - \dfrac{2+6}{7+23} = \dfrac{2+1}{5}$

$$\tfrac{13}{15} - \tfrac{8}{30} = \tfrac{3}{5}$$
$$\tfrac{13}{15} - \tfrac{4}{15} = \tfrac{9}{15}$$

Example 4: Solve the equation $\dfrac{x}{x-b} - \dfrac{x+2a}{x+b} = \dfrac{a^2+b^2}{x^2-b^2}$ for x.

$$x(x+b) - (x+2a)(x-b) = a^2 + b^2$$
$$x^2 + bx - x^2 - 2ax + bx + 2ab = a^2 + b^2$$
$$2x(b-a) = a^2 - 2ab + b^2$$
$$x = \frac{b-a}{2}$$

Rules

1. *Clear the equation of fractions by multiplying each term by the lowest common multiple of the denominators.*
2. *Transpose all terms containing the unknown to the left side of the equation and all other terms to the right. When transposing a term from one side to another, always change its sign.*
3. *Collect terms and divide by the coefficient of the unknown quantity.*

Note: If a fraction is preceded by a minus sign and the numerator is a polynomial, avoiding errors in clearing fractions will be easier if the numerator is enclosed in parentheses as shown in Examples 3 and 4. If this is not done, great care must be taken to change the sign of each term of the numerator when the denominator is removed.

EXERCISE 2.7

Solve the following equations for x:

1. $10x - 4 = 2x - 12$
2. $14x - 9 - 2x = 15 + 5x + 25$
3. $13 + 2x - (x + 6 + 3x) + (5x - 12) = 76$
4. $1.2x - (0.3x + 0.4x - 2.5) + 7.5 = 14.5 - (1.0x + 0.5x)$
5. $0.7(x + 1.13) = 0.05(2.1 - 2x) + 0.4$
6. $\dfrac{3x + 7}{2} = \dfrac{16x - 3}{7}$ 9. $3x + \dfrac{x}{3} = \dfrac{40}{3}$
7. $\dfrac{9x}{8} - \dfrac{x}{4} = \dfrac{8x - 1}{9}$ 10. $3x - \dfrac{x}{7} = 20$
8. $\dfrac{x}{3} + 10 = 17$ 11. $21 - 2x + \dfrac{x}{3} = \dfrac{4x}{3} - \left(\dfrac{4x}{9} + \dfrac{6x}{27}\right)$
12. $25 - \left(\dfrac{x}{5} + x\right) + \dfrac{x}{0.2} = 7x - 7$
13. $\dfrac{2x}{3} + 2\dfrac{2}{3} - \dfrac{x}{11} = \dfrac{8x}{11} + 1$
14. $\dfrac{x}{2} + \dfrac{x}{3} - \dfrac{x}{4} + \dfrac{3x}{10} - \dfrac{5x}{12} = 7$
15. $\dfrac{x - 1}{2} + \dfrac{x - 2}{3} + \dfrac{x - 3}{4} = \dfrac{5x - 1}{6}$
16. $\dfrac{x + 2}{x + 1} - \dfrac{x + 3}{x + 2} = \dfrac{x + 5}{x + 4} - \dfrac{x + 6}{x + 5}$
    Hint: Simplify each side first.

17. $1 - \dfrac{ab}{x} = \dfrac{7}{ab} - \dfrac{49}{abx}$

18. $a(x - a - 2\,b) + b(x - b) + c(x + c) = 0$

19. $\dfrac{x - 1}{a - 1} - \dfrac{x - 1}{x - 1} = \dfrac{x^2 - a^2}{(a - 1)(a - 1)}$

20. $\dfrac{4\,x + 7}{10} - \dfrac{12\,x + 7}{5\,x - 24} = \dfrac{2\,x + 1}{5}$

21. $\dfrac{6}{3\,x + 4} - \dfrac{1}{x + 2} = \dfrac{2}{2\,x + 1}$

22. $\dfrac{7\,x + 23}{21} - \dfrac{x + 9}{4\,x + 14} = \dfrac{23}{70} + \dfrac{x + 1}{3}$

23. $\left(\dfrac{c}{d} + \dfrac{d}{c}\right)x = \left(\dfrac{c}{d} - \dfrac{d}{c}\right) - 2\,x$

24. $\dfrac{x + 1.05}{2.1} + 1.702 = \dfrac{2\,x - 0.1}{3.7}$

25. $\dfrac{x + 0.08}{12.2} = \dfrac{1.57 - x}{3.05}$

APPLICATIONS OF LINEAR EQUATIONS

Many formulas were given in arithmetic for computing various volumes and areas. The equations were nearly always solved for the unknown quantity and the answer was obtained by direct substitution.

Many practical problems require the solution of a formula for different letters. Since the formula is an ordinary equation, the algebraic methods in the preceding sections can be applied.

Example 1: The area of a circle $A = \pi R^2$. Solve for R.

$$\pi R^2 = A$$

Divide by π $\qquad\qquad R^2 = \dfrac{A}{\pi}$

Extract square root $\qquad R = \sqrt{\dfrac{A}{\pi}}$

Example 2: The area of a triangle $A = \frac{1}{2}\,bh$. Solve for b.

$$A = \tfrac{1}{2}\,bh$$

Clear fractions $\qquad\quad bh = 2\,A$

Divide by h $\qquad\qquad b = \dfrac{2\,A}{h}$

Example 3: The area of a trapezoid $A = \frac{1}{2}(a + b)h$. Solve for a.

$$A = \tfrac{1}{2}(a + b)h$$
$$2A = ah + bh$$
$$ah = 2A - bh$$
$$a = \frac{2A}{h} - b$$

Example 4: Find the altitude of a trapezoid of area 88 sq in. and bases 12 in. and 10 in. respectively.

$$A = \tfrac{1}{2}(a + b)h$$
$$2A = (a + b)h$$
$$h = \frac{2A}{a + b} = \frac{2(88)}{12 + 10} = 8 \text{ in.}$$

In solving problems by algebraic methods, the most difficult part is to write the equation relating the known values to the unknown. When this has been done, the resulting equation can be solved by the usual methods. The following suggestions will be helpful:

1. *Represent the unknown quantity by one of the final letters of the alphabet, x, y, or z. If there is more than one unknown, use a different letter for each one.*
2. *Write an equation or equations in accordance with the conditions stated in the problem. An independent equation is required for each unknown.*
3. *Solve the equation or equations for the unknowns.*
4. *Check the obtained values by substitution in the original problem.*

Example 5: A triangle has a perimeter of 32 in. The longest side is 8 in. longer than the shortest side, and the shortest side is 3 in. shorter than the third side. Find the length of the three sides.

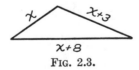
Fig. 2.3.

Let x = length of the shortest side in inches.

Then $x + 8$ = length of longest side, since the **longest side is** 8 in. longer than the shortest side.

$$x + 3 = \text{length of third side}$$

The perimeter equals

$$x + (x + 3) + (x + 8) = 32$$
$$3\,x + 11 = 32$$
$$3\,x = 21$$
$$x = 7 \text{ in.}$$
$$x + 3 = 10 \text{ in.}$$
$$x + 8 = 15 \text{ in.}$$

These results can be checked by trial in the original problem.

It is frequently necessary to find an unknown dimension on a drawing. By writing an equation containing the unknown distance and the known measurements, the unknown quantity can be determined. Lines and triangles must often be drawn to obtain the equation, and sometimes the Pythagorean theorem $a^2 + b^2 = c^2$ is useful.

Example 6: Find the radius R.

Construct a right triangle and put on the dimensions in terms of R, as shown in Fig. 2.5. By the Pythagorean theorem

$$R^2 = (R - \tfrac{1}{2})^2 + (1)^2$$
$$R^2 = R^2 - R + \tfrac{1}{4} + 1$$
$$R = \tfrac{1}{4} + 1 = \tfrac{5}{4}$$

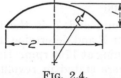

FIG. 2.4.

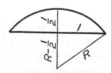

FIG. 2.5.

There are no rules for deciding what lines to draw or what triangles to solve in this type of problem. Experience usually enables one to make a good guess, but even then several trials may be necessary to obtain a satisfactory equation. A few suggestions may help.

Suggestions

1. *Always try to form a triangle in which some of the dimensions are known.*
2. *Connect the centers of any circles which are tangent to each other.*

3. *Try to form right triangles by drawing lines parallel or per-pendicular to the lines of the figure.*
4. *Write the dimensions on the sides of the triangles, either in numbers or in terms of the unknown.*
5. *Write an equation involving the unknown and solve it for the unknown.*

EXERCISE 2.8

Given	Find		Given	Find
1. $A = \frac{1}{2}(a + b)h$	b	9.	$d = \sqrt{a^2 + b^2 + c^2}$	b
2. $A = 4\pi R^2$	R	10.	$V = \frac{1}{6}\pi h(3R^2 + h^2)$	R
3. $V = \frac{4}{3}\pi R^3$	R	11.	$\dfrac{x}{a} + \dfrac{y}{b} = 2$	y
4. $C = \frac{5}{9}(F - 32)$	F			
5. $HP = \dfrac{2\pi NT}{33,000}$	N	12.	$(x - h)^2 + y^2 = h^2$	h
		13.	$x + y = xy$	x
6. $I = P(1 + nr)$	n	14.	$x^2 + y^2 + z^2 = r^2$	y
7. $I = P(1 + r)^n$	r	15.	$D = vt + \frac{1}{2}gt^2$	v
8. $d = \dfrac{D}{L^2}(L^2 - a^2)$	L			

16. The formula for the horsepower of a motor is

$$HP = \frac{2\pi NT}{33,000}$$

where N is revolutions per minute and T is the torque in pound-feet. Solve the formula for T and determine the torque developed by a 10-HP motor running at 1750 rpm. How would the formula be changed if N were stated in revolutions per second?

17. A room is 4 ft longer than it is wide. If the length is decreased 2 ft and the width is increased 1 ft, the area will be decreased by 8 sq ft. Find the dimensions of the room.

18. The total resistance R_T of a circuit containing three pure resistances R_1, R_2 and R_3 in parallel is given by

$$\frac{1}{R_T} = \frac{1}{R_1} + \frac{1}{R_2} + \frac{1}{R_3}$$

Solve the equation for R_T and find the value of R_T when $R_1 = 10$ ohms, $R_2 = 5$ ohms, $R_3 = 8$ ohms.

19. What resistance must be placed in parallel with two others in parallel with values of 15 and 20 ohms respectively to give a total resistance for the circuit of 5 ohms? *Hint:* See Problem 18.

20. If air is a mixture of approximately 4 parts of nitrogen to 1 part of oxygen, how many cubic feet of each are there in a room 10 ft by 14 ft by 10 ft high?

21. The formula for changing Fahrenheit degrees to temperature centigrade is $C = \frac{5}{9}(F - 32)$, where C is in degrees centigrade and F is in degrees Fahrenheit. At what temperature do the two thermometers read the same?

22. The speed of sound at a temperature $T°C$ is
$$V = 33,130 + 60.7T \text{ cm/sec}$$
Derive an equation giving V in feet per second when T is in degrees Fahrenheit. *Hint:* See Problem 21.

23. Work out a formula for changing feet per second to miles per hour. Let F = ft per sec and M = mph.

24. The volume of a hollow cylinder is given by the equation
$$V = \pi R^2 h - \pi r^2 h$$
where R = outside radius, r = inside radius, and h = height. Solve for r and find the thickness of a metal cylinder which has a volume of 1660 cu in., a height of 4 ft, and an outside radius of 6 in.

25. Given the equation $H = 1,600,000 \dfrac{b_1 - b_2}{b_1 + b_2} (1 + 0.004\, t)$, solve for t.

26. Solve the equation $Q = \dfrac{K(t_2 - t_1)AT}{d}$ for t_1.

27. A traveler on a train notices that 4.5 times the number of telegraph poles per minute the train passes equals the speed of the train in miles per hour. Find the distance between the poles.

28. Find x.

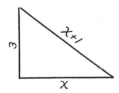

29. Find x.

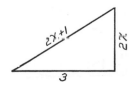

30. Find x.

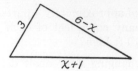

31. Find the shaded area in terms of D.

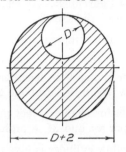

32. Find R in terms of D.

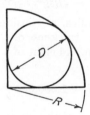

33. Find x.

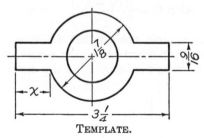

TEMPLATE.

34. Find d in terms of R.

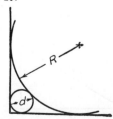

35. Find D.

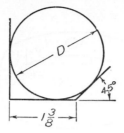

36. Find R.

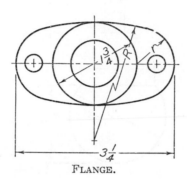

FLANGE.

HOUSING

37. Find x.

COVER PLATE.

38. Find R and x.

39. Find x and y.

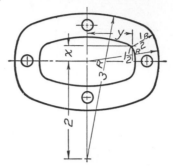

40. Find D.

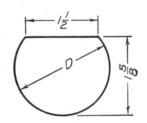

41. Find r

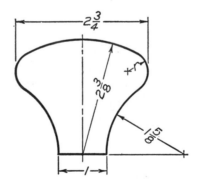

42. Find x.

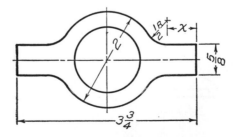

43. Find r.

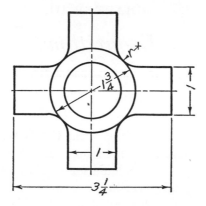

44. Find r and R.

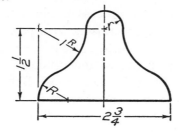

CHAPTER III

Logarithms

Historical Note

The word logarithm comes from the Greek *logos* meaning proportion, and *arithmos* meaning number. Logarithms are numbers employed in calculation. They greatly simplify multiplication, division, raising to powers, and extracting roots, and make it easy to solve problems which might otherwise be extremely difficult, if not impossible. With logarithms, multiplication is reduced to a process of addition, division becomes a process of subtraction, raising to a power involves simple multiplication, and extracting roots is done by division.

Logarithms were invented independently by John Napier, a Scotchman (1550–1617), and Joost Bürgi, a Swiss (1552–1632). Napier first expounded them in his *Mirifici Logarithmorum Canonis Descriptio* (1614). The logarithms they invented are not the same as those used today.[1] The first logarithms to the base 10 were published by Henry Briggs (1561–1630) in collaboration with Napier. Briggs gave the logarithms of the numbers from 1 to 20,000 and 90,000 to 100,000 to 14 decimal places. Later Adrian Vlacq in Holland completed the tables from 20,000 to 90,000 and shortened them to 10 decimal places. Tables of natural logarithms were published in 1619 by John Speidell in London.

Definition of Logarithm

The logarithm of a number to a given base is the power to which the base must be raised to give the number. Thus if

$$N = b^x, \qquad x = \log_b N$$

---

[1] Naperian logarithms are often confused with natural logarithms, which are connected by the relation

$$\text{Nap. log } n = 10^7 \left\{ \text{nat. log} \left(\frac{10^7}{n} \right) \right\}$$

This last equation is read, "x equals the logarithm of N to the base b." The base is written to the right and a little below the word log. It can be any positive number except 1.

Example: Find $\log_3 9$.

Since
$$3^2 = 9$$
$$\log_3 9 = 2$$

Similarly, since
$$5^4 = 625$$
$$\log_5 625 = 4$$

and since
$$10^3 = 1000$$
$$\log_{10} 1000 = 3$$

Base of Logarithms

Any positive real number except 1 can be taken as the base. A negative number is not usually considered to have a logarithm. The base of the common or Briggsian system is 10, and the corresponding common logarithms are used for most computing. This is a natural base because it fits into the decimal system.

The other base sometimes used is the number $2.71828 \cdots$, represented by the letter e, which gives the natural or hyperbolic logarithms. Natural logarithms are discussed later in this chapter.

Properties of Logarithms

The laws of logarithms are similar to the laws of exponents, since the logarithm of a number is the exponent of the base which gives the number.

1. *The logarithm of a product is the sum of the logarithms of the factors.*

   Proof: Let $\quad\quad M = b^x \quad$ and $\quad N = b^y$

   Then $\quad\quad\quad M(N) = b^{x+y}$

   and $\quad\quad\quad \log_b MN = x + y$

   This gives the rule for multiplication by logarithms

   $$\log_b MN = \log_b M + \log_b N$$

   since $\quad\quad x = \log_b M \quad$ and $\quad y = \log_b N$

   Similarly the theorem can be proved for the product of three or more factors.

2. *The logarithm of a quotient is the logarithm of the numerator minus the logarithm of the denominator.*

   Proof: If $\quad M = b^x \quad$ and $\quad N = b^y$

   $$\frac{M}{N} = \frac{b^x}{b^y} = b^{x-y}$$

   and $\qquad \log_b \frac{M}{N} = x - y$

   This gives the rule for division by logarithms

   $$\log_b \frac{M}{N} = \log_b M - \log_b N$$

   since $x = \log_b M \quad$ and $\quad y = \log_b N$ as before.

3. *The logarithm of a power of a number is the logarithm of the number multiplied by the exponent of the power.*

   Proof: If $\quad M = b^x \quad$ then $\quad M^n = b^{nx}$

   Therefore $\qquad \log_b M^n = nx$

   Since $x = \log_b M$, this gives the rule for raising to a power with logarithms

   $$\log_b M^n = n \log_b M$$

   If the exponent is a fraction, multiply first by the numerator and then divide the result by the denominator.

4. *The logarithm of a root of a number equals the logarithm of the number divided by the index of the root.*

   Proof: Since $\sqrt[n]{M} = b^{\frac{x}{n}} \quad$ when $\quad M = b^x$

   $$\log_b \sqrt[n]{M} = \frac{x}{n}$$

   This gives the rule for extracting roots with logarithms

   $$\log_b \sqrt[n]{M} = \frac{1}{n} \log_b M$$

5. *The logarithm of the reciprocal of a number is equal to* − 1
times the logarithm of the number.

Proof: If
$$M = b^x$$

$$\frac{1}{M} = b^{-x}$$

$$\log_b \frac{1}{M} = -x$$

This gives the rule

$$\log_b \frac{1}{M} = -\log_b M$$

6. *The logarithm of 1 to any base is zero.*

Proof: Since $b^0 = 1$, if b does not equal zero,

$$\log_b 1 = 0$$

7. *The logarithm of the base b is 1.*

Proof: Since
$$b^1 = b$$

$$\log_b b = 1$$

8. *The logarithm of zero to any base greater than 1 is negative
infinity.*

Proof: Since $b^{-\infty} = \dfrac{1}{b^\infty} = 0$ when b is greater than 1,

$$\log_b 0 = -\infty$$

This means that as the number approaches the limit zero,
its logarithm is negative and increases in absolute value
without limit.

Common Logarithms

Ten is the base of the common or Briggsian system of logarithms and all logarithm tables are calculated to this base
unless otherwise stated. The advantage of this system is that
the decimal part of the logarithm is always the same for a
given sequence of numbers and does not change when the

decimal point is moved. The following table shows the logarithms to base 10 of certain powers of 10:

x	1000	100	10	1	0.1	0.01	0.001
$\log_{10} x$	3	2	1	0	-1	-2	-3

It is easily seen that no other numbers in this range have integers for their logarithms. Thus, for a number between 10 and 100, the logarithm is 1 plus a decimal fraction. The integral part of the logarithm (number ahead of the decimal point) is called the **characteristic,** and the decimal part is called the **mantissa.** It has been agreed *always to make the mantissa positive,* but the characteristic may be either positive or negative. The logarithm is the characteristic plus the mantissa.

Moving the decimal point of a number corresponds to multiplying or dividing by a power of 10. Thus

$$273.6 = 27.36 \times 10$$
$$= 2.736 \times 10^2$$
$$= 2736 \times 10^{-1}, \text{ etc.}$$

Multiplying a number by 10 increases the characteristic of its logarithm by 1, because

$$\log 10 N = \log 10 + \log N$$
$$= 1 + \log N$$
since $$\log 10 = 1$$

Similarly, multiplying a number by 10^n increases the characteristic by n, and dividing by 10^n decreases the characteristic by n.

Examination of the table shows that the logarithm of 15 is 1 plus the mantissa. Applying the above rule gives:

$$\log 15 \quad = \quad 1. + \text{mantissa}$$
$$\log 150 \quad = \quad 2. + \text{mantissa}$$
$$\log 15{,}000 = \quad 4. + \text{mantissa}$$
$$\log 1.5 \quad = \quad 0. + \text{mantissa}$$
$$\log 0.015 \quad = -2. + \text{mantissa}$$

It is easily seen that the mantissa of a logarithm is independent of the position of the decimal point for a given sequence of figures. Moving the decimal point affects only the characteristic of the logarithm.

Determining the Characteristic

Since the characteristic of the logarithm of a number between 1 and 10 is zero, the above consideration gives the following rules for logarithms to the base 10:

1. *The characteristic of the logarithm of a number greater than 1 is positive and is 1 less than the number of digits to the left of the decimal point.*
2. *The characteristic of the logarithm of a positive number less than 1 is negative and is numerically 1 more than the number of zeros between the decimal point and the first significant figure.*

Thus, if the logarithm of 2376.4 is 3.37592,

$$\log 23.764 \quad = \quad 1.37592$$
$$\log 2.3764 \quad = \quad 0.37592$$
$$\log 0.23764 \quad = -\ 1.37592$$
$$\log 0.0023764 = -\ 3.37592$$

When the characteristic is negative, 10 is added to the characteristic and subtracted at the right of the mantissa. Thus -1 is written $9 - 10$, -4 becomes $6 - 10$, and -13 could be written $7 - 20$. The negative portion should always be a multiple of -10. If this were not done, the mantissa would be a positive decimal and the characteristic would be a negative integer. This number is neither all positive nor all negative and is difficult to use in calculations.

Tables of Logarithms

For use in computations, tables giving mantissas of the logarithms of successive numbers have been calculated. The number of decimal places used for a computation depends upon the accuracy required. Tables to four, five, six, seven, ten, fourteen, or more places have been published. For most calculations, four or five places are used. Five-place tables give five significant figures in the result, but the last figure is not always exact.

The first column of a five-place table of logarithms gives the first three figures of the number and is headed by the letter N, meaning number. The fourth figure is found at the top of one of the other ten columns, numbered 0, 1, 2, 3, $\cdots$ 9. Thus, to find log 2.736, first find 273 in the N-column (Tables, p. 9). The mantissa required will be found in the horizontal line, in the column headed 6. It is 43712. Since the first two figures of the mantissa are the same for several lines, they appear only in one line to save repetition.

As a guide to rounding off five-place mantissas to four places, when the last figure is 5 it is written $\bar{5}$ if the half is to be dropped, and is an ordinary 5 if it is to be added.

To Find the Logarithm of a Number

1. *When the number has four figures.*

   Find the first three figures in the N-column. The mantissa will be found in that horizontal line, in the column headed by the fourth figure of the number.

Example: Find log 503.6

The characteristic is 2. Find 503 in the N-column, and go to the 6-column. The mantissa is 70209. Thus

Similarly
$$\log 503.6 = 2.70209$$
$$\log 69.85 = 1.84417$$
$$\log 0.007684 = 7.88559 - 10$$
$$\log 3804 = 3.58024$$
$$\log 0.03238 = 8.51028 - 10$$

2. *When the number has less than four figures.*

   Determine the characteristic in the regular way. To find the mantissa, add enough zeros to make four places, and locate it in the tables as you do any other mantissa.

Example: Find log 28.

The characteristic is 1, and the mantissa is the same as the mantissa of log 2800. This gives

$$\log 28 = 1.44716$$

Similarly
$$\log 1.59 = 0.20140$$
$$\log 8 = 0.90309$$
$$\log 0.065 = 8.81291 - 10$$

3. *When the number has five or more figures.*

In this case interpolation is necessary. This process assumes that the increase in the logarithm is proportional to the increase of the number for small changes in the number.

Example: Find log 59.543.

From the tables
$$10 \left\{ 3 \left\{ \begin{array}{l} \log 59.540 = 1.77481 \\ \log 59.543 = \quad ? \\ \log 59.550 = 1.77488 \end{array} \right\} x \right\} 7$$

Since the change in the logarithm is assumed to be proportional to the change in the number, the proportion becomes,

$$\frac{x}{7} = \frac{3}{10} \quad \text{or} \quad x = 2.1$$

Rounding off to the nearest whole number gives 2. This must be added to the smaller logarithm because the difference, *x*, was figured from that logarithm. If the amount to be added ends in 0.5, take the nearest even number. Thus

$$\log 59.543 = 1.77483$$

Similarly
$$\log 765.37 = 2.88387$$
$$\log 0.18247 = 9.26119 - 10$$
$$\log 162{,}780 = 5.21160$$
$$\log 0.01739613 = 8.24045 - 10$$

Note: *When five-place logarithms are used, the amount to be added when interpolating should always be rounded off to the nearest whole number.* The mantissas given in the table are not exact but are rounded off to five decimal places. The last figure may be as much as half a unit from the correct value. The interpolation assumes that they are all exact; therefore it cannot be used to obtain results closer than the last place given in the tables. It is a mistake to work to more than five decimal places when using five-place tables.

EXERCISE 3.1

1. Find the logarithms of the following numbers:

146.8	Ans. 2.16673	500,000
1.517	Ans. 0.18099	7,500,000,000
943.7		27.850
8.260		6.345
705		178.2
56.21		4560
2145		325
3.142		

2. Find the logarithms of the following numbers:

467.6	Ans. 2.66987	7.0
61.68	Ans. 1.79014	73,680,000
3.786		14×10^{11}
1885		3.176×10^{14}
819		962.1
2.02		6.17
631,900		11.97
5.291		

3. Find the logarithms of the following numbers:

0.728	Ans. $9.86213 - 10$	0.0000008710
0.0531		0.0516
0.4620		0.273
0.00078		0.00005627
0.00542		0.009800

4. Find the logarithms of the following numbers:

0.2850	Ans. $9.45484 - 10$	0.0000007260
0.0358		0.00001471
0.9080		9.247×10^{-16}
0.00013		0.007239
0.00146		257.9×10^{-28}

5. Find the logarithms of the following numbers:

7.2483	Ans. 0.86024	0.0034786
45.167		0.0631545
938.51		100,056
0.34285		1046.38
6738.25		327.85

6. Find the logarithms of the following numbers:

6.7219 Ans. 0.82749	0.00078899
89.042	0.033445
162.72	2.71828
0.0629517	3.14159
94,938.32	9.8696×10^{-13}

To Find the Number Corresponding to a Given Logarithm

In most cases when a problem has been solved with logarithms, it is necessary to find the number corresponding to the logarithm of the answer. This number is often called the **antilogarithm**. The mantissa is used to find the sequence of figures, and the characteristic determines the position of the decimal point.

1. *When the mantissa is given exactly in the table.*

In this case the first three figures are given in the *N*-column, and the fourth figure is at the top of the column containing the mantissa.

Example 1: Find the antilogarithm of 2.93125.

In the logarithm tables find the mantissa 93125. This is in the line that has 853 in the *N*-column and in the column with 6 at the top. The significant figures are therefore 8536. Since the characteristic is 2, there are three figures ahead of the decimal point. Thus

$$\text{antilog } 2.93125 = 853.60$$

The 0 is put on the end to show it came out even. This should always be done to give five significant figures.

Example 2: Find the antilogarithm of 7.89221 − 10.

From the tables, the significant figures are 7802. Since the characteristic is 7 − 10, or − 3, two zeros are placed after the decimal point. Thus

$$\text{antilog } (7.89221 - 10) = 0.0078020$$

2. *When the mantissa is not given exactly in the table.*

In this case find two consecutive mantissas such that the given mantissa is between them. The number corresponding to the smaller mantissa gives the first four figures of the result, and the fifth figure can be determined by interpolation by assuming that for small differences the change in the logarithm is proportional to the change in the number.

Example: Find the antilogarithm of 1.41536.

From the tables

$$10\left\{x\left\{\begin{matrix}\log 26.020 = 1.41531 \\ \log\ \ ?\ \ = 1.41536\end{matrix}\right\}5\atop\log 26.030 = 1.41547\right\}16$$

The proportion is

$$\frac{x}{10} = \frac{5}{16} \qquad \text{and} \qquad x = 3.1 \text{ or } 3$$

to the nearest whole number. This must be added to the smaller number. This gives

$$\text{antilog } 1.41536 = 26.023$$

When working with five-place tables, do not use more than 5 significant figures in the result. If the proportion gives 5 in the first decimal place, use the nearest even number when rounding off.

Example: Find the antilogarithm of 6.53879 − 10.

From the tables

$$10\left\{x\left\{\begin{matrix}\log 0.00034570 = 6.53870 - 10 \\ \log\ \ ?\ \ = 6.53879 - 10\end{matrix}\right\}9\atop\log 0.00034580 = 6.53882 - 10\right\}12$$

This proportion becomes

$$\frac{x}{10} = \frac{9}{12} \qquad \text{and} \qquad x = 7.5 \text{ or } 8$$

Thus   antilog $(6.53879 - 10) = 0.00034578$

The 8 was taken instead of 7 to make an even number.

Interpolation can also be done by the tables of proportional parts included with the logarithm tables in the column headed P.P. They give the tabular differences multiplied by tenths. A sample is shown at the right. Thus four-tenths of 12 is 4.8, etc. This would be rounded off to 5 when interpolating. In the last example, the tabular difference was 12 and the difference between the mantissas was 9. To find the fifth figure, follow down the second column of the table headed 12 to the figure nearest 9. In this case it is halfway between 8.4 and 9.6. Use the even figure in the first column, or 8.

12	
1	1.2
2	2.4
3	3.6
4	4.8
5	6.0
6	7.2
7	8.4
8	9.6
9	10.8

EXERCISE 3.2

1. Find the antilogarithms of the following:

2.72082	Ans. 525.80	1.90356
7.99989 − 10	Ans. 0.0099975	9.60210 − 10
0.04415		7.65376 − 10
8.30016 − 10		0.25416
3.89172		1.00090

2. Find the antilogarithms of the following:

3.96047	Ans. 9130.0	2.89745
8.67031 − 10	Ans. 0.046807	7.83706
0.01292		8.68157 − 20
9.23855 − 10		2.56721 − 10
4.57548		9.30869

3. Find the antilogarithms of the following:

2.91917	Ans. 830.18	8.22318 − 10
8.16211 − 10		9.89771
3.01002		6.38327
2.19827		8.11219 − 10
7.88994		3.99715

4. Find the antilogarithms of the following:

1.00517	7.17617 − 10
2.19002	6.22853 − 10
4.01287 − 20	0.00011
2.19927	9.00132 − 10
8.29005 − 10	14.99998 − 20

Multiplication Using Logarithms

Rule 1 states: The logarithm of a product is the sum of the logarithms of the factors.

Example: Multiply 27.386(0.0039682)(1.7643).

From the tables

$$\log 27.386 = 1.43753$$
$$\log 0.0039682 = 7.59859 - 10$$
$$\log 1.7643 = 0.24657$$
$$\log N = \overline{9.28269 - 10}$$
$$N = 0.19173$$

If negative quantities occur in the computation, treat them as if they were positive and determine the sign of the result later by inspection.

Example: Multiply $3.8076(-1.8725)(28.1)$.

From the tables

$$\log 3.8076 = 0.58065$$
$$\log 1.8725 = 0.27242$$
$$\log 28.1 = \underline{1.44871}$$
$$\log N = 2.30178$$
$$N = -200.35$$

DIVISION USING LOGARITHMS

Rule 2 states: The logarithm of a quotient is the logarithm of the numerator minus the logarithm of the denominator.

Example 1: Divide 17.476 by 2.3964.

$$\log 17.476 = 1.24244$$
$$\log 2.3964 = \underline{0.37956}$$
$$\log N = 0.86288$$
$$N = 7.2925$$

Example 2: Calculate $\dfrac{27.32(1628.3)(0.073)}{18761(2.3)(9.764)}$.

$$\log 27.32 = 1.43648 \qquad \log 18761 = 4.27325$$
$$\log 1628.3 = 3.21173 \qquad \log 2.3 = 0.36173$$
$$\log 0.073 = \underline{8.86332 - 10} \qquad \log 9.764 = \underline{0.98963}$$
$$\log \text{Num.} = 13.51153 - 10 \qquad \log \text{Den.} = 5.62461$$
$$\log \text{Den.} = \underline{5.62461}$$
$$\log N = 7.88692 - 10$$
$$N = 0.0077076$$

EXERCISE 3.3

1. Multiply, using logarithms:

    750(1437)
    0.36285(0.00854)(72483)
    67.2(321.56)(14.86)(0.1045)
    438.15(6.258)(94672)
    0.00427(0.0000326)(0.0008623)

2. Multiply, using logarithms:

    854(94672)
    15(0.21)(145)
    871(1.2389)(17.4317)
    2.71828(3.14159)
    0.007165(17.8516)(2.817)(10^{-5})

3. Divide, using logarithms:

$$\frac{7548}{26.1} \qquad \frac{93.826}{1.0482} \qquad \frac{0.093478}{728.3}$$

$$\frac{346}{52875} \qquad\qquad \frac{17.82}{369.39}$$

4. Divide, using logarithms:

$$\frac{72.749}{1.732} \qquad \frac{28.986}{7465.98} \qquad \frac{0.000714}{0.0189674}$$

$$\frac{17.38 \times 10^{-7}}{283.190} \qquad \frac{1.00065}{0.00018}$$

5. Evaluate, using logarithms:

$$\frac{5534(0.02374)}{3.246(18.944)(2.3)}$$

6. Evaluate, using logarithms:

$$\frac{5.9637(0.33506)(\pi)(19.689)}{4.0962(57637)(0.0068375)}$$

7. Evaluate, using logarithms:

$$\frac{84(17.16)(2.974)(1.73849)(7.2816)}{17834(0.00016)(1.118)(2.99816)}$$

8. Evaluate, using logarithms:

$$\frac{100(16.543)(111.23)(88.466)(2.993)}{(17 + 4.6)(2.986 + 11.22)(13 - 4.11)}$$

COLOGARITHMS

The cologarithm of a number is the logarithm of the **reciprocal** of the number. It is also known as the **arithmetical complement.** Rule 5 states: The logarithm of the reciprocal of a number is equal to -1 times the logarithm of the number. Thus

$$\text{colog } 2 = \log \tfrac{1}{2} = -\log 2$$

Adding the cologarithm of a number has the same effect as subtracting the logarithm. To divide two numbers, add the logarithm of the numerator to the cologarithm of the denominator. This makes it possible to put all the logarithms and cologarithms in one column, as in multiplication by logarithms. The cologarithm is obtained by subtracting the logarithm from $10.00000 - 10$, which keeps the mantissa positive.

Example 1: Find colog 17.68.

$$
\begin{array}{rl}
& 10.00000 - 10 \\
\log 17.68 = & \underline{1.24748} \\
\text{colog } 17.68 = & 8.75252 - 10
\end{array}
$$

This can be done mentally by subtracting each figure of the logarithm from 9, except the last one, which is subtracted from 10.

Example 2: Calculate $\dfrac{27.32(1628.3)(0.073)}{18761(2.3)(9.764)}$.

This is the same as Example 2 in the preceding section.

$$
\begin{array}{rl}
\log 27.32 = & 1.43648 \\
\log 1628.3 = & 3.21173 \\
\log 0.073 = & 8.86332 - 10 \\
\text{colog } 18761 = & 5.72675 - 10 \\
\text{colog } 2.3 = & 9.63827 - 10 \\
\text{colog } 9.764 = & \underline{9.01037 - 10} \\
\log N = & 7.88692 - 10 \\
N = & 0.0077076 \quad \text{as before}
\end{array}
$$

POWERS OF NUMBERS

The logarithm of a power of a number is the logarithm of the number multiplied by the exponent of the power.

Example 1: Find $(1.782)^4$.

$$
\begin{array}{rl}
\log 1.782 = & 0.25091 \\
4 \log 1.782 = & 1.00364 \\
N = & 10.084
\end{array}
$$

Example 2: Find $(0.084)^{1.406}$.

$$
\begin{array}{rl}
\log 0.084 = & 8.92428 - 10 \\
1.406 \log 0.084 = & 12.54754 - 14.06 \\
\text{Subtract} & \underline{4.06 \qquad - 4.06} \\
\log N = & 8.48754 - 10 \\
N = & 0.030729
\end{array}
$$

In the case of negative characteristics, always add or subtract an amount which will make the characteristic a whole number. It would be extremely difficult to do Example 2 without logarithms.

ROOTS OF NUMBERS

The logarithm of a root of a number equals the logarithm of the number divided by the index of the root.

Example 1: Find $\sqrt{7.3865}$.

$$\log 7.3865 = 0.86844$$
$$\tfrac{1}{2}\log 7.3865 = 0.43422$$
$$\sqrt{7.3865} = 2.7178$$

Example 2: Find $\sqrt[1.7]{0.384}$.

$$\log 0.384 = 9.58433 - 10$$
$$= 16.58433 - 17$$
$$\frac{1}{1.7}\log 0.384 = 9.75549 - 10$$
$$\sqrt[1.7]{0.384} = 0.56950$$

Note that 7 was added to and subtracted from the logarithm so that 1.7 would exactly go into the negative part of the characteristic to give -10. Always add or subtract the proper amount so that the index of the root will go evenly into the negative part of the characteristic.

EXERCISE 3.4

1. Find the cologarithms of the following numbers:

22.741	Ans. 8.64319 − 10	0.000625
0.001468	Ans. 2.83327	17.983
1.0112		223.06
0.031456		177.88
8.9798		2111.364
10046		0.071122

2. Find the cologarithms of the following numbers:

10.144	Ans. 8.99379 − 10	6374.6
0.000223	Ans. 3.65170	0.0042349
5.8136		0.000024235
0.025702		0.423400
0.00072605		3340.98
842.62		54.1547

3. Raise to the powers indicated:

2^{32}	0.00058^3
17^6	0.07128^2
0.00452^5	$0.505^{0.56}$
1.2483^3	$21.082^{0.64}$
728.651^4	$0.032956^{-0.32}$

4. Raise to the powers indicated:

12^5 π^2

2.07^3 $e^{2\pi}$

0.899^4 $0.00148^{0.71}$

2.5786^5 $196.223^{1.406}$

707.11^2 $0.0726^{-0.914}$

5. Find the indicated roots:

$\sqrt[3]{3.14159}$ $\sqrt[3]{71.6428}$

$\sqrt[5]{785263}$ $\sqrt{0.03857}$

$\sqrt[32]{2.0000}$ $\sqrt{0.000048215}$

$\sqrt{17854.315}$ $\sqrt{0.000005261}$

$\sqrt[4]{0.0218576}$ $\sqrt[3]{0.0068431}$

6. Find the indicated roots:

$\sqrt[3]{2.71828}$ $\sqrt[3]{3.5700}$

$\sqrt[4]{962.013}$ $\sqrt[14]{395.24}$

$\sqrt[12]{2.0000}$ $\sqrt{0.00001011}$

$\sqrt{425.58}$ $\sqrt{0.0002965}$

$\sqrt[5]{0.00952}$ $\sqrt[3]{0.004116}$

7. Calculate, using cologarithms for the denominator:

$$\frac{5534(0.02374)}{\sqrt[3]{1785}(3.246)^3(8.963)}$$

8. Solve by using cologarithms for the denominator:

$$\frac{2185(0.156)(9.42)(0.051)}{\sqrt{275}(\sqrt[3]{321})(0.062)(5758)}$$

9. Solve by using cologarithms for the denominator:

$$\frac{\sqrt{3586} \times \sqrt[3]{72843}(0.111)(6.28)}{\sqrt[3]{345} \times \sqrt[3]{512} \times 0.0004}$$

10. Solve by using cologarithms for the denominator:

$$\frac{5.9637(0.33506)(\pi)(19.689)}{4.0962(57637)(0.0068375)}$$

11. Solve with logarithms and cologarithms.

$$\frac{\sqrt[4]{57654.00} \times \sqrt{\pi} \times 3.569}{0.00796(1.1)(15)}$$

12. Solve with logarithms and cologarithms.

$$\frac{0.00000000001742(19386.4)}{19.984(1.7 \times 10^{-11})(2 + 3.964)}$$

Natural Logarithms

Natural logarithms are similar to common logarithms to the base 10, and are used in advanced mathematics and theoretical work. In higher mathematics it has been found that the simplest form of equations involving logarithms is obtained by using a special number, designated by e, for the base of logarithms. This base cannot be expressed exactly, but is a continued decimal $2.71828\cdots$. Charles Hermite (1822–1901) showed in 1873 that e is not an algebraic number. The use of this base eliminates certain numerical constants from the equations and simplifies the form. Since formulas common in technical work are frequently expressed with natural logarithms or as e to some power, natural logarithms will now be explained. In engineering work the natural logarithm of a number N is usually written $\log_e N$. Where no base is indicated, the base 10 is understood. Thus $\log N$ is understood to mean $\log_{10} N$. The same base must be used throughout a given set of tables.

Relation Between Natural and Common Logarithms

The relation between natural and common logarithms is very simple.

Let
$$x = \log_{10} N$$
then
$$10^x = N$$

Now take natural logarithms of both sides of this equation.

$$\log_e 10^x = \log_e N$$
or
$$x \log_e 10 = \log_e N$$

From the first equation, $x = \log_{10} N$
therefore
$$\log_{10} N \,(\log_e 10) = \log_e N$$

The value of $\log_e 10$ has been computed and is given in the tables as
$$\log_e 10 = 2.30258509\cdots$$

This gives, by division

$$\frac{1}{\log_e 10} = 0.43429448 \cdots$$

If these values are substituted in the equation relating the two systems, the following formulas are evident:

$$\log_e N = 2.30259 \log_{10} N$$
$$\log_{10} N = 0.434294 \log_e N$$

The first equation shows that the natural logarithm of a number is always $2.30259 \cdots$ times the common logarithm. Natural logarithms can be used to multiply, divide, etc., just as common logarithms are used. Tables of natural logarithms, as well as of common logarithms, are presented in the back of this book. If natural logarithm tables are not available, merely look up the number in the common logarithm tables and multiply the value by 2.30259.

One important difference in the tables must be kept in mind. In the common logarithm tables the mantissa was independent of the decimal point, and the characteristic was determined by the decimal point. This was true because 10 is the base of the decimal system as well as the base of common logarithms. In the natural logarithm tables this is not the case. Both the characteristic and mantissa are given in the tables. This means that care must be used to look up the number in the right part of the tables because the characteristic and mantissa both change with decimal point. $\log_e 12$ and $\log_e 120$ are in different parts of the table. The heading of the tables tells the series of numbers that is included in each section.

Example 1: Given $\log_{10} 7.65 = 0.88366$, find $\log_e 7.65$.

$$\log_e 7.65 = 2.30259 \log_{10} 7.65$$
$$= 2.30259(0.88366)$$
$$= 2.03471$$

Example 2: Given $\log_e 604 = 6.40357$, find $\log_{10} 604$.

$$\log_{10} 604 = 0.434294 \log_e 604$$
$$= 0.434294(6.40357)$$
$$= 2.78104$$

Example 3: Multiply 2.75(1.76)(1.75) with natural logarithms.

From the natural logarithm tables,

$$\begin{aligned}
\log_e 2.75 &= 1.01160 \\
\log_e 1.76 &= 0.56531 \\
\log_e 1.75 &= \underline{0.55962} \\
\log_e N &= 2.13653 \\
N &= 8.470
\end{aligned}$$

The table of natural logarithms in the back of the book goes from 0 to 1109. A few numbers beyond 1000 are given to aid in interpolation where the differences are large. For values of N greater than 1109 use the equation

$$\begin{aligned}
\log_e 10\,N &= \log_e N + \log_e 10 \\
&= \log_e N + 2.30259
\end{aligned}$$

Example 1: Find $\log_e 8740$.

$$\begin{aligned}
\log_e 874 &= 6.77308 \\
\log_e 10 &= \underline{2.30259} \\
\log_e 8740 &= 9.07567
\end{aligned}$$

Example 2: The equation for the tension of a belt on a pulley just held from slipping by friction is

$$T_2 = T_1 e^{0.01745 fA}$$

BELT ON PULLEY.

where T_1 and T_2 are the tensions of the belt on the two sides of the pulley, e is the base of natural logarithms, f is the coefficient of friction, and A is the angle in degrees of contact of the belt on the pulley. Find the least pull (T_1) required to keep the belt from slipping if the tension on the other side is 550 lb, the angle of contact is 160° and $f = 0.40$.

Take the natural logarithms of both sides of the equation

$$\begin{aligned}
\log_e T_2 &= \log_e T_1 + \log_e e^{0.01745 fA} \\
&= \log_e T_1 + 0.01745\,fA \log_e e \\
&= \log_e T_1 + 0.01745\,fA
\end{aligned}$$

since $\log_e e = 1$ by Rule 7. Substitute the values in the equation.

$$\begin{aligned}
\log_e 550 &= \log_e T_1 + 0.01745(0.40)(160) \\
6.30992 &= \log_e T_1 + 1.11680 \\
\log_e T_1 &= 5.19312 \\
T_1 &= 180.0 \text{ lb}
\end{aligned}$$

EXPONENTIAL EQUATIONS

Sometimes in advanced mathematical problems the unknown in an equation occurs in the exponent of a number. When this happens, the problem can often be solved by taking logarithms of both sides of the equation and solving the resulting equation by ordinary algebra.

Example: Given $6^x = 42$, find x.

Taking logarithms of both sides of the equation gives

$$x \log 6 = \log 42$$
$$x = \frac{\log 42}{\log 6} = \frac{1.62325}{0.77815} = 2.0860$$

Notice that the equation gives x and not $\log x$. This means that it is not necessary to find the antilogarithm of 2.0860, for this is the answer. The logarithms can be either to base 10 or base e. The same result will be obtained either way. *The logarithms must be treated as ordinary numbers, and not subtracted as in logarithmic division.*

Example: Given $4^{x+y} = 5$ and $3^x = 6^y$. Find x and y.

Take logarithms of both sides of the first equation.

$$(x + y) \log 4 = \log 5$$

Substitute values for the logarithms

$$0.60206(x + y) = 0.69897$$
$$x + y = \frac{0.69897}{0.60206} = 1.16096$$

This shows that the two numbers are to be divided. Even though they are logarithms they are to be divided by arithmetic. In order to divide them by logarithms the logarithm of each one must be looked up in the tables, the results subtracted, and the antilogarithm taken. *Always do exactly what the equation says, regardless of whether the numbers may have been logarithms originally.*

Similarly, the logarithms of both sides of the second equation give

$$x \log 3 = y \log 6$$
$$0.47712\,x = 0.77815\,y$$
$$x = \frac{0.77815}{0.47712}\,y = 1.63093\,y$$

Substitute this value for x in the other equation.

$$1.63093\,y + y = 1.16096$$

Add the two y terms together.

$$2.63093 \, y = 1.16096$$

$$y = \frac{1.16096}{2.63093} = 0.44127$$

From the first equation

$$x = 1.16096 - 0.44127 = 0.71969$$

EXERCISE 3.5

1. Calculate, using natural logarithms,
$$\frac{3.56(8.81)(98,000)(10.08)}{656(11,080)(1.17)}$$

2. Calculate, using natural logarithms,
$$\frac{\sqrt{8.06}(96)^2(17.6 + 34.8)(984)}{91(5.48)(10,960)}$$

3. Given $\log_e 873 = 6.77194$, find $\log_{10} 8.73$. Note the change in decimal point.

4. Given $\log_e 3.12 = 1.13783$, find $\log_{10} 31.2$.

b. Given $\log_{10} 7716 = 3.88739$, find $\log_e 771.6$.

6. Given $\log_{10} 878.6 = 2.94379$, find $\log_e 8.786$.

7. Solve the following equations by the use of logarithms:

$$2^x = 25 \qquad\qquad \left\{ \begin{array}{l} 3^{x+y} = 4 \\ 2^y = 5^{x+1} \end{array} \right.$$
$$8^x = 3$$
$$2^{2x} = 64$$

8. Solve each of the following equations by the use of logarithms:

$$3^x = 16 \qquad\qquad \left\{ \begin{array}{l} 6^{x+y} = 4^y \\ 3^x = 5^{y-1} \end{array} \right.$$
$$7^x = 1.48$$
$$3^x = 2(4^x)$$

9. Solve for x if $3^{x+2}(2^{x+1}) = 7^{3x}$

10. Solve for x if $4^{2x+1} \div 6^{x-1} = 5^x$

11. Find x if $\dfrac{e^x - e^{-x}}{e^x + e^{-x}} = 0.945$, where e is the base of natural logarithms.

12. Find x if $e^{x^2} \div e^{-x^2} = 5$, where e is the base of natural logarithms.

13. Solve for i when $E = 6$ volts, $R = 12$ ohms, $t = 0.03$ sec, and $L = 0.4$ henry in the equation for the current in a circuit containing resistance and inductance in series.

$$i = \frac{E}{R}\left(1 - e^{-\frac{Rt}{L}}\right)$$

e is the base of natural logarithms.

14. Find the time required for the current i to reach a value of 0.12 amp in the following equation if $E = 18$ volts, $R = 7.3$ ohms, $L = 1.74$ henry.

$$i = \frac{E}{R}\left(1 - e^{-\frac{Rt}{L}}\right)$$

e is the base of natural logarithms.

Hint: Substitute the numbers and simplify as much as possible before taking natural logarithms.

15. The following expression is used to find the area of a triangle when the three sides are known:

$$A = \sqrt{s(s - a)(s - b)(s - c)}$$

where $s = \frac{1}{2}(a + b + c)$ and a, b, and c are the three sides. Find the area of a triangle of sides 21.72 in., 14.33 in., and 25.86 in.

16. The area of a circle is 1973.6 sq in. Find the radius.

17. The equation for the work done by a perfect gas in expanding at constant temperature is

$$W = p_1 V_1 \log_e \frac{V_2}{V_1}$$

Find W if $p_1 = 387$, $V_1 = 132$, and $V_2 = 363$.

18. The equation for the expansion of a perfect gas at constant entropy is

$$P_1 V_1^{1.406} = P_2 V_2^{1.406}$$

Find V_2 if $P_1 = 18.0$, $P_2 = 36.4$, $V_1 = 19.3$.

19. The equation for the maximum deflection of a beam of uniform cross section, loaded transversely and supported freely at the ends, is

$$d = \frac{Wa}{3\,EIc}\left[\frac{b(a + c)}{3}\right]^{\frac{3}{2}}$$

Find d if $W = 8500$ lb; $E = 29.8 \times 10^6$; $I = 21.8$ in^4. ; $a = 42$ in.; $b = 102$ in.; $c = 144$ in.

Note: The dimension of I is in^4. This means inches to the fourth power such as would be obtained by squaring square inches. The 4 should not be substituted in the equation; it is part of the units.

20. The equation for the mean effective pressure in a simple steam engine is

$$p_m = P\,\frac{(1 + \log_e R)}{R} - p$$

Find p_m if $P = 107$ lb per in^2., $p = 15.8$ lb per in^2., $R = 3.64$

21. The flow of saturated steam through a nozzle is given approximately by

$$W = 60 \frac{A p^{0.97}}{\sqrt{x}}$$

Find W if $A = 0.168$, $p = 86.5$ and $x = 0.98$.

22. The skin frictional resistance of a surface on an airplane is given by the equation,

$$R = 0.00000778\ L^{0.93} V^{1.86} b$$

Find R if $L = 12.5$ ft, $V = 206$ ft per sec, $b = 3.25$ ft.

23. The horsepower required to compress a gas in a single-stage air compressor is

$$HP = \frac{144}{33,000} \frac{n}{n - 1} P_1 V_1 \left[\left(\frac{P_2}{P_1} \right)^{\frac{n-1}{n}} - 1 \right]$$

Find the horsepower required to compress 250 cu ft per minute from a pressure of 15 lb per sq in. to 275 lb per sq in., if $n = 1.26$.

Hint: First work out the ratio $\frac{P_2}{P_1}$ to its power completely, subtract 1, and then multiply by the other factors.

24. The current in amperes in a capacitive circuit consisting of a condenser C and a resistance R in series is given by

$$i = \frac{E}{R} e^{-\frac{t}{RC}}$$

Find i if $E = 16.1$ volts, $R = 8.7$ ohms, $C = 0.0000061$ farad and $t = 0.00002$ sec. e is the base of natural logarithms.

25. The equation for the flow of water over a contracted rectangular weir is given by the following equation:

$$Q = 3\tfrac{1}{3} \left(b - \frac{2\,H}{10} \right) [(H + h)^{\frac{3}{2}} - h^{\frac{3}{2}}]$$

where Q is in cu ft per sec. Find Q if $H = 0.25$ ft; $b = 0.31$ ft; $h = 0.0026$ ft.

Hint: Work out each term in the brackets first, and then subtract.

26. The temperature of a body cooling in moving air is given by the equation

$$T = T_0 e^{-kt}$$

where t is the time in seconds, T is the difference in temperature between the body and the air, T_0 is the initial temperature difference, and k is the radiation constant. Find the time for the difference in temperature to fall from 38° C to 21° C if

$$k = 0.00145$$

27. The air pressure at an altitude h is given approximately by the equation

$$p = 14.7 \, e^{-0.0000375h}$$

where h is in ft and p is in lb per sq in. Find the air pressure at an altitude of 16,500 ft.

28. According to scientific measurements, a 180-lb man falling from an airplane will drop 1200 ft in 11 sec and then have a constant velocity of fall of 173 ft per sec. The equation for his velocity is approximately

$$V = 173(1 - e^{-\frac{32.1}{173}t})$$

where t is the time in seconds and e is the base of natural logarithms. Find his velocity at the end of six seconds.

29. The total length of a freely hanging wire or rope is given by the following equation

$$S = a(e^{\frac{x}{a}} - e^{-\frac{x}{a}})$$

where a is a constant depending on the horizontal tension and the weight per ft, and x is one-half the span. Find the length of a telephone wire hanging between two poles 350 ft apart if $a = 2150$ and e is the base of natural logarithms.

30. The heat flow per hour through a pipe is given by the equation

$$Q = \frac{2 \, \pi KL(T_1 - T_2)}{\log_e \frac{r_2}{r_1}}$$

where K is a constant depending on the material, L is the length of the pipe, T_1 is the inside temperature, T_2 is the outside temperature, r_2 is the outside radius and r_1 is the inside radius. Find the loss in Btu's per minute through a pipe 60 ft long, if the inside temperature is 280° F., the outside temperature 268° F., the outside diameter is 10 in., the inside diameter is 9 in. and $K = 240$.

CHAPTER IV

Plane Geometry

THE SUBJECT OF PLANE GEOMETRY DEALS WITH THE PROPERTIES, measurements, and relations of lines, angles and surfaces in one plane. The theory starts out with certain axioms and postulates so self-evident that they must be admitted as true as soon as the terms in which they are expressed are clearly understood. Starting with these basic truths, logical steps are used to prove other propositions or theorems. Some of these axioms and postulates follow.

Axioms

An axiom is a general truth and need not relate to geometry.

1. *In any process, any quantity may be substituted for its equal.*
2. *Quantities which are equal to the same quantity, or to equal quantities, are equal to each other.*
3. *If equals are added to equals, the sums are equal.*
4. *If equals are subtracted from equals, the differences are equal.*
5. *If equals are multiplied by equals, the products are equal.*
6. *If equals are divided by equals, the quotients are equal. In this case the divisor must not be zero.*
7. *The whole is equal to the sum of all its parts and is greater than any of its parts.*

Postulates

A postulate is a geometric statement admitted without proof.

1. *A straight line can be drawn between any two points and it will be the shortest line between the two points.*
2. *Only one straight line can be drawn between two points.*
3. *Through a given point not more than one line can be drawn parallel to a given line.*

4. *A geometric figure may be moved in space without any change in form or size.*

5. *Two straight lines can intersect at but one point.*

The following definitions are to be used in the proofs of theorems which follow.

Definitions

1. An **angle** is formed when two straight lines are drawn from a common point. The common point is called the **vertex** and the two straight lines are called the **sides** of the angle.

2. If the two sides of an angle extend in opposite directions from the vertex so that they form a straight line, the angle is called a **straight angle.**

3. Two angles with a common side and a common vertex are called **adjacent angles.**

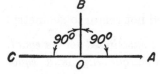

FIG. 4.1.—RIGHT ANGLES.

4. Half of a straight angle is a **right angle.** Thus in Fig. 4.1 angles *AOB* and *BOC* are equal to each other and are each equal to half of straight angle *AOC*.

5. Two angles are called **complementary** if their sum is a right angle.

6. Two angles are called **supplementary** if their sum is a straight angle.

7. Angles are usually measured in **degrees.** There are 90 degrees in a right angle, 180 degrees in a straight angle, and 360 degrees in a full circle. A degree is often divided into sixty equal parts called **minutes,** and the minute can be divided into sixty equal parts called **seconds.** These units are abbreviated as °, ′, ″, respectively. Thus 10 degrees, 12 minutes and 18 seconds is written 10° 12′ 18″.

8. An **acute angle** is an angle less than 90 degrees and an **obtuse angle** is an angle greater than 90 degrees but less than 180 degrees.

9. Two straight lines are **perpendicular** if they are at right

angles to each other. In Fig. 4.1, lines *OB* and *CA* are perpendicular.

FIG. 4.2.—PARALLEL LINES.

10. Two straight lines in the same plane are said to be **parallel** if they never intersect no matter how far they are extended.

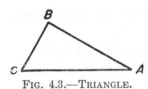
FIG. 4.3.—TRIANGLE.

11. A **triangle** is a portion of a plane enclosed by three straight lines. In Fig. 4.3 the triangle *ABC* is formed by the straight lines *AB*, *BC* and *CA*.

12. A **parallelogram** is a quadrilateral with opposite sides parallel. In Fig. 4.4 sides *BC* and *AD* are parallel and sides *AB* and *DC* are parallel.

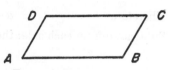
FIG. 4.4.—PARALLELOGRAM.

13. A **right triangle** is a triangle with one right angle. The side opposite the right angle is called the **hypotenuse**. In Fig. 4.5 side *BC* is the hypotenuse.

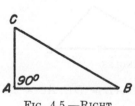
FIG. 4.5.—RIGHT TRIANGLE.

14. An **isosceles triangle** is a triangle with two equal sides.

15. A **scalene triangle** is any triangle that does not have any two sides equal.

16. An **equilateral triangle** is a triangle with three equal sides.

17. An **equiangular triangle** is a triangle with three equal angles.

18. When two straight lines intersect, the angles that have a common vertex and in which the sides of one are the prolongation through the vertex of the other are called **vertical angles**. In Fig. 4.6 angles *DOB* and *COA* are vertical angles. Similarly, angles *AOD* and *COB* are also vertical angles.

19. Two geometric figures are **congruent** if they can be placed

one upon the other so they will coincide everywhere simultaneously.

CONGRUENT TRIANGLES

Proposition 1. *If two straight lines intersect, the vertical angles formed are equal.*

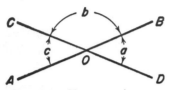

FIG. 4.6.—VERTICAL ANGLES.

Given: The two intersecting straight lines AB and CD.

Prove: Angles a and c are equal.

Proof:

$$a + b = 180°$$
$$c + b = 180°$$

Therefore $\qquad a + b = c + b \qquad$ by Axiom 2.

Subtract b from each side; then

$$a = c \qquad \text{by Axiom 4.}$$

Proposition 2. *Two triangles are congruent if two sides and the included angle of one are equal respectively to two sides and the included angle of the other.*

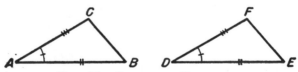

FIG. 4.7.—CONGRUENT TRIANGLES.

Given: The two triangles ABC and DEF with $AB = DE$, $AC = DF$ and $\angle A$ equal to $\angle D$.

Prove: The triangles are congruent.

Proof: Place triangle ABC upon triangle DEF so vertex A coincides with vertex D, side AB falls along DE, and side AC falls along DF. Then point B will coincide with point E since $AB = DE$ and point C will coincide with point F since $AC = DF$. Therefore side BC coincides with side EF by Postulate 2. The two triangles are thus congruent since all the parts can be made to coincide simultaneously.

A **corollary** to a geometric proposition is another geometric proposition that can be proved easily by the given proposition.

Corollary. *Two right triangles are congruent if the two legs of one triangle are equal respectively to the two legs of the other.*

Since the included angles are both right angles, Proposition 2 applies.

Proposition 3. *Two triangles are congruent if a side and the two adjacent angles of one are equal respectively to a side and the two adjacent angles of the other.*

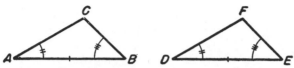

FIG. 4.8.—CONGRUENT TRIANGLES.

Given: The two triangles *ABC* and *DEF* with *AB* = *DE*, ∠*A* = ∠*D*, and ∠*B* = ∠*E*.

Prove: The triangles are congruent.

Proof: Place triangle *ABC* upon triangle *DEF* so vertex *A* coincides with vertex *D*, vertex *B* coincides with vertex *E*, side *AC* lies along side *DF*, and side *BC* lies along side *EF*. Then points *C* and *F* will coincide because the two straight lines can intersect in only one point. The two triangles are therefore congruent since all the parts can be made to coincide simultaneously.

Corollary. *Two right triangles are congruent if a leg and the adjacent acute angle of one are equal respectively to a leg and the adjacent acute angle of the other.*

Proposition 4. *In any isosceles triangle the angles opposite the equal sides are equal.*

Given: Isosceles triangle *ABC* with *AC* = *BC*.
Prove: ∠*A* = ∠*B*.

Proof: Draw line *CD* to bisect ∠*C*. Then *AC* = *BC*, *CD* = *CD* identically and ∠*ACD* = ∠*DCB*. Hence triangles *ACD* and *BCD* are congruent by Proposition 2. Therefore ∠*A* = ∠*B* because they are corresponding parts of congruent triangles.

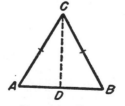

FIG. 4.9.—ISOS-
CELES TRIANGLE.

Corollary 1. *The bisector of the vertex angle of an isosceles triangle is perpendicular to the base and bisects the base.*

Extend the proof of Proposition 4.

Corollary 2. *If a triangle is equilateral it is also equiangular.*

Apply Proposition 4 twice.

Proposition 5. *If two angles of a triangle are equal, the sides opposite these angles are equal.*

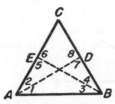

FIG. 4.10.—ISOS-
CELES TRIANGLE.

Given: Triangle ABC with $\angle A = \angle B$.

Prove: Side AC = side BC.

Proof: Draw line AD bisecting $\angle A$ and line BE bisecting $\angle B$. Since $\angle A = \angle B$, $\angle 1 = \angle 2 = \angle 3 = \angle 4$ by Axiom 6. $AB = AB$ identically. Therefore triangles ABD and ABE are congruent by Proposition 3. This means that $\angle 5 = \angle 7$ and $AD = BE$ since they are corresponding parts of congruent triangles. Likewise $\angle 6 = \angle 8$ since these two angles have equal supplements.

In triangles ADC and BEC, $\angle 2 = \angle 4$, $\angle 6 = \angle 8$, and $AD = BE$ as just proved. Therefore triangles ADC and BEC are congruent by Proposition 3. Hence $AC = BC$ since they are corresponding parts of congruent triangles.

Proposition 6. *Two triangles are congruent if the three sides of one are equal respectively to the three sides of the other.*

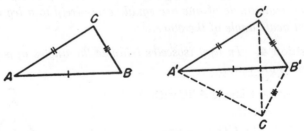

FIG. 4.11.—CONGRUENT TRIANGLES.

Given: Triangles ABC and $A'B'C'$ with $AB = A'B'$, $AC = A'C'$, and $BC = B'C'$.

Prove: The triangles are congruent.

Proof: Place triangle ABC so point A lies on point A', side AB lies along side $A'B'$, and vertex C is opposite vertex C', as shown in Fig. 4.11.

Draw line CC'. Then in isosceles triangle $A'C'C$, $\angle A'C'C$ = $\angle A'CC'$ by Proposition 4. Similarly in triangle $C'CB'$, $\angle CC'B'$ = $\angle C'CB'$. Then $\angle A'C'C + \angle CC'B' = \angle A'CC' + \angle C'CB'$ by Axiom 3. Therefore $\angle A'C'B' = \angle A'CB'$ by Axiom 7 and triangles $A'B'C'$ and $A'B'C$ are congruent by Proposition 2. Hence triangles ABC and $A'B'C'$ are congruent since each one is equal to triangle $A'B'C'$.

EXERCISE 4.1

1. Find angle θ.

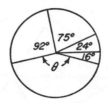

2. Find angle θ.

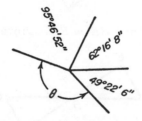

3. A wheel has seven spokes spaced at equal distances along the rim. Find the angle between adjacent spokes, in degrees, minutes and seconds.

4. Find the complement of each of the following angles: 38°, 61°, 64° 42′, 84° 31′, 26° 13′ 48″, 81° 49′ 17″.

5. Find the supplement of each of the following angles: 124°, 37°, 105° 35′, 171° 48′, 179° 0′ 18″, 29° 18′ 49″.

6. Prove that if two adjacent angles are supplementary, the angle between the bisectors of the angles is a right angle.

7. Divide the following angles by three: 26°, 38° 14′, 289° 15′ 12″, 125° 16′ 11″.

8. Two angles are supplements and one is 5° larger than the other. Find the angles.

9. How many degrees does the hour hand of a clock turn in 25 minutes?

10.   Prove that $AC = BC$.

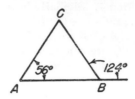

11. Prove that the bisector of one vertical angle bisects the other.

12.   Prove that $\angle a = \angle b$.

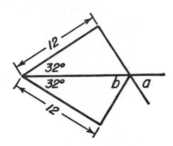

13.   Given $AB = BC$ and $BE = BD$.   Prove $\angle A = \angle C$.

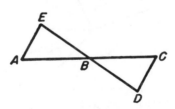

14.   Prove that the diagonals of a square are equal.

15.   Prove that $\angle a = \angle b$.

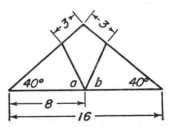

16.   Prove that the lines joining the midpoints of an equilateral triangle form an equilateral triangle half as large as the original triangle.

17. In the square $ABCD$, points E and F are the midpoints of the sides shown. Prove that $\angle DFC = \angle BEA$.

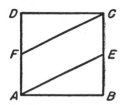

18. On sides AB and BC of any triangle ABC, equilateral triangles BAE and BCD are constructed, with points E and D outside the triangle. If AD and CE are drawn, prove that these two lines are equal.

PERPENDICULAR AND PARALLEL LINES

Proposition 7. *Only one perpendicular can be drawn from a given external point to a given line, and this perpendicular is the shortest line that can be drawn from the external point to the line.*

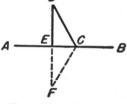

FIG. 4.12.—PERPEN-DICULAR TO LINE.

Given: Line AB, external point D, DE perpendicular to AB, and some other line DC from D to the line AB.

Prove: DC is not perpendicular to AB and DE is shorter than DC.

Proof: Extend DE to point F so $DE = EF$. Draw line FC. Then DCF is not a straight line by Proposition 2.

Side DE = side EF by construction. $\angle DEC = \angle FEC$ since both equal $90°$. $EC = EC$ identically. Therefore triangles DEC and FEC are congruent by Proposition 2, and $\angle DCE = \angle ECF$ because they are corresponding parts of congruent triangles. Since $\angle DCF$ is not a straight angle, angles DCE and ECF are not right angles; each is half of an angle not equal to a straight angle. Therefore DC is not perpendicular to AB.

Line DCF is greater than DEF by Postulate 1.

$$DE = \text{one half of } DEF.$$
$$DC = \text{one half of } DCF.$$

Therefore DC is greater than DE since it is the half of the greater distance.

Proposition 8. *An exterior angle of a triangle is greater than either opposite interior angle.*

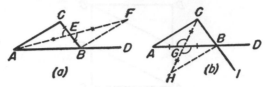

FIG. 4.13.—EXTERIOR ANGLE.

Given: Triangle ABC and exterior angle DBC which is opposite the interior angles A and C.

Prove: $\angle DBC$ is greater than either $\angle A$ or $\angle C$.

Proof: Draw line AE to the midpoint of BC and extend until $AE = EF$ as shown in Fig. 4.13a. Then in triangles AEC and BEF, $AE = EF$ by construction, $CE = EB$ by construction, and $\angle CEA = \angle BEF$ since they are vertical angles (Proposition 1). Therefore triangles AEC and BEF are congruent by Proposition 2. Hence $\angle FBC = \angle C$ since they are corresponding parts of congruent triangles. But $\angle DBC$ is greater than $\angle FBC$; the whole is greater than any of its parts. Therefore $\angle DBC$ is greater than $\angle C$ because a quantity may be substituted for its equal in any process.

In exactly the same manner, using Fig. 4.13b and the construction shown, where G is the midpoint of AB, it can be proved that $\angle ABI$ is greater than $\angle A$. But $\angle ABI = \angle DBC$ since they are vertical angles. Hence $\angle DBC$ is greater than $\angle A$.

Proposition 9. *If two straight lines in the same plane are cut by a transversal and if a pair of the alternate interior angles are equal, the two straight lines are parallel.*

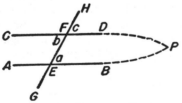

FIG. 4.14.—PARALLEL LINES.

Given: Two straight lines AB and CD cut by the transversal GH at points E and F respectively so that $\angle a = \angle b$.

Prove: Lines AB and CD are parallel.

Proof: Suppose for the moment that AB and CD prolonged meet at a point P. Then, by Proposition 8, $\angle b$ is greater than $\angle a$. But this is impossible since $\angle a = \angle b$. Therefore the two straight lines cannot intersect and are parallel.

Corollary 1. *If two straight lines in the same plane are cut by a transversal and if a pair of corresponding angles are equal, the two straight lines are parallel.*

In Fig. 4.14, if $\angle a = \angle c$, then $\angle a = \angle b$ because $\angle b = \angle c$ (vertical angles) and Proposition 9 can be used.

Corollary 2. *If two straight lines in the same plane are each perpendicular to a third straight line, the two lines are parallel.*

Corollary 3. *If two straight lines in the same plane are cut by a transversal and if the sum of the two interior angles on the same side of the transversal is equal to a straight angle, the two straight lines are parallel.*

Proposition 10. *If two parallel lines are cut by a transversal, the alternate interior angles are equal.*

Given: Parallel lines AB and CD cut by a transversal EF at points G and H respectively.

Prove: $\angle e = \angle f$.

Proof: Suppose for the moment that $\angle f$ does not equal $\angle e$. Draw the line IJ through point H so $\angle g = \angle e$. Then line IJ is parallel to line AB by Proposition 9. But line CD is parallel to line AB. Therefore lines CD and IJ coincide since through a given point not more than one line can be drawn parallel to a given line (Postulate 3).

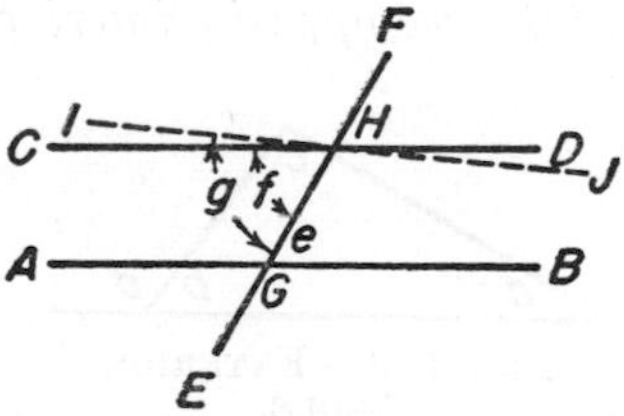

FIG. 4.15.—PARALLEL LINES.

Corollary 1. *If two parallel lines are cut by a transversal, the corresponding angles are equal.*

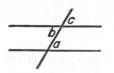

FIG. 4.16.—PARALLEL LINES.

Since $\angle b = \angle c$ by Proposition 1, and $\angle a = \angle b$ by Proposition 10, then $\angle a = \angle c$ by Axiom 2.

Corollary 2. *If two parallel lines are cut by a transversal, the sum of the two interior angles on the same side of the transversal is equal to a straight angle.*

Since $\angle b + \angle c = 180°$ and $\angle a = \angle b$, then $\angle a + \angle c = 180°$.

Corollary 3. *If a line is perpendicular to one of two parallel lines it is perpendicular to the other also, if all are in the same plane.*

FIG. 4.17.—
PARALLEL LINES.

Proposition 11. *The sum of the interior angles of a triangle is a straight angle.*

Given: Triangle *ABC.*

Prove: $\angle a + \angle b + \angle c = 1$ straight angle $= 180°.$

Proof: Draw a line *DE* through vertex *C* and parallel to side *AB.*

Then $\angle c + \angle d + \angle e = 1$ straight angle. But $\angle d = \angle a$ and $\angle e = \angle b$ by Proposition 10. Therefore $\angle a + \angle b + \angle c = 1$ straight angle, by substituting $\angle a$ for $\angle d$ and $\angle b$ for $\angle e$ (Axiom 1).

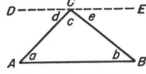

FIG. 4.18.—TRIANGLE.

Corollary 1. *An exterior angle of a triangle is equal to the sum of the two opposite interior angles.*

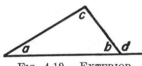

FIG. 4.19.—EXTERIOR ANGLE.

$\angle a + \angle b + \angle c = \angle b + \angle d.$ Subtract $\angle b$ from each side of the equation. Then $\angle a + \angle c = \angle d.$

Corollary 2. *In any right triangle the two acute angles are complementary.*

Corollary 3. *If an acute angle of one right triangle equals an acute angle of another right triangle, the other acute angles of the two triangles are equal.*

Corollary 4. *Two right triangles are congruent if the hypotenuse and an acute angle of one are equal respectively to the hypotenuse and an acute angle of the other.*

Prove by Corollary 3 and Proposition 3.

Corollary 5. *Two right triangles are congruent if a leg and either acute angle of one are equal respectively to a leg and the corresponding acute angle of the other.*

Corollary 6. *If two angles of one triangle are equal respectively to two angles of a second triangle, the third angle of the first triangle is equal to the third angle of the second.*

Corollary 7. *If any two angles and a side of one triangle are equal respectively to two angles and the corresponding side of the second triangle, the two triangles are congruent.*

This can be proved by Corollary 6 and Proposition 3

Corollary 8. *Each angle of an equilateral triangle or of an equiangular triangle is 60°.*

EXERCISE 4.2

1. $AB = BC$. $\angle DBC = 116°$. Find $\angle A$.

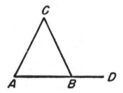

2. $\angle A = 40°$. OC bisects $\angle C$ and OB bisects $\angle B$. Find $\angle BOC$.

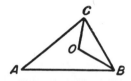

3. $\angle B = 2 \angle A$. Find A and B.

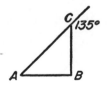

4. Given $AB = AC$, $BD = BC = CE$, and $\angle A = 95°$. Find $\angle D$ and $\angle BCD$.

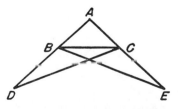

5. Given $\angle EBC = 151° 15'$, CD bisects $\angle C$ and DA bisects $\angle A$. Find $\angle CDA$.

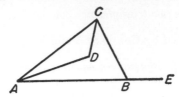

6. Given $\angle AEC = \angle BDC = 90°$ and the angles shown. Find $\angle EAB$ and $\angle CAB$.

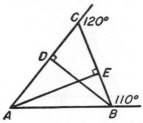

7. Given parallel lines AB and CD cut by transversal EF at points G and H respectively. $\angle FHD = 50°$. Find $\angle EGB$.

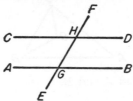

8. Given BD parallel to AC and the angles shown. Find $\angle FBD$ and $\angle C$.

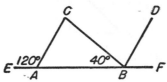

9. Given DE parallel to AC and the angles shown. Prove $DE = BE$.

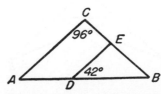

10. Given AD parallel to BC and AB parallel to DC, $\angle BDC = 90°$ and $\angle BEC = 144°$. Find $\angle BAC$.

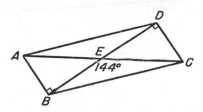

11. Given $AD = DC$, DE parallel to AB, and DF parallel to BC. Prove EF is parallel to AC.

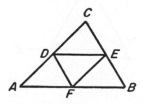

12. Given $\angle ABC = 90°$, AB parallel to DC, and $AE = CE$. Prove $BE = ED$ and $\angle A = \angle D$.

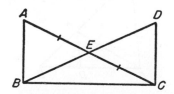

13. Given $\angle D = 90°$ and the other angles as shown. Find $\angle E$.

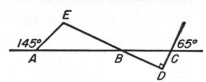

14. Find $\angle A$.

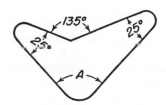

15.   Find $\angle A$.

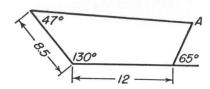

16.   Given isosceles triangle ABC with DA bisecting $\angle A$ and DB bisecting $\angle B$. Prove $\angle D = \angle EBC$.

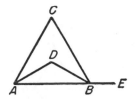

17.   Given triangle ABC with CD bisecting $\angle C$ and AE parallel to CD. Prove $CE = CA$.

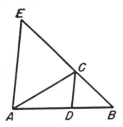

PARALLEL AND PERPENDICULAR ANGLES

Proposition 12.   *Two angles are equal if they have their sides parallel, right side to right side and left side to left side.*

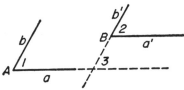

FIG. 4.20.—PARALLEL ANGLES.

Corollary 1 of Proposition 10. equals $\angle 3$.

Given: Angles A and B with side a parallel to side a', and side b parallel to side b'.

Prove: $\angle 1 = \angle 2$.

Proof: Prolong sides a and b' until they intersect to form $\angle 3$. Then $\angle 1 = \angle 3$ and $\angle 2 = \angle 3$ by Therefore $\angle 1 = \angle 2$ since each one

Corollary. *Two angles are supplementary if they have their sides parallel, right side to left side and left side to right side.*

Given: Angles *A* and *B* with side *a* parallel to side *a'* and side *b* parallel to side *b'*.

Prove: ∠1 + ∠2 = 180°.

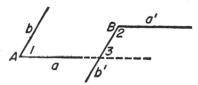

FIG. 4.21.—PARALLEL ANGLES.

Proof: Extend side *a* until it intersects side *b'*. Then ∠1 = ∠3 by Corollary 1 of Proposition 10. ∠2 + ∠3 = 180° by Corollary 2 of Proposition 10. Therefore ∠1 + ∠2 = 180° by substituting ∠1 for ∠3.

Proposition 13. *Two angles are equal if they have their sides perpendicular, right side to right side and left side to left side.*

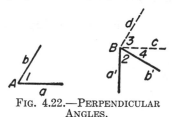

FIG. 4.22.—PERPENDICULAR ANGLES.

Given: Angles *A* and *B* with sides *a* and *a'* perpendicular and sides *b* and *b'* perpendicular.

Prove: ∠*A* = ∠*B*.

Proof: Construct ∠3 at vertex *B* with sides parallel to ∠1 as shown. Then ∠2 + ∠4 = 90° and ∠3 + ∠4 = 90°. Therefore ∠2 = ∠3 since angles with equal complements are equal. But ∠3 = ∠1 by Proposition 12. Hence ∠1 = ∠2 since each equals ∠3.

Corollary. *Two angles are supplementary if they have their sides perpendicular, right side to left side and left side to right side respectively.*

Proposition 14. *Two right triangles are congruent if the hypotenuse and a side of one are equal respectively to the hypotenuse and a side of the other.*

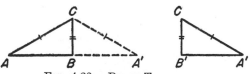

FIG. 4.23.—RIGHT TRIANGLES.

Given: Two right triangles *ABC* and *A'B'C'* with *AC* = *A'C'*, *BC* = *B'C'* and ∠*B* = ∠*B'* = 90°.

Prove: The triangles are congruent.

Proof: Place triangle $A'B'C'$ so side $B'C'$ coincides with side BC and vertex A' is opposite vertex A, as shown in Fig. 4.23. Then ABA' is a straight line since it is the sum of two right angles ABC and $A'BC$. $AA'C$ is therefore an isosceles triangle, and $\angle A = \angle A'$ by Proposition 4. The two triangles are therefore congruent by Corollary 4 of Proposition 11.

EXERCISE 4.3

1. Given DE perpendicular to AB, DF perpendicular to AC, and the angles shown. Find $\angle A$.

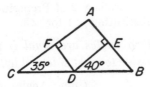

2. Given $\angle ACB = 90°$, $\angle CDB = 90°$. Prove that $\angle BCD = \angle CAB$.

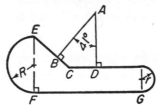

3. Given AB perpendicular to EC, AD perpendicular to CD, EF perpendicular to FG, and FG parallel to CD. Find $\angle FEB$.

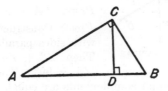

4. Find $\angle x$.

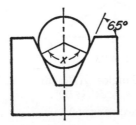

5. The edge of a 30°–60° drawing triangle is moved along a straight line as shown. Show that the sides are always parallel to the original position.

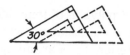

6. A 45° drawing triangle is used to draw the angle shown. Find ∠x.

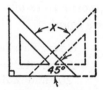

7. Show two ways to use the two triangles above to draw two perpendicular lines, one at 15° with the horizontal.

8. Find ∠x.

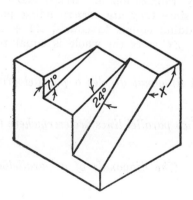

9. Find ∠x.

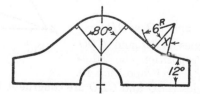

PARALLELOGRAMS

Definitions

1. A **quadrilateral** is a polygon of four sides.
2. A **parallelogram** is a quadrilateral whose opposite sides are parallel. If the interior angles are all right angles it is called a **rectangle**. If all four sides of a rectangle are equal it is called a **square**.

Proposition 15. *The opposite sides of a parallelogram are equal and the opposite angles are equal.*

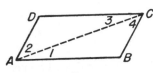

FIG. 4.24.—PARALLELO-GRAM.

Given: Parallelogram $ABCD$.

Prove: $AB = DC$, $AD = BC$, $\angle B = \angle D$ and $\angle A = \angle C$.

Proof: Draw diagonal AC. Then $\angle 1 = \angle 3$ and $\angle 2 = \angle 4$ by Proposition 10. $AC = AC$ identically. Therefore triangles ABC and CDA are congruent by Proposition 3. Hence $AB = DC$, $AD = BC$ and $\angle D = \angle B$ since they are corresponding parts of congruent triangles. By adding equals to equals, $\angle 1 + \angle 2 = \angle 3 + \angle 4$. Therefore $\angle A = \angle C$ since the whole is equal to the sum of its parts.

Corollary 1. *A diagonal divides a parallelogram into two congruent triangles.*

Corollary 2. *Two parallel lines are everywhere the same distance apart.*

Proposition 16. *The diagonals of a parallelogram bisect each other.*

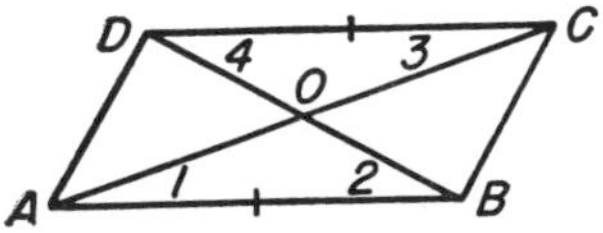

Given: Parallelogram $ABCD$ with diagonals AC and BD intersecting at point O.

Prove: $AO = OC$ and $BO = OD$.

Proof: In triangles ABO and CDO, $AB = CD$ by Proposition 15. $\angle 1 = \angle 3$ and $\angle 2 = \angle 4$ by Proposition 10.

FIG. 4.25.—PARALLELO-GRAM.

Therefore triangles ABO and CDO are congruent by Proposition 3.

Hence $AO = OC$ and $BO = OD$ since they are corresponding parts of congruent triangles.

EXERCISE 4.4

1. Prove that if two successive angles of a parallelogram are bisected, the triangle formed is a right triangle.

2. In the right triangle ABC, the line CE is drawn to the midpoint E of hypotenuse AB and extended to point D so $CE = DE$. Prove that if the lines AD and BD are drawn, the figure $ABCD$ is a rectangle.

3. Prove that any two consecutive angles of a parallelogram are supplementary.

4. Prove that if two sides of a quadrilateral are equal and parallel the figure is a parallelogram.

5. Prove that if the midpoints of the sides of a parallelogram are joined successively, another parallelogram is formed.

6. Given a parallelogram $ABCD$ and diagonal AC bisecting $\angle A$. Prove $AB = BC$.

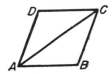

7. Given a parallelogram $ABCD$, diagonal AC, and perpendiculars to the diagonal BF and DE. Prove that $DE = BF$.

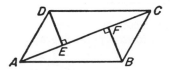

8. The diagonals of a parallelogram intersect at point O. Prove that any other straight line through point O with ends on the parallelogram will be bisected by O.

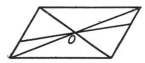

9. Prove that if three or more parallel lines intercept equal segments on one transversal, they intercept equal segments on all intersecting lines.

10. The proposition in Problem 9 is often used to divide a given line into a given number of equal parts. Suppose line AB is to be divided into eight equal parts. Draw any line AC and divide into eight equal parts as shown. Draw BC. Then lines parallel to BC, through the points marked on AC, will divide AB equally as shown.

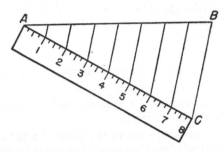

11. Prove that two parallelograms are congruent if they have two sides and the included angle of one equal to two sides and the included angle of the other.

12. Prove that the bisectors of the internal angles of a parallelogram form a rectangle.

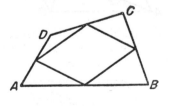

13. Show that the lines connecting the midpoints of successive sides of a quadrilateral form a parallelogram.

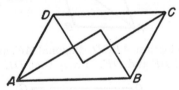

CIRCLES

Definitions

1. A **circle** is a closed curved line, in a plane, all points of which are equidistant from a point within called the **center**.

2. The **circumference** is the length of the circle.

3. The **radius** of a circle is the distance from the center to any point on the circle.

4. Any straight line through the center of the circle, with its ends on the circle, is called a **diameter**.

5. A **chord** is any straight line with its ends on the circle.

6. An **arc** is any portion of a circle.

7. A **semicircle** is half a circle. A quarter of a circle is often called a **quadrant**.

8. A **tangent** to a circle is a straight line that touches the circle at only one point.

9. A **secant** is any straight line that intersects a circle in two points.

FIG. 4.26.—SECANT AND TANGENT.

10. A **central angle** is an angle with its vertex at the center of the circle and two radii of the circle for sides.

 ∠ *AOB* is a central angle.

FIG. 4.27.—CENTRAL ANGLE.

11. An **inscribed angle** is an angle with its vertex on the circle, and two chords for sides.

 ∠ *AOB* is an inscribed angle.

FIG. 4.28.—IN-SCRIBED ANGLE.

12. An angle is said to **intercept** the arc cut off between its sides. The arc is said to **subtend** the angle.

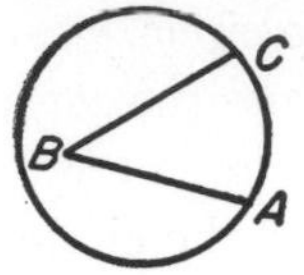

Angle *B* intercepts the arc *AC*, and arc *AC* subtends the angle *B*.

FIG. 4.29.—
INTERCEPTED
ARC.

13. A **sector** of a circle is the area bounded by two radii and the intercepted arc.

Area *AOB* is a sector of the circle.

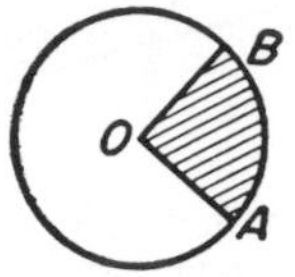

FIG. 4.30.—
SECTOR OF
CIRCLE.

14. A **segment** of a circle is the area bounded by a chord and the intercepted arc.

Area *ABC* is a segment of the circle.

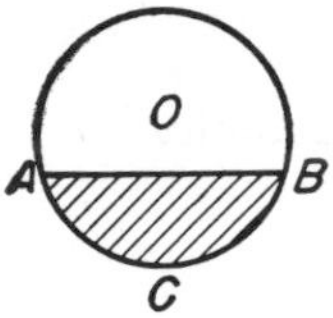

FIG. 4.31.—
SEGMENT OF
CIRCLE.

Postulates

From the preceding definitions, it is apparent that the following geometrical properties of a circle are true.

1. *All radii of the same circle or of equal circles are equal.*
2. *If the centers of two equal circles are made to coincide, and if the circles lie in the same plane, the circles will coincide everywhere.*
3. *A point is inside a circle, on a circle, or outside a circle according to whether the distance from the center is less than, equal to, or greater than the radius.*

4. *A straight line through a point within a circle cuts the circle in two points.*

5. *If the end points of two arcs of the same or of equal circles in the same plane can be made to coincide, the arcs are equal, since they will then coincide at all other points if the centers are on the same side of the arcs.*

6. *If, in the same circle or in equal circles, two central angles are equal, the arcs which they intercept are equal; and conversely, if in the same circle or in equal circles two arcs are equal, the central angles which they subtend are equal.*

This is easily proved by placing one figure upon the other and noting that all parts coincide.

7. *A central angle is measured by its intercepted arc.*

It follows from this assumption that in the same circle or in equal circles two central angles have the same ratio as their intercepted arcs. For example, in a given circle, if the arc is made twice as long, the central angle will be doubled.

Proposition 17. *A diameter of a circle which is perpendicular to a chord of the circle bisects the chord and the arc subtended by it.*

Given: Circle *ADBC* with center *O* and diameter *AB* perpendicular to chord *CD*.

Prove: *CE* = *ED* and arc *AC* = arc *AD*.

Proof: Draw radii *CO* and *DO*. Then right triangles *CEO* and *DEO* are congruent by Proposition 14. Hence *CE* = *ED* because they are corresponding parts of congruent triangles. Likewise ∠*COE* = ∠*DOE* for the same reason. Therefore arc *CA* = arc *AD* because they subtend equal central angles.

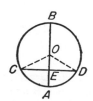

Fig. 4.32.—
DIAMETER PERPENDICULAR TO CHORD.

Corollary 1. *The perpendicular bisector of a chord passes through the center of the circle.*

Corollary 2. *A diameter that bisects a chord (not a diameter) of a circle is perpendicular to the chord.*

Proposition 18. *A tangent to a circle is perpendicular to the radius drawn to the point of contact.*

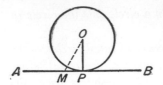

FIG. 4.33.—TANGENT TO A CIRCLE.

Given: Line AB tangent to circle O at point P and radius OP.

Prove: AB perpendicular to OP.

Proof: By Proposition 7 a perpendicular is the shortest line that can be drawn from an external point to the line. Draw any other line through the center O to intersect the line at a point M. Then M is outside the circle and OM is greater than OP. Therefore OM cannot be perpendicular to AB. Since OP is the shortest line that can be drawn to line AB it is perpendicular to AB.

Corollary 1. *A straight line perpendicular to a radius at its extremity on the circle is tangent to the circle.*

Corollary 2. *A perpendicular to a tangent to a circle at the point of contact passes through the center of the circle.*

Proposition 19. *Tangents drawn from an external point to a circle are equal and make equal angles with the line joining the external point and the center of the circle.*

Given: Circle with center O an external point P, the two tangents PA and PB, and line PO connecting point P to the center of the circle.

Prove: $PA = PB$ and $\angle BPO = \angle APO$.

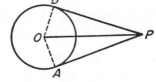

FIG. 4.34.—TANGENTS FROM EXTERNAL POINT.

Proof: Draw radii OA and OB to the points of tangency. Then $OA = OB$ since they are radii of the same circle, $OP = OP$ identically, and $\angle OBP = \angle OAP$ because they are both right angles by Proposition 18. Hence triangles OAP and OBP are congruent by Proposition 14. Therefore $PA = PB$ and $\angle OPB = \angle OPA$ since they are corresponding parts of congruent triangles.

Proposition 20. *An angle inscribed in a circle is measured by one half the intercepted arc.*

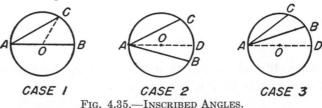

CASE 1   CASE 2   CASE 3

FIG. 4.35.—INSCRIBED ANGLES.

Given: Circle with center O and inscribed angle BAC.

Prove: $\angle BAC$ is measured by one half of arc BC.

Proof: Case 1. One side is a diameter of the circle.

Draw radius CO. Then triangle OAC is isosceles since $OA = OC$. By Proposition 4, $\angle OAC = \angle OCA$, and by Corollary 1 of Proposition 11, $\angle BOC = \angle OAC + \angle OCA$. Therefore $\angle OAC = \frac{1}{2}\angle BOC$. But $\angle BOC$ is measured by arc BC. Hence $\angle OAC$ is measured by one half of arc BC.

Case 2. Center of circle within the angle.

Draw diameter AD through vertex A. Then $\angle DAC$ is measured by $\frac{1}{2}$ arc DC and $\angle DAB$ is measured by $\frac{1}{2}$ arc BD by Case 1. Therefore $\angle BAC = \angle BAD + \angle DAC$ is measured by $\frac{1}{2}$ arc $BD + \frac{1}{2}$ arc $DC = \frac{1}{2}$ arc BC.

Case 3. Center of circle outside the angle.

This is proved in a manner similar to that used in Case 2 by subtracting $\frac{1}{2}$ arc DB from $\frac{1}{2}$ arc DC.

Corollary 1. *An angle inscribed in a semicircle is a right angle.*

Corollary 2. *All inscribed angles which subtend the same arc of a circle are equal.*

EXERCISE 4.5

1. A regular polygon of n sides is inscribed in a circle. Use inscribed angles to prove that each interior angle is $\dfrac{n-2}{n}(180°)$.

2. The exterior angle of a regular polygon is 72°. Find the number of sides.

3. Find $\angle A$.

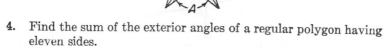

4. Find the sum of the exterior angles of a regular polygon having eleven sides.

5. Show that if the two sides of a carpenter's square are kept in contact with two nails, the vertex will describe a semicircle.

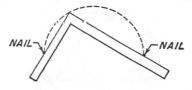

6. The length of a tangent from an external point to a circle 80 inches in diameter is 46 inches. Find the distance from the external point to the center of the circle.

7. Given radius AO, chord CD parallel to AO, and diameter BC. Prove arc $BD = 2$ arc AC.

8. Prove that if an isosceles triangle is inscribed in a circle, the two equal sides are equidistant from the center.

9. Prove that if two tangents are drawn to a circle from an external point, the line joining the external point to the center of the circle bisects the chord joining the two points of tangency.

10. Two circles are tangent to line OA at point A. Tangents are drawn from point O to the circles as shown. Prove $OB = OC$.

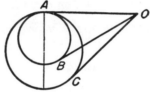

11. Two circles are tangent to line AB at point O. Prove that line AB bisects tangent CD and that $CD = EF$.

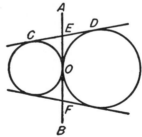

12. A quadrilateral is circumscribed about a circle. Prove that $AB + CD = CA + BD$.

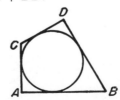

13. Three circles are tangent as shown, and triangle ABC is formed by connecting the centers.   Prove that the perimeter of triangle ABC equals the diameter of the large circle.

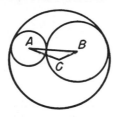

14. Prove that an angle formed by a tangent and a chord drawn to the tangent point is measured by one half the intercepted arc.

15. Two circles are tangent at point O and have a common external tangent AB. Prove $\angle BOA = 90°$.

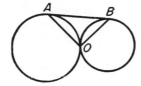

CHAPTER V

Quadratic Equations

SO FAR THE UNKNOWN IN THE ALGEBRAIC EQUATIONS HAS BEEN to the first power. In applied problems, however, squares, cubes and higher powers often occur. A **quadratic function** is one which contains the second power of one unknown quantity. It may or may not contain the first power.

Examples: 1. $x^2 = 9$ A pure quadratic
             2. $x^2 = 6\,x$ An incomplete quadratic
             3. $x^2 + 5\,x = 6$ A complete quadratic

Several methods for solving quadratic equations will be explained. The four most common are:

1. Graphic method
2. Factoring
3. Completing the square
4. Quadratic formula

The values of the unknown that satisfy the equation are called the *roots of the equation.*

Graph of a Quadratic Function

It is often useful to plot the graph of a quadratic function. The roots of a quadratic equation can then be determined from the graph, and the curve is often helpful in discussing the solutions. The U-shaped curve which is obtained is called a **parabola.**

Consider the function $x^2 - 3\,x - 4$. To draw this graph set it equal to y. Then

$$y = x^2 - 3\,x - 4$$

Assume different values for x and calculate y for each one. Thus, if $x = 1$, $y = (1)^2 - 3(1) - 4 = -6$. Make out a table showing the values of y corresponding to the assumed value of x.

$$y = x^2 - 3x - 4$$

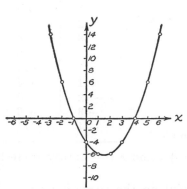

x	y
1	-6
2	-6
3	-4
4	0
5	$+6$
6	$+14$
0	-4
-1	0
-2	$+6$
-3	$+14$

FIG. 5.1.—A QUADRATIC FUNCTION.

Plot the calculated values of x and y and draw a smooth curve through the points. It is not necessary to use the same scale on both the x and y axes. In this case the value of y was $+14$ when x was 6. The scale for y was chosen so that the curve extends approximately equal distances along both axes.

Solving a Quadratic Equation Graphically

The roots of the quadratic function are the points where the curve intersects the x-axis. There are three possible cases. The curve may intersect the axis in two points, it may be tangent at one point, or it may not intersect the axis at all. In the first case, there will be two real roots; in the second case the two roots are real and equal, and in the third case the roots are imaginary.

Example 1: Solve the equation $x - x^2 + 6 = 0$ for x by the graphic method.

Set the function equal to y and make out a table of calculated values of y for each assumed value for x.

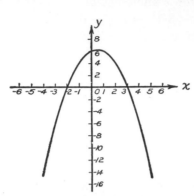

FIG. 5.2.—TWO REAL ROOTS.

$$y = -x^2 + x + 6$$

x	y
0	$+6$
1	$+6$
2	$+4$
3	0
4	-6
5	-14
-1	$+4$
-2	0
-3	-6
-4	-14

The roots are seen to be $x = +3$ and $x = -2$; they are real and unequal.

The highest, or lowest, point on the curve is always given by one-half the coefficient of x divided by the coefficient of x^2 with the sign changed. In this case the highest point is

$$x = \frac{\frac{1}{2}(+1)}{+1} = +\frac{1}{2}$$

If the coefficient of x^2 is negative, the point is a maximum; if it is positive, the point is a minimum. The values of x should be selected so that they fall above and below this point by equal amounts. The accuracy of the roots is determined by the accuracy in plotting the points and the care used in drawing the smooth curve through them.

Example 2: Solve the equation

$$2x^2 - 8x + 8 = 0$$

for x by the graphic method.

Divide by 2 to simplify the equation.

$$x^2 - 4x + 4 = 0$$

Then $y = x^2 - 4x + 4$ and the minimum point occurs when $x = 2$.

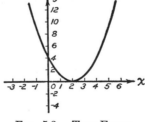

FIG. 5.3.—TWO EQUAL ROOTS.

$$y = x^2 - 4x + 4$$

x	y
2	0
3	$+1$
4	$+4$
5	$+9$
1	$+1$
0	$+4$
-1	$+9$

In this case the roots are equal and $x = +2$.

Example 3: Solve the equation $x^2 - 5x + 8 = 0$ for x graphically.

$$y = x^2 - 5x + 8$$

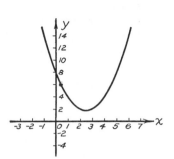

x	y
$2\frac{1}{2}$	$+1.75$
3	$+2$
4	$+4$
5	$+8$
6	$+14$
2	$+2$
1	$+4$
0	$+8$
-1	$+14$

FIG. 5.4.—TWO IMAGINARY ROOTS.

Since the curve does not intersect the x-axis, the two roots are imaginary.

EXERCISE 5.1

Plot the following quadratic functions:

1. $x^2 - 2x - 3$
2. $x^2 - 2x - 8$
3. $x^2 - 6x + 5$
4. $4x^2 - 4x + 15$
5. $6x^2 - 13x - 5$
6. $14x^2 + 17x - 12$
7. $7x - 3x^2 - 2$
8. $x - x^2 - 1$
9. $6x - x^2 - 9$
10. $x^2 - 6$

Solve the following equations for x by the graphic method:

11. $x^2 - 3x + 2 = 0$
12. $x^2 - 2x - 8 = 0$
13. $2x^2 + 7x + 6 = 0$
14. $2x^2 + 3x - 2 = 0$
15. $x - 6x^2 = 3$
16. $2x^2 = 7x + 1$
17. $3x^2 - 18x + 27 = 0$
18. $x^2 + 2x - 5 = 0$
19. $2x^2 + 20x + 50 = 0$
20. $x^2 + 13x + 43 = 0$

THE PURE QUADRATIC

A pure quadratic contains the second power of the unknown and a constant term; the first power of the unknown is missing. These equations are solved by first getting the term containing the unknown to the left side of the equation and the remaining terms to the right side, and then extracting the square root of each side of the equation.

Example 1: Solve the equation $x^2 = 9$ for x.

$$x^2 = 9$$
$$\sqrt{x^2} = \sqrt{9}$$
$$x = \pm\, 3$$

Check: If $x = +\,3$
$$x^2 = (+\,3)^2 = 9$$
If $x = -\,3$
$$x^2 = (-\,3)^2 = 9$$

Thus the equation is satisfied.

The $\pm$ sign (read plus or minus) means that the answer may be either plus 3 or minus 3. This is true because either a $+\,3$ or a $-\,3$ will give $+\,9$ when squared. Since there is nothing in the problem that tells which answer to use, they both are given. Often in a practical problem there is a good reason why one of the answers is impossible or has no meaning. Unless there is a definite reason why one cannot be used, always state both.

Example 2: Solve the equation $x^2 + 18 = 82$ for x.

Rearrange terms. $\qquad x^2 = 82 - 18 = 64$
Extract the square root. $\quad x = \pm 8$

Check: If $x = +\,8$, $(+\,8)^2 + 18 = 64 + 18 = 82$
If $x = -\,8$, $(-\,8)^2 + 18 = 64 + 18 = 82$

Example 3: Solve the equation $x^2 - 7 = 15$ for x.

$$x^2 - 7 = 15$$
$$x^2 = 22$$
$$x = \sqrt{22} = \pm 4.6904$$

The square root may be worked out by arithmetic or looked up in the tables of square roots.

The Incomplete Quadratic

An incomplete quadratic contains the first and second powers of the unknown, but does not contain a constant term.

Example 1: Solve the equation $x^2 = 6\,x$ for x.

Rearrange terms. $\qquad\qquad\qquad\qquad\quad x^2 - 6\,x = 0$
Factor. $\qquad\qquad\qquad\qquad\qquad\qquad x(x - 6) = 0$
Set each factor equal to zero. $\qquad\qquad\quad x = 0$
and $\qquad\qquad\qquad\qquad\qquad\qquad\quad x - 6 = 0$
Hence $\qquad\qquad\qquad\qquad\qquad\qquad\quad x = 6 \text{ or } 0$

Check: If $x = 0$, $(0)^2 - 6(0) = 0$
If $x = 6$, $(6)^2 - 6(6) = 36 - 36 = 0$

Example 2: Solve the equation $7 x^2 - 11 x = 0$ for x.

Factor. $\qquad x(7 x - 11) = 0$

Then $\qquad\qquad x = 0$

and $\qquad\qquad 7 x - 11 = 0$

$\qquad\qquad\qquad 7 x = 11$

Hence $\qquad\qquad x = \frac{11}{7} = 1\frac{4}{7}$ or 0

Check: If $x = 0$, $\qquad 7(0)^2 - 11(0) = 0$

$\quad$ If $x = 1\frac{4}{7}$, $\quad 7(\frac{11}{7})^2 - 11(\frac{11}{7}) = \frac{121}{7} - \frac{121}{7} = 0$

THE COMPLETE QUADRATIC

The first and second powers of the unknown both appear in a complete quadratic. Sometimes these can be solved by factoring, and sometimes it is necessary to use other methods, such as completing the square, or the quadratic formula.

Solution by Factoring

Example 1: Solve the equation $x^2 - 6 x + 8 = 0$ for x.

This may be factored to give $(x - 4)(x - 2) = 0$.

Since the product of two factors is zero, one or both of them must equal zero. Therefore

$\qquad x - 4 = 0 \qquad$ *Check:* If $x = 4$

$\qquad\qquad x = 4 \qquad\qquad (4)^2 - 6(4) + 8 = 16 - 24 + 8 = 0$

or $\quad x - 2 = 0 \qquad$ If $x = 2$

$\qquad\qquad x = 2 \qquad\qquad (2)^2 - 6(2) + 8 = 4 - 12 + 8 = 0$

There are two answers to this problem; either of them satisfies the equation.

Example 2: Solve the equation $6 x^2 + 11 x + 4 = 0$ for x by factoring.

Factor. $\qquad\qquad (3 x + 4)(2 x + 1) = 0$

Set each factor equal to zero.

$3 x + 4 = 0 \qquad$ *Check:* If $x = -\frac{4}{3}$

$\quad 3 x = -4 \qquad\quad 6(-\frac{4}{3})^2 + 11(-\frac{4}{3}) + 4 = \frac{96}{9} - \frac{44}{3} + 4$

$\quad\quad x = -\frac{4}{3} \qquad\qquad\qquad\qquad\qquad = \frac{32}{3} - \frac{44}{3} + \frac{12}{3} = 0$

and

$2 x + 1 = 0 \qquad$ If $x = -\frac{1}{2}$

$\quad 2 x = -1 \qquad\quad 6(-\frac{1}{2})^2 + 11(-\frac{1}{2}) + 4 = \frac{6}{4} - \frac{11}{2} + 4$

$\quad\quad x = -\frac{1}{2} \qquad\qquad\qquad\qquad\qquad = \frac{3}{2} - \frac{11}{2} + \frac{8}{2} = 0$

The equation is satisfied.

Completing the Square

In this method the left side of the equation is arranged so that it contains all the unknowns and also is a perfect square.

The square root of both sides of the equation is then taken and the resulting equation is solved for the unknown.

Example 1: Solve the equation $x^2 = 24 - 10\,x$ for x.

First rearrange the terms.

$$x^2 + 10\,x = 24$$

In order to make the left side a perfect square, a certain amount must be added to it. To find this amount, divide the coefficient of the x term by 2 and square the result. Add this amount to both sides of the equation.

$$x^2 + 10\,x + (5)^2 = 24 + (5)^2 = 49$$

The left side is now a perfect square, and the equation may be rewritten

$$(x + 5)^2 = 49$$

Extract the square root of both sides of the equation.

$$x + 5 = \pm 7$$

Then $\quad x + 5 = 7 \qquad$ and $\qquad x + 5 = -7$
so $\qquad\quad x = 2 \qquad$ or $\qquad\quad x = -12.$

Check: If $x = 2$ $\qquad\qquad$ If $x = -12$
$\quad (2)^2 + 10(2) = 4 + 20 = 24 \qquad (-12)^2 + 10(-12) = 144 - 120 = 24$

Both roots of the equation check.

Example 2: Solve the equation $6\,x^2 = 18\,x + 168$ for x.

Rearrange the terms.

$$6\,x^2 - 18\,x = 168$$

Before the method of completing the square can be used, the equation must be changed so the coefficient of x^2 *is 1.*
Divide by 6.

$$x^2 - 3\,x = 28$$

Complete the square.

$$x^2 - 3\,x + (\tfrac{3}{2})^2 = 28 + (\tfrac{3}{2})^2 = 28 + \tfrac{9}{4}$$
$$= \tfrac{112}{4} + \tfrac{9}{4} = \tfrac{121}{4}$$

so $\qquad\qquad (x - \tfrac{3}{2})^2 = \tfrac{121}{4}$

Extract the square root.

$$x - \tfrac{3}{2} = \pm\, \tfrac{11}{2}$$

Then $\quad x - \tfrac{3}{2} = +\tfrac{11}{2} \qquad$ and $\qquad x - \tfrac{3}{2} = -\tfrac{11}{2}$
$\qquad\quad x = \tfrac{3}{2} + \tfrac{11}{2} = \tfrac{14}{2} \qquad\qquad\qquad x = \tfrac{3}{2} - \tfrac{11}{2} = -\tfrac{8}{2}$
$\qquad\quad x = 7 \qquad\qquad\qquad\qquad\qquad\quad x = -4$

Check: If $x = 7$ $\qquad\qquad$ If $x = -4$
$\quad 6(7)^2 - 18(7) = 294 - 126 \qquad 6(-4)^2 - 18(-4) = 96 + 72$
$\qquad\qquad\qquad\qquad = 168 \qquad\qquad\qquad\qquad\qquad\qquad = 168$

Rules for Completing the Square

1. *Rearrange the equation, if necessary, to the form* $x^2 + bx = c$. *If the coefficient of* x^2 *is not 1, divide the whole equation by the coefficient.*

2. *Divide the coefficient of* x *by 2, square the result, and add this amount to each side of the equation. The left side of the equation is now a perfect square.*

3. *Extract the square root of both sides of the equation. Put a $\pm$ sign in front of the result on the right side.*

4. *Solve the two equations obtained by Rule 3.*

5. *Check the obtained results by substitution in the original equation.*

In most practical problems, the resulting quadratic equations cannot be factored, and they usually contain decimals. The solution in this case is the same as in Examples 1 and 2.

Example 3: Solve the equation $2.7\,x^2 = 8.802\,x + 16.254$ for x by completing the square.

$$2.7\,x^2 - 8.802\,x = + 16.254$$
$$x^2 - 3.26\,x = + 6.02 \qquad \text{Rule 1}$$
$$x^2 - 3.26\,x + (1.63)^2 = + 6.02 + (1.63)^2$$
$$= + 6.02 + 2.6569$$
$$= + 8.6769 \qquad \text{Rule 2}$$
$$x - 1.63 = \sqrt{8.6769} = \pm\, 2.9456^+$$
$$x = 1.63 \pm 2.9456$$
$$= 4.5756 \qquad \text{or} \qquad - 1.3156$$

Check: If $x = 4.5756$

$$2.7(4.5756)^2 - 8.802(4.5756) = 56.528 - 40.275 = 16.253$$

This checks within 0.001.

If $x = -1.3156$

$$2.7(-1.3156)^2 - 8.802(-1.3156) = 4.673 + 11.580 = 16.253$$

This also checks within 0.001.

There is usually a small error in the check because the values of x are not exact, since the square root seldom comes out even. The error in the check depends on the accuracy used in finding the root.

EXERCISE 5.2

Solve the following pure quadratic equations for x.

1. $4 x^2 + 3 = 67$
2. $5 x^2 - 12 = 113$
3. $2 x^2 + 25 = 475$
4. $3 x^2 = 81$
5. $10 x^2 - 9 = 1$

6. $14 x^2 - 9 = 47$
7. $8 = 35 - 3 x^2$
8. $115 = 15 + 4 x^2$
9. $6 x^2 + 12 = 738$
10. $10 x^2 + 160 = 1600$

Solve the following equations for x by factoring:

11. $x^2 + 3 x - 18 = 0$
12. $x^2 + 9 x + 18 = 0$
13. $x^2 - 11 x + 30 = 0$
14. $6 x^2 + 60 x + 150 = 0$
15. $30 x^2 + 37 x - 84 = 0$

16. $6 x^2 = 36 x - 54$
17. $x^2 + 144 = 25 x$
18. $74 x - 1225 = x^2$
19. $x^2 - 4 ax = - 3 a^2$
20. $x^2 + kx = ax + ak$

Solve the following equations for x by completing the square:

21. $x^2 - 5 x - 14 = 0$
22. $x^2 - 180 - 8 x = 0$
23. $x^2 + 140 = - 27 x$
24. $6 x^2 - 5 x = 6$
25. $5 x^2 + 8 = 14 x$

26. $0.2 x^2 - 3.5 + 0.9 x = 0$
27. $3 x^2 - 10 - 13 x = 0$
28. $10 = 7 x^2 + 9 x$
29. $21 a^2 - 4 ax - x^2 = 0$
30. $x^2 - 4 ab - 2 ax + 2 bx = 0$

QUADRATIC FORMULA

A general formula for solving all types of complete quadratic equations can be worked out. This may be used to find the roots of the equation by substituting the values of the coefficients directly in the formula. This formula is used for most practical problems, since the equation can seldom be factored and usually the coefficients involve decimals.

First put the general quadratic equation in the standard form

$$ax^2 + bx + c = 0 \qquad a \neq 0$$

where a, b and c may be either letters or numbers. It is necessary that $a \neq 0$, for if $a = 0$, the equation is not a quadratic.

Then transpose c. $ax^2 + bx = - c$

$$x^2 + \frac{b}{a} x = - \frac{c}{a}$$ Rule 1, page 161

$$x^2 + \frac{b}{a}x + \left(\frac{b}{2\,a}\right)^2 = -\frac{c}{a} + \left(\frac{b}{2\,a}\right)^2 \qquad \text{Rule 2}$$

$$x^2 + \frac{b}{a}x + \frac{b^2}{4\,a^2} = -\frac{c}{a} + \frac{b^2}{4\,a^2} = \frac{b^2 - 4\,ac}{4\,a^2}$$

$$x + \frac{b}{2\,a} = \pm\frac{\sqrt{b^2 - 4\,ac}}{2\,a} \qquad \text{Rule 3}$$

Transposing $$x = -\frac{b}{2\,a} \pm \frac{\sqrt{b^2 - 4\,ac}}{2\,a}$$

Hence $$x = \frac{-b \pm \sqrt{b^2 - 4\,ac}}{2\,a}$$

If x_1 and x_2 are the two roots of the equation, then

$$x_1 = \frac{-b + \sqrt{b^2 - 4\,ac}}{2\,a} \quad \text{and} \quad x_2 = \frac{-b - \sqrt{b^2 - 4\,ac}}{2\,a}$$

Anyone who needs to solve practical quadratic equations should memorize the quadratic formula and use it when the factors are not obvious.

Example 1: Solve the equation $2\,x^2 - 13\,x + 16 = 0$ for x, using the quadratic formula.

Here $$a = +2$$
$$b = -13$$
$$c = +16$$

$$x = \frac{-(-13) \pm \sqrt{(-13)^2 - 4(2)(16)}}{2(2)}$$

$$= \frac{13 \pm \sqrt{169 - 128}}{4} = \frac{13 \pm \sqrt{41}}{4}$$

$$= \frac{13 \pm 6.4031^+}{4}$$

$$x_1 = \frac{13 + 6.4031}{4} = \frac{19.4031}{4} = 4.8508$$

$$x_2 = \frac{13 - 6.4031}{4} = \frac{6.5969}{4} = 1.6492$$

Check: If $x = 4.8508$

$2(4.8508)^2 - 13(4.8508) + 16 = 47.060 - 63.060 + 16 = 0$

If $x = 1.6492$

$2(1.6492)^2 - 13(1.6492) + 16 = 5.4396 - 21.4396 + 16 = 0$

Both roots satisfy the equation.

Example 2: Solve the equation $x^2 + kx = jx + jk$ for x, using the quadratic formula.

Rearrange.
$$x^2 + (k - j)x - jk = 0$$
$$a = +1$$
$$b = k - j$$
$$c = -jk$$

$$x = \frac{-(k - j) \pm \sqrt{(k - j)^2 - 4(1)(-jk)}}{2(1)}$$

$$= \frac{-k + j \pm \sqrt{k^2 - 2jk + j^2 + 4jk}}{2}$$

$$= \frac{-k + j \pm \sqrt{k^2 + 2jk + j^2}}{2} = \frac{-k + j \pm (k + j)}{2}$$

$$x_1 = \frac{-k + j + k + j}{2} = \frac{2j}{2} = j$$

$$x_2 = \frac{-k + j - k - j}{2} = \frac{-2k}{2} = -k$$

The check is left for the student.

NATURE OF THE ROOTS OF A QUADRATIC EQUATION

The two roots of the complete quadratic equation $ax^2 + bx + c = 0$ were shown to be

$$x_1 = \frac{-b + \sqrt{b^2 - 4ac}}{2a} \quad \text{and} \quad x_2 = \frac{-b - \sqrt{b^2 - 4ac}}{2a}$$

When a, b and c are real numbers, it is evident that $b^2 - 4ac$ may be positive, negative or zero. This expression is called the **discriminant** of the quadratic equation. Examination of the expressions for x_1 and x_2 shows that when $b^2 - 4ac > 0$ the two roots are real and unequal. If $b^2 - 4ac$ is a perfect square, the roots are rational; and if it is not a perfect square, the roots are irrational.

If $b^2 - 4ac < 0$, the roots are unequal and imaginary. For example, in the equation $x^2 + 3x + 4 = 0$,

$$b^2 - 4ac = (3)^2 - 4(1)(4) = 9 - 16 = -7$$

The roots are therefore imaginary.

If $b^2 - 4ac = 0$, the two roots x_1 and x_2 are equal, real and rational.

EXERCISE 5.3

Solve the following equations, using the quadratic formula.

1. $x^2 - 8x + 15 = 0$

2. $x^2 + x - 20 = 0$

3. $y^2 - 2y - 143 = 0$

4. $y^2 - ay + by = ab$

5. $x^2 + mx = 2m^2$

6. $0.2x^2 - 0.22x = 0.12$

7. $2.1x^2 - 1.3x - 2.0 = 0$

8. $0.9x^2 - 8.9x = 11$

9. $5.8R^2 + 4R + 0.3 = 0$

10. $7.1R - 3.1R^2 = -10.1$

11. $-0.03 + 0.12R^2 = 0.011R$

12. $7.5r^2 - 0.1 = 3.17r$

13. $(\frac{3}{4}R)^2 + \frac{7}{32} = \frac{13}{16}R$

14. $\frac{5}{8}R = 1\frac{3}{4}R^2 - 2\frac{1}{2}$

15. $1.022a^2 + 6.01a = 20.3$

16. $3.14z^2 = 0.16 + 4.07z$

17. $5.0625x = -6.25x^2 + 3.75$

18. $0.315x^2 = 2.00x - 3.01$

19. $15.987R^2 - 3.012R + 0.0511 = 0$

20. $0.25x^2 - 0.61x + 0.3721 = 0$

21. $\dfrac{9}{10x} + \dfrac{1}{x+1} = 1$

22. $\dfrac{1}{6x-1} + \dfrac{3x}{4x-5} = 0$

23. $(1.25 - R)^2 - R^2 = (R + 0.75)^2$

24. $(0.3125 + x)^2 + (2.125 - x)^2 = 16$

25. $\dfrac{3}{x} - 7 = \dfrac{5}{x-1}$

26. Find R and r.

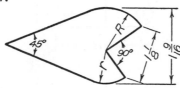

27. Find R.

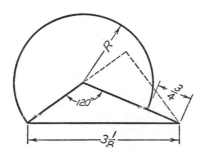

28. Find R.

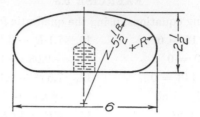

29. Find R and shaded area.

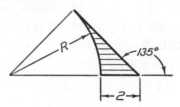

30. Find R.

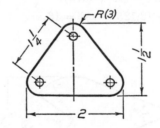

31. Find x.

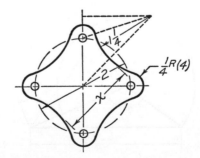

32. Find the diameter D.

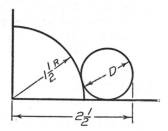

33. The shaded area is 1.60 sq in. Find a and b.

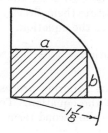

34. Find the distance x.

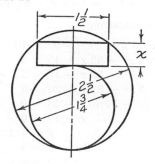

EQUATIONS INVOLVING RADICALS

An equation which contains the unknown under a radical sign is called a **radical equation**. In most practical problems the root indicated is the square root. Such an equation can frequently be reduced to a quadratic equation. The following examples show the method of freeing the equation of radicals.

Example 1: Solve the equation $\sqrt{x + 16} = 2 + \sqrt{x}$ for x.

$$\sqrt{x + 16} = 2 + \sqrt{x}$$

Square both sides. $\qquad x + 16 = 4 + 4\sqrt{x} + x$

Simplify. $\qquad 4\sqrt{x} = 12$

$$\sqrt{x} = 3$$

so $\qquad x = 9$

Check: If $x = 9$, $\qquad \sqrt{9 + 16} = 2 + \sqrt{9}$

$$5 = 2 + 3 = 5$$

The original equation should always be used for the check, for this is an important part of the problem. When an equation is squared, either a plus term or a minus term becomes plus, and this often causes extraneous roots to enter the solution. The best way to test the roots is to substitute them directly in the original equation.

The result $x = 9$ satisfies the equation.

Example 2: Solve the equation $\sqrt{3x - 5} - \sqrt{4x - 4} + \sqrt{x - 9} = 0$ for x.

In order to simplify the squaring process, transpose one of the terms to the right side of the equation. To decrease the chance of an error in sign, transpose the second term.

$$\sqrt{3x - 5} + \sqrt{x - 9} = \sqrt{4x - 4}$$

Squaring $\quad 3x - 5 + 2(\sqrt{3x - 5})(\sqrt{x - 9}) + x - 9 = 4x - 4$

Collecting terms and transposing

$$2\sqrt{(3x - 5)(x - 9)} = 10$$
$$\sqrt{3x^2 - 32x + 45} = 5$$

Squaring again $\qquad 3x^2 - 32x + 45 = 25$

so $\qquad 3x^2 - 32x + 20 = 0$

Factoring $\qquad (x - 10)(3x - 2) = 0$

Then $\qquad x - 10 = 0$

$$x = +10$$

and $\qquad 3x - 2 = 0$

$$x = +\tfrac{2}{3}$$

Note: If the student is not quite sure how to square both sides of the equation, the surest way is to set the expression down and actually multiply it. When the sum of two radicals is squared, the result should be treated as a binomial.

$$(\sqrt{x} + \sqrt{y})^2 \text{ is not } x + y, \text{ but rather}$$
$$(\sqrt{x} + \sqrt{y})^2 = x + 2(\sqrt{x})(\sqrt{y}) + y$$

Be sure to include the middle term.

Check: If $x = 10$

$$\sqrt{3(10) - 5} - \sqrt{4(10) - 4} + \sqrt{10 - 9} = \sqrt{25} - \sqrt{36} + \sqrt{1}$$
$$= 5 - 6 + 1 = 0$$

This checks the equation. Never use a $\pm$ sign when extracting the root; always use the sign indicated before the radical in the original equation when checking.

If $x = \frac{2}{3}$

$$\sqrt{3(\tfrac{2}{3})] - 5} - \sqrt{4(\tfrac{2}{3}) - 4} + \sqrt{\tfrac{2}{3} - 9} = \sqrt{-3} - \sqrt{-\tfrac{4}{3}} + \sqrt{-\tfrac{25}{3}} \neq 0$$

This value for x does not satisfy the equation; it is an extraneous root which was introduced in the squaring process.

Example 3: Solve the equation $\sqrt{1 + x\sqrt{x^2 + 12}} = 1 + x$ for x.

Squaring both sides

$$1 + x\sqrt{x^2 + 12} = 1 + 2x + x^2$$
$$x\sqrt{x^2 + 12} = 2x + x^2$$

Squaring again $x^2(x^2 + 12) = 4x^2 + 4x^3 + x^4$

Transposing and collecting terms

$$4x^3 - 8x^2 = 0$$
$$4x^2(x - 2) = 0$$
$$4x^2 = 0 \qquad \text{and} \qquad x - 2 = 0$$
$$x = 0 \qquad\qquad\qquad x = 2$$

Check: If $x = 0$ $\sqrt{1 + 0\sqrt{0 + 12}} = 1 + 0$

$$\sqrt{1} = 1$$
$$1 = 1$$

If $x = 2$ $\sqrt{1 + 2\sqrt{2^2 + 12}} = 1 + 2$

$$\sqrt{1 + 2(4)} = 1 + 2$$
$$\sqrt{9} = 3$$
$$3 = 3$$

Both roots satisfy the equation.

The student may wonder why an x was not canceled out in the second step, thus simplifying the equation. *Any expression containing the unknown should never be canceled out of an equation.* It may result in cancelling out a root, or it may result in dividing by zero. In this example it would have canceled the root $x = 0$.

EXERCISE 5.4

1. $x - 2 + \sqrt{x + 1} = 0$
2. $\sqrt{3x + 4} - 2\sqrt{2x + 2} = -3$
3. $\sqrt{4x + 21} + \sqrt{x + 2} = 4$

4. $\sqrt{2x+7} + \sqrt{x} = 2\sqrt{x+3}$

5. $\sqrt{y} + \sqrt{y+3a^2} = \sqrt{y+8a^2}$

6. $3\sqrt{y^2-9} + 3 = 3y$

7. $1 + \sqrt{(3-5x)^2 + 16} = 6 - 2x$

8. $R - \dfrac{a^2}{\sqrt{R^2-a^2}} + \sqrt{R^2-a^2} = 0$

9. $\sqrt{2R + \sqrt{10R+1}} = 1 + \sqrt{2R}$

10. $2x + \sqrt{4x^2-1} = 8x - 4\sqrt{4x^2-1}$

11. $\sqrt{1.7R + 3.25} + \sqrt{6.5 + R} = 10.5$

12. $\sqrt{(2.5+R)^2 - 2.5^2} = 5.5 - \sqrt{12.25 + R^2}$

13. $2x - 1.75 = \sqrt{(x+10.5)^2 - 16.25}$

14. $\sqrt{R^2 - 16R + 20.25} = \sqrt{R^2 - 12.5R - 16.25} + 1.75$

15. $2\sqrt{x^2+a^2} + \sqrt{x^2-3a^2} = 4a$

16. Find D.

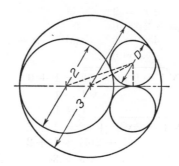

17. Find D.

Hint: $\sqrt{\left(\dfrac{D}{2}\right)^2 - \left(\dfrac{D}{2} - \dfrac{3}{4}\right)^2} + \sqrt{\left(\dfrac{D}{2}\right)^2 - \left(\dfrac{D}{2} - 1\tfrac{1}{8}\right)^2} = 3$

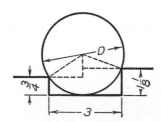

18. Find x.

Hint: $\sqrt{(2)^2 - \left(\dfrac{x}{2}\right)^2} - \sqrt{(1\frac{1}{4})^2 - \left(\dfrac{x}{2}\right)^2} = 2 + \frac{1}{4} - 1\frac{1}{4}$

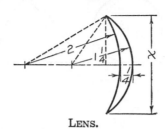

LENS.

19. Find x.

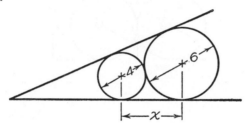

20. The perimeter of the trapezoid is 220 ft. Find the altitude h.

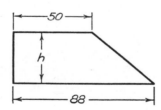

21. Find the altitude h.

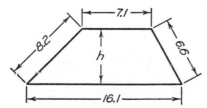

22. Find the distance x.

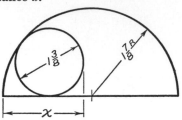

23. Find the diameter D.

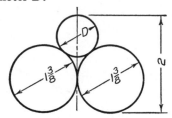

CHAPTER VI

Simultaneous Equations

A LINEAR FUNCTION IS A FUNCTION IN WHICH THE VARIABLES occur only in the first degree, are multiplied by constants, and combined only by addition and subtraction.

GRAPH OF A LINEAR FUNCTION

It is often useful to plot a graph of a function in order to give a picture of the way the function varies. If y is a linear function of x, such as $y = ax + b$, the graph of the function can be plotted.

Example: Plot a graph of the function $y = 2x + 3$.

Make a table of calculated values of y for each assumed value for x.

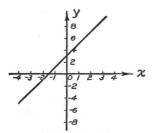

$$y = 2x + 3$$

x	y
0	3
1	5
2	7
-1	1
-2	-1
-3	-3
$-\frac{3}{2}$	0

FIG. 6.1.—LINEAR FUNCTION OF x.

The graph is seen to be a straight line. A linear function always gives a straight-line graph when plotted in this way.

If the function is known to have a straight-line graph, two points will determine the line. The easiest way to find two points is first to let $x = 0$ to obtain a value for y, and then to let $y = 0$ to obtain a corresponding value for x. These two points arc the points where the line cuts the y and x axes. As a check, a third point should be calculated.

Two Linear Equations in Two Unknowns

It frequently happens that two unknowns occur in one linear equation. In the preceding example $y = 2x + 3$. Evidently there is a different value for y corresponding to each value of x. The value of either x or y may be known. In this case the corresponding value of y or x can be obtained by solving the equation after the one known value has been substituted in it.

Usually the value of both x and y is unknown. In order to solve in this case, there must be two independent equations. Two linear equations are said to be independent when one cannot be obtained from the other by multiplying each term of one by the same non-zero constant.

Three general methods for solving for the two unknowns will now be explained:

1. Graphic solution
2. Elimination by addition and subtraction
3. Elimination by substitution

Graphic Solution

If the graphs of two linear equations in two unknowns are plotted on the same coordinate axes, the point where the two straight lines intersect will have as coordinates one pair of values (x, y) which satisfies both of the equations at the same time. The equations are said to be satisfied simultaneously by this point.

Example: Plot the graph of the two equations

$$x + y = 5$$
$$3x - y = 7$$

and determine the values of x and y which give a common solution.

Make a table of values for x and y for each equation, and plot the points on the same axes.

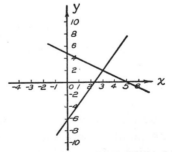

FIG. 6.2.—GRAPHIC SOLUTION.

$x + y = 5$

x	y
0	5
5	0
2	3

$3x - y = 7$

x	y
0	-7
$2\frac{1}{3}$	0
1	-4

The lines intersect at the point (3, 2), so the common solution is $x = 3$ and $y = 2$. If these values are substituted in the two equations, they will satisfy both.

Note: It may happen that the two lines are parallel. In this case the two equations are inconsistent and have no common solution. If both equations give the same line, they are not independent; one is a multiple of the other.

Elimination by Addition and Subtraction

If the coefficients of either x or y are the same in both equations, that unknown may be eliminated by addition or subtraction, depending upon the signs of the coefficients. If the coefficients of an unknown are not the same, they can be made the same by multiplying one or both of the equations by the proper constants.

Example 1: Solve the equations

$$x + y = 5$$
$$3x - y = 7$$

for x and y by addition or subtraction.

Add the first equation to the second.

$$
\begin{array}{ll}
\begin{aligned}
x + y &= 5 \\
\underline{3x - y} &= \underline{7} \\
4x &= 12 \\
x &= 3
\end{aligned}
&
\begin{aligned}
&\text{Substitute } x = 3 \text{ in the first equation.} \\
&3 + y = 5 \\
&y = 5 - 3 = 2
\end{aligned}
\end{array}
$$

Check: Substitute both values in the second equation.

$$3(3) - 2 = 7$$

The solution $x = 3$, $y = 2$ checks the graphic method described in the preceding section.

Suppose x is to be eliminated instead of y. Multiply the first equation by 3, and subtract the second.

$$
\begin{array}{ll}
\begin{aligned}
3x + 3y &= 15 \\
\underline{3x - y} &= \underline{7} \\
4y &= 8 \\
y &= 2
\end{aligned}
&
\begin{aligned}
x + 2 &= 5 \\
x &= 3
\end{aligned}
\end{array}
$$

Subtract

Sometimes it is necessary to multiply each equation by a constant to make the coefficients alike.

Example 2: Solve the equations

$$4x + 5y = 31$$
$$3x + 2y = 18$$

simultaneously for x and y.

Either unknown may be eliminated. Suppose we select x. To make both coefficients the same, multiply the first equation by 3 and the second by 4; this gives

$$12\,x + 15\,y = 93$$
$$12\,x + 8\,y = 72$$

Subtract
$$7\,y = 21$$
$$y = 3$$

From the first equation

$$4\,x + 5(3) = 31$$
$$4\,x = 31 - 15 = 16$$
$$x = 4$$

Check: Substitute the values $x = 4$, $y = 3$ in the second equation.

$$3(4) + 2(3) = 12 + 6 = 18$$

The same method could have been used to eliminate y instead of x.

Sometimes the coefficients are letters instead of numbers. The same method of solution can be used.

Example 3: Solve the equations

$$ax + by = m$$
$$cx - dy = n$$

for x and y.

Multiply the first equation by c and the second by a.

$$acx + bcy = cm$$
$$acx - ady = an$$

Subtract
$$bcy + ady = cm - an$$
$$(bc + ad)y = cm - an$$
$$y = \frac{cm - an}{bc + ad}$$

In order to find x, this value for y may be substituted in either of the original equations. Since this gives a complicated fraction, suppose we solve for x in the same way that we found y.

Multiply the first equation by d and the second by b.

$$adx + bdy = dm$$
$$bcx - bdy = bn$$

Add
$$adx + bcx = dm + bn$$
$$(ad + bc)x = dm + bn$$
$$x = \frac{dm + bn}{ad + bc}$$

The check is left for the student.

In many engineering problems the coefficients involve decimals. The solution is the same as before.

Example 4: Solve the equations

$$4.17\,x + 3.01\,y = 32.10$$
$$3.2\,x - 1.75\,y = 2.63$$

for x and y.

Multiply the first equation by 3.2 and the second by 4.17.

$$13.344\,x + 9.632\,y = 102.72$$
$$\underline{13.344\,x - 7.2975\,y = 10.9671}$$

Subtract $\quad\qquad 16.9295\,y = 91.7529$

$$y = 5.419^{+}$$

Substitute this value for y in the first equation.

$$4.17\,x + 3.01(5.419) = 32.10$$
$$4.17\,x + 16.311 = 32.10$$
$$4.17\,x = 32.10 - 16.311 = 15.789$$
$$x = 3.786^{+}$$

Check: Substitute both values in the second equation.

$$3.2(3.786) - 1.75(5.419) = 12.115 - 9.483 = 2.632$$

This checks within 0.002. The amount of the error depends upon the accuracy used in solving the equations.

EXERCISE 6.1

Construct the graph of the following equations:

1. $x + y = 6$
2. $2\,x - y = 4$
3. $3\,x - 5\,y = 30$
4. $x = y - 6$
5. $x = 2\,y + 3$
6. $3\,x + 6\,y = 27$

7. $1.7\,y - 5.1\,x = 11.9$
8. $(x + 3)^2 = y + x^2 + 4$
   Hint: Simplify first.
9. $x - 5 = y + 8$
10. $2\,x + \sqrt{3}\,y = 7$

Solve the following simultaneous equations by the graphic method and also by addition and subtraction.

11. $x - y = 6$
    $2\,x - 7\,y = -18$
12. $4\,x - 5\,y = 5$
    $5\,x + 4\,y = 37$
13. $8\,x - y = -20$
    $3\,y + 4\,x = 4$
14. $x = 2 + 3\,y$
    $y = 3\,x + 26$
15. $0.2\,x = 1.7 - 2\,y$
    $0.2\,y = 0.03\,x + 0.15$

16. $0.3\,x + 0.51\,y = 0.687$
    $0.7\,x + 1.1\,y = 1.54$
17. $7\,x - 3\,y = 40$
    $13\,x + 23\,y = 560$
18. $24\,x - 8\,y = 0$
    $11\,x + 13\,y = 62.5$
19. $9\,x + 8\,y = 6.2$
    $0.3\,y = 1.7 - 2.9\,y$
20. $0.02\,x - 1.17\,y = 2.28$
    $3.9\,x - 0.003\,y = 2.91$

Solve for x and y by the method of addition and subtraction.

21. $ax + by = 6$
$bx + ay = 3 \qquad a \neq b$

22. $y + 3\,ax = 9\,a$
$x + 2\,y = 3$

23. $2.17\,x - 3.01\,y = 12.16$
$3.19\,x + 0.17\,y = 9.17$

24. $4.19\,x - 2.15\,y - 3.29 = 0$
$-1.05\,x + 3.73\,y - 1.57 = 0$

25. $u = 8.25\,x - 3.96\,y$
$v = -5.18\,x + 5.75\,y$

26. $4 - y = 3\,x$
$41 - x = 3(1 - y)$

27. $\dfrac{3\,x}{4} + \dfrac{2\,y}{3} = 21$

$\dfrac{x}{2} + \dfrac{3\,y}{4} = 19$

28. $\dfrac{3}{x} - \dfrac{5}{y} = 10$

$\dfrac{2}{x} - \dfrac{1}{y} = 13$

Hint: Solve for $\dfrac{1}{x}$ and $\dfrac{1}{y}$.

29. $\dfrac{1}{x + 1} + \dfrac{2}{x - y} = 0$

$\dfrac{x + y}{3} - \dfrac{x}{7} = 8$

30. $ay - bx + xy = 0$
$by - ax + xy = 0$

Elimination by Substitution

In this method, one of the equations is solved for one unknown in terms of the other. This expression is next substituted in the second equation. The resulting equation is then solved for the remaining unknown.

Example 1: Solve the equations

$$2\,x + y = 22$$
$$x - y = 5$$

for x and y by the substitution method.
From the second equation

$$x = y + 5$$

Substitute this in the first equation.

$$2(y + 5) + y = 22$$
$$2\,y + 10 + y = 22$$
$$3\,y = 12$$
$$y = 4$$

and $\qquad\qquad x = y + 5 = 4 + 5 = 9$

Check: $\qquad\quad 2(9) + 4 = 18 + 4 = 22$

and $\qquad\qquad\quad 9 - 4 = 5$

Both equations are satisfied.

Example 2: Solve the equations

$$0.5\,x + 0.70\,y = 1.25$$
$$0.12\,x - 0.08\,y = 3.6$$

for x and y.

Solve the first equation for x.

$$0.5\,x = 1.25 - 0.70\,y$$
$$x = 2.50 - 1.40\,y$$

Substitute this in the second equation.

$$0.12(2.50 - 1.40\,y) - 0.08\,y = 3.6$$
$$0.300 - 0.168\,y - 0.08\,y = 3.6$$
$$- 0.248\,y = 3.300$$
$$y = -\,13.31^-$$
$$x = 2.50 - 1.40(-\,13.31)$$
$$= 2.50 + 18.63 = 21.13^-$$

Check: Substitute these values in the second equation.

$$0.12(21.13) - 0.08(-\,13.31) = 2.5356 + 1.0648 = 3.6004$$

This checks within 0.0004.

EXERCISE 6.2

Solve the following simultaneous equations by elimination by substitution.

1.
$$2\,y = 7\,x - 17$$
$$3\,x + 5\,y = 19$$

2.
$$2\,x - y = 12$$
$$x + 2\,y = 11$$

3.
$$7\,x - 6\,y = 38$$
$$3\,x - 2\,y = 18$$

4.
$$5\,x - 2\,y = 13$$
$$x + 3\,y = 23$$

5.
$$3\,x - y = 19$$
$$y + 3\,x = 29$$

6.
$$2\,x - 3\,y = 5$$
$$4\,y + x = 19$$

7.
$$5\,x - 5\,y = 40$$
$$x + y = 10$$

8.
$$x + 4 = y - 4$$
$$2(x + 2) = 24 - y$$

9.
$$(x + 1) + (y - 2) = 14$$
$$(x - 1) - (y - 3) = 1$$

10.
$$\frac{x + y}{3} + \frac{x - y}{4} = 11$$
$$\frac{x + y}{2} - \frac{x - y}{3} = 8$$

11.
$$\frac{x + y}{5} - \frac{y - x}{5} = \frac{3\,x - y}{8} + \frac{2(y - x) - 10}{5} + 1$$
$$5\,x = 3\,y$$

12.
$$ax + by = a^2 + 2\,a + b^2$$
$$bx + ay = a^2 + 2\,b + b^2$$

13. $\dfrac{x}{n+m} + \dfrac{y}{n-m} = 2$

$\dfrac{x}{m} - \dfrac{y}{n} = \dfrac{n}{m} + \dfrac{m}{n}$

14. $\dfrac{2x+3y}{5} + \dfrac{y+6}{7} = 2$

$\frac{1}{3}(2x-5y) + \frac{1}{4}(x+7) = 1$

15. $3.25x - 1.17y = 22.34$
$7.19x + 0.13y = 18.20$

16. $3x = 7.2y - 11.00$
$6.29y = 3 + 4x$

17. $0.022x - 3.001y = 22.1$
$0.136y + 1.11x = 9.13$

18. $0.28x - 1.35y = 3.02$
$0.93x + 2.2y = 1.91$

Three Linear Equations in Three Unknowns

Thus far we have learned to solve two linear equations in two unknowns. But problems in engineering often involve three or more unknowns. These can be solved by the same general methods as were used for two linear equations in two unknowns.

If a linear equation in three variables is plotted, it results in a plane. Two such equations give two planes. If these two planes intersect, only the points on the line of intersection lie on both planes and can satisfy both equations. A third equation will give a third plane. If this plane intersects the line of intersection of the other two, there will be one point which lies on all three planes. The coordinates of this point will be the required values of the three unknowns.

In order for the three planes to intersect in a point, no two of the planes can be parallel, and the third one cannot be parallel to the line of intersection of the other two. For this reason it is necessary that the three equations be independent, and there must be as many equations as there are unknowns.

Since it is difficult to construct planes in space and find the lines of intersection, the graphic method is not used.

The three equations can be solved by the method of substitution. This requires great care to prevent an endless cycle of substitution which never could be reduced to an answer. Careful choice is necessary to make sure that the right letter is eliminated each time.

The method of elimination by addition and subtraction is the one which is used in practice. This is very similar to the corresponding method for two unknowns. The following examples illustrate it:

Example 1: Solve the following equations for x, y and z.

$$x + y - z = 1 \qquad (1)$$
$$2x - y + 2z = 9 \qquad (2)$$
$$x - y - 2z = -9 \qquad (3)$$

The first step is to decide which unknown is to be eliminated first; usually it makes little difference. However, once it is decided, it must not be changed in the middle of the problem. Suppose we start by eliminating x from the first two equations. Multiply the first equation by 2 and subtract the second.

$$2x + 2y - 2z = 2$$
$$2x - y + 2z = 9$$

Subtract $\qquad \overline{3y - 4z = -7} \qquad (4)$

This equation now has two unknowns. To solve it we need another equation in y and z. This can be obtained by eliminating x from Eq 1 and 3 or from Eq 2 and 3; it makes little difference which. Let us take Eq 1 and 3.

$$x + y - z = 1 \qquad (1)$$
$$x - y - 2z = -9 \qquad (3)$$

Subtract $\qquad \overline{2y + z = 10} \qquad (5)$

Eq 4 and 5 can now be solved for y and z. Multiply Eq 5 by 4 and add this to Eq 4. This eliminates z, because the coefficients of z are now equal.

$$3y - 4z = -7$$
$$8y + 4z = 40$$

Add $\qquad \overline{11y = 33}$
$$y = 3$$

This value for y can be substituted in *any* of the other equations, since they are all true. We shall use Eq 5.

$$2(3) + z = 10$$
$$z = 10 - 6 = 4$$

The values for y and z can be substituted in Eq 1, 2 or 3 to give x. Suppose we select Eq 1, and use Eq 2 and 3 for the check.

$$x + 3 - 4 = 1$$
$$x = 2$$

Check: Eq 2 $\quad 2(2) - 3 + 2(4) = 4 - 3 + 8 = 9$
Eq 3 $\quad 2 - 3 - 2(4) = 2 - 3 - 8 = -9$

The three equations are satisfied.

Sometimes, in the case of three linear equations in three unknowns, one or more of the equations may contain only two unknowns. This is often confusing. The following example shows how to solve such a case.

Example 2: Solve the following equations for x, y and z.

$$3\,x + 6\,y = 12 \tag{1}$$
$$3\,y - z = -1 \tag{2}$$
$$x = y + z \tag{3}$$

Suppose we eliminate x first. The second equation does not contain x, so it is already in the proper form. Eliminate x from Eq 1 and 3. Multiply Eq 3 by 3 and subtract this from Eq 1.

$$3\,x + 6\,y \qquad\quad = 12$$
$$3\,x - 3\,y - 3\,z = 0$$

Subtract $\qquad\quad \overline{9\,y + 3\,z = 12}$

or $\qquad\qquad\quad 3\,y + z = 4 \tag{4}$

Subtract Eq 2 from Eq 4 to eliminate y.

$$3\,y + z = 4$$
$$3\,y - z = -1$$

Subtract $\qquad\quad \overline{2\,z = 5}$

$$z = 2.5$$

Substitute in Eq 2.

$$3\,y - 2.5 = -1$$
$$3\,y = 1.5$$
$$y = 0.5$$

Use Eq 1 to find x.

$$3\,x + 6(0.5) = 12$$
$$3\,x = 9$$
$$x = 3.0$$

Check: Substitute these values in Eq 3.

$$x = y + z$$
$$3.0 = 0.5 + 2.5 = 3.0$$

The values satisfy the equations.

In practical engineering problems, the coefficients of the unknowns are often decimals, and the equations must frequently be simplified before the solution is begun. The method of solution is the same as before, although the calculations may be more involved.

Example 3: The following equations for the three currents I_1, I_2 and I_3 in an electric circuit are to be solved for the three unknowns:

$$- 12 + 0.5\,I_1 + 6(I_1 + I_2 + I_3) + 3(I_1 + I_2) + I_1 = 0 \qquad (1)$$
$$- 10 + 0.4\,I_2 - 1.5\,I_3 + 3(I_1 + I_2) = 0 \qquad (2)$$
$$6(I_1 + I_2 + I_3) + 1.5\,I_3 - 6 + 0.3(I_2 + I_3) = 0 \qquad (3)$$

Note: I_1, I_2 and I_3 should be considered as single letters. I_1 is read I sub 1, I_2 is read I sub 2, and I_3 is read I sub 3. The subscripts identify the three I's.

Simplify Eq 1

$$- 12 + 0.5\,I_1 + 6\,I_1 + 6\,I_2 + 6\,I_3 + 3\,I_1 + 3\,I_2 + I_1 = 0$$
$$10.5\,I_1 + 9\,I_2 + 6\,I_3 = 12 \qquad (1)$$

Simplify Eq 2

$$- 10 + 0.4\,I_2 - 1.5\,I_3 + 3\,I_1 + 3\,I_2 = 0$$
$$3\,I_1 + 3.4\,I_2 - 1.5\,I_3 = 10 \qquad (2)$$

Simplify Eq 3

$$6\,I_1 + 6\,I_2 + 6\,I_3 + 1.5\,I_3 - 6 + 0.3\,I_2 + 0.3\,I_3 = 0$$
$$6\,I_1 + 6.3\,I_2 + 7.8\,I_3 = 6 \qquad (3)$$

Let us eliminate I_1 first. Multiply Eq 2 by 3.5 and subtract this from Eq 1.

$10.5\,I_1 +$	$9\,I_2 +$	$6\,I_3 =$	12	(1)
$10.5\,I_1 +$	$11.9\,I_2 -$	$5.25\,I_3 =$	35	(2)

Subtract $\qquad\qquad - 2.9\,I_2 + 11.25\,I_3 = - 23 \qquad (4)$

Now eliminate I_1 from Eq 2 and 3. Multiply Eq 2 by 2 and subtract Eq 3.

$$6\,I_1 + 6.8\,I_2 - 3.0\,I_3 = 20 \qquad (2)$$
$$6\,I_1 + 6.3\,I_2 + 7.8\,I_3 = 6 \qquad (3)$$

Subtract $\qquad\qquad 0.5\,I_2 - 10.8\,I_3 = 14 \qquad (5)$

Eq 4 and 5 contain I_2 and I_3 only. To eliminate I_2, multiply Eq 5 by 5.8 and add to Eq 4.

$$- 2.9\,I_2 + 11.25\,I_3 = - 23 \qquad (4)$$
$$+ 2.9\,I_2 - 62.64\,I_3 = 81.2$$

Add $\qquad\qquad\qquad - 51.39\,I_3 = 58.2$
$$I_3 = - 1.132^+$$

Substitute this value of I_3 in Eq 4.

$$- 2.9\,I_2 + 11.25(- 1.132) = - 23$$
$$2.9\,I_2 + 12.735 = 23$$
$$2.9\,I_2 = 10.265$$
$$I_2 = 3.540^-$$

Substitute these values for I_2 and I_3 in Eq 1 to find I_1.

$$10.5\,I_1 + 9(3.540) + 6(- 1.132) = 12$$
$$10.5\,I_1 + 31.86 - 6.792 = 12$$
$$10.5\,I_1 = - 13.068$$
$$I_1 = - 1.245^-$$

The check is left for the student.

EXERCISE 6.3

Solve the following equations for the unknowns:

1.
$$2x - y + z = 5$$
$$3x + 2y - z = 9$$
$$x + 5y + 3z = 37$$

2.
$$7x + 10y - z = -2$$
$$-2x - 5y + 9z = 68$$
$$x + 7y - 4z = -44$$

3.
$$3x + 4y - 7z = 1$$
$$4.5x + 8.0y + 10.5z = 5$$
$$12x + 5y - 21z = 2.25$$

4.
$$3x + 7y + 1.2z = 8.32$$
$$4x - 3y + 0.6z = -4.24$$
$$1.1x - 4y - 7.1z = -0.208$$

5.
$$8x - 4y + z = 24$$
$$6x + y - z = 84$$
$$x - 3y - 4z = -80$$

6.
$$\frac{x}{2} + \frac{y}{3} + \frac{z}{4} = 124$$

$$\frac{x}{3} + \frac{y}{4} + \frac{z}{5} = 94$$

$$\frac{x}{4} + \frac{y}{5} + \frac{z}{6} = 76$$

7.
$$\frac{1}{x} + \frac{1}{y} + \frac{1}{z} = 2$$

$$\frac{1}{y} + \frac{1}{z} + \frac{1}{u} = 3$$

$$\frac{1}{x} + \frac{1}{z} + \frac{1}{u} = 4$$

$$\frac{1}{x} + \frac{1}{y} + \frac{1}{u} = 6$$

Hint: Add the four equations, divide by 3, and subtract each equation in turn from the one obtained.

8.
$$1.5 I_1 + 3 I_2 = 6$$
$$3 I_1 - I_3 = -1$$
$$I_1 = I_2 + I_3$$

9.
$$4 + 0.5 I_1 - 3 I_2 + 2 + I_1 = 0$$
$$-3 + I_3 - 3 I_2 + 2 = 0$$
$$I_1 + I_2 + I_3 = 0$$

10.
$$3w + x + 2y - z = 22$$
$$4x - y + 3z = 35$$
$$4w + 3x - 2y = 19$$
$$2w + 4y + 2z = 46$$

11.
$$w + x + y - z = 2$$
$$w + x - y + z = 4$$
$$w - x + y + z = 6$$
$$x - w + y + z = 8$$

12.
$$2.3x + 1.7y - 2.5z = u$$
$$9.2x - 3.1y - 0.9z = v$$
$$10.3x + 0.1y + 3.9z = w$$

GRAPH OF A SECOND-DEGREE FUNCTION

In earlier sections we have seen how to draw the graph of a quadratic function and of a linear function. This procedure will now be extended to include the graph of a general second-degree function. The method is very similar to that shown for the quadratic function, and will be illustrated by the following examples:

Example 1: Plot the graph of $x^2 + y^2 = 25$.
First, solve the equation for y.

$$y = \sqrt{25 - x^2}$$

Assume values for x and calculate the corresponding values of y. Plot the points and connect them with a smooth curve.

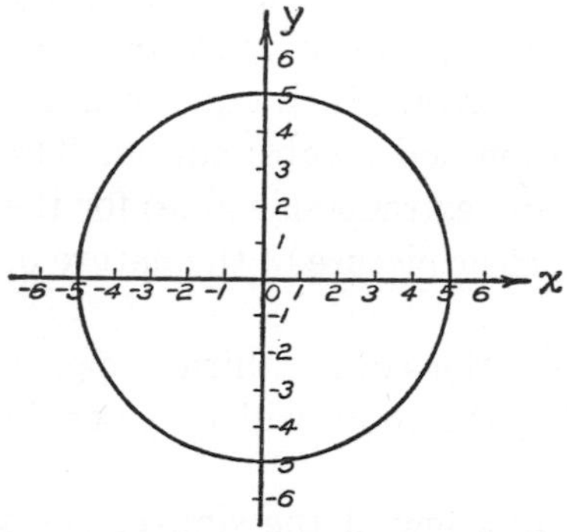

FIG. 6.3.—CIRCLE.

$$y = \sqrt{25 - x^2}$$

x	y
0	± 5
± 1	± 4.90
± 2	± 4.58
± 3	± 4
± 4	± 3
± 5	0

If x is greater in absolute value than 5, y will be the square root of a negative number, which is imaginary. Thus there is no graph to the right of $x = 5$ or to the left of $x = -5$.

When the same scale is used on both axes, the graph is seen to be a circle.

Example 2: Plot the graph of $x^2 - y^2 = 25$.
Solve the equation for y.

$$y = \sqrt{x^2 - 25}$$

Make a table of assumed values of x and the corresponding values for y, as in Example 1.

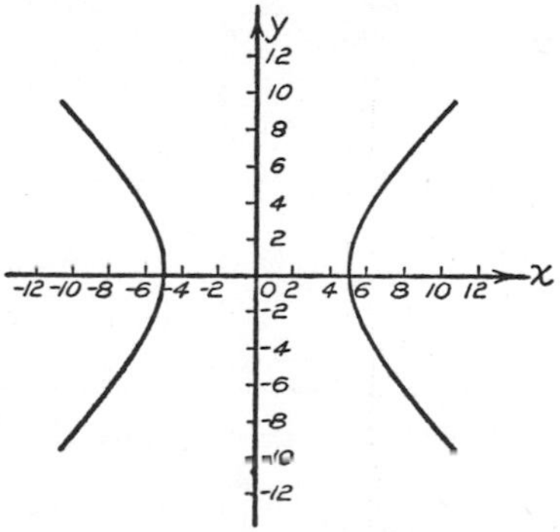

FIG. 6.4.—HYPERBOLA.

$$y = \sqrt{x^2 - 25}$$

x	y
± 5	0
± 6	± 3.32
± 7	± 4.90
± 8	± 6.24
± 9	± 7.48

If x is less in absolute value than 5, y will be imaginary. Therefore there is no graph between $x = + 5$ and $x = - 5$.

This curve is common in more advanced mathematics and is called a hyperbola.

SIMULTANEOUS QUADRATIC FUNCTIONS

The preceding sections explained how to solve linear simultaneous equations in two or more unknowns. Frequently simultaneous equations are not linear; one or more of them may be of the second or a higher degree. Such equations are usually solved graphically or by the method of substitution. The graphic method is helpful in avoiding extraneous values for the unknowns; furthermore, it gives a clear picture of the nature of the solution.

A discussion of the solution of equations of the third or higher degree and the methods of finding the roots will be given in Chapter VII.

The following examples illustrate a few of the simpler cases that can be solved by elementary methods:

Example 1: Solve the equations

$$x^2 + 4 y^2 = 16 \qquad (1)$$
$$x - 2 y = 2 \qquad (2)$$

simultaneously for x and y.

Plot the graphs of the two equations on the same axes. Make tables of corresponding values of x and y as in preceding examples of linear and quadratic functions.

$$x^2 + 4 y^2 = 16$$

x	y
0	± 2
± 1	± 1.94
± 2	± 1.73
± 3	± 1.32
± 4	0

$$x - 2 y = 2$$

x	y
0	$- 1$
2	0
1	$- \frac{1}{2}$

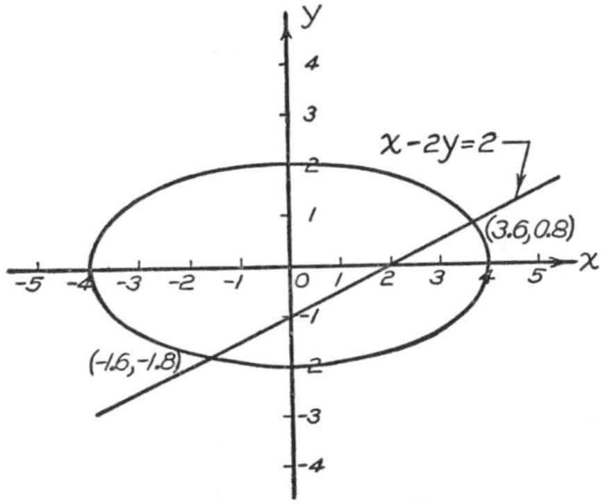

FIG. 6.5.—SIMULTANEOUS EQUATIONS.

The two graphs intersect in two points $(3.6, 0.8)$ and $(-1.6, -1.8)$. Therefore the solution is

$$\left. \begin{array}{l} x = 3.6 \\ y = 0.8 \end{array} \right\} \quad \text{and} \quad \left. \begin{array}{l} x = -1.6 \\ y = -1.8 \end{array} \right\} \quad \text{approximately}$$

A more exact solution can be obtained algebraically by the method of substitution. Solve Eq 2 for x in terms of y

$$x = 2y + 2$$

and substitute in Eq 1.

$$(2y + 2)^2 + 4y^2 = 16$$

Simplify $\qquad 4y^2 + 8y + 4 + 4y^2 = 16$

$$8y^2 + 8y - 12 = 0$$

or $\qquad\qquad 2y^2 + 2y - 3 = 0$

Solve by the quadratic formula.

$$y = \frac{-2 \pm \sqrt{(2)^2 - 4(2)(-3)}}{2(2)}$$

$$= \frac{-2 \pm \sqrt{28}}{4} = \frac{-2 \pm 5.2915}{4}$$

So $\qquad y_1 = \dfrac{-2 + 5.2915}{4} = 0.8229-$

and $\qquad y_2 = \dfrac{-2 - 5.2915}{4} = -1.8229-$

In order to find the corresponding values of x, these values of y_1 and y_2 are substituted in one of the original equations. If Eq 1 is used, the graph shows that there are two values of x, one plus and one minus, for each value of y. It is necessary to use great care to select the right one. If Eq 2 is used, there is only one value of x for each value of y. Therefore, to decrease the chances of an error, use the linear equation to find x and Eq 1 for checking.

$$x - 2y = 2 \qquad\qquad\qquad (2)$$
$$x_1 - 2(0.8229-) = 2$$
$$x_1 = 1.6458- + 2 = 3.6458-$$
$$x_2 - 2(-1.8229-) = 2$$
$$x_2 = -3.6458- + 2 = -1.6458-$$

Hence the solution is

$$\left. \begin{array}{l} x_1 = 3.6458- \\ y_1 = 0.8229- \end{array} \right\} \qquad \left. \begin{array}{l} x_2 = -1.6458- \\ y_2 = -1.8229- \end{array} \right\}$$

Check: $\qquad\qquad\qquad x^2 + 4y^2 = 16 \qquad\qquad\qquad (1)$

At (x_1, y_1) $\quad (3.6458)^2 + 4(0.8229)^2 = 13.292 + 2.709 = 16.001$

At (x_2, y_2) $\quad (-1.6458)^2 + 4(-1.8229)^2 = 2.709 + 13.292 = 16.001$

Both results check within 0.001.

In Example 1, one equation was linear and the second quadratic. Frequently neither equation is linear. This will be illustrated in the following example:

Example 2: Solve the equations

$$x^2 + 2.3\,y^2 = 20.7 \tag{1}$$
$$xy = 3.68 \tag{2}$$

simultaneously for x and y.
A graphic solution is shown in Fig. 6.6.

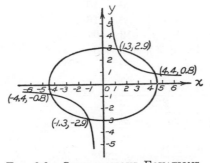

$$x^2 + 2.3\,y^2 = 20.7$$

x	y
0	± 3.00
± 1	± 2.93
± 2	± 2.69
± 3	± 2.26
± 4	± 1.43
± 4.55	0

$$xy = 3.68$$

x	y
± 1	± 3.68
± 2	± 1.84
± 3	± 1.23
± 4	± 0.92
± 5	± 0.74

FIG. 6.6.—SIMULTANEOUS EQUATIONS.

The two graphs intersect in four points, $(4.4, 0.8)$, $(1.3, 2.9)$, $(-4.4, -0.8)$ and $(-1.3, -2.9)$. Therefore the four solutions are, approximately:

$$\left.\begin{array}{l} x_1 = 4.4 \\ y_1 = 0.8 \end{array}\right\} \quad \left.\begin{array}{l} x_2 = 1.3 \\ y_2 = 2.9 \end{array}\right\} \quad \left.\begin{array}{l} x_3 = -4.4 \\ y_3 = -0.8 \end{array}\right\} \quad \left.\begin{array}{l} x_4 = -1.3 \\ y_4 = -2.9 \end{array}\right\}$$

The equations will now be solved algebraically by the method of substitution.

From Eq 2
$$x = \frac{3.68}{y}$$

Substitute in Eq 1.

$$\left(\frac{3.68}{y}\right)^2 + 2.3\,y^2 = 20.7$$
$$13.5424 + 2.3\,y^4 = 20.7\,y^2$$

Transpose. $\quad 2.3\,y^4 - 20.7\,y^2 + 13.5424 = 0$

This is a biquadratic equation, and can be solved for y^2 by the quadratic formula.

$$y^2 = \frac{20.7 \pm \sqrt{(20.7)^2 - 4(2.3)(13.5424)}}{2(2.3)}$$
$$= \frac{20.7 \pm \sqrt{303.90}}{4.6}$$
$$= 0.71022 \quad \text{or} \quad 8.2898$$

Extract the square root.

$$y = \pm 0.8427 \quad \text{or} \quad \pm 2.8792$$

From Eq 2

$$x = \pm 4.3668 \quad \text{or} \quad \pm 1.2781$$

Eq 2 was used instead of Eq 1 to find x because it gives a single value for x. Eq 2 would give two values of x for each value of y. The solutions are:

$$\left.\begin{array}{l} x_1 = 4.3668 \\ y_1 = 0.8427 \end{array}\right\} \quad \left.\begin{array}{l} x_2 = 1.2781 \\ y_2 = 2.8792 \end{array}\right\} \quad \left.\begin{array}{l} x_3 = -4.3668 \\ y_3 = -0.8427 \end{array}\right\} \quad \left.\begin{array}{l} x_4 = -1.2781 \\ y_4 = -2.8792 \end{array}\right\}$$

The check by Eq 1 is left for the student.

Example 3: Solve the following equations for x and y:

$$x = \sqrt{y^2 - 2y} + 1 \qquad (1)$$
$$x + y = 5 \qquad (2)$$

Solve Eq 2 for x.

$$x = -y + 5$$

and substitute in Eq 1.

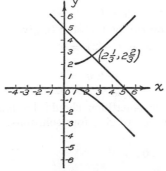

FIG. 6.7.—SIMULTANEOUS EQUATIONS.

$x + y = 5$	
x	y
0	5
5	0
2	3

$x = \sqrt{y^2 - 2y} + 1$	
y	x
0, 2	1
3, −1	2.73
4, −2	3.82
5, −3	4.87
6, −4	5.90

$$-y + 5 = \sqrt{y^2 - 2y} + 1$$
$$\sqrt{y^2 - 2y} = 4 - y$$

Square

$$y^2 - 2y = 16 - 8y + y^2$$
$$6y = 16$$
$$y = 2\tfrac{2}{3}$$

From Eq 2

$$x = 2\tfrac{1}{3}$$

There is no graph for Eq 1 to the left of $x = 1$. The positive sign of the radical is indicated so it cannot be negative, and thus $x = 1$ is the smallest value x can have. This solution is in agreement with the graphic solution.

EXERCISE 6.4

Draw the graphs of the following second-degree functions.

1. $x^2 + y^2 = 25$

2. $x^2 - y^2 = 25$

3. $x^2 + 4 y^2 = 16$

4. $x^2 - 4 y^2 = 16$

5. $y^2 = 4 x$

6. $x^2 + y^2 = 2 x + 2 y$

7. $x^2 - y^2 = x - y$

8. $4(x - 3)^2 + 9 y^2 = 36$

9. $x^2 - 2 x - y^2 = 0$

10. $x^2 - y^2 = 2 x - 1$

Solve the following equations by both graphic and algebraic methods. Set down each corresponding pair of values which constitute a solution.

11. $x^2 + y^2 = 41$
$x - y = 1$

12. $x^2 - y^2 = 40$
$2 x - y = 13$

13. $y^2 = 7 x$
$x + 2 y = 12$

14. $x^2 + 9 y^2 = 36$
$x - 3 y - 6 = 0$

15. $x^2 - 4 x + y^2 - 4 y + 4 = 0$
$x + y = 3$

16. $x^2 - y^2 + 16 = 0$
$y^2 - 8 x = 0$

17. $x^2 + 2 y^2 = 8$
$2 x^2 - 2 y^2 - 3 xy - 2 x + 4 y = 0$

Hint: The second equation can be factored to give
$$(x - 2 y)(2 x + y - 2) = 0$$
This is equivalent to
$$x - 2 y = 0$$
and
$$2 x + y - 2 = 0.$$
Each of these two linear equations should be plotted and solved with the first equation to give four solutions.

18. $x^2 - y^2 = 25$
$(2 x - y)(x + 3 y - 3) = 0$
Hint: See Problem 17.

19. $x^2 = 4 y$
$y^2 = 3 x^2 + 4$

20. $x^2 - 2 xy + y^2 = 4$
$x^2 + y^2 = 4$

21. $x^2 + y^2 = 32$
$xy = 16$

22. $x + y^2 - 6 = 0$
$x^2 = 3 y^2$

23. Find x and y.

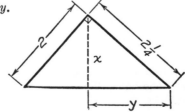

24. Find x and y.

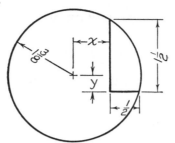

25. Find the radius R.

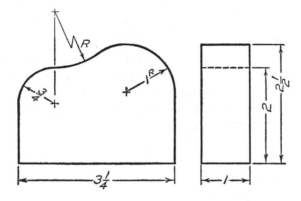

CHAPTER VII

Graphs

Rectangular Coordinates

In the preceding chapters graphs were used to plot algebraic equations to show how the functions varied, to find approximate solutions to equations, and to sort out extraneous roots from the desired roots. In each case the graph was plotted with rectangular coordinates. Such curves are very useful in engineering studies because they are much easier to interpret than the original equations and they can be used to present large amounts of data in concise form. A graph can be used to plot data, to observe trends in the data, and to estimate values between the plotted points.

Any convenient scale can be used and it is not necessary to use the same units on each axis. When convenient, the zero point should be shown, but occasionally the range of the variables may be such that this is impracticable.

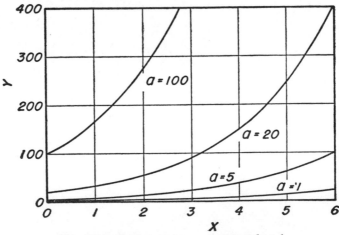

FIG. 7.1.—GRAPH OF $y = a\,e^{bx}$, WHEN $b = \frac{1}{2}$.

Sometimes rectangular coordinates are not completely satisfactory because the curves may be too crowded in some parts of
the range and too far apart in others. When the curves are too
crowded in one part of the graph it is often necessary to replot a
small section of the graph to a larger scale.

The curves in Fig. 7.1 show the plot on rectangular coordinates of the equation $y = a\, e^{1/2\, x}$ for various values of a. For
small values of a and x the graph is hard to read. This section
has been replotted to a larger scale in Fig. 7.2. There is some

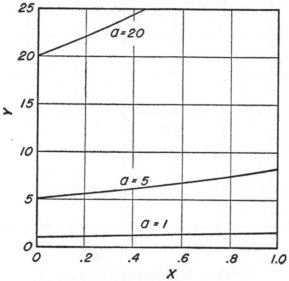

FIG. 7.2.—ENLARGED GRAPH OF $y = a\, e^{\frac{1}{2}x}$

improvement, but the vertical scale is still too crowded between 0 and 10. The lower left corner of this graph could be
replotted to an even larger scale, but this would not solve the
problem completely. What is needed is a vertical scale that is
stretched for small values of y and compressed for large values
of y.

Semi-Log Coordinate Paper

The graph of $y = \log_{10} x$ is shown in Fig. 7.3. For large values
of x the curve flattens out; the rate of increase is less and less.

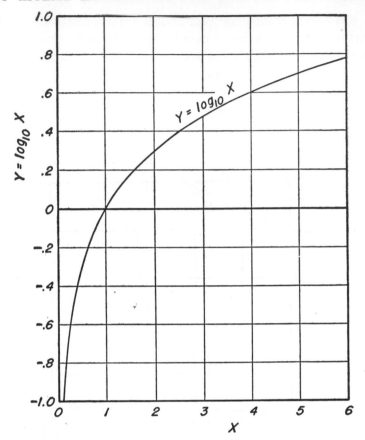

FIG. 7.3.—GRAPH OF $y = \log_{10} x$.

For small values of x (between 0 and 1) the curve is very steep. If the vertical scale of a graph is constructed so that the ordinate is proportional to the logarithm of the number instead of to the number itself, the part of the range corresponding to large values of y will be compressed, and the scale will be expanded for small values of y.

Fig. 7.4 shows the same graph that is plotted in Fig. 7.1, but on a semi-log scale for the y axis. The curves are no longer crowded near the origin and they are now straight lines. This makes it much easier to plot the curve because it is necessary to

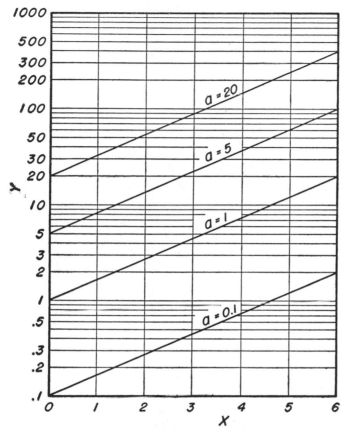

FIG. 7.4.—GRAPH OF $y = a\,e^{bx}$ WHEN $b = \frac{1}{2}$.

compute only two points for each value of a and draw a straight line. It should be noted that all the curves have the same slope.

A useful property of this method of plotting is that once a curve is drawn for one value of a, the curve for any other value of a can be drawn by locating the new value of a on the y axis and drawing a straight line through this point and parallel to the original line.

If a is held constant in the equation $y = a\,e^{bx}$ and the b in the exponent is varied, the slopes of the curves are different but all intersect at a common point given by $x = 0$ and $y = a$, as shown in Fig. 7.5.

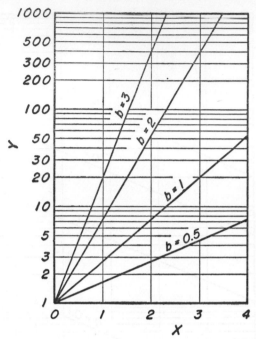

FIG. 7.5.—GRAPH OF $y = a\, e^{bx}$ WHEN $a = 1$.

A comparison of Figs. 7.4 and 7.5 shows that the coefficient a determines the point where the straight line intersects the y axis and the exponent b determines the slope of the line.

Although the preceding examples were for the number e raised to a variable exponent, this is not necessary. Any constant number to a first-degree exponent will give a straight line. Fig. 7.6 shows the graphs of some other simple functions.

An important advantage of the logarithmic scale is that percentage fluctuations of the variable are always shown on the same basis. On a linear scale, a 10 per cent change at the low end of the scale would not be very great when compared to a 10 per cent change at the top of the scale. The logarithmic graph emphasizes a given percentage change in exactly the same way, regardless of the magnitude of the quantity. Thus it is often unnecessary to compute the actual percentage change, since the graph shows the information directly.

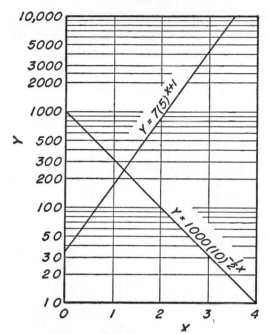

FIG. 7.6.—GRAPHS OF FUNCTIONS.

Log Coordinate Paper

It is often convenient to use a logarithmic scale on both axes, as shown in Fig. 7.7. Such graph paper is useful when plotting equations of the form $y = a x^n$, where a and n are constants; it is called log paper. Each section of the paper corresponding to a change in value of ten times, as from 1 to 10 or from 10 to 100, is called a cycle; and the paper comes in various types, such as 1 cycle on each axis, 1 by 2 cycle, 2 by 2 cycle, 2 by 3 cycle, etc. Both the semi-log and the log scales can be obtained on thick bond paper, on thin tracing paper, or on tracing cloth, and in various sizes and colors.

Whenever an equation can be reduced to a form

$$\log y = \log a + n \log x$$

where a and n are constants, the graph will be a straight line on log paper. The slope of the line will be equal to n, and the y intercept at the line $x = 1$ will be a.

Since this equation can represent multiplication, division, raising to powers, or extraction of roots, if the constants a and n are chosen properly, equations representing all such operations can be plotted as straight lines on log paper. The graph can be obtained by computing two points and drawing a straight line through the points.

Fig. 7.7 shows a graph of the area of a circle for various radii,

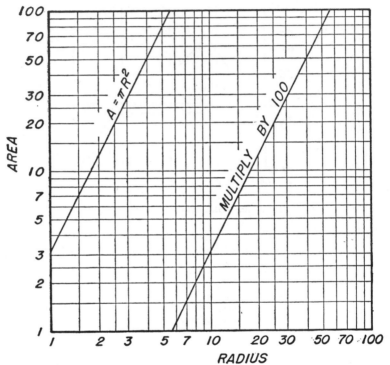

FIG. 7.7.—AREA OF CIRCLES, $A = \pi R^2$.

$A = \pi R^2$. Since this can be reduced to the equation

$$\log A = \log \pi + 2 \log R$$

the intercept for unit radius will be Area $= \pi$, and the straight line will be determined by one other point. This chart illustrates another advantage of such paper. When the curve runs off the top of the chart, it can be moved down and continued, if the proper multiplier is given. It is not necessary to add another sheet of paper to continue the graph. This same shift can be made on semi-log paper.

Empirical Equations

In engineering work it is often necessary to obtain an approximate equation from a series of measured points. Often this is done by plotting the points on log paper to see if they lie approximately on a straight line. When they do, it is easy to write the equation of the line.

For example, suppose that a wheel is rolling down a uniform slope, and the position of the wheel is measured at the end of each second. The following table shows the results of such an experiment.

Time in Seconds	Distance in Feet
0	0
1	5.3
2	21.0
3	52.0
4	86.0

When the points are plotted, as in Fig. 7.8, they are seen to lie approximately on a straight line. The small departures from the straight line are due to small inaccuracies in the measurements, in the measuring instruments, small imperfections in the materials, in the smoothness of the slope, etc. In such work the data are smoothed out by correcting the slight errors. A straightedge is moved about until the fit is as good as possible, with the deviations on each side about equal. This line of best fit intersects the line $t = 1$ at $d = 5.5$ and the slope of the line is 2; the line rises two units of distance vertically for each unit of distance horizontally. The equation of the line is therefore $d = 5.5\, t^2$.

It should be noted that a log scale has no zero point, and therefore cannot be used if the function goes from positive to

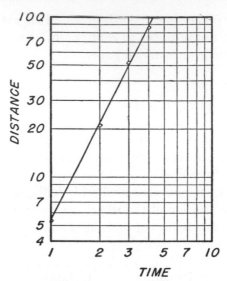

Fig. 7.8.—Variation of Distance with Time.

negative. The values for a particular cycle can be assigned to make the data fit the paper properly. Thus each distance on Fig. 7.7 can be multiplied by the proper power of 10 to give the desired range of distances.

Polar Coordinate Paper

In many engineering studies it is desired to plot the variation of some quantity with angle, measured from a given line taken as zero degrees. This can be done on polar coordinate paper. This paper has a series of radial lines starting from the origin to represent the angles, and a uniformly spaced series of concentric circles, with center at the origin, to represent the magnitude of the quantity, as shown in Fig. 7.9. Ordinarily the circles are drawn to provide a linear scale along each radius, but occasionally a logarithmic scale is used.

The curve in Fig. 7.9 shows the voltage pickup of a certain television receiving antenna as it is rotated about its axis. Much more voltage is picked up in the direction of 0° than in any other direction, and in most cases the antenna should be oriented so the transmitting station is in this direction. If

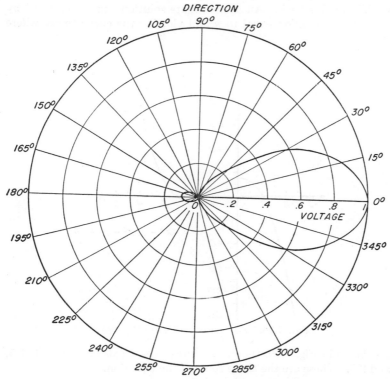

FIG. 7.9.—DIRECTIVITY OF TELEVISION ANTENNA.

the antenna is pointed away from the station, $\theta = 180°$, only about one-tenth as much voltage will be developed by the antenna. This directivity can sometimes be used to suppress an unwanted signal.

Graphic Solution of Equations

The solution of practical problems often leads to equations that cannot be solved by any of the algebraic methods given in this book. Usually an approximate root of the equation can be obtained by plotting the function to see where it goes through zero.

Example 1: Solve the equation $4x^3 - 12x^2 - x + 15 = 0$ for x.

This is called a cubic equation because it is a third-degree polynomial. The method of solution by algebra is too complicated to explain in this book. An approximate solution can be obtained by setting the equation equal to y and plotting the curve to see where $y = 0$.

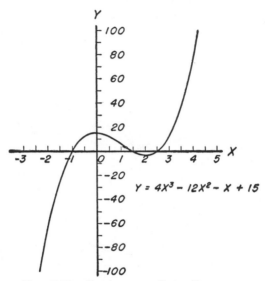

FIG. 7.10.—SOLUTION OF CUBIC EQUATION.

As shown in Fig. 7.10, the curve crosses the x axis at $x = -1$, 1.5, and 2.5. These are the three roots of the equation.

Example 2: A compressed air tank has the shape of a cylinder with hemispherical ends. The over-all length is 36 inches, and the volume is 10 gallons. Find the diameter.

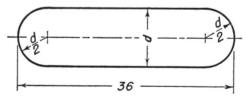

FIG. 7.11.—COMPRESSED AIR TANK.

The volume of a sphere is $\frac{4}{3}\pi r^3$, where r is the radius. One gallon = 231 cu in. The equation becomes

$$V = \tfrac{4}{3}\pi(d/2)^3 + \pi(d/2)^2(36 - d) = 10(231)$$

This can be simplified to

$$2d^3 - 3d^3 + 108d^2 = 2310(12)/\pi$$

or
$$d^3 - 108d^2 + 8823.55 = 0$$

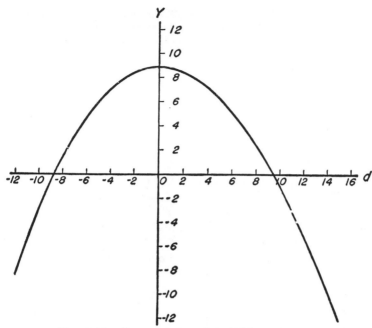

FIG. 7.12.—GRAPH OF $y = d^3 - 108d^2 + 8823.55$.

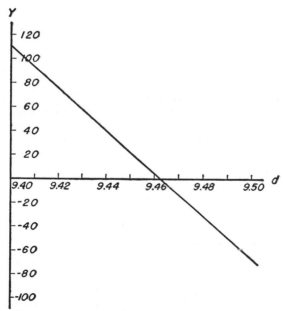

FIG. 7.13.—GRAPH OF $y = d^3 - 108d^2 + 8823.55$.

The graph of this curve is shown in Fig. 7.12. There is one root at $x = -8.70$, and one at $x = 9.45$; a third one occurs at $x = +107.2$ but is not shown. Obviously the correct one is $x = 9.45$. When a small portion of the curve is plotted to a larger scale, as shown in Fig. 7.13, the result can be read more accurately as 9.4628. This is accurate enough for any practical need.

EXERCISE 7.1

1. If \$1.00 is drawing 6 per cent compound interest, plot the amount of the principal and interest at the end of each year for ten years. How long will it take for the interest to equal 50 per cent of the principal? Use one cycle of semi-log paper. Draw a second curve showing the corresponding growth of \$5.00.

2. Plot a graph of the reciprocals of the numbers from 1 to 10. Use log scales.

3. One side of a line has a logarithmic scale from 1 to 10, and on the other side is a logarithmic scale from 1 to 0.1. Show that adjacent numbers are reciprocals.

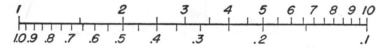

4. Plot a graph showing the number of gallons in a right circular cylinder of heights 6, 8, 12, and 15 inches, as a function of the diameter, for all diameters from 1 to 15 inches. Use log paper.

5. The period of a simple pendulum is given by the equation $T = 2\pi\sqrt{L/g}$ where L is the length in inches, g is the acceleration of gravity = 386 in. per sec.^{2}, and T is the period in seconds. Plot a curve on log paper to show the period of pendulums of lengths 10 to 100 inches. How long a pendulum has a period of one second?

6. The relation between the temperature in centigrade degrees and the degrees of the Fahrenheit scale is given by the equation

$$F = \tfrac{9}{5}C + 32$$

Plot a graph showing this relation. At what temperature do the two thermometers read the same?

7. The air pressure at an altitude h is given approximately by the equation

$$p = 14.7\, e^{-0.0000375h}$$

where h is in feet and p is in pounds per square inch. Plot a graph on semi-log paper to show the pressure for altitudes from 0 to 50,000 feet.

8. Solve the equations
$$y = 3(10)^{1-x}$$
and
$$y = \log_e (x + 1)$$

simultaneously by plotting on semi-log paper.

9. Plot a graph on log paper showing square roots and cube roots of the numbers from 1 to 1000.

10. How can the following equation be plotted so that it will be a straight line on log paper?
$$y = \frac{x + 1}{x}$$

11. Solve the equation
$$x^3 - 1.5\,x^2 + x - 2 = 0$$

for x. What causes the curve to level off between $x = 0$ and $x = 1$?

12. Solve the equation
$$x^4 - 6.2\,x^3 + 14.41\,x^2 - 14.88\,x + 5.76 = 0$$
graphically for the four roots.

CHAPTER VIII

Trigonometry with Applications

Introduction

Trigonometry is an important branch of mathematics that is of great value in many practical problems. It deals with the measurement of angles and triangles. If sufficient parts of a triangle are given to construct the triangle, it is possible to calculate approximately to any desired degree of accuracy all the remaining sides and angles by trigonometry. This requires the use of the trigonometric ratios or functions such as sine, cosine, tangent, cotangent, secant and cosecant.

Although trigonometry is primarily concerned with triangles, it also has many other uses, all of which deal with investigations of angles. It enables the calculation of many distances and angles that cannot be directly measured. For example, the distance to a star or across a river can be determined by means of measured angles if at least one side of the triangle is known. Obviously these distances could not be measured with a regular scale.

ANGLES

An angle is generated by the rotation of a line segment or ray about one of its ends; the original position of the line segment is called the **initial side,** and the final position the **terminal side.** An angle can be considered as the opening between two lines drawn from the same point. If the rotation of the line segment is taken in a counterclockwise direction, the angle generated is positive, and if the rotation is in the opposite direction, the angle is negative. Since the rotating line segment may be revolved as often as desired, angles can be of any size whatever.

Thus in Fig. 8.1, suppose a line segment OP starts from position OX and rotates about O in a counterclockwise direction to the terminal position OP. Then angle A, indicated by the curved arrow, will be generated. If the counterclockwise

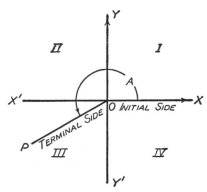

direction of rotation is defined as positive, then angle A is *positive*, as indicated by the direction of the arrow. When the rotation of OP is clockwise, starting from OX, the angle generated is *negative*.

FIG. 8.1.—ANGLE AND QUADRANTS.

When a set of X and Y axes is used in the generation of angles as in Fig. 8.1, the generation is *always* started from line OX, called the initial side. The angle is said to be in the first, second, third or fourth quadrant depending upon which of the four corners marked I, II, III or IV contains the terminal side. Thus in Fig. 8.1, angle A lies in the third quadrant.

It is obvious that angles can be of any size, either positive or negative, since the angle can lie in any quadrant. If the terminal side turns from OX to OY, it generates a right angle, or 90°. When it turns another 90° to OX', it generates 180°, or two right angles. One complete revolution is 360°, and another complete revolution is 720°. If the rotation were in the opposite direction, the angles would contain the same number of degrees but would all be negative.

A right angle is divided into 90 equal parts or **degrees** (°), each degree is divided into 60 equal parts or **minutes** ('), and each minute is further divided into 60 equal parts called **seconds** ("). An angle of 49 degrees, 36 minutes and 18 seconds is written 49° 36′ 18″.

Since the above definition of an angle is so general as to cover any amount of rotation of the generating line, it is easily seen that any given position of the generating line can represent a whole series of angles, each differing from the next one in the series by 360°. Thus in Fig. 8.2, angle A of 30° is generated by rotating the generating line OP in a counterclockwise direction

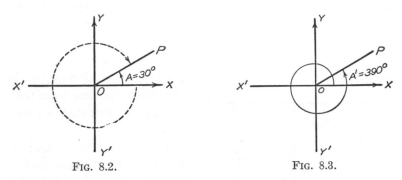

FIG. 8.2. FIG. 8.3.

from the initial position OX through 30°. In Fig. 8.3, however, the generating line has been rotated a full revolution from the initial position plus 30° more. Hence, although the generating line has the same terminal position in both cases, the angle generated in the first case is 30°, and that generated in the second case is 360° + 30° = 390°. By a second full revolution an angle of 2 × 360° + 30° = 750° would be generated, and the generating line would again have the same terminal position. Hence for n revolutions, the angle generated would be n × 360° + 30°.

Suppose the generating line in Fig. 8.2 had been rotated in a clockwise direction as indicated by the dotted arrow. Then the angle generated would have been equal to − 330°. An additional clockwise rotation of 360° would generate an angle of − 360° + (− 330°) = − 690°, having the same terminal position; n complete revolutions in addition to the − 330° would generate an angle of − n × 360° + (− 330°) = − (n × 360° + 330°). It is now evident that in addition to an endless series of *positive* angles, any given terminal position of the generating line also represents an endless series of *negative* angles.

EXERCISE 8.1

Use a protractor to construct the following angles, and state the quadrant in which each lies.

1. 22°; 150°; − 170°; 380°; 780°; − 20°; − 745°; 225°; 330°
2. 24°; 160°; − 160°; 390°; 760°; − 15°; − 750°; 230°; 330°
3. 30°; 150°; − 175°; 380°; 770°; − 40°; − 760°; 335°; 220°
4. 35°; 165°; − 160°; 380°; 750°; − 10°; − 745°; 225°; 325°

ANGULAR MEASUREMENT

Several systems are used for the measurement of angles. The two in most common use are the *degree* or *sexagesimal* system; and the *radian* or *circular measure* system.

The degree system is the system with which nearly everyone is familiar and has already been discussed in the preceding section.

Radians

Although it may not seem so upon first acquaintance, the radian or circular system is much more convenient than the degree system for certain applications, particularly theoretical investigations.

A radian is defined as the angle at the center of a circle which intercepts an arc equal in length to the radius.

Thus in Fig. 8.4, if arc *XP* is equal in length to radius *OX* or *r*, the central angle *POX* is equal to one radian.

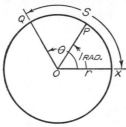

FIG. 8.4.

Suppose now it is desired to find some other angle such as *QOX*. If the length of the arc *QPX* is known, the number of radians in angle *QOX* can be found by determining the number of times the radius r will go into the arc length QPX. In mathematical symbols, if angle QOX is denoted by the Greek letter θ,[1] and arc QPX by s, then

$$\theta = \frac{s}{r} \text{ radians}$$

or $$\text{Angle} = \frac{\text{Arc}}{\text{Radius}}$$

Length of an Arc

If the above equation is written in the form

$$s = r\theta$$

it becomes a formula for finding the arc length intercepted by a central angle θ when the radius of the circle and the number of radians in angle θ are known. This important formula should be carefully memorized, since it will be needed in many of the applied problems.

Example: Find the angle subtended at the center of a circle of radius 6 in. by an arc of length 9 in.

$$\theta = \frac{s}{r} = \frac{9}{6} = 1.5 \text{ radians}$$

Relation Between Degrees and Radians

The circumference of a circle is 2π times the radius. Therefore, from the definition of a radian:

One revolution $= 2\pi$ radians

and also   One revolution $= 360°$

[1] Greek letters are frequently used to denote angles in mathematics, and various other quantities in mechanics. The Greek alphabet is as follows:

A	α	Alpha	N	ν	Nu
B	β	Beta	Ξ	ξ	Xi
Γ	γ	Gamma	O	o	Omicron
Δ	δ	Delta	Π	π	Pi
E	ϵ	Epsilon	P	ρ	Rho
Z	ζ	Zeta	Σ	σ	Sigma
H	η	Eta	T	τ	Tau
Θ	θ	Theta	Υ	υ	Upsilon
I	ι	Iota	Φ	ϕ	Phi
K	κ	Kappa	X	χ	Chi
Λ	λ	Lambda	Ψ	ψ	Psi
M	μ	Mu	Ω	ω	Omega

Thus 2π radians $= 360°$

and therefore   **1 radian** $= \dfrac{360°}{2\pi} = \dfrac{180°}{\pi} = $ **57.2957795°** [2]

Similarly, since $360° = 2\pi$ radians

$$1° = \frac{2\pi}{360} = \frac{\pi}{180} = \textbf{0.0174532925 radians}$$

In order to change radians to degrees, accurate to seconds, it is necessary to use figures accurate to at least five decimal places.

Example 1: Change 1.74 radians to degrees, minutes, and seconds.

$$1 \text{ radian} = 57.29578°$$
$$1.74 \text{ radians} = 1.74(57.29578)$$
$$= 99.69466°$$

Since $1° = 60'$
$$0.69466° = 0.69466(60)'$$
$$= 41.6796'$$

Similarly $0.6796' = 0.6796(60)''$
$$= 40.8''$$

Thus $1.74 \text{ radians} = 99° \, 41' \, 40.8''$

Example 2: Change $37° \, 14' \, 19''$ to radians.

First change the minutes and seconds to decimals of a degree.

Since $1' = 60''$
$$19'' = \tfrac{19}{60} = 0.31667'$$

Similarly $14.31667' = \dfrac{14.31667}{60}$
$$= 0.238611°$$

Thus $37° \, 14' \, 19'' = 37.238611°$

Now change to radians.

Since $1° = 0.01745329$ radian
$$37.238611° = 37.238611(0.01745329)$$
$$= 0.64993 \text{ radian}$$

[2] The ratio of the circumference to the diameter of a circle, known as π, cannot be exactly determined. Lambert proved in 1761 that this ratio is incommensurable, and in 1881 Lindemann showed it to be transcendental. In 1873 W. Shank presented to the Royal Society of London a computation for π correct to 707 places. The first 30 places are

$$\pi = 3.141{,}592{,}653{,}589{,}793{,}238{,}462{,}643{,}383{,}279 \cdots$$

It is often convenient to express angles in radians as multiples of π. Since $360° = 2\pi$ radians, $90° = \frac{1}{2}\pi$ radians, $45° = \frac{1}{4}\pi$ radians, etc. It is only necessary to multiply the degrees by $\frac{\pi}{180}$ to change to radians.

Thus
$$135° = 135\left(\frac{\pi}{180}\right) = \frac{3}{4}\pi \text{ radians}$$

Use of Radian Tables

There are tables in the back of the book for changing degrees to radians. They give the number of radians corresponding to each degree, as well as to minutes and seconds. To find the total number of radians, the number of radians corresponding to the degrees, minutes and seconds are placed in a column and added.

Example: Change 14° 19′ 26″ to radians.

From the tables,

$$
\begin{array}{rl}
14° & = 0.24435 \text{ radian} \\
19' & = 0.00553 \\
26'' & = \underline{0.00013} \\
14° \ 19' \ 26'' & = 0.25001 \text{ radian}
\end{array}
$$

To change radians to degrees, minutes and seconds, first find in the tables the largest number of radians corresponding to a whole number of degrees that is contained in the given number. Subtract this to obtain the remainder which gives the radians corresponding to minutes. Find the largest number of radians corresponding to a whole number of minutes that is contained in the remainder and subtract. If there is a remainder, look it up in the tables to get the seconds.

Example: Change 1.22409 radians to degrees, minutes and seconds.

From the tables

$$
\begin{array}{rl}
& 1.22409 \\
70° = & \underline{1.22173} \text{ radians} \\
& 0.00236 \\
8' = & \underline{0.00233} \\
6'' = & \overline{0.00003} \\
1.22409 \text{ radians} = & 70° \ 8' \ 6''.
\end{array}
$$

AREA OF A CIRCULAR SECTOR

Fig. 8.5 shows an area BOA bounded by two radii and an arc of a circle, which is called a **sector**. It is shown in geometry that the area of a circular sector is equal to the area of a triangle having a base equal to the arc and an altitude equal to the radius. This gives the area of BOA as

$$A = \frac{rs}{2}$$

However, since $s = r\theta$, substitution for s gives

$$A = \tfrac{1}{2}\, r^2\theta$$

where θ *must be expressed in radians.*

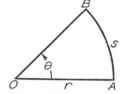

FIG. 8.5.

Example: Find the area of a circular sector having a radius of 6 ft, if the central angle is 30°.

$$30° = 30(0.01745) = 0.5235 \text{ radian}$$

Area
$$= \tfrac{1}{2}\, r^2\theta = \tfrac{1}{2}(6)^2(0.5235)$$
$$= 9.423 \text{ sq ft.}$$

EXERCISE 8.2

1. Change the following degrees, minutes and seconds to decimals, without the use of tables:

   37° 48′ 16″   28° 7′ 19″
   14° 8′ 17″   114° 19′ 38″

2. Work Problem 1 with the help of tables.

3. Change the following angles to radians, correct to *four* decimal places, without the use of tables:

   16°   19° 54′ 17″
   28.67°   26° 18′ 29″

4. Work Problem 3 with the help of tables.

5. Change the following angles to degrees, minutes and seconds without using tables:

   1.678 radians $\tfrac{3}{8}\,\pi$ radians
   $\tfrac{9}{16}$ radian

6. Work Problem 5 with tables.

7. Change the following angles to degrees, minutes and seconds without using tables:

   0.0765 radian $\tfrac{27}{64}$ radian
   3.1416 radians

8. Work Problem 7 with tables.

9. Change the following angles to degrees, minutes and seconds without using tables:

2.3146 radians $\qquad$ $\frac{7}{11} \pi$ radians

$\frac{38}{49}$ radian

10. Work Problem 9 with tables.

11. How many radians in each corner of a pentagon?

12. A motor is making 1750 rpm. How many radians per second is this?

13. What is the radius of a circle in which an arc 2 ft long subtends an angle of 38°? Use radians.

14. Find the length of an arc intercepted by a central angle of 49° in a circle of 9 in. radius.

15. A man at latitude 45° N goes 500 miles north. Find his new latitude. The radius of the earth is 3960 miles.

16. The latitude of Rochester, New York, is 43° 10′ 10″ N. What is the shortest distance to the north pole? Use the radius given in Problem 15.

17. Find the distance between degree marks on a circle 9 in. in diameter.

18. The maximum safe rim velocity of a cast-iron flywheel is 100 ft per sec. How many radians per second would this be for a wheel 28 in. in diameter?

19. A 17-in. pulley makes 870 rpm. What is the belt speed in miles per hour?

20. An automobile has 16 × 7.00 tires. How many rpm does the wheel make at 50 mph?

21. How many radians does the minute hand of a watch turn through in 1 hr 55 min?

22. Find the length of the circular arc from A to B.

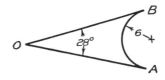

23. Find angle θ.

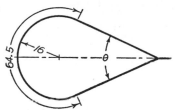

24. Find θ in degrees, minutes and seconds.

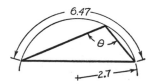

25. Find the arc length x.

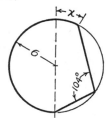

26. Find the arc length x.

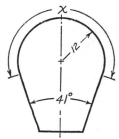

27. Find the distance from A to B along the center line.

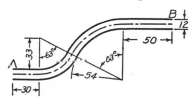

28. Find the area of the shaded figure.

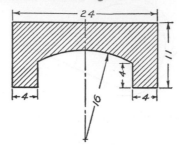

29. Find θ.

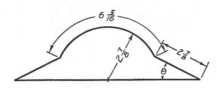

30. The area of the shaded portion is 1550. Find angle θ.

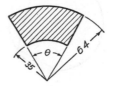

TRIGONOMETRIC FUNCTIONS

By the use of trigonometric functions of angles, it is possible to solve many problems that would be very difficult to solve by geometry. For example, if two sides of a right triangle are known, the angles can be determined as accurately as necessary for all values of the sides. This requires the use of trigonometric ratios, or functions.

In Fig. 8.6, angle C is the right angle in triangle ABC, and therefore AB is the *hypotenuse*. BC is

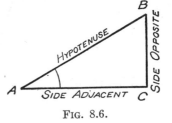

FIG. 8.6.

called the *side opposite* angle A and AC is the *side adjacent* to angle A. It is important to be able properly to identify these sides regardless of the position of the triangle.

Fig. 8.7 shows another triangle similar to that in Fig. 8.6 but to a different scale so that the hypotenuse is of unit length.

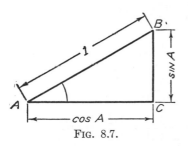

FIG. 8.7.

The **sine** of angle A (abbreviated sin A) is defined as the *side opposite divided by the hypotenuse.* Since the hypotenuse is equal to 1, the side opposite is numerically equal to sin A.

Similarly, the *side adjacent divided by the hypotenuse* is defined as the **cosine** of A (written cos A). Again, since the hypotenuse is 1 the side adjacent is equal numerically to cos A.

If another right triangle is drawn so that the adjacent side is 1, as in Fig. 8.8, the side opposite is equal, by definition, to the

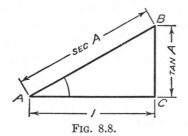

FIG. 8.8.

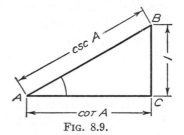

FIG. 8.9.

tangent of A, or tan A. The hypotenuse, which is numerically the same as the hypotenuse divided by the adjacent side, is defined as the **secant** of A, or sec A. In Fig. 8.9 is shown a right triangle with the side opposite equal to 1. The side adjacent is defined as the **cotangent** of A, or cot A. The hypotenuse is equal to the **cosecant** of A, or csc A.

To obtain a combined picture of the six trigonometric ratios, draw a circle with radius equal to 1, as shown in Fig. 8.10, and an angle A at the center. Draw the perpendiculars BC, ED, FO and FG. Then, by definition,

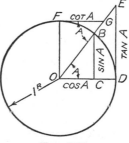

FIG. 8.10.

$$\sin A = \frac{\text{side opposite}}{\text{hypotenuse}} = \frac{BC}{1} = BC$$

$$\cos A = \frac{\text{side adjacent}}{\text{hypotenuse}} = \frac{OC}{1} = OC$$

$$\tan A = \frac{\text{side opposite}}{\text{side adjacent}} = \frac{DE}{1} = DE$$

$$\cot A = \frac{\text{side adjacent}}{\text{side opposite}} = \frac{1}{\tan A} = \frac{FG}{FO} = FG$$

$$\sec A = \frac{\text{hypotenuse}}{\text{side adjacent}} = \frac{1}{\cos A} = \frac{OE}{OD} = OE$$

$$\csc A = \frac{\text{hypotenuse}}{\text{side opposite}} = \frac{1}{\sin A} = \frac{OG}{OF} = OG$$

It is easy to see that for different-sized similar triangles these ratios are always the same, because the corresponding parts of similar figures are proportional. Therefore, the values of these ratios are the same for right similar triangles of any size, but they change for angles of different sizes. For a definite angle, there is one, and only one, value for each trigonometric ratio.

How to Find the Trigonometric Functions for a Given Angle

All the ratios have been calculated mathematically for all the angles. They are usually listed to five decimal places in tables for each minute of angle from 0° to 90°. They can also be found graphically by measurement.

Example: Find the six trigonometric functions of 35° graphically.

Draw an angle of 35° with a protractor. Let the hypotenuse AB be an even length, say 3 in. Draw a perpendicular from B to AC and measure the two sides carefully. The six trigonometric functions can then be calculated by substituting these values in the equations defining the functions. Thus

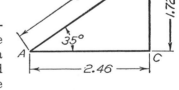

$$\sin 35° = \frac{1.72}{3} = 0.573 \qquad \cot 35° = \frac{2.46}{1.72} = 1.430$$

$$\cos 35° = \frac{2.46}{3} = 0.820 \qquad \sec 35° = \frac{3}{2.46} = 1.220$$

$$\tan 35° = \frac{1.72}{2.46} = 0.699 \qquad \csc 35° = \frac{3}{1.72} = 1.744$$

In this way a table giving all the functions for any angle can be made.

The values listed in such a table would be approximate, owing to unavoidable inaccuracy in making the necessary constructions and measurements. By advanced methods which will not be explained here, tables of various degrees of accuracy have been made, giving the numerical values of the sine, cosine, tangent and cotangent for any desired acute angle. These four functions are the ones most used in practical work. The secant and cosecant functions are seldom used; but if their values are needed, they can be easily calculated from the cosine and sine functions respectively, as will be shown later. For all ordinary applications the usual tables computed to four or five decimal places are sufficiently accurate. For special classes of work such as is encountered in extended surveys, astronomy and the use of certain instruments of high precision, tables to six, seven and even ten decimal places are available. A five-place table is used for the work in this course.

Both natural or numerical values and logarithmic values of the trigonometric functions of any acute angle, expressed in degrees and minutes, can be read directly from the tables of *Natural Sines and Cosines, Natural Tangents and Cotangents,* and *Logarithmic Functions* in the back of this book. For the present only the natural functions will be considered.

To find a function of an angle which is not an integral number of minutes, the process of **interpolation** is used. This can be easily understood from examples.

Example 1: Find sin 36° 28.7′.

From the tables

$$1\left\{ 0.7 \left\{ \begin{array}{ll} \sin 36° 28' & = 0.59436 \\ \sin 36° 28.7' & = \quad ? \end{array} \right\} x \\ \sin 36° 29' & = 0.59459 \end{array} \right\} 23$$

Since 28.7′ lies $\frac{7}{10}$ of the distance between 28′ and 29′, sin 36° 28.7′ should be $\frac{7}{10}$ of the distance between 0.59436 and 0.59459. The whole difference is 0.59459 − 0.59436 = 0.00023, or, if the decimal point is neglected, 23.

Taking $\frac{7}{10}$ of this difference, or 16 to the nearest whole number, and adding it to the sine of the smaller angle gives 0.59436 + 0.00016 = 0.59452.

Note: Since a five-place table was used, the 16.1 was rounded off to 16, as only five places can be used in the answer.

Example 2: Find cot 23° 13′ 43″.

From the tables

$$60\left\{43\left\{\begin{array}{ll}\cot 23° 13′ & = 2.3313 \\ \cot 23° 13′ 43″ = & ?\end{array}\right\}x \atop \cot 23° 14′ \quad = 2.3294\right\}19$$

The proportion becomes

$$\frac{x}{19} = \frac{43}{60} \quad \text{so} \quad x = 13.6 \quad \text{or} \quad 14$$

Since the angle is increasing, the cotangent is decreasing. Therefore, in order for the answer to come between the two values, the difference, 14, must be subtracted from 2.3313.

Note: When interpolating, always work from the smaller angle and not from the smaller number.

The result is

$$2.3313 − 0.0014 = 2.3299$$

As before, x was rounded off to the nearest whole number.

Example 3: Given cos θ = 0.64041. Find the acute angle θ.

From the tables

$$60\left\{x\left\{\begin{array}{ll}\cos 50° 10′ & = 0.64056 \\ \cos \theta & = 0.64041\end{array}\right\}15 \atop \cos 50° 11′ = 0.64033\right\}23$$

The proportion becomes

$$\frac{x}{60} = \frac{15}{23} \quad \text{or} \quad x = 39.1$$

The angle is therefore

$$\theta = 50° 10′ 39″$$

Examination of the tables of Natural Sines and Cosines or of Natural Tangents and Cotangents shows that angles from 0° to 45° are given at the top of the pages and those between 45°

and 90° are given at the bottom of the pages. There is a column of minutes at the left and another at the right. The one at the left starts with zero at the top of the column and increases to 60 at the bottom. It is to be used with the angles at the top of the page, between 0° and 45°. The column of minutes at the right starts with zero at the bottom of the column and increases to 60 at the top. It is used with the angles at the bottom of the page, between 45° and 90°.

In Example 3 the number 0.64041 could not be found in the column headed cos at the top of the page; it was given in the column which was marked cos at the bottom. This meant that the angle at the bottom of the page was to be used, and the minutes were found in the minute column on the right.

EXERCISE 8.3

Fill in the blank spaces in the tables below.

1.

θ	$\sin \theta$	$\cos \theta$	$\tan \theta$	$\cot \theta$
41° 15′ 20″				
73° 29′ 45″				
	0.22641			
		0.23730		
			1.3477	
				0.77382

2.

θ	$\sin \theta$	$\cos \theta$	$\tan \theta$	$\cot \theta$
42° 16′ 25″				
80° 28′ 51″				
	0.26541			
		0.28407		
			2.65331	
				0.32011

3.

θ	sin θ	cos θ	tan θ	cot θ
35° 17′ 33″				
89° 32′ 14″				
	0.27770			
		0.29075		
			3.4389	
				0.96013

4.

θ	sin θ	cos θ	tan θ	cot θ
20° 14′ 55″				
73° 45′ 10″				
	0.28311			
		0.30324		
			1.3475	
				0.95200

RELATIONS BETWEEN THE FUNCTIONS

The six trigonometric functions are related by several fundamental equations. These relations are of considerable importance and are discussed in great detail in more advanced courses in trigonometry. Here, however, it will be sufficient to consider only a few of them without making any attempt at an extended study. For the sake of convenience the definitions of the six functions are repeated below. In the right triangle ABC

$$\sin A = \frac{a}{c}; \qquad \cos A = \frac{b}{c}$$

$$\tan A = \frac{a}{b}; \qquad \cot A = \frac{b}{a}$$

$$\sec A = \frac{c}{b}; \qquad \csc A = \frac{c}{a}$$

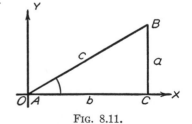

FIG. 8.11.

By the Pythagorean theorem, in Fig. 8.11,

$$a^2 + b^2 = c^2 \tag{1}$$

Dividing this equation by c^2 gives

$$\frac{a^2}{c^2} + \frac{b^2}{c^2} = 1$$

But $\dfrac{a}{c} = \sin A$ and $\dfrac{b}{c} = \cos A$. Substituting these terms in the last equation, we have

$$\sin^2 A + \cos^2 A = 1 \tag{2}$$

This is true for all values of angle A. This equation is very important and should be memorized. Since it holds true for all values of A, it is called an **identity**.

If we divide Eq 1 by b^2, we have

$$\frac{a^2}{b^2} + 1 = \frac{c^2}{b^2}$$

Making the substitutions $\dfrac{a}{b} = \tan A$ and $\dfrac{c}{b} = \sec A$ gives

$$\tan^2 A + 1 = \sec^2 A \tag{3}$$

Dividing Eq 1 by a^2 gives

$$1 + \frac{b^2}{a^2} = \frac{c^2}{a^2}$$

But since $\dfrac{b}{a} = \cot A$ and $\dfrac{c}{a} = \csc A$, substitution gives

$$\cot^2 A + 1 = \csc^2 A \tag{4}$$

From the definitions of the functions it is seen that

$$\frac{\sin A}{\cos A} = \frac{\dfrac{a}{c}}{\dfrac{b}{c}} = \frac{a}{c}\left(\frac{c}{b}\right) = \frac{a}{b}$$

But

$$\frac{a}{b} = \tan A$$

and therefore

$$\tan A = \frac{\sin A}{\cos A} \tag{5}$$

Likewise it can be shown that

$$\cot A = \frac{\cos A}{\sin A} \tag{6}$$

All these identities should be memorized.

Reciprocal Relations

The six trigonometric functions are reciprocal in pairs.

Since $\quad \sin A = \dfrac{a}{c} \qquad$ and $\qquad \csc A = \dfrac{c}{a}$

$\qquad \sin A = \dfrac{1}{\csc A} \qquad$ and $\qquad \csc A = \dfrac{1}{\sin A}$

Similarly, $\cos A = \dfrac{b}{c} \qquad$ and $\qquad \sec A = \dfrac{c}{b}$

hence $\qquad \cos A = \dfrac{1}{\sec A} \qquad$ and $\qquad \sec A = \dfrac{1}{\cos A}$

Again, $\quad \tan A = \dfrac{a}{b} \qquad$ and $\qquad \cot A = \dfrac{b}{a}$

therefore $\tan A = \dfrac{1}{\cot A} \qquad$ and $\qquad \cot A = \dfrac{1}{\tan A}$

These equations are general and hold for all angles.

Functions of Complementary Angles

Since the sum of the three angles of any triangle is 180°, it follows that in any right triangle the sum of the two acute angles is 90°. Hence, the two acute angles are complementary. From Fig. 8.11 it is easily seen that a function of an acute angle is equal to the cofunction of the complement of that angle. Thus in Fig. 8.11, by definition:

$$\sin A = \frac{a}{c}; \qquad \cos B = \frac{a}{c}, \qquad \text{so} \qquad \sin A = \cos B$$

$$\cos A = \frac{b}{c}; \qquad \sin B = \frac{b}{c}, \qquad \text{so} \qquad \cos A = \sin B$$

$$\tan A = \frac{a}{b}; \qquad \cot B = \frac{a}{b}, \qquad \text{so} \qquad \tan A = \cot B$$

$$\cot A = \frac{b}{a}; \qquad \tan B = \frac{b}{a}, \qquad \text{so} \qquad \cot A = \tan B$$

$$\sec A = \frac{c}{b}; \qquad \csc B = \frac{c}{b}, \qquad \text{so} \qquad \sec A = \csc B$$

$$\csc A = \frac{c}{a}; \qquad \sec B = \frac{c}{a}, \qquad \text{so} \qquad \csc A = \sec B$$

These equations can be rewritten:

$$\sin \alpha = \cos (90° - \alpha) \qquad \cot \alpha = \tan (90° - \alpha)$$
$$\cos \alpha = \sin (90° - \alpha) \qquad \sec \alpha = \csc (90° - \alpha)$$
$$\tan \alpha = \cot (90° - \alpha) \qquad \csc \alpha = \sec (90° - \alpha)$$

Trigonometric Identities

There are many other relations between the functions than those given above. From one of the identities already proved, others can be developed. Substitutions from one identity to another give new results. The following examples illustrate the method.

Example 1: Prove that $\sin \alpha = \dfrac{1}{\pm\sqrt{1 + \cot^2 \alpha}}$.

Start with the identity

$$\sin \alpha = \frac{1}{\csc \alpha}$$

and substitute for the cosecant the value obtained from the identity

$$\csc^2 \alpha = 1 + \cot^2 \alpha$$
$$\csc \alpha = \pm\sqrt{1 + \cot^2 \alpha}$$

This gives the result

$$\sin \alpha = \frac{1}{\pm\sqrt{1 + \cot^2 \alpha}}$$

Example 2: Prove that $\dfrac{1}{\tan \alpha} + \dfrac{1}{\cot \alpha} = \sec \alpha \csc \alpha$.

Since $\qquad \dfrac{1}{\tan \alpha} = \dfrac{\cos \alpha}{\sin \alpha} \qquad$ and $\qquad \dfrac{1}{\cot \alpha} = \dfrac{\sin \alpha}{\cos \alpha}$

$$\frac{1}{\tan \alpha} + \frac{1}{\cot \alpha} = \frac{\cos \alpha}{\sin \alpha} + \frac{\sin \alpha}{\cos \alpha} = \frac{\cos^2 \alpha + \sin^2 \alpha}{\sin \alpha \cos \alpha} = \frac{1}{\sin \alpha \cos \alpha}$$

since $\qquad\qquad \sin^2 \alpha + \cos^2 \alpha = 1 \qquad\qquad$ from Eq 2.

But $\qquad \dfrac{1}{\sin \alpha} = \csc \alpha \qquad$ and $\qquad \dfrac{1}{\cos \alpha} = \sec \alpha$

hence $\qquad \dfrac{1}{\tan \alpha} + \dfrac{1}{\cot \alpha} = \sec \alpha \csc \alpha$

Example 3: Prove that $\dfrac{\cot^2 \theta \cos^2 \theta}{\cos \theta + \cot \theta} = \cot \theta - \cos \theta$.

$$\frac{\cot^2 \theta \cos^2 \theta}{\cos \theta + \cot \theta} = \frac{\dfrac{\cos^2 \theta}{\sin^2 \theta}(\cos^2 \theta)}{\cos \theta + \dfrac{\cos \theta}{\sin \theta}} = \frac{\dfrac{\cos^4 \theta}{\sin^2 \theta}}{\dfrac{\sin \theta \cos \theta + \cos \theta}{\sin \theta}}$$

$$= \frac{\cos^4 \theta}{\sin^2 \theta}\left(\frac{\sin \theta}{\cos \theta (\sin \theta + 1)}\right) = \frac{\cos^3 \theta}{\sin \theta (1 + \sin \theta)}$$

Multiply numerator and denominator by $1 - \sin \theta$.

$$\frac{\cos^3 \theta (1 - \sin \theta)}{\sin \theta (1 - \sin^2 \theta)} = \frac{\cos \theta (1 - \sin \theta)}{\sin \theta} = \cot \theta - \cos \theta$$

since $\qquad 1 - \sin^2 \theta = \cos^2 \theta$

Note: It is usually a good idea to change everything to sine and cosine before trying to transform one expression into another. Always try to avoid radicals whenever possible.

EXERCISE 8.4

1. Given $\sin A = \frac{3}{5}$, find $\cos A$ and $\tan A$.
2. Given $\tan A = 1.328$, find $\cos A$ and $\sin A$.
3. Given $\tan 30° = \dfrac{\sqrt{3}}{3}$, find $\cot 60°$.
4. Given $\tan B = \tan A$ and $A + B = 90°$, find A and B.
5. Given $\sin A = \cos 2A$, find A.
6. Given $\cot 2A = \tan 3A$, find A.

Prove the following identities:

7. $\sin \alpha \sec \alpha \cot \alpha = 1$
8. $\sin \alpha \cot \alpha = \cos \alpha$
9. $1 - \sin^2 \beta = \dfrac{\sin^2 \beta}{\tan^2 \beta}$
10. $\dfrac{1 - \sin^2 \beta}{1 + \tan^2 \beta} = \cos^4 \beta$
11. $1 - \cos^2 \beta = \dfrac{\cos^2 \beta}{\cot^2 \beta}$
12. $\tan \gamma + \cot \gamma = \sec \gamma \csc \gamma$
13. $\dfrac{\sin x - \sqrt{1 - 2 \sin x \cos x}}{\cos x - \sqrt{1 + 2 \sin x \cos x}} = - \cot x$

    Hint: Substitute $\sin^2 x + \cos^2 x$ for the **1**.
14. $\cos x = \pm \dfrac{\sqrt{\csc^2 x - 1}}{\csc x}$
15. $\csc x = \pm \dfrac{\sec x}{\sqrt{\sec^2 x - 1}}$
16. $\sec x = \pm \dfrac{\sqrt{1 + \cot^2 x}}{\cot x}$
17. Given $\cos a = \frac{7}{24}$, find the other five functions of a.
18. Given $\cos \beta : \sin \beta = 15 : 17$, find all six functions of β.
19. Express $\sin \beta$ in terms of each of the other five functions of β.

20. Express cos β in terms of each of the other five functions of β.

21. Express tan β in terms of each of the other five functions of β.

Right Triangles

It is possible to construct any triangle when one side and two other parts are given. If the triangle is drawn accurately to scale, the unknown parts can be measured directly from the figure. In engineering it is often necessary to calculate these parts more accurately than they can be measured. This is easily done by means of the trigonometric ratios, and the calculation can be carried out to as many significant figures as there are in the table of functions. This process is known as solving the triangle.

In solving a triangle it is important that some definite order be followed. The suggestions below are valuable.

Suggestions

1. Carefully construct the triangle to scale by means of compass, ruler and protractor. The computed values can then be roughly checked by measurement from the figure.

2. State the given and the required parts, then select and write down the formulas which you need in the solution. In choosing the formulas, select for each part required the formula that contains this part and two of the known parts. Thus, in Fig. 8.12, if angle A and side b are two known parts and side c is a required part, use the equation $\cos A = \dfrac{b}{c}$ because it contains the given parts and the required part c. Solving this formula for c gives

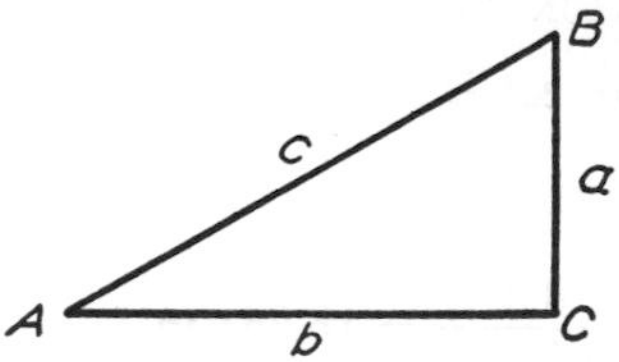

$$c = \frac{b}{\cos A}$$

Fig. 8.12.

3. Substitute the known values in the formulas and obtain the required part by evaluation.

4. Check your results by measuring, or by using other formulas than those used in the solution.

Example 1: Given $c = 5$ in. and $A = 32°$, find a, b, and B.

$$\text{Given}\begin{cases} A = 32° \\ c = 5 \text{ in.} \end{cases} \quad \text{Find}\begin{cases} B = 58°\,^3 \\ b = 4.2402 \text{ in.} \\ a = 2.6496 \text{ in.} \end{cases}$$

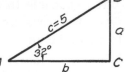

FORMULAS

$a = c \sin A \qquad B = 90° - A$

$b = c \cos A$

COMPUTATION

$a = 5 \sin 32° = 5(0.52992) = 2.6496$ in.

$b = 5 \cos 32° = 5(0.84805) = 4.2402$ in.

$B = 90° - 32° = 58°$

CHECK

$a^2 + b^2 = c^2$

$2.6496^2 = 7.0204$

$4.2402^2 = \underline{17.9793}$ CHECK: $5^2 = 25$

$c^2 = 24.9997$

Example 2: Given $a = 6.32$ in. and $b = 13.88$ in., find A, B, and c.

$$\text{Given}\begin{cases} a = 6.32 \text{ in.} \\ b = 13.88 \text{ in.} \end{cases} \quad \text{Find}\begin{cases} A = 24°\,28'\,52'' \\ B = 65°\,31'\,8'' \\ c = 15.251 \text{ in.} \end{cases}$$

FORMULAS

$\tan A = \dfrac{a}{b} \qquad \cot B = \dfrac{a}{b}$

$c = \dfrac{a}{\sin A}$

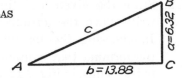

COMPUTATION

$\tan A = \dfrac{6.32}{13.88} = 0.45533 = \cot B$

$A = 24°\,28'\,52''$

$B = 65°\,31'\,8''$

$c = \dfrac{6.32}{\sin 24°\,28'\,52''} = \dfrac{6.32}{0.41439} = 15.251$ in.

CHECK

$a^2 + b^2 = c^2$

$6.32^2 = 39.94$

$13.88^2 = \underline{192.65}$ CHECK: $15.251^2 = 232.59$

$c^2 = 232.59$

[3] To be filled in when problem has been solved.

Solution of Right Triangle Without Tables

It often happens that it is necessary to find the angle in a right triangle when trigonometric tables are not available. This can be done as follows.[4] An approximation, when A is less than 45°, is

$$A = \left(\frac{a}{b + 2c}\right) 172°$$

The error of this approximation is very small, as shown by Fig. 8.13. At 20° the approximation is too large by 0.69

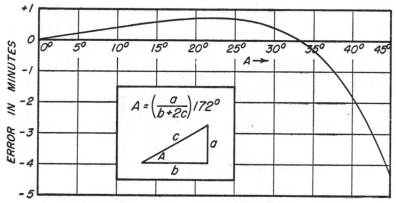

FIG. 8.13.—ERROR OF APPROXIMATION.

minute, at 30° it is 0.40 minute too large, and at 45° the approximation is too small by 4.38 minutes.

If A is greater than 45°, solve for the other acute angle first. If two sides of the triangle are given, the third can be found by the Pythagorean theorem. The accuracy of the approximation can be improved, for the smaller values of A, by using the constant 171.8873° (= 3 radians). The curve of Fig. 8.13 is then tangent to the zero-error axis. The resulting errors are:

Angle A	5°	10°	15°	20°	25°	30°
Error in minutes	−0.00010	−0.0031	−0.024	−0.100	−0.309	−0.777

[4] J. S. Frame, "Solving a Right Triangle Without Tables," *American Mathematical Monthly*, Vol. 50, December, 1943, pp. 622–623.

LENGTH OF A CHORD AND AREA OF A SEGMENT OF A CIRCLE

In Fig. 8.14, let BC be a chord in a circle of radius r, which subtends an angle θ at the center of the circle. Draw OD so

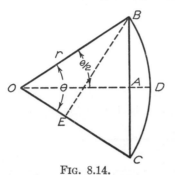

that it bisects θ. The angle at A is a right angle. From the figure, $BA = r \sin \frac{1}{2}\theta$ and the length of chord

$$BC = 2\,r \sin \tfrac{1}{2}\theta$$

The area of triangle OBC can be found by drawing BE perpendicular to OC. The area is $\frac{1}{2}\overline{OC} \times \overline{BE}$, but $BE = r \sin \theta$ and $OC = r$. Therefore, the area of $OBC = \frac{1}{2}r^2 \sin \theta$. The area of the sector $OBDC$ was

FIG. 8.14.

shown on page 213 to be $\frac{1}{2}r^2\theta$. Subtracting the two areas gives the area of the segment BCD.

$$\text{Area of segment} = \tfrac{1}{2}r^2\theta - \tfrac{1}{2}r^2 \sin \theta = \tfrac{1}{2}r^2\,(\theta - \sin \theta)$$

where θ must be in radians.

EXERCISE 8.5

Solve the following right triangles:

	Given		Find
1.	$a = 13$	$A = 41°$	b, c, B
2.	$a = 17$	$A = 26°$	b, c, B
3.	$a = 25$	$A = 49°$	b, c, B
4.	$a = 18$	$A = 22°$	b, c, B
5.	$b = 9.5$	$A = 52° 10'$	a, c, B
6.	$b = 11.2$	$A = 28° 15'$	a, c, B
7.	$b = 17.9$	$A = 31° 10'$	a, c, B
8.	$b = 26.3$	$A = 45° 42'$	a, c, B
9.	$c = 22.5$	$A = 38° 4'$	a, b, B
10.	$c = 31.6$	$A = 29° 19'$	a, b, B
11.	$c = 94.2$	$A = 41° 10'$	a, b, B
12.	$c = 14.9$	$A = 23° 3'$	a, b, B
13.	$b = 32$	$B = 75° 13'$	a, c, A
14.	$b = 14$	$B = 24° 5'$	a, c, A
15.	$b = 13$	$B = 17° 9'$	a, c, A
16.	$b = 62$	$B = 52° 30'$	a, c, A

17.   Determine angle θ.

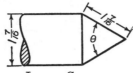

LATHE CENTER.

18.   Determine distances X and Y.

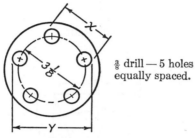

$\frac{3}{8}$ drill — 5 holes
equally spaced.

RETAINING COVER.

19.   Find angle θ.

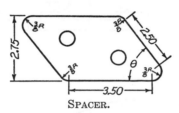

SPACER.

20.   Find distance x.

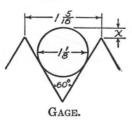

GAGE.

21.   Find angle β.

CUTTING FORM.

22. Find distance x.

23. Find distance y.

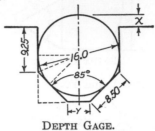

DEPTH GAGE.

24. Determine angle β.

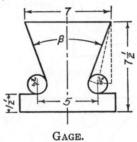

GAGE.

25. Determine angle θ.

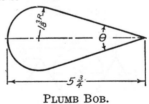

PLUMB BOB.

26. Find x and y.

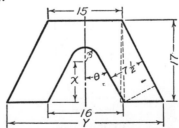

27. Find angle β.

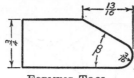

FORMING TOOL.

28. Find angle α.

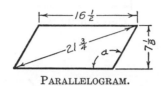

PARALLELOGRAM.

29. How far does the upper piece rise when the wedge moves ahead 2 in.?

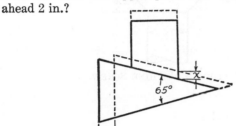

30. Find radii R and r.

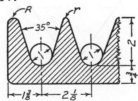

DRIVING SHEAVE GROOVE FOR WIRE ROPE TRANSMISSION.

31. Find distance x.

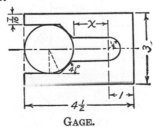

GAGE.

82. Find x and θ.

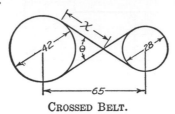

CROSSED BELT.

33. Find x.

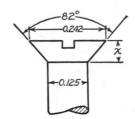

FLAT-HEAD MACHINE SCREW.

34. Find distances x and y.

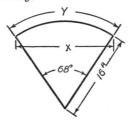

35. Prove $X = \dfrac{D}{2} - \sqrt{\left(\dfrac{D}{2}\right)^2 - \left(\dfrac{W}{2}\right)^2}$

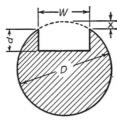

KEYWAY.

36. Find θ and the shaded area.

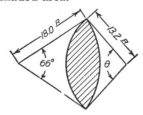

37. Find the shaded area.

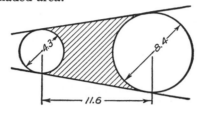

38. Prove $d = D \tan^2 \dfrac{180 - \theta}{4} = D - \dfrac{2\,d \sin \frac{1}{2}\theta}{1 - \sin \frac{1}{2}\theta}.$

39. Prove $d^2 = cD.$

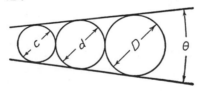

40. Find the shaded area.

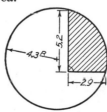

CIRCULAR CUTTER.

41. Find the length of key seat x.

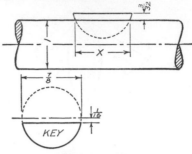

WOODRUFF KEY.

FUNCTIONS OF LARGE ANGLES

In a preceding section a set of definitions for the trigonometric functions of acute angles was given and later it was shown how these functions could be calculated and used in the solution of right triangles. Trigonometry is not restricted to the solution of right triangles; for, as will be shown later, there are certain special relations between the sides and functions of the angles of all triangles which make it possible to solve any type.

There are five kinds or types of triangles; right, isosceles, equilateral, acute scalene, and obtuse scalene. The first three are already quite familiar. A **scalene triangle** is any triangle, not a right triangle, in which no two sides or angles are equal. An **acute scalene triangle** is one in which all the angles are acute. In an **obtuse scalene triangle**, two of the angles are acute and one is obtuse, that is, greater than 90°. The method for solving right triangles has already been shown. Isosceles and equilateral triangles can be solved by the same method by breaking them up into two equal right triangles, but the scalene type requires the use of the above-mentioned special relations or formulas. An attempt to solve the obtuse scalene triangle leads to difficulty because the solution requires the use of sines, cosines, tangents, etc., of obtuse angles. Thus far the trigonometric functions of acute angles only have been defined and discussed.

The first difficulty in applying the above methods to the

functions of obtuse angles lies in defining the various functions. For acute angles like θ in triangle OPM in Fig. 8.15, the functions were defined in terms of the hypotenuse, side opposite, and side adjacent to θ. For the sake of convenience, these definitions are repeated in the first three columns below.

$$\sin \theta = \frac{MP}{OP} = \frac{\text{side opposite}}{\text{hypotenuse}} = \frac{y}{r} = \frac{\text{ordinate of } P}{\text{distance from } P \text{ to } O}$$

$$\cos \theta = \frac{OM}{OP} = \frac{\text{side adjacent}}{\text{hypotenuse}} = \frac{x}{r} = \frac{\text{abscissa of } P}{\text{distance from } P \text{ to } O}$$

$$\tan \theta = \frac{MP}{OM} = \frac{\text{side opposite}}{\text{side adjacent}} = \frac{y}{x} = \frac{\text{ordinate of } P}{\text{abscissa of } P}$$

$$\cot \theta = \frac{OM}{MP} = \frac{\text{side adjacent}}{\text{side opposite}} = \frac{x}{y} = \frac{\text{abscissa of } P}{\text{ordinate of } P}$$

$$\sec \theta = \frac{OP}{OM} = \frac{\text{hypotenuse}}{\text{side adjacent}} = \frac{r}{x} = \frac{\text{distance from } P \text{ to } O}{\text{abscissa of } P}$$

$$\csc \theta = \frac{OP}{MP} = \frac{\text{hypotenuse}}{\text{side opposite}} = \frac{r}{y} = \frac{\text{distance from } P \text{ to } O}{\text{ordinate of } P}$$

Suppose OP is now rotated to the position OP', generating an angle θ' lying in the second quadrant, and the perpendicular $P'M'$ is dropped to $X'X$. It is required to find the sine of θ'. According to the definition used earlier for acute angles, the sine should be the side opposite θ' divided by the hypotenuse of the triangle $OP'M'$. But what is meant by the side opposite θ'? For unlike θ, which lies inside the triangle formed by OP, $X'X$, and the perpendicular PM drawn to $X'X$ (thereby making

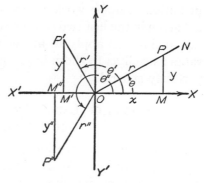

Fig. 8.15.

θ one of the angles of the triangle), θ' lies outside and is not one of the angles of the triangle $OP'M'$. A similar difficulty is met in defining any of the other functions of θ', for interpreting what is meant by the side adjacent to θ' is just as hard as it is for the side opposite. It is evident that although the old definitions worked well for acute angles, they are not sufficiently general to cover all angles; they break down when the attempt is made to use them for angles greater than 90°. Therefore, in considering functions of angles greater than 90°, a new set of definitions is necessary which includes angles greater than 90° as well as angles less than 90°.

Look at Fig. 8.15 and consider the sine of the acute angle θ. By the old definition, $\sin \theta = \dfrac{MP}{OP}$. But if P is considered as a point in the plane of the X and Y axes, then MP is equal to the ordinate, y, of P, and OP equals the distance r from P to O. Hence, the sine of θ is equal to the ordinate of P divided by the distance from P to O. It is easily seen that this definition does not depend upon the quadrant in which the angle lies.

Similarly, the definition of the cosine can be changed so that the side adjacent becomes the abscissa of P, thus making the definition general. In a similar manner, by using ordinates and abscissas of P and the distance from P to O instead of the terms "side opposite," "side adjacent," and "hypotenuse," new definitions can be worked out for the other functions. They are given in the last two columns of the tabulation above. These new definitions apply to angles in the third and fourth quadrants as well as to those in the first and second, and hence are perfectly general.

Functions of Large Angles in Terms of Angles of Less Than 90°

In the preceding section one of the difficulties involved in considering the functions of large angles was overcome, namely, the difficulty of defining them. Another difficulty lies in the fact that the usual tables go only to 90°. Hence it is necessary to find out how to use the tables when larger angles are involved. As a start, consider the sine, cosine, and tangent of some angle in the second quadrant. Suppose this angle is 150°.

Draw an angle of 150° and form the triangle OPM, where OP is any convenient length and PM is perpendicular to OM. Evidently the angle inside the triangle is 30°. The sine of 150° is defined as

$$\sin 150° = \frac{\text{ordinate of } P}{\text{distance from } P \text{ to } O} = \frac{MP}{OP}$$

Construct another triangle $OP'M'$ in the first quadrant, with $OP' = OP$ and at 30° to the X-axis. Since both triangles are

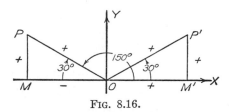

FIG. 8.16.

the same size, it is evident that $MP = M'P'$, and both are positive. Also $OP = OP'$, and both are positive by definition.

Note: The distance from P to O is always taken positive regardless of the quadrant in which the angle lies. Evidently

$$\sin 150° = \frac{MP}{OP} = \frac{M'P'}{OP'} = \sin 30°$$

Similarly the cosine can also be calculated.

$$\cos 150° = \frac{OM}{OP} = \frac{-OM'}{OP'} = -\cos 30°$$

OM is negative because it is measured to the left. This makes the cosine negative. Likewise

$$\tan 150° = \frac{MP}{OM} = \frac{M'P'}{-OM'} = -\tan 30°$$

It is thus clear that all the functions of angles lying in the second quadrant can be obtained in terms of angles which are less than 90°. To do this, draw the required angle and the triangle as shown. Put the proper + or − sign on each side, remembering that the hypotenuse is always +. Determine the sign of the result by taking the proper ratio. Remember that 2 minus signs give a plus. *Always work from 180° or 360°*

and not from 90° or 270°. If the angles are computed from 90° or 270°, the sine must be changed to cosine, and all the others to their corresponding cofunctions. If a general angle θ had been taken instead of 150°, the general formulas would become, for the second quadrant:

$$\sin \theta = \sin (180° - \theta)$$
$$\cos \theta = - \cos (180° - \theta)$$
$$\tan \theta = - \tan (180° - \theta)$$
$$\cot \theta = - \cot (180° - \theta)$$
$$\sec \theta = - \sec (180° - \theta)$$
$$\csc \theta = \csc (180° - \theta)$$

Notice that the sine and cosecant always have the same sign; also the cosine and secant; and the tangent and cotangent. In a similar manner sets of formulas can be worked out for angles lying in the other quadrants.

FUNCTIONS OF NEGATIVE ANGLES

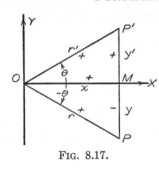

FIG. 8.17.

It is often necessary to find the functions of negative angles. To do this, draw the angle as before, starting at OX and going around clockwise. Complete the triangle and put on the proper signs, as shown in Fig. 8.17.
Then

$$\sin (- \theta) = \frac{MP}{OP} = \frac{- MP'}{OP'} = - \sin \theta$$

The others are determined in the same way. The formulas become:

$$\sin (- \theta) = - \sin \theta$$
$$\cos (- \theta) = + \cos \theta$$
$$\tan (- \theta) = - \tan \theta$$
$$\cot (- \theta) = - \cot \theta$$
$$\sec (- \theta) = + \sec \theta$$
$$\csc (- \theta) = - \csc \theta$$

The following table is convenient for determining the proper sign of the functions in the four quadrants.

Function	Sin	Cos	Tan	Cot	Sec	Csc
Quadrant						
I	+	+	+	+	+	+
II	+	−	−	−	−	+
III	−	−	+	+	−	−
IV	−	+	−	−	+	−

FUNCTIONS OF SPECIAL ANGLES

The values of the functions for certain special angles can be worked out easily. The most useful ones are listed in the table below:

Angle	Sin	Cos	Tan	Cot
0°	0	1	0	∞
30°	$\frac{1}{2}$	$\frac{1}{2}\sqrt{3}$	$\frac{\sqrt{3}}{3}$	$\sqrt{3}$
45°	$\frac{1}{2}\sqrt{2}$	$\frac{1}{2}\sqrt{2}$	1	1
60°	$\frac{1}{2}\sqrt{3}$	$\frac{1}{2}$	$\sqrt{3}$	$\frac{\sqrt{3}}{3}$
90°	1	0	∞	0
180°	0	− 1	0	∞
270°	− 1	0	∞	0
360°	0	1	0	∞

SOME SPECIAL TRIGONOMETRIC FORMULAS

In many practical problems and in the simplification of trigonometric equations, it becomes necessary to have formulas for the sum and difference, as well as for double and half angles. Some of these are listed below, without proof, for convenient reference.

$$\sin (\alpha + \beta) = \sin \alpha \cos \beta + \cos \alpha \sin \beta$$
$$\cos (\alpha + \beta) = \cos \alpha \cos \beta - \sin \alpha \sin \beta$$
$$\sin (\alpha - \beta) = \sin \alpha \cos \beta - \cos \alpha \sin \beta$$
$$\cos (\alpha - \beta) = \cos \alpha \cos \beta + \sin \alpha \sin \beta$$
$$\sin \alpha + \sin \beta = 2 \sin \tfrac{1}{2}(\alpha + \beta) \cos \tfrac{1}{2}(\alpha - \beta)$$
$$\sin \alpha - \sin \beta = 2 \cos \tfrac{1}{2}(\alpha + \beta) \sin \tfrac{1}{2}(\alpha - \beta)$$
$$\cos \alpha + \cos \beta = 2 \cos \tfrac{1}{2}(\alpha + \beta) \cos \tfrac{1}{2}(\alpha - \beta)$$
$$\cos \alpha - \cos \beta = - 2 \sin \tfrac{1}{2}(\alpha + \beta) \sin \tfrac{1}{2}(\alpha - \beta)$$
$$A \sin \beta + B \cos \beta = \sqrt{A^2 + B^2} \cos (\beta - \alpha)$$

where
$$\tan \alpha = \frac{A}{B}$$

$$\sin 2\alpha = 2 \sin \alpha \cos \alpha$$
$$\cos 2\alpha = \cos^2 \alpha - \sin^2 \alpha = 1 - 2 \sin^2 \alpha$$
$$= 2 \cos^2 \alpha - 1$$
$$\sin \tfrac{1}{2}\alpha = \pm \sqrt{\frac{1 - \cos \alpha}{2}}$$

Use the $+$ sign if $\frac{\alpha}{2}$ is in quadrants I or II, the $-$ sign if $\frac{\alpha}{2}$ is in III or IV.

$$\cos \tfrac{1}{2}\alpha = \pm \sqrt{\frac{1 + \cos \alpha}{2}}$$

Use the $+$ sign if $\frac{\alpha}{2}$ is in quadrants I or IV, the $-$ sign if $\frac{\alpha}{2}$ is in II or III.

GRAPHS OF THE TRIGONOMETRIC FUNCTIONS

If the values of the trigonometric functions are taken from the tables and the proper sign is used for each quadrant, the graphs of the functions can be plotted. The x-axis should be the angle and it can be in either degrees or radians.

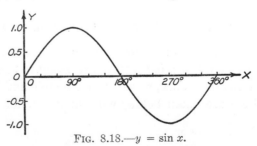

FIG. 8.18.—$y = \sin x$.

Fig. 8.18 shows the graph of $y = \sin x$. It starts at zero when $x = 0°$ and increases to 1 when $x = 90°$. It then decreases to zero at 180°. Since the sine is negative from 180° to 360°, the curve decreases to -1 at 270° and then increases to zero at 360°. At 360° it starts again and continues as before. For negative angles the curve is the same, being negative from zero to $-180°$, and positive from $-180°$ to $-360°$. The maximum value is 1 and all the arcs are exactly the same shape.

The graph of $y = \cos x$ is similar to the sine wave, except that it is shifted 90° to the left as shown in Fig. 8.19. When $x = 0°$, $\cos x = 1$ and it decreases to zero at 90°. From 90° to 270°

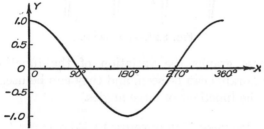

FIG. 8.19.—$y = \cos x$.

it is negative, and at 270° it starts increasing from zero until it becomes 1 at 360°. Beyond 360° it repeats the cycle.

The graph of $y = \tan x$ starts at zero when $x = 0°$ and increases rapidly. As it approaches $x = 90°$ it becomes infinite. As it passes $x = 90°$ it suddenly jumps to $-\infty$ and then begins to rise until it is again zero at 180°. Starting at 180° it repeats the same cycle.

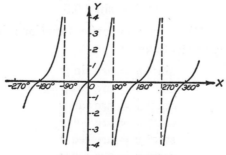

FIG. 8.20.—$y = \tan x$.

Fig. 8.21 shows the graph of $y = \cot x$. It is similar to that of the tangent. It is infinite at $x = 0$, decreases to zero at $x = 90°$, and goes to $-\infty$ at $x = 180°$. From there it repeats the cycle.

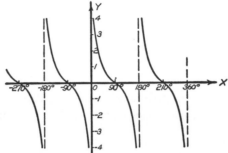

FIG. 8.21.—$y = \cot x$.

From these graphs the variation of the function in the different quadrants can be seen, and they can be used to check the sign of the functions of large angles.

INVERSE TRIGONOMETRIC FUNCTIONS

If the equation $y = \sin x$ is solved for x when y is not stated numerically, it can be written

$$x = \sin^{-1} y$$

The symbolic notation $\sin^{-1} y$ is called the **arc sine** of y or the **inverse sine** of y. The equation should be interpreted "x is an angle whose sine is y." Thus since

$$\sin 30° = 0.5$$
$$30° = \sin^{-1} 0.5$$

Similarly the other trigonometric functions have inverse functions. They are as follows:

$$\sin^{-1} y = \text{arc sin } y$$
$$\cos^{-1} y = \text{arc cos } y$$
$$\tan^{-1} y = \text{arc tan } y$$
$$\cot^{-1} y = \text{arc cot } y$$
$$\sec^{-1} y = \text{arc sec } y$$
$$\csc^{-1} y = \text{arc csc } y$$

The -1 is not an exponent but a symbol. The inverse function always represents an angle.

Example 1: Find $\tan^{-1} 1$.

If
$$y = \tan^{-1} \mathbf{1}$$
$$\tan y = 1$$
Hence
$$y = 45°$$

Example 2: Find $\cos^{-1} 0.75$.

If
$$y = \cos^{-1} 0.75$$
$$\cos y = 0.75$$
so from the tables
$$y = 41° 24' 35''$$

EXERCISE 8.6

Look up all six functions of the following angles:

1. $256° 13' 27''$
2. $199° 28' 59''$
3. $798° 26' 57''$
4. $1987° 24' 39''$

5. $-587° 47' 19''$
6. $-601° 18' 29''$
7. $-197° 22' 38''$
8. $-967° 33' 48''$

Prove the following identities:

9. $\sin \alpha \tan \alpha + \cos \alpha = \sec \alpha$

10. $\dfrac{\cos \alpha + \cot \alpha}{\cos \alpha \cot \alpha} = \sec \alpha + \tan \alpha$

11. $(\sin x + \cos x)^2 = 1 + \sin 2x$

12. $\dfrac{\cot^2 x}{1 + \cot^2 x} = \cos^2 x$

13. $\sin 3x = 3 \sin x - 4 \sin^3 x$
Hint: $\sin 3x = \sin (2x + x)$.

14. $\cos 6x = 32 \cos^6 x - 48 \cos^4 x + 18 \cos^2 x - 1$
Hint: $\cos 6x = \cos 2(3x)$.

15. $\dfrac{\sin x + \sin y}{\cos x + \cos y} = \tan \frac{1}{2}(x + y)$

16. $\sin (x + y) \sin (x - y) = \sin^2 x - \sin^2 y$

17. $2 \sin \frac{1}{2}(A + B) \cos \frac{1}{2}(A - B) = \sin A + \sin B$

18. If $A + B + C = 180°$, prove that
$$\tan A + \tan B + \tan C = (\tan A)(\tan B)(\tan C)$$

19. Given: $\cos 3x + \cos 2x + 1 = 0$. Find x.

20. Given: $3 \cos x - \sin^2 x = 0$. Find x.

SOLUTION OF OBLIQUE TRIANGLES

Methods for solving any type of triangle will be developed in this section. As was stated before, a triangle can be solved when one side and any two other parts are given. This can be done by drawing the triangle and measuring the unknown parts, or by using mathematical methods. Accurate methods of checking will be introduced which will eliminate errors of computation. To save time and to make the process easier to understand, a special form for making computations is introduced; this should be followed.

In practice it is always possible to break up a triangle into two right triangles by dropping a perpendicular from one vertex to the opposite side. These two triangles can be solved to obtain the solution of the whole triangle. Actually it is simpler to derive a formula in this way and use it for solving the triangles directly. Two general formulas are used: the sine law and the cosine law. These will now be developed.

LAW OF SINES

In any triangle, the length of a side divided by the sine of the angle opposite this side is equal to the length of any other side divided by the sine of the angle opposite that side.

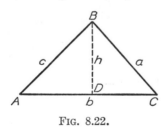

FIG. 8.22.

Draw an oblique triangle ABC with altitude h, as in Fig. 8.22. It is easy to see that

$$h = c \sin A = a \sin C$$

Dividing by $\sin A \sin C$ gives

$$\frac{a}{\sin A} = \frac{c}{\sin C}$$

In a similar way, by drawing a perpendicular from C to AB,

$$\frac{a}{\sin A} = \frac{b}{\sin B}$$

Combine these two equations.

$$\frac{a}{\sin A} = \frac{b}{\sin B} = \frac{c}{\sin C}$$

This is the law of sines for any plane triangle.

LAW OF COSINES

In any triangle, the square of a side equals the sum of the squares of the other two sides minus twice the product of these two sides multiplied by the cosine of the angle between them.

Using the same figure as before, we see that

$$h^2 = c^2 - \overline{AD}^2 \qquad \text{in triangle } ABD$$
$$h^2 = a^2 - \overline{DC}^2$$
$$= a^2 - (b - \overline{AD})^2 \qquad \text{in triangle } BCD$$

Equating these two values for h^2 gives

$$c^2 - \overline{AD}^2 = a^2 - (b - \overline{AD})^2$$
$$= a^2 - b^2 + 2\,b\overline{AD} - \overline{AD}^2$$

Rearrange terms and cancel $\overline{AD}^2$.

$$a^2 = b^2 + c^2 - 2\,b\overline{AD}$$

Since $\overline{AD} = c \cos A$, the equation becomes

$$a^2 = b^2 + c^2 - 2\,bc \cos A$$

It should be noticed that if A is greater than $90°$, the cosine is negative, which changes the sign of the last term.

In a similar manner, by drawing a perpendicular to each of the other two sides, corresponding equations for the other sides can be derived. The three equations are:

$$a^2 = b^2 + c^2 - 2\,bc \cos A$$
$$b^2 = a^2 + c^2 - 2\,ac \cos B$$
$$c^2 = a^2 + b^2 - 2\,ab \cos C$$

CHECKING THE SOLUTION OF OBLIQUE TRIANGLES

The solution of a triangle can be checked by drawing a figure to scale and measuring the required parts, but this is not accurate. A very convenient equation which can be used is

$$\frac{a - b}{c} = \frac{\sin \frac{1}{2}(A - B)}{\cos \frac{1}{2} C}$$

This is known as Mollweide's equation, after the German astronomer Karl Mollweide (1774–1825). Because this equation contains all six parts of the triangle, it checks all parts simultaneously. To check with logarithms it can be rearranged to read

$$a - b = \frac{c \sin \frac{1}{2}(A - B)}{\cos \frac{1}{2} C}$$

The right side of the equation is computed with logarithms and the result should agree with the left side which can be computed by ordinary subtraction. In case angle B is greater than A, $\sin \frac{1}{2}(A - B)$ will be negative. Since the logarithm of a negative number cannot be taken, treat it as a positive number and place a minus sign in front of the product.

Example 1: Given two angles and a side of a triangle, find the other sides and angle.

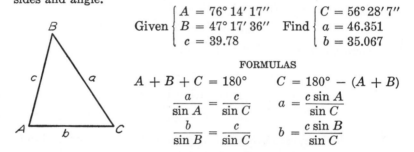

$$\text{Given}\begin{cases} A = 76° \, 14' \, 17'' \\ B = 47° \, 17' \, 36'' \\ c = 39.78 \end{cases} \quad \text{Find}\begin{cases} C = 56° \, 28' \, 7'' \\ a = 46.351 \\ b = 35.067 \end{cases}$$

FORMULAS

$$A + B + C = 180° \qquad C = 180° - (A + B)$$

$$\frac{a}{\sin A} = \frac{c}{\sin C} \qquad a = \frac{c \sin A}{\sin C}$$

$$\frac{b}{\sin B} = \frac{c}{\sin C} \qquad b = \frac{c \sin B}{\sin C}$$

LOGARITHMIC FORMULAS

$$\log a = \log c + \log \sin A + \text{colog} \sin C$$
$$\log b = \log c + \log \sin B + \text{colog} \sin C$$

COMPUTATION

$$C = 180° - (76° \, 14' \, 17'' + 47° \, 17' \, 36'') = 56° \, 28' \, 7''$$

$\log c = 1.59966$	$\log c = 1.59966$
$\log \sin A = 9.98735 - 10$	$\log \sin B = 9.86619 - 10$
$\text{colog} \sin C = 0.07905$	$\text{colog} \sin C = 0.07905$
$\log a = 1.66606$	$\log b = 1.54490$
$a = 46.351$	$b = 35.067$

Check: Use Mollweide's equation.

$$\frac{a - b}{c} = \frac{\sin \frac{1}{2}(A - B)}{\cos \frac{1}{2} C} \quad \text{or} \quad a - b = \frac{c \sin \frac{1}{2}(A - B)}{\cos \frac{1}{2} C}$$

$$a - b = 11.284 \qquad\qquad \log c = 1.59966$$
$$c = 39.78 \qquad \log \sin \frac{1}{2}(A - B) = 9.39778 - 10$$
$$\tfrac{1}{2}(A - B) = 14° \, 28' \, 20'' \qquad \text{colog} \cos \tfrac{1}{2} C = 0.05501$$
$$\tfrac{1}{2} C = 28° \, 14' \, 4'' \qquad \log (a - b) = 1.05245$$
$$a - b = 11.284$$

First draw the figure to scale and then select the formulas to be used and solve them for the unknown part. From these write the logarithmic formulas by inspection. Always arrange the work in columns and look up all the logarithms at the same time. Work out the values to be used for the check in the first column, and in the second column substitute them in the formula. The check should come out within 4 or 5 in the fifth figure if five-place logarithms are used.

Solution of a Triangle When Two Sides and an Angle Opposite One of Them Are Given

In a problem of this type there are, unfortunately, two possible solutions. This is made clear by the sketch below. Consider a triangle ABC in which $a = 1.5$ in., $c = 2.0$ in., and $A = 40°$. To construct the triangle, lay off $c = 2.0$ in. at an

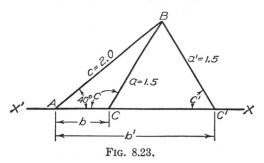

Fig. 8.23.

angle of $40°$ with the line $X'X$. From B swing an arc of radius 1.5 in. From B draw a line passing through the intersection of the arc and the line $X'X$. The arc intersects $X'X$ in two places, and hence two triangles ABC and ABC', both of which satisfy the given conditions, can be drawn. It should be noticed that in one of these triangles C is obtuse, and in the other C' is acute. Also angles C and C' are connected by the relationship $$C' = 180° - C$$

Fortunately in practice this ambiguous situation is seldom encountered because it is usually known beforehand whether angle C of the triangle under consideration is obtuse or acute. The triangle is then solved as follows: Application of the law of sines determines one of the two unknown angles; from the relation $A + B + C = 180°$ the remaining unknown angle is found; a second application of the sine law determines the other unknown side.

Example 2: Solve the triangle above in which $A = 40°$, $a = 1.5$ and $c = 2.0$.

$$\text{Given} \begin{cases} A = 40° \\ a = 1.5 \\ c = 2.0 \end{cases} \quad \text{Find} \begin{cases} b = 0.75924 \\ B = 18°\ 59'\ 15'' \\ C = 121°\ 0'\ 45'' \end{cases} \begin{cases} b' = 2.3049 \\ B' = 81°\ 0'\ 45'' \\ C' = 58°\ 59'\ 15'' \end{cases}$$

FORMULAS

$$\frac{c}{\sin C} = \frac{a}{\sin A} \qquad \sin C = \frac{c \sin A}{a} = \sin C'$$

$$C' = 180° - C \qquad B = 180° - A - C$$

$$A + B + C = 180° \qquad B' = 180° - A - C'$$

$$\frac{b}{\sin B} = \frac{a}{\sin A} \qquad b = \frac{a \sin B}{\sin A}$$

$$b' = \frac{a \sin B'}{\sin A}$$

COMPUTATION

$\log c = 0.30103$	$\log a = 0.17609$
$\log \sin A = 9.80807 - 10$	$\log \sin B = 9.51236 - 10$
$\text{colog } a = 9.82391 - 10$	$\text{colog } \sin A = 0.19193$
$\log \sin C = 9.93301 - 10$	$\log b = 9.88038 - 10$
	$b = 0.75924$

$C = 121°\ 0'\ 45''$
$C' = 58°\ 59'\ 15''$

$\log a = 0.17609$
$\log \sin B' = 9.99464 - 10$
$\text{colog } \sin A = 0.19193$

$B = 18°\ 59'\ 15''$
$B' = 81°\ 0'\ 45''$

$\log b' = 0.36266$
$b' = 2.3049$

Check:

$$a - b = \frac{c \sin \frac{1}{2}(A - B)}{\cos \frac{1}{2} C}$$

$a - b = 0.74076$
$c = 2.0$
$\frac{1}{2}(A - B) = 10°\ 30'\ 23''$
$\frac{1}{2} C = 60°\ 30'\ 22''$

$\log c = 0.30103$
$\log \sin \frac{1}{2}(A - B) = 9.26089 - 10$
$\text{colog } \cos \frac{1}{2} C = 0.30774$
$\log (a - b) = 9.86966 - 10$
$a - b = 0.74073$

$a - b' = -0.8049$
$c = 2.0$
$\frac{1}{2}(A - B') = -20°\ 30'\ 23''$
$\frac{1}{2} C' = 29°\ 29'\ 38''$

$\log c = 0.30103$
$\log \sin \frac{1}{2}(A - B') = 9.54446 - 10$
$\text{colog } \cos \frac{1}{2} C = 0.06027$
$\log (a - b') = 9.90576 - 10$
$a - b' = -0.8049$

Solution of a Triangle When Two Sides and the Included Angle Are Given

This case requires the use of the law of cosines. By applying this law the unknown side is first computed. An application of the sine law will determine one of the two unknown angles. The other angle is then found most easily by using the relation $A + B + C = 180°$.

Example 3: Given $c = 48$, $a = 35$, $B = 110°$ in triangle ABC. Find b, A, and C.

Given $\begin{cases} a = 35 \\ c = 48 \\ B = 110° \end{cases}$ Find $\begin{cases} b = 68.397 \\ A = 28° 44' 31'' \\ C = 41° 15' 29'' \end{cases}$

FORMULAS

$$b^2 = a^2 + c^2 - 2\,ac \cos B$$

$$\frac{a}{\sin A} = \frac{b}{\sin B} \quad \text{or} \quad \sin A = \frac{a \sin B}{b}$$

$$C = 180° - A - B$$

COMPUTATION

$\log 2 = 0.30103$	$a^2 = 1225$
$\log a = 1.54407$	$c^2 = 2304$
$\log c = 1.68124$	$2\,ac \cos B = 1149.2\,^5$
$\log \cos B = 9.53405 - 10$	$b^2 = 4678.2$
3.06039	$b = 68.397$

$\log a = 1.54407$

$\log \sin B = 9.97299 - 10$

$\text{colog } b = 8.16496 - 10$

$\log \sin A = 9.68202 - 10$

$A = 28°44'31''$

$C = 180° - 28° 44' 31'' - 110°$

$= 41° 15' 29''$

Check:

$a - b = -33.397$

$c = 48$

$\frac{1}{2}(A - B) = -40° 37' 45''$

$\frac{1}{2} C = 20° 37' 45''$

$\log c = 1.68124$

$\log \sin \frac{1}{2}(A - B) = 9.81368 - 10$

$\text{colog } \cos \frac{1}{2} C = 0.02878$

$\log (a - b) = 1.52370$

$a - b = -33.396$

---

[5] *Note:* Since B is in the second quadrant, the cosine is negative. This minus sign changes the other sign to plus, and all the numbers are added.

Solution of a Triangle When Three Sides Are Given

In this case two applications of the cosine law will determine two of the angles. The third is then determined by means of the relationship $A + B + C = 180°$. A second method can be employed as follows: Find one of the angles by means of the cosine law; then find another by applying the sine law; finally determine the remaining angle as was done above. Of the two methods, the first is more convenient because the cosine law must be used to find the first angle, and once all the sides have been squared, a second application of the cosine law is quite simple.

Example 4: Given a triangle whose sides are 7, 12, and 15, find the three angles.

$$\text{Given} \begin{cases} a = 7 \\ b = 15 \\ c = 12 \end{cases} \quad \text{Find} \begin{cases} A = 27° \, 15' \, 56'' \\ B = 100° \, 58' \, 51'' \\ C = 51° \, 45' \, 11'' \end{cases}$$

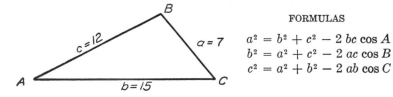

FORMULAS

$$a^2 = b^2 + c^2 - 2\,bc \cos A$$
$$b^2 = a^2 + c^2 - 2\,ac \cos B$$
$$c^2 = a^2 + b^2 - 2\,ab \cos C$$

COMPUTATION

$$\cos A = \frac{225 + 144 - 49}{2(15)(12)} = \frac{320}{360} = 0.88889$$
$$A = 27° \, 15' \, 56''$$

$$\cos B = \frac{49 + 144 - 225}{2(7)(12)} = \frac{-32}{168} = -0.19048$$
$$B = 100° \, 58' \, 51''$$

$$\cos C = \frac{49 + 225 - 144}{2(7)(15)} = \frac{130}{210} = 0.61905$$
$$C = 51° \, 45' \, 11''$$

Check:

$$\begin{array}{r} 27° \, 15' \, 56'' \\ 100° \, 58' \, 51'' \\ \underline{51° \, 45' \, 11''} \\ 179° \, 59' \, 58'' \end{array}$$

Note: If angle C were calculated by subtracting A and B from 180°, the results could not be checked by adding the three angles. To use this check, the three angles must all be calculated by the sine or cosine laws.

AREA OF AN OBLIQUE TRIANGLE

The area of any oblique triangle can be readily found by trigonometry. In the triangle ABC in Fig. 8.24, the area is by geometry,

$$\text{Area} = \tfrac{1}{2}\overline{AB}h.$$

Since $h = b \sin A$, and $\overline{AB} = c$, the equation becomes

$$\text{Area} = \tfrac{1}{2}\, bc \sin A$$

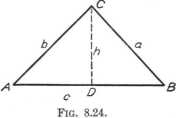

In case the three sides only are known, the area is given by the following formula:

FIG. 8.24.

$$\text{Area} = \sqrt{s(s - a)(s - b)(s - c)}$$

where

$$s = \tfrac{1}{2}(a + b + c)$$

RADIUS OF INSCRIBED CIRCLE

The radius of a circle inscribed in any triangle whose sides are a, b, and c is given by the formula

$$r = \frac{\sqrt{s(s - a)(s - b)(s - c)}}{s}$$

where $s = \tfrac{1}{2}(a + b + c)$ as before.

RADIUS OF CIRCUMSCRIBED CIRCLE

Let O be the center of a circle of radius R circumscribed about oblique triangle ABC. Draw the diameter AH. Then $\angle ACH = 90°$ and $\angle B = \angle H$, unless B is an obtuse angle, in which case $\angle B + \angle H = 180°$. In triangle ACH

$$AH = \frac{b}{\sin H} = \frac{b}{\sin B}$$

By the law of sines we have

$$2R = \frac{a}{\sin A} = \frac{b}{\sin B} = \frac{c}{\sin C}$$

An alternate formula, when the three sides are given, is

$$R = \frac{abc}{4\sqrt{s(s - a)(s - b)(s - c)}}$$

where $s = \frac{1}{2}(a + b + c)$.

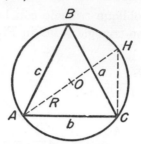

FIG. 8.25.—RADIUS OF
CIRCUMSCRIBED
CIRCLE.

EXERCISE 8.7

1. Given $a = 3$, $A = 36°$, $C = 66°$; find b, c, B.
2. Given $a = 4$, $A = 41°$, $C = 65°$; find b, c, B.
3. Given $a = 2$, $A = 23°$, $C = 70°$; find b, c, B.
4. Given $a = 5$, $A = 34°$, $C = 80°$; find b, c, B.
5. Given $a = 328$, $B = 37°$, $C = 111°$; find b, c, A.
6. Given $a = 300$, $B = 40°$, $C = 110°$; find b, c, A.
7. Given $a = 294$, $B = 35°$, $C = 113°$; find b, c, A.
8. Given $a = 316$, $B = 34°$, $C = 109°$; find b, c, A.

Solve the following four triangles. All angles are acute.
9. Given $a = 460$, $b = 538$, $A = 42°$; find c, B, C.
10. Given $a = 320$, $b = 400$, $A = 40°$; find c, B, C.
11. Given $a = 600$, $b = 995$, $A = 36°$; find c, B, C.
12. Given $a = 5$, $b = 6$, $A = 41°$; find c, B, C.

Solve the following four obtuse triangles:
13. Given $b = 45.8$, $c = 56.3$, $B = 20° 14'$; find a, A, C (2 solutions).
14. Given $b = 52.3$, $c = 71.4$, $B = 19° 10'$; find a, A, C (2 solutions).
15. Given $b = 109.6$, $c = 82.3$, $B = 25° 30'$; find a, A, C (1 solution).
16. Given $b = 81.4$, $c = 69.8$, $B = 32° 40'$; find a, A, C (1 solution).

Solve the following triangles:
17. Given $A = 35°$, $b = 16.2$, $c = 14.8$; find a, B, C.
18. Given $A = 40°$, $b = 18.3$, $c = 21.6$; find a, B, C.
19. Given $A = 50°$, $b = 19.1$, $c = 31.1$; find a, B, C.

20. Given $A = 33°$, $b = 26.2$, $c = 42.3$; find a, B, C.

21. Given $a = 51.3$, $b = 34.7$, $C = 126°$; find c, A, B.

22. Given $a = 55.8$, $b = 30.1$, $C = 129°$; find c, A, B.

23. Given $a = 53.1$, $b = 35.3$, $C = 119°$; find c, A, B.

24. Given $a = 60.2$, $b = 38.4$, $C = 132°$; find c, A, B.

25. Given $a = 61$, $b = 56$, $c = 44$; find A, B, C.

26. Given $a = 60$, $b = 55$, $c = 43$; find A, B, C.

27. Given $a = 63$, $b = 57$, $c = 42$; find A, B, C.

28. Given $a = 64$, $b = 58$, $c = 46$; find A, B, C.

29. Given $a = 9.1$, $b = 12.5$, $c = 17.6$; find area of triangle.

30. Given $a = 9.3$, $b = 12.4$, $c = 17.5$; find area of triangle.

31. Given $a = 8.8$, $b = 12.3$, $c = 17.8$; find area of triangle.

32. Given $a = 92$, $b = 126$, $c = 174$; find area of triangle.

33. Wishing to determine the height of mountain, a man walks along the slope 750 yd from A to B in the same vertical plane as the top of the mountain. The line BA is nearly level, but point B is 45 ft higher than point A. The angle of elevation of the mountaintop at B is $47° 38'$ and at A it is $10° 29'$.
    a. What is the height of the mountain above point A?
    b. What is the distance from A to a point directly under the mountaintop, measured on a level line?

34. Two straight roads come together with an angle of 60° between them. A sign on the road says it is 18.5 miles to the nearest town on one road and 12.0 miles to another town along the second road. How far apart are the two towns?

35. A man 6 ft tall standing in the street notices that the angle of elevation of the top of a house is 46° and the second story window is 21°. He knows he is 38 ft from the house. How high is the top of the house above the street?

36. A and B are two positions on opposite sides of a hill and C is a point on top of the hill which is visible from both A and B. From A to C is 16 miles and the angle of elevation is $4° 12'$. From B to C is 13 miles, and the angle of elevation is $6° 18'$. How much higher is A than B?

37. A chord 10 ft long in a circle subtends a certain angle at the center. A chord 16 ft long subtends twice as large an angle. Without using tables, find the diameter of the circle.

38. Two sides of a triangular lot are 76 ft and 84 ft. The angle between them is 135°. Find the length of the third side and the area in acres.

39. A regular pentagon has an area of 174 sq in. Find the length of each side and of a diagonal.

40. On the bank of a river, the angle of elevation of a tree on the other bank is 38° and 75 ft farther back it is 22°. Find the height of the tree and the width of the stream.

41. The three sides of a triangular field are 17.38 rods, 24.13 rods and 30.89 rods. How many acres in the field?

42. A surveyor is running a straight line and when he gets to point A he finds a swamp which he cannot go through. He turns left 42° and goes 1170 ft to point C. Then he turns right 23° and goes 2380 ft to D. At point D he turns right 78°. How far must he go to locate point B which is on the same straight line as A, and how far is it from A to B?

43. A boat has a radio with a range of 300 miles. If shore stations are placed along the coast at intervals of 225 miles, how far out can the boat sail parallel to the shore and always be in communication with the shore?

44. If tangent 18° = $\dfrac{\sqrt{5}-1}{\sqrt{10+2\sqrt{5}}}$, find cos 36° without using tables.

45. Three circular gardens, each with a diameter of 64 ft are on a level plot of ground. The center-to-center distances are 73 ft, 81 ft and 88 ft respectively. Find the dimensions of the smallest triangular piece of ground which will just include the gardens, and the number of acres in this triangle.

46. The area of a triangle is 2586 sq ft and two of the sides are 75 and 85 ft. Find two possible values for the third side.

47. A gas company proposes to build a cylindrical tank on a triangular piece of ground. The measurements of the lot which can most easily be made are the sides. A surveyor finds that $a = 78.3$ ft, $b = 82.2$ ft, and $c = 110.7$ ft. Find the diameter of the largest tank which can be built on the lot.

48. Find the area $ABCD$.

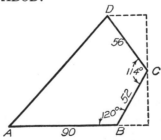

49. Find the diameter D.

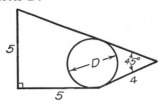

50. Find the shaded area, in acres.

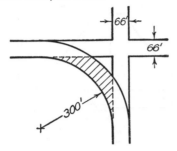

51. Find x and y.

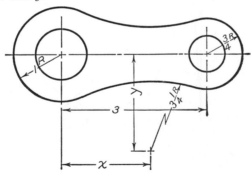

52. Find x.

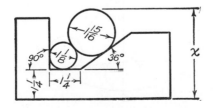

53.   If $a - b = 1.5$, find a and b.

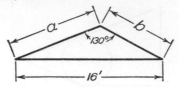

54.   Find the angle θ.

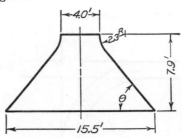

55.   Find the angle β.

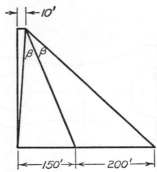

56.   Find the angle through which the smaller cylinder rotates in rolling from A to B.

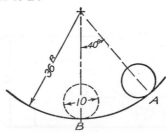

57. Find the angle θ.

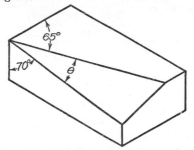

58. Find the angle θ.

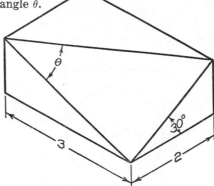

59. Find the diameter D.

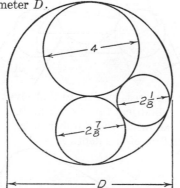

Hint: Let a, b, and c be the three radii, R the radius of the large circle, and α, β, and γ the three angles at the center of the large circle of radius R formed by connecting the centers of the circles. Then

$$\cos \alpha = \frac{(R - a)^2 + (R - c)^2 - (a + c)^2}{2(R - a)(R - c)} \quad (1)$$

$$= 1 - \frac{2\,ac}{(R - a)(R - c)} \quad (2)$$

$$\cos \beta = 1 - \frac{2\,bc}{(R - c)(R - b)} \quad (3)$$

$$\cos \gamma = 1 - \frac{2\,ab}{(R - a)(R - b)} \quad (4)$$

If $\alpha + \beta = \gamma$, then

$$\cos \gamma - \cos \alpha \cos \beta = -\sin \alpha \sin \beta$$

Square both sides of the equation and simplify to

$$\cos^2 \alpha + \cos^2 \beta + \cos^2 \gamma - 2 \cos \alpha \cos \beta \cos \gamma = 1 \quad (5)$$

Substitute the numerical values in equations 2, 3, and 4, simplify, and substitute in equation 5 to find R.

60.   Find the diameter D.

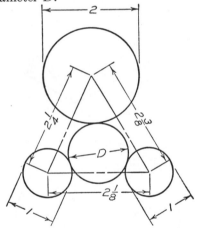

Hint: Use a process similar to that given in Problem 59.

61.   A horizontal cylindrical tank is 6 ft in diameter and 12 ft long. Plot a graph showing the number of gallons of liquid in the tank as a function of the depth h.

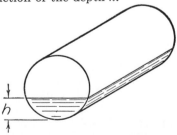

62. The shaded area of the circle is one-third of the total area. Find the distance D.

Hint: Derive an equation for the central angle subtended by the chord and solve for the angle graphically.

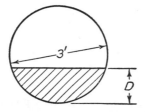

63. In the right triangle shown, the two distances x are equal. Find the angle θ.

Hint: If $y = \cos^2 \theta$, show that $y^3 - y^2 + 2y - 1 = 0$. Solve this equation for y graphically and find θ.

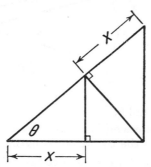

64. Line CD bisects angle C. Find the distance x.

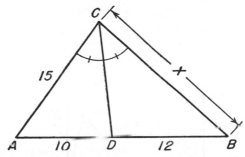

65. The chord of the circle shown is 4 inches long, and the subtended arc is 5 inches. Find the radius R.

Hint: If the central angle is 2 θ, show that sin θ = 0.8 θ, where θ is in radians. Solve for θ graphically.

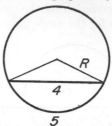

66. The two tangents from an external point to a circle have the same length as the major arc cut off by the tangents. Find the angle θ between the tangents.

Hint: Show that tan θ + 2 θ = 2π.

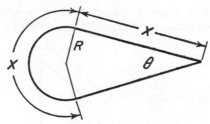

67. The distances from an internal point to three corners of a square are as shown. Find x.

Hint: Use the cosine law three times to derive expressions for x. Eliminate the cosine terms by means of the equations

$$\cos (\alpha + \beta) = \cos \alpha \cos \beta - \sin \alpha \sin \beta$$
and $\quad \sin^2 \alpha + \cos^2 \alpha = 1$

Show that x is given by the equation

$$x^4 - 10.25 x^2 + 18.28125 = 0$$

This can be solved by the quadratic formula.

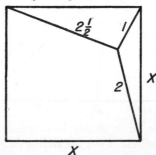

68. Derive a formula for the area of the shaded part of the circle.

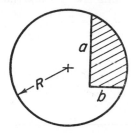

69. The trapezoid shown is to be divided into four equal areas by lines parallel to the bases, as shown. Find x, y and z.

Hint: Use the formula in Chapter I for the area of a trapezoid to set up simultaneous equations for a, b and c in terms of x, y, and z. Solve for x, y and z, knowing that $a = 8 + \frac{1}{4}x$, etc.

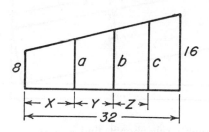

70. Three circles are inscribed in a 3-inch circle as shown. Find the diameter D.

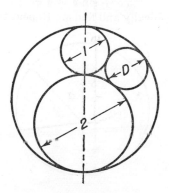

71. In the triangle shown, $x + y = 15$. Find x and y.

Hint: Use the cosine law to show that

$$5^2 = x^2 + (15 - x)^2 - \frac{2(15 - x)x^2}{\sqrt{x^2 + 3^2}}$$

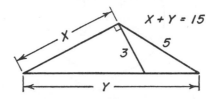

72. A rectangle 3 inches wide is inscribed in the larger rectangle as shown. Find the length L.

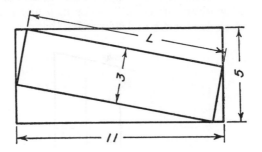

73. In the 10-inch circle shown, find α, β and γ so the three areas are equal.

Hint: If θ is the central angle subtended by the arc intercepted by α, show that

$$5\theta + \sin \theta = \tfrac{5}{3}\pi$$

Solve for θ graphically and find α. Repeat the process to find γ.

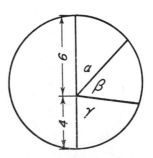

74. Find r/R so the arc of the smaller circle cuts off one sixth of the area of the larger circle.

Hint: If 2α is the angle subtended by the arc of radius r and 2θ is the angle subtended by the arc of radius R, show that

$$r^2(2\alpha - \sin 2\alpha) + R^2(2\theta - \sin 2\theta) = \tfrac{1}{3}\pi R^2$$
$$r \sin \alpha = R \sin \theta$$
$$r = 2R\cos\alpha$$

These lead to the equation

$$4\cos^2\alpha\,(2\alpha - \sin 2\alpha) + 2\pi - 4\alpha + \sin 4\alpha = \tfrac{1}{3}\pi$$

Solve for α graphically and find r/R.

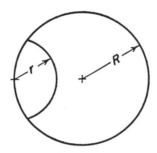

75. A new highway is to be built to the specifications shown. Find the number of square feet to be cut and the number to be filled at this cross section.

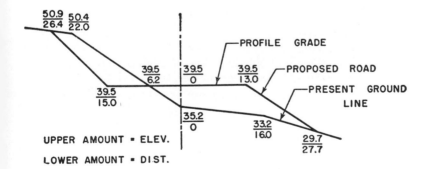

76. A traffic circle is to be constructed at the intersection of two highways as shown. Find the number of square feet of paving within the four lines where the arcs of radius R_1 begin. The center circle is not paved. Find the length of curbing to be constructed. Include the center circle.

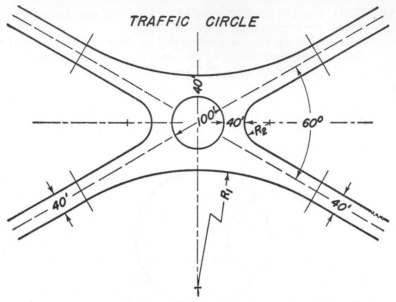

TRAFFIC CIRCLE

77. Find the number of acres in the plot of ground described as follows:

"Beginning at the intersection of the Northern line of High Street, with the Eastern boundary of Lot No. 12, hereinafter referred to; running thence Northerly along said Eastern boundary line of Lot 12, and the Eastern boundary line of Lots 13 and 14, one-hundred-twelve (112) feet; thence at right angles Westerly, sixty-six (66) feet; thence South 15° 16′ West, ninety-two (92) feet to the Northern line of High Street; thence Easterly along said Northern line of High Street, ninety-three and 17/100 (93.17) feet, more or less, to the point of beginning."

Hint: High Street does not run exactly East and West.

78. A hollow cast-iron sphere weighs 20 pounds and the outside diameter is 10 inches. If cast iron weighs 0.260 pound per cubic inch, find the thickness of the wall of the sphere.

79. The equation for the conical pendulum is

$$v^2 = gl \sin \theta \tan \theta$$

where v is the velocity of the ball, l is the length of the string, g is the acceleration of gravity, and θ is the angle the string makes with the vertical. Find θ if $v = 10$ ft per sec, $l = 12$ ft, and $g = 32.2$ ft per sec².

Hint: Show that $\cos^2 \theta + 0.2588 \cos \theta - 1 = 0$. Solve for $\cos \theta$ with the quadratic formula.

Answers

EXERCISE 1.1

1. 146. **3.** $\frac{32}{7}$. **5.** 150. **7.** $\frac{22}{81}$. **9.** $- 7$. **11.** $\frac{2111}{121}$.
13. $581\frac{13}{55}$. **15.** 97.4 hr. **17.** 36.7 sec. **19.** 2973 lb.
21. $184.44 **23.** 700 rpm. **25.** 35,160 lb. **27.** $55.29;
$1.16.

EXERCISE 1.2

1. $\frac{57}{64}$ in. **3.** $\frac{15}{64}$ in. **5.** 485. **7.** 1.840 in. **9.** 12 hr.
11. 1. **13.** $22\frac{178}{213}$. **15.** $2\frac{70}{169}$. **17.** $\frac{11}{23}$; $\frac{17}{37}$; $\frac{47}{87}$. **19.** $3\frac{21}{32}$ in.
21. $3\frac{1}{2}$ thousandths in. **23.** 104.

EXERCISE 1.3

1. 639.6394. **3.** 547.273125. **5.** $\frac{19}{20}$; $1\frac{48}{125}$; $\frac{1}{12}$; $\frac{1}{15}$.
7. 88.23925; 24.28272; 71.2263 $\times$ 10⁻⁶. **9.** 3.1044; 1.3711;
0.007929; 58476.

EXERCISE 1.4

1. 93.75; 0.32085; 0.4240625; 2622.402. **3.** 40; 881.43; 1.0426;
0.360; 1.966. **5.** $360.13. **7.** $6.00. **9.** $6.63. **11.** 113.5 lb.

EXERCISE 1.5

1. $16\frac{2}{3}$ days. **3.** 13.74 cu ft. **5.** 92.8 rpm. **7.** 24 mph.

EXERCISE 1.6

1. 1.769 ft. **3.** 19 ft 3 in. **5.** 4.684 in. **7.** 17 ft $3\frac{1}{2}$ in.
9. 3.20. **11.** 193 ft 3 in. **13.** 5.35 in.; 6.38 in.; 10.70 in.

EXERCISE 1.7

1. 107.4 in. **3.** $4.20. **5.** 17 in. **7.** 7.85 gr per cc.
9. 8.43 lb. **11.** 1.045 lb per pint. **13.** $9\frac{23}{32}$ in. **15.** 1035 gr
per sq cm. **17.** 208 tons. **19.** 2554 rpm. **21.** 2.589998 sq km.
23. 54.059 miles. **25.** 0.0680 sq in.; 0.247 lb per ft. **27.** 0.00782
lb per in. **29.** 65.23 cu yd. **31.** 7.77 sq ft. **33.** 9.896 sq in.
35. 3.520 in. **37.** 3 lb 14.8 oz. **39.** 511 bolts. **41.** 362.64 cu in.;
115 lb 14 oz. **43.** 48.57 cu in. **45.** 1.7873 cu in.; 8.10 oz.
47. 16.341 cu ft. **49.** 3.61 in. **51.** 7050 gal. **53.** 46.6 mph.
55. 45 sheets. **57.** 132 per min.

EXERCISE 2.1

1. $12\,a + 9\,b + 40\,c + 6\,d.$ **3.** $-4\,a + 19\,b + 17\,c - 14\,d.$
5. $-9\,y^2 + 38\,z + 13\,x^3.$ **7.** $30\,a^{\frac{3}{2}} - 27\,b^{\frac{3}{2}} + 10\,c^{\frac{3}{2}}.$
9. $a - b - c - d.$ **11.** $5\,y^2 + xy - x^2.$ **13.** $3\,x - 3\,a + 4\,b.$
15. $19\,a - b + 2\,c + 5.$ **17.** $-3\,a + 2\,b.$ **19.** $-2\,x - 1.$

EXERCISE 2.2

1. $24\,abc.$ **3.** $-48\,abc.$ **5.** $30\,ab.$ **7.** $b^2 - c^2.$
9. $a^2c^2 - 36.$ **11.** $a^2 - b^2 + 2\,bc - c^2.$ **13.** $10\,x^2 - 14\,x - 12.$
15. $6\,a^4 - 41\,a^2 - 7.$ **17.** $5\,a^4b^4 + 27\,a^2b^2c - 18\,c^2.$
19. $x^2 - y^2 - 2\,yz - z^2.$ **21.** $y^4 - 9\,x^2 + 12\,x - 4.$ **23.** $a^4 + a^2b^2 + b^4.$
25. $y^4 - 4\,y^2 + 4\,y - 1.$ **27.** $x^2 + 4\,x.$ **29.** $\pi(-\frac{3}{4}\,x^2 + 5\,x + 25).$
31. $\frac{\pi}{4}(4\,r^2 - x^2).$ **33.** $\frac{\pi}{4}(R^2 - r^2) + 15\,R + R^2.$ **35.** $\dfrac{31\,\pi ab^2}{24}.$

EXERCISE 2.3

1. $y - 4.$ **3.** $x^2 + 3\,x + 9.$ **5.** $x^7 - x^6 + 2\,x^5 - 2\,x^4 + 3\,x^3 - 3\,x^2 + 4\,x - 1.$ **7.** $2\,x^2 - 3\,xy + y^2.$ **9.** $y^2 - 2\,y + 1 - \dfrac{y - 1}{y^2 - y - 2}.$ **11.** $x^5 + x^4y + x^3y^2 + x^2y^3 + xy^4 + y^5.$
13. $1 + x + x^2 + x^3 + x^4 + \cdots.$ **15.** $x^5 - 2\,x^4 + 4\,x^3 - 8\,x^2 + 16\,x + 6.$
17. $x^4 - 2\,x^3 + 4\,x^2 - 8\,x - 3.$ **19.** $x^2 + x - 5.$
21. $14\,y^2 - 11\,y + \dfrac{8\,y - 1}{y^2 + y + 1}.$ **23.** $7\,y^3 - 5\,y^2 - 6\,y - 2.$
25. $x^2 - 4\,x - 3.$ **27.** $3\,y^2 - 4\,y + 2.$ **29.** $b^2 + bx - 2\,bd - 2\,dx + 4\,d^2.$

EXERCISE 2.4

1. $6\,axy(2\,a - 4\,xy + 3\,a^2x).$ **3.** $x^6(x^4 + x^3 - x^2 + x - 1).$
5. $3\,ab(ab + 1)(ab + 1).$ **7.** $(x^2 - 2)(x - 1).$ **9.** $(a - b - c)(y - 1).$ **11.** $(x + 4)(x + 4).$ **13.** $(3\,xy + 1)(3\,xy + 1).$
15. $(3\,a + 3\,b + 4)(3\,a + 3\,b + 4).$ **17.** $(x^2 - 7)(x^2 + 7).$
19. $(x + a)(x - a).$ **21.** $(2\,a - 3\,b - 3\,x - y)(2\,a - 3\,b + 3\,x + y).$
23. $(x^a - y^b)(x^a + y^b).$ **25.** $(x + 6)(x + 5).$ **27.** $(9 + x)(3 - x).$
29. $(x^2 - 18\,b^3)(x^2 + 2\,b^3).$ **31.** $(x^2 - 10\,b^2)(x^2 + 11\,b^2).$
33. $3(a + 16)(a - 8).$ **35.** $(3\,a - 4)(3\,a - 10).$
37. $(3\,b - a)(b - 3\,a).$ **39.** $(5\,a - 1)(3\,a + 4).$
41. $(7\,x - 5)(3\,x + 2).$ **43.** $(9\,x^3 - 2)(x^3 + 5).$
45. $b(a - b)(a + b).$ **47.** $b(x - 13)(x + 3).$
49. $(a - 3\,b - 5\,c)(a - 3\,b - 5\,c).$

EXERCISE 2.5

1. $\dfrac{9\,ax^2}{4\,b}$. **3.** $\dfrac{rt^3}{3}$. **5.** $-\,2\,x^2 - 3\,xy$. **7.** $-\dfrac{ab}{1 + a}$.

9. $\dfrac{4\,x^2 - 11\,x + 2}{x(2\,x - 1)}$. **11.** $\dfrac{2\,x + y}{3\,x^2(2\,x - y)}$. **13.** $\dfrac{2(x + 2)}{3}$.

15. $9\,x + 3$. **17.** $\dfrac{6\,c}{(c - b)b}$. **19.** $\dfrac{t + 3}{t + 1}$. **21.** $\dfrac{6\,a + 1}{a - 2}$.

EXERCISE 2.6

1. 2. **3.** 1. **5.** 16. **7.** $5\sqrt{2}$. **9.** $\frac{1}{4}\sqrt[3]{4}$. **11.** $3\sqrt{2\,a - 1}$.

13. $4\sqrt{2\,a^2 - a}$. **15.** $3\,a^2(x - y)\sqrt{2(x - y)}$. **17.** $\dfrac{a^3}{y}\sqrt[n]{6}$.

19. $-\,0.3\sqrt[3]{4}$. **21.** $a^{\frac{3}{8}}y^{\frac{6}{8}}x^{\frac{7}{5}}$. **23.** $3\,x(3\,x^2 - xy^2)^{\frac{1}{2}}$. **25.** $\sqrt{a - b}$.

27. $\dfrac{\sqrt{2}}{2}$. **29.** $\left(\dfrac{1}{y} - \dfrac{1}{x}\right)\sqrt{xy}$. **31.** $\sqrt[3]{3\,x^2y}$. **33.** $\dfrac{\sqrt{x - y}}{x - y}$.

35. $\dfrac{\sqrt{2}}{2}$. **37.** $3\sqrt{42}$. **39.** 3. **41.** $x^{\frac{1}{2}} + x^{\frac{1}{4}}y^{\frac{1}{4}} + y^{\frac{1}{2}}$. **43.** $6\,x^2$.

45. $6\,a^2 - 7\,a^{\frac{5}{3}} - 19\,a^{\frac{4}{3}} + 5\,a + 9\,a^{\frac{2}{3}} - 2\,a^{\frac{1}{3}}$. **47.** $a^2 - a^{-2}$.

49. x.

EXERCISE 2.7

1. $-\,1$. **3.** 27. **5.** $-\,0.3575$. **7.** 8. **9.** 4. **11.** 9.

13. 11. **15.** 7. **17.** $ab + 7$. **19.** a or $-\,1$. **21.** $-\,8$.

23. $\dfrac{c - d}{c + d}$. **25.** 1.24.

EXERCISE 2.8

1. $b = \dfrac{2\,A - ah}{h}$. **3.** $R = \sqrt[3]{\dfrac{3\,V}{4\,\pi}}$. **5.** $N = \dfrac{33000\,HP}{2\,\pi T}$.

7. $r = \sqrt[n]{\dfrac{I}{P}} - 1$. **9.** $b = \sqrt{d^2 - a^2 - c^2}$. **11.** $y = \dfrac{b(2\,a - x)}{a}$.

13. $x = \dfrac{y}{y - 1}$. **15.** $v = \dfrac{D}{t} - \dfrac{1}{2}\,gt$. **17.** 10 by 14 ft.

19. 12 ohms. **21.** $-\,40°$ F. **23.** $M = \frac{15}{22}\,F$.

25. $t = \dfrac{(b_1 + b_2)H + 1{,}600{,}000(b_2 - b_1)}{6400(b_1 - b_2)}$. **27.** 396 ft. **29.** 2.

31. $\pi(D + 1)$. **33.** 0.7307 in. **35.** 1.9445 in. **37.** 0.2831 in.

39. $x = \frac{5}{16}$ in.; $y = 0.9499$ in. **41.** 0.446 in. **43.** 0.405 in.

EXERCISE 3.3

1. 1,077,800; 224.61; 33,556; 259,590,000; 1.2004×10^{-10}.

3. 289.19; 89.512; 0.00012835; 0.0065438; 0.048241. **5.** 0.92890.

7. 5673.9.

EXERCISE 3.4

3. 4,295,000,000; 24,138,000; 1.8867 $\times$ 10^{-12}; 1.9452; 28.189 $\times$ 10^{-10}; 1.9511 $\times$ 10^{-10}; 0.0050809; 0.68209; 7.0356; 2.9803.   **5.** 1.4646; 15.101; 1.0219; 133.62; 0.38450; 4.1533; 0.19639; 0.0069437; 0.0022937; 0.18985.   **7.** 0.035330.   **9.** 77,678.   **11.** 746.37.

EXERCISE 3.5

1. 3.6432.   **3.** 0.94101.   **5.** 6.64848.   **7.** $x = 4.6439$; $x = 0.52832$;

$x = 3;$ $\begin{cases} x = -0.31911; \\ y = 1.5810. \end{cases}$ **9.** 0.71438.   **11.** 1.78284.   **13.** 0.297 amp.

15. 155.61 sq in.   **17.** 51,676.   **19.** 0.640 in.   **21.** 770.5.
23. 65.23 hp.   **25.** 0.1099 cfs.   **27.** 7.917 lb per sq in.
29. 350.5 ft.

EXERCISE 4.1

1. 153°.   **3.** 51° 25′ 43″.   **5.** 56°, 74° 25′.   **7.** 8° 40′, 12° 44′ 40″.
9. 12.5°.

EXERCISE 4.2

1. 58°.   **3.** $A = 45°, B = 90°$.   **5.** 104° 22′ 30″.   **7.** 130°·
13. 120°   **15.** 68°.

EXERCISE 4.3

1. 95°.   **3.** 49°.   **9.** 28°.

EXERCISE 4.5

3. 108°.

EXERCISE 5.1

11. $x = 1$ or 2.   **13.** $x = -\frac{3}{2}$ or -2.   **15.** Imaginary.
17. $x = 3$.   **19.** $x = -5$.

EXERCISE 5.2

1. $x = \pm 4$.   **3.** $x = \pm 15$.   **5.** $x = \pm 1$.   **7.** $x = \pm 3$.
9. $x = \pm 11$.   **11.** $x = 3$ or -6.   **13.** $x = 5$ or 6.
15. $x = \frac{7}{6}$ or $-\frac{12}{5}$.   **17.** $x = 9$ or 16.   **19.** $x = a$ or $3a$.
21. $x = -2$ or 7.   **23.** $x = -7$ or -20.   **25.** $x = \frac{4}{5}$ or 2.
27. $x = 5$ or $-\frac{2}{3}$.   **29.** $x = -7a$ or $3a$.

EXERCISE 5.3

1. $x = 3$ or 5.   **3.** $y = -11$ or 13.   **5.** $x = -2m$ or m.
7. $x = -\frac{5}{7}$ or $\frac{4}{3}$.   **9.** $R = -0.60402$ or -0.08563.

11. $R = 0.54793$ or $- 0.45626$. **13.** $R = 1.0865$ or 0.3579.
15. $a = - 8.2796$ or $+ 2.39901$. **17.** $x = - 1.2791$ or $+ 0.46909$.
19. $R = 0.16955$ or 0.018851. **21.** $x = \frac{3}{2}$ or $- \frac{3}{5}$.

23. $R = - 2 \pm \sqrt{5}$. **25.** $x = \dfrac{5 \pm \sqrt{- 59}}{14}$. **27.** $R = 1.416$ in.

29. $R = 4.828$; Area $= 2.502$. **31.** $x = 1.560$ in.
33. $a = 1.577$ or 1.015 in.; $b = 1.015$ or 1.577 in.

EXERCISE 5.4

1. $x = 0$. **3.** $x = - \frac{17}{9}$. **5.** $y = a^2$. **7.** $x = 0$ or $\frac{10}{21}$.
9. $R = 0$ or 8. **11.** $R = 16.930$. **13.** $x = 11.884$.
15. $x = \pm \sqrt{3}\, a$. **17.** $D = 3.3845$ in. **19.** $x = 4.899$ in.
21. $h = 5.781$ in. **23.** $D = 0.8613$ in.

EXERCISE 6.1

11. $x = 12$; $y = 6$. **13.** $x = - 2$; $y = 4$. **15.** $x = 0.4$;
$y = 0.81$. **17.** $x = 13$; $y = 17$. **19.** $x = 0.21667$; $y = 0.53125$.
21. $x = \dfrac{6\,a - 3\,b}{a^2 - b^2}$; $y = \dfrac{3\,a - 6\,b}{a^2 - b^2}$. **23.** $x = 2.9756$;
$y = - 1.8946$. **25.** $x = 0.21356\,u + 0.14708\,v$; $y = 0.19239\,u + 0.30641\,v$. **27.** $x = 13.455$; $y = 16.364$. **29.** $x = 6.16$;
$y = 20.48$.

EXERCISE 6.2

1. $x = 3$; $y = 2$. **3.** $x = 8$; $y = 3$. **5.** $x = 8$; $y = 5$.
7. $x = 9$; $y = 1$. **9.** $x = 7$; $y = 8$. **11.** $x = 30$; $y = 50$.
13. $x = m + n$; $y = n - m$. **15.** $x = 2.7390$; $y = - 11.486$.
17. $x = 9.1193$; $y = - 7.2974$.

EXERCISE 6.3

1. $x = 2$; $y = 4$; $z = 5$. **3.** $x = \frac{1}{3}$; $y = \frac{1}{4}$; $z = \frac{1}{7}$. **5.** $x = 12$;
$y = 20$; $z = 8$. **7.** $u = \frac{1}{3}$; $x = \frac{1}{2}$; $y = 1$; $z = - 1$. **9.** $I_1 = - 3.0$;
$I_2 = 0.5$; $I_3 = 2.5$. **11.** $w = 1$; $x = 2$; $y = 3$; $z = 4$.

EXERCISE 6.4

11. $\left.\begin{array}{l} x = - 4 \\ y = - 5 \end{array}\right\}$ $\left.\begin{array}{l} 5 \\ 4 \end{array}\right\}$. **13.** $\left.\begin{array}{l} x = 2.9349 \\ y = 4.5326 \end{array}\right\}$ $\left.\begin{array}{l} 49.0651 \\ - 18.5326 \end{array}\right\}$.
15. $\left.\begin{array}{l} x = 0.1771 \\ y = 2.8229 \end{array}\right\}$ $\left.\begin{array}{l} 2.8229 \\ 0.1771 \end{array}\right\}$. **17.** $\left.\begin{array}{l} x = 0 \\ y = 2 \end{array}\right\}$, $\left.\begin{array}{l} x = - \frac{16}{9} \\ y = - \frac{14}{9} \end{array}\right\}$;
$\left.\begin{array}{l} x = \frac{4}{3}\sqrt{3} \\ y = \frac{2}{3}\sqrt{3} \end{array}\right\}$; $\left.\begin{array}{l} x = - \frac{4}{3}\sqrt{3} \\ y = - \frac{2}{3}\sqrt{3} \end{array}\right\}$. **19.** $x = \pm\, 7.0213$; $y = 12.3246$.

21. $x = 4$, $\quad -4$.
$\ y = 4$, $\quad -4$.

23. $x = 1.495$ in.; $y = 1.682$ in.

25. $R = 1\frac{1}{2}$ in.

EXERCISE 7.1

1. 6.95 years. **5.** 9.78 in. **11.** $1.63600, -0.068000 \pm 1.10357\, i$.

EXERCISE 8.2

1. $37.80444°$; $14.13805°$; $28.12195°$; $114.32723°$. **3.** 0.2793 rad; 0.5004 rad; 0.3474 rad; 0.4592 rad. **5.** $96°\,8'\,33''$; $32°\,13'\,44''$; $67°\,30'\,00''$. **7.** $4°\,22'\,59''$; $180°\,0'\,2''$; $24°\,10'\,18''$. **9.** $132°\,37'\,1''$; $44°\,26'\,1''$; $114°\,32'\,44''$. **11.** 1.88496 rad. **13.** 3.0156 ft. **15.** $52°\,14'\,4''$ N. **17.** 0.0785 in. **19.** 44.00 mph. **21.** 12.043 rad. **23.** $\theta = 50°\,58'\,25''$. **25.** 2.932 in. **27.** 188.86 ft. **29.** $\theta = 27°\,5'\,57''$.

EXERCISE 8.4

1. $\cos A = \frac{4}{5}$; $\tan A = \frac{3}{4}$. **3.** $\cot 60° = 0.57735$. **5.** $A = 30°$.
17. $\sin a = 0.95652$; $\tan a = 3.2795$; $\cot a = 0.30493$; $\sec a = 3.4286$; $\csc a = 1.0455$.

19. $\sin \beta = \sqrt{1 - \cos^2 \beta} = \dfrac{\tan \beta}{\sqrt{1 + \tan^2 \beta}}$
$= \dfrac{1}{\sqrt{1 + \cot^2 \beta}} = \dfrac{\sqrt{\sec^2 \beta - 1}}{\sec \beta} = \dfrac{1}{\csc \beta}$.

21. $\tan \beta = \dfrac{\sin \beta}{\sqrt{1 - \sin^2 \beta}}$
$= \dfrac{\sqrt{1 - \cos^2 \beta}}{\cos \beta} = \dfrac{1}{\cot \beta} = \sqrt{\sec^2 \beta - 1} = \dfrac{1}{\sqrt{\csc^2 \beta - 1}}$.

EXERCISE 8.5

1. $b = 14.955$; $c = 19.815$; $B = 49°$. **3.** $b = 21.732$; $c = 33.125$; $B = 41°$. **5.** $a = 12.233$; $c = 15.488$; $B = 37°\,50'$. **7.** $a = 10.826$; $c = 20.920$; $B = 58°\,50'$. **9.** $a = 13.873$; $b = 17.714$; $B = 51°\,56'$. **11.** $a = 62.007$; $b = 70.913$; $B = 48°\,50'$. **13.** $a = 8.4448$; $c = 33.095$; $A = 14°\,47'$. **15.** $a = 42.126$; $c = 44.086$; $A = 72°\,51'$. **17.** $\theta = 60°$. **19.** $\theta = 53°\,7'\,49''$. **21.** $\beta = 38°\,37'\,30''$. **23.** $y = 4.5150$ in. **25.** $\theta = 36°\,38'\,6''$. **27.** $\beta = 29°\,6'\,10''$. **29.** $x = 2.548$ in. **31.** $x = 1.3931$ in. **33.** $x = 0.0673$ in. **37.** Area $= 39.843$ sq in. **41.** $x = 0.8173$ in.

EXERCISE 8.6

1. $\sin \alpha = -0.97123$; $\cos \alpha = -0.23812$; $\tan \alpha = +4.0787$; $\cot \alpha = +0.24518$; $\sec \alpha = -4.1996$; $\csc \alpha = -1.0296$. **3.** $\sin \alpha = +0.97975$; $\cos \alpha = +0.20023$; $\tan \alpha = +4.8929$; $\cot \alpha =$

$+ 0.20438$; sec $\alpha = + 4.9940$; csc $\alpha = + 1.0207$.   **5.** sin $\alpha =$
$+ 0.74067$;   cos $\alpha = - 0.67187$;   tan $\alpha = - 1.1024$;   cot $\alpha =$
$- 0.90710$; sec $\alpha = - 1.4884$; csc $\alpha = + 1.3501$.   **7.** sin $\alpha =$
$+ 0.29866$;   cos $\alpha = - 0.95436$;   tan $\alpha = - 0.31294$;   cot $\alpha =$
$- 3.1955$; sec $\alpha = - 1.0479$; csc $\alpha = + 3.3482$.   **19.** $x = 49° 21' 14''$
or $310° 38' 46''$.

EXERCISE 8.7

1. $b = 4.9923$; $c = 4.6626$; $B = 78°$.   **3.** $b = 5.1115$;
$c = 4.8099$; $B = 87°$.   **5.** $b = 372.49$; $c = 577.84$; $A = 32°$.
7. $b = 318.22$; $c = 510.70$; $A = 32°$.   **9.** $c = 686.18$;
$B = 51° 29' 54''$; $C = 86° 30' 6''$.   **11.** $c = 938.96$; $B = 77° 5' 40''$;
$C = 66° 54' 20''$.   **13.** $a = 94.282$; $A = 134° 36' 29''$;
$C = 25° 9' 31''$; $a' = 11.370$; $A' = 4° 55' 31''$; $C' = 154° 50' 29''$.
15. $a = 178.00$; $A = 135° 38' 21''$; $C = 18° 51' 39''$.
17. $a = 9.4170$; $B = 80° 39' 0''$; $C = 64° 21' 0''$.
19. $a = 23.841$; $B\rfloor = 37° 51' 28''$; $C = 92° 8' 32''$.
21. $c = 76.997$; $A = 32° 37' 3''$; $B = 21° 22' 57''$.
23. $c = 76.700$; $A = 37° 15' 53''$; $B = 23° 44' 7''$.
25. $A = 74° 5' 19''$; $B = 61° 59' 22''$; $C = 43° 55' 19''$
27. $A = 77° 24' 20''$; $B = 62° 0' 20''$; $C = 40° 35' 20''$
29. Area $= 54.059$.   **31.** Area $= 49.434$.   **33.** 163.87 yd;
885.62 yd.   **35.** 45.35 ft.   **37.** $D = 16\frac{2}{3}$ ft.
39. Side $= 10.0564$ in.; diagonal $= 16.271$ in.   **41.** 1.3060 acres.
43. 278 miles.   **45.** 175.086 ft; 211.062 ft; 194.270 ft; 0.366 acres.
47. $D = 47.4$ ft.   **49.** $D = 3.050$.   **51.** $x = 1.844$ in.;
$y = 3.829$ in.   **53.** $a = 9.570$ ft; $b = 8.070$ ft.
55. $\beta = 21° 27' 33''$.   **57.** $\theta = 31° 36' 22''$.   **59.** $D = 6.8815$ in.
63. $40° 59' 7''$.   **65.** 2.2102.   **67.** 2.81969.   **69.** 10.33202, 8.26442,
7.09238.   **71.** 5.70941, 9.29059.   **73.** $43° 12' 47''$, $54° 33' 35''$,
$82° 13' 38''$.   **75.** 70.19 sq ft, 120.29 sq ft.   **77.** 0.1832 acres.
79. $28° 29'$.

Index

Tables

MATHEMATICAL
TABLES

HARPER & ROW, PUBLISHERS

NEW YORK, EVANSTON, AND LONDON

MATHEMATICAL TABLES

Contents

LOGARITHMS OF NUMBERS

Numbers 100-150 Logs 00000-17869

N	0	1	2	3	4	5	6	7	8	9
100	00 000	00 043	00 087	00 130	00 173	00 217	00 260	00 303	00 346	00 389
101	432	475	518	561	604	647	689	732	775	817
102	860	903	945	988	01 030	01 072	01 115	01 157	01 199	01 242
103	01 284	01 326	01 368	01 410	452	494	536	578	620	662
104	703	745	787	828	870	912	953	995	02 036	02 078
105	02 119	02 160	02 202	02 243	02 284	02 325	02 366	02 407	449	490
106	531	572	612	653	694	735	776	816	857	898
107	938	979	03 019	03 060	03 100	03 141	03 181	03 222	03 262	03 302
108	03 342	03 383	423	463	503	543	583	623	663	703
109	743	782	822	862	902	941	981	04 021	04 060	04 100
110	04 139	04 179	04 218	04 258	04 297	04 336	04 376	04 415	04 454	04 493
111	532	571	610	650	689	727	766	805	844	883
112	922	961	999	05 038	05 077	05 115	05 154	05 192	05 231	05 269
113	05 308	05 346	05 385	423	461	500	538	576	614	652
114	690	729	767	805	843	881	918	956	994	06 032
115	06 070	06 108	06 145	06 183	06 221	06 258	06 296	06 333	06 371	408
116	446	483	521	558	595	633	670	707	744	781
117	819	856	893	930	967	07 004	07 041	07 078	07 115	07 151
118	07 188	07 225	07 262	07 298	07 335	372	408	445	482	518
119	555	591	628	664	700	737	773	809	846	882
120	07 918	07 954	07 990	08 027	08 063	08 099	08 135	08 171	08 207	08 243
121	08 279	08 314	08 350	386	422	458	493	529	565	600
122	636	672	707	743	778	814	849	884	920	955
123	991	09 026	09 061	09 096	09 132	09 167	09 202	09 237	09 272	09 307
124	09 342	377	412	447	482	517	552	587	621	656
125	691	726	760	795	830	864	899	934	968	10 003
126	10 037	10 072	10 106	10 140	10 175	10 209	10 243	10 278	10 312	346
127	380	415	449	483	517	551	585	619	653	687
128	721	755	789	823	857	890	924	958	992	11 025
129	11 059	11 093	11 126	11 160	11 193	11 227	11 261	11 294	11 327	361
130	11 394	11 428	11 461	11 494	11 528	11 561	11 594	11 628	11 661	11 694
131	727	760	793	826	860	893	926	959	992	12 024
132	12 057	12 090	12 123	12 156	12 189	12 222	12 254	12 287	12 320	352
133	385	418	450	483	516	548	581	613	646	678
134	710	743	775	808	840	872	905	937	969	13 001
135	13 033	13 066	13 098	13 130	13 162	13 194	13 226	13 258	13 290	322
136	354	386	418	450	481	513	545	577	609	640
137	672	704	735	767	799	830	862	893	925	956
138	988	14 019	14 051	14 082	14 114	14 145	14 176	14 208	14 239	14 270
139	14 301	333	364	395	426	457	489	520	551	582
140	14 613	14 644	14 675	14 706	14 737	14 768	14 799	14 829	14 860	14 891
141	922	953	983	15 014	15 045	15 076	15 106	15 137	15 168	15 198
142	15 229	15 259	15 290	320	351	381	412	442	473	503
143	534	564	594	625	655	685	715	746	776	806
144	836	866	897	927	957	987	16 017	16 047	16 077	16 107
145	16 137	16 167	16 197	16 227	16 256	16 286	316	346	376	406
146	435	465	495	524	554	584	613	643	673	702
147	732	761	791	820	850	879	909	938	967	997
148	17 026	17 056	17 085	17 114	17 143	17 173	17 202	17 231	17 260	17 289
149	319	348	377	406	435	464	493	522	551	580
150	17 609	17 638	17 667	17 696	17 725	17 754	17 782	17 811	17 840	17 869
N	0	1	2	3	4	5	6	7	8	9

P.P.

	43	42	41
1	4.3	4.2	4.1
2	8.6	8.4	8.2
3	12.9	12.6	12.3
4	17.2	16.8	16.4
5	21.5	21.0	20.5
6	25.8	25.2	24.6
7	30.1	29.4	28.7
8	34.4	33.6	32.8
9	38.7	37.8	36.9

	40	39	38
1	4.0	3.9	3.8
2	8.0	7.8	7.6
3	12.0	11.7	11.4
4	16.0	15.6	15.2
5	20.0	19.5	19.0
6	24.0	23.4	22.8
7	28.0	27.3	26.6
8	32.0	31.2	30.4
9	36.0	35.1	34.2

	37	36	35
1	3.7	3.6	3.5
2	7.4	7.2	7.0
3	11.1	10.8	10.5
4	14.8	14.4	14.0
5	18.5	18.0	17.5
6	22.2	21.6	21.0
7	25.9	25.2	24.5
8	29.6	28.8	28.0
9	33.3	32.4	31.5

	34	33	32
1	3.4	3.3	3.2
2	6.8	6.6	6.4
3	10.2	9.9	9.6
4	13.6	13.2	12.8
5	17.0	16.5	16.0
6	20.4	19.8	19.2
7	23.8	23.1	22.4
8	27.2	26.4	25.6
9	30.6	29.7	28.8

	31	30	29
1	3.1	3.0	2.9
2	6.2	6.0	5.8
3	9.3	9.0	8.7
4	12.4	12.0	11.6
5	15.5	15.0	14.5
6	18.6	18.0	17.4
7	21.7	21.0	20.3
8	24.8	24.0	23.2
9	27.9	27.0	26.1

Numbers 150–200 Logs 17609–30298

N	0	1	2	3	4	5	6	7	8	9
150	17 609	17 638	17 667	17 696	17 725	17 754	17 782	17 811	17 840	17 869
151	898	926	955	984	18 013	18 041	18 070	18 099	18 127	18 156
152	18 184	18 213	18 241	18 270	298	327	355	384	412	441
153	469	498	526	554	583	611	639	667	696	724
154	752	780	808	837	865	893	921	949	977	19 005
155	19 033	19 061	19 089	19 117	19 145	19 173	19 201	19 229	19 257	285
156	312	340	368	396	424	451	479	507	535	562
157	590	618	645	673	700	728	756	783	811	838
158	866	893	921	948	976	20 003	20 030	20 058	20 085	20 112
159	20 140	20 167	20 194	20 222	20 249	276	303	330	358	385
160	20 412	20 439	20 466	20 493	20 520	20 548	20 575	20 602	20 629	20 656
161	683	710	737	763	790	817	844	871	898	925
162	952	978	21 005	21 032	21 059	21 085	21 112	21 139	21 165	21 192
163	21 219	21 245	272	299	325	352	378	405	431	458
164	484	511	537	564	590	617	643	669	696	722
165	748	775	801	827	854	880	906	932	958	985
166	22 011	22 037	22 063	22 089	22 115	22 141	22 167	22·194	22 220	22 246
167	272	298	324	350	376	401	427	453	479	505
168	531	557	583	608	634	660	686	712	737	763
169	789	814	840	866	891	917	943	968	994	23 019
170	23 045	23 070	23 096	23 121	23 147	23 172	23 198	23 223	23 249	23 274
171	300	325	350	376	401	426	452	477	502	528
172	553	578	603	629	654	679	704	729	754	779
173	805	830	855	880	905	930	955	980	24 005	24 030
174	24 055	24 080	24 105	24 130	24 155	24 180	24 204	24 229	254	279
175	304	329	353	378	403	428	452	477	502	527
176	551	576	601	625	650	674	699	724	748	773
177	797	822	846	871	895	920	944	969	993	25 018
178	25 042	25 066	25 091	25 115	25 139	25 164	25 188	25 212	25 237	261
179	285	310	334	358	382	406	431	455	479	503
180	25 527	25 551	25 575	25 600	25 624	25 648	25 672	25 696	25 720	25 744
181	768	792	816	840	864	888	912	935	959	983
182	26 007	26 031	26 055	26 079	26 102	26 126	26 150	26 174	26 198	26 221
183	245	269	293	316	340	364	387	411	435	458
184	482	505	529	553	576	600	623	647	670	694
185	717	741	764	788	811	834	858	881	905	928
186	951	975	998	27 021	27 045	27 068	27 091	27 114	27 138	27 161
187	27 184	27 207	27 231	254	277	300	323	346	370	393
188	416	439	462	485	508	531	554	577	600	623
189	646	669	692	715	738	761	784	807	830	852
190	27 875	27 898	27 921	27 944	27 967	27 989	28 012	28 035	28 058	28 081
191	28 103	28 126	28 149	28 171	28 194	28 217	240	262	285	307
192	330	353	375	398	421	443	466	488	511	533
193	556	578	601	623	646	668	691	713	735	758
194	780	803	825	847	870	892	914	937	959	981
195	29 003	29 026	29 048	29 070	29 092	29 115	29 137	29 159	29 181	29 203
196	226	248	270	292	314	336	358	380	403	425
197	447	469	491	513	535	557	579	601	623	645
198	667	688	710	732	754	776	798	820	842	863
199	885	907	929	951	973	994	30 016	30 038	30 060	30 081
200	30 103	30 125	30 146	30 168	30 190	30 211	30 233	30 255	30 276	30 298
N	0	1	2	3	4	5	6	7	8	9

P.P.

	29	28
1	2.9	2.8
2	5.8	5.6
3	8.7	8.4
4	11.6	11.2
5	14.5	14.0
6	17.4	16.8
7	20.3	19.6
8	23.2	22.4
9	26.1	25.2

	27	26
1	2.7	2.6
2	5.4	5.2
3	8.1	7.8
4	10.8	10.4
5	13.5	13.0
6	16.2	15.6
7	18.9	18.2
8	21.6	20.8
9	24.3	23.4

	25	24
1	2.5	2.4
2	5.0	4.8
3	7.5	7.2
4	10.0	9.6
5	12.5	12.0
6	15.0	14.4
7	17.5	16.8
8	20.0	19.2
9	22.5	21.6

	23	22
1	2.3	2.2
2	4.6	4.4
3	6.9	6.6
4	9.2	8.8
5	11.5	11.0
6	13.8	13.2
7	16.1	15.4
8	18.4	17.6
9	20.7	19.8

	21
1	2.1
2	4.2
3	6.3
4	8.4
5	10.5
6	12.6
7	14.7
8	16.8
9	18.9

Numbers 200–250   Logs 30103–39950

N	0	1	2	3	4	5	6	7	8	9
200	30 103	30 125̅	30 146	30 168	30 190	30 211	30 233	30 255̅	30 276	30 298
201	320	341	363	384	406	428	449	471	492	514
202	535	557	578	600	621	643	664	685	707	728
203	750	771	792	814	835	856	878	899	920	942
204	963	984̅	31 006	31 027	31 048	31 069	31 091	31 112	31 133	31 154
205	31 175̅	31 197	218	239	260	281	302	323	345̅	366
206	387	408	429	450	471	492	513	534	555	576
207	597	618	639	660	681	702	723	744	765̅	785
208	806	827	848	869	890	911	931	952	973	994
209	32 015̅	32 035	32 056	32 077	32 098	32 118	32 139	32 160	32 181	32 201
210	32 222	32 243	32 263	32 284	32 305̅	32 325	32 346	32 366	32 387	32 408
211	428	449	469	490	510	531	552	572	593	613
212	634	654	675̅	695̅	715	736	756	777	797	818
213	838	858	879	899	919	940	960	980	33 001	33 021
214	33 041	33 062	33 082	33 102	33 122	33 143	33 163	33 183	203	224
215	244	264	284	304	325̅	345̅	365̅	385	405	425̅
216	445	465	486	506	526	546	566	586	606	626
217	646	666	686	706	726	746	766	786	806	826
218	846	866	885	905	925	945	965	985̅	34 005	34 025̅
219	34 044̅	34 064	34 084	34 104	34 124	34 143	34 163	34 183	203	223
220	34 242	34 262	34 282	34 301	34 321	34 341	34 361	34 380	34 400	34 420
221	439	459	479	498	518	537	557	577	596	616
222	635	655̅	674	694	713	733	753	772	792	811
223	830	850	869	889	908	928	947	967	986	35 005
224	35 025̅	35 044	35 064	35 083	35 102	35 122	35 141	35 160	35 180	199
225	218	238	257	276	295	315̅	334	353	372	392
226	411	430	449	468	488	507	526	545	564	583̅
227	603	622	641	660	679	698	717	736	755	774̅
228	793	813	832	851	870	889	908	927	946	965
229	984	36 003	36 021	36 040	36 059	36 078	36 097	36 116	36 135	36 154
230	36 173	36 192	36 211	36 229	36 248	36 267	36 286	36 305̅	36 324	36 342
231	361	380	399	418	436	455	474	493	511	530
232	549	568	586	605	624	642	661	680	698	717
233	736	754	773	791	810	829	847	866	884	903
234	922	940	959	977	996	37 014	37 033	37 051	37 070	37 088
235	37 107	37 125	37 144	37 162	37 181	199	218	236	254	273
236	291	310	328	346	365̅	383	401	420	438	457
237	475̅	493	511	530	548	566	585̅	603	621	639
238	658	676	694	712	731	749	767	785	803	822
239	840	858	876	894	912	931	949	967	985̅	38 003
240	38 021	38 039	38 057	38 075	38 093	38 112	38 130	38 148	38 166	38 184
241	202	220	238	256	274	292	310	328	346	364
242	382	399	417	435	453	471	489	507	525̅	543
243	561	578	596	614	632	650	668	686	703	721
244	739	757	775̅	792	810	828	846	863	881	899
245	917	934	952	970	987	39 005	39 023	39 041	39 058	39 076
246	39 094	39 111	39 129	39 146	39 164	182	199	217	235̅	252
247	270	287	305̅	322	340	358	375	393	410	428
248	445	463	480	498	515	533	550	568	585	602
249	620	637	655̅	672	690	707	724	742	759	777
250	39 794	39 811	39 829	39 846	39 863	39 881	39 898	39 915	39 933	39 950
N	0	1	2	3	4	5	6	7	8	9

P.P.

	22	21
1	2.2	2.1
2	4.4	4.2
3	6.6	6.3
4	8.8	8.4
5	11.0	10.5
6	13.2	12.6
7	15.4	14.7
8	17.6	16.8
9	19.8	18.9

	20
1	2.0
2	4.0
3	6.0
4	8.0
5	10.0
6	12.0
7	14.0
8	16.0
9	18.0

	19
1	1.9
2	3.8
3	5.7
4	7.6
5	9.5
6	11.4
7	13.3
8	15.2
9	17.1

	18
1	1.8
2	3.6
3	5.4
4	7.2
5	9.0
6	10.8
7	12.6
8	14.4
9	16.2

	17
1	1.7
2	3.4
3	5.1
4	6.8
5	8.5
6	10.2
7	11.9
8	13.6
9	15.3

Numbers 250–300   Logs 39794–47842

N	0	1	2	3	4	5	6	7	8	9
250	39 794	39 811	39 829	39 846	39 863	39 881	39 898	39 915	39 933	39 950
251	967	985	40 002	40 019	40 037	40 054	40 071	40 088	40 106	40 123
252	40 140	40 157	175	192	209	226	243	261	278	295
253	312	329	346	364	381	398	415	432	449	466
254	483	500	518	535	552	569	586	603	620	637
255	654	671	688	705	722	739	756	773	790	807
256	824	841	858	875	892	909	926	943	960	976
257	993	41 010	41 027	41 044	41 061	41 078	41 095	41 111	41 128	41 145
258	41 162	179	196	212	229	246	263	280	296	313
259	330	347	363	380	397	414	430	447	464	481
260	41 497	41 514	41 531	41 547	41 564	41 581	41 597	41 614	41 631	41 647
261	664	681	697	714	731	747	764	780	797	814
262	830	847	863	880	896	913	929	946	963	979
263	996	42 012	42 029	42 045	42 062	42 078	42 095	42 111	42 127	42 144
264	42 160	177	193	210	226	243	259	275	292	308
265	325	341	357	374	390	406	423	439	455	472
266	488	504	521	537	553	570	586	602	619	635
267	651	667	684	700	716	732	749	765	781	797
268	813	830	846	862	878	894	911	927	943	959
269	975	991	43 008	43 024	43 040	43 056	43 072	43 088	43 104	43 120
270	43 136	43 152	43 169	43 185	43 201	43 217	43 233	43 249	43 265	43 281
271	297	313	329	345	361	377	393	409	425	441
272	457	473	489	505	521	537	553	569	584	600
273	616	632	648	664	680	696	712	727	743	759
274	775	791	807	823	838	854	870	886	902	917
275	933	949	965	981	996	44 012	44 028	44 044	44 059	44 075
276	44 091	44 107	44 122	44 138	44 154	170	185	201	217	232
277	248	264	279	295	311	326	342	358	373	389
278	404	420	436	451	467	483	498	514	529	545
279	560	576	592	607	623	638	654	669	685	700
280	44 716	44 731	44 747	44 762	44 778	44 793	44 809	44 824	44 840	44 855
281	871	886	902	917	932	948	963	979	994	45 010
282	45 025	45 040	45 056	45 071	45 086	45 102	45 117	45 133	45 148	163
283	179	194	209	225	240	255	271	286	301	317
284	332	347	362	378	393	408	423	439	454	469
285	484	500	515	530	545	561	576	591	606	621
286	637	652	667	682	697	712	728	743	758	773
287	788	803	818	834	849	864	879	894	909	924
288	939	954	969	984	46 000	46 015	46 030	46 045	46 060	46 075
289	46 090	46 105	46 120	46 135	150	165	180	195	210	225
290	46 240	46 255	46 270	46 285	46 300	46 315	46 330	46 345	46 359	46 374
291	389	404	419	434	449	464	479	494	509	523
292	538	553	568	583	598	613	627	642	657	672
293	687	702	716	731	746	761	776	790	805	820
294	835	850	864	879	894	909	923	938	953	967
295	982	997	47 012	47 026	47 041	47 056	47 070	47 085	47 100	47 114
296	47 129	47 144	159	173	188	202	217	232	246	261
297	276	290	305	319	334	349	363	378	392	407
298	422	436	451	465	480	494	509	524	538	553
299	567	582	596	611	625	640	654	669	683	698
300	47 712	47 727	47 741	47 756	47 770	47 784	47 799	47 813	47 828	47 842
N	0	1	2	3	4	5	6	7	8	9

P.P.

	18		17		16		15		14
1	1.8		1.7		1.6		1.5		1.4
2	3.6		3.4		3.2		3.0		2.8
3	5.4		5.1		4.8		4.5		4.2
4	7.2		6.8		6.4		6.0		5.6
5	9.0		8.5		8.0		7.5		7.0
6	10.8		10.2		9.6		9.0		8.4
7	12.6		11.9		11.2		10.5		9.8
8	14.4		13.6		12.8		12.0		11.2
9	16.2		15.3		14.4		13.5		12.6

Numbers 300–350		Logs 47712–54518									
N	**0**	**1**	**2**	**3**	**4**	**5**	**6**	**7**	**8**	**9**	**P.P.**
300	47 712	47 727	47 741	47 756	47 770	47 784	47 799	47 813	47 828	47 842	**15**
301	857	871	885	900	914	929	943	958	972	986	1 · 1.5
302	48 001	48 015	48 029	48 044	48 058	48 073	48 087	48 101	48 116	48 130	2 · 3.0
303	144	159	173	187	202	216	230	244	259	273	3 · 4.5
304	287	302	316	330	344	359	373	387	401	416	4 · 6.0
305	430	444	458	473	487	501	515	530	544	558	5 · 7.5
306	572	586	601	61$\bar{5}$	629	643	657	671	686	700	6 · 9.0
307	714	728	742	756	770	78$\bar{5}$	799	813	827	841	7 · 10.5
308	855	869	883	897	911	926	940	954	968	982	8 · 12.0
309	996	49 010	49 024	49 038	49 052	49 066	49 080	49 094	49 108	49 122	9 · 13.5
310	49 136	49 150	49 164	49 178	49 192	49 206	49 220	49 234	49 248	49 262	**14**
311	276	290	304	318	332	346	360	374	388	402	1 · 1.4
312	415	429	443	457	471	485	499	513	527	541	2 · 2.8
313	554	568	582	596	610	624	638	651	665	679	3 · 4.2
314	693	707	721	734	748	762	776	790	803	817	4 · 5.6
315	831	84$\bar{5}$	859	872	886	900	914	927	941	95$\bar{5}$	5 · 7.0
316	969	982	996	50 010	50 024	50 037	50 051	50 06$\bar{5}$	50 079	50 092	6 · 8.4
317	50 106	50 120	50 133	147	161	174	188	202	215	229	7 · 9.8
318	243	256	270	284	297	311	32$\bar{5}$	338	352	365	8 · 11.2
319	379	393	406	420	433	447	461	474	488	501	9 · 12.6
320	50 51$\bar{5}$	50 529	50 542	50 556	50 569	50 583	50 596	50 610	50 623	50 637	
321	651	664	678	691	70$\bar{5}$	718	732	745	759	772	
322	786	799	813	826	840	853	866	880	893	907	
323	920	934	947	961	974	987	51 001	51 014	51 028	51 041	
324	51 05$\bar{5}$	51 068	51 081	51 09$\bar{5}$	51 108	51 121	13$\bar{5}$	148	162	17$\bar{5}$	
325	188	202	215	228	242	255	268	282	295	308	
326	322	335	348	362	375	388	402	41$\bar{5}$	428	441	
327	45$\bar{5}$	468	481	49$\bar{5}$	508	521	534	548	561	574	
328	587	601	614	627	640	654	667	680	693	706	
329	720	733	746	759	772	786	799	812	825	838	
330	51 851	51 86$\bar{5}$	51 878	51 891	51 904	51 917	51 930	51 943	51 957	51 970	**13**
331	983	996	52 009	52 022	52 035	52 048	52 061	52 07$\bar{5}$	52 088	52 101	1 · 1.3
332	52 114	52 127	140	153	166	179	192	205	218	231	2 · 2.6
333	244	257	270	284	297	310	323	336	349	362	3 · 3.9
334	37$\bar{5}$	388	401	414	427	440	453	466	479	492	4 · 5.2
335	504	517	530	543	556	569	582	595	608	621	5 · 6.5
336	634	647	660	673	686	699	711	724	737	750	6 · 7.8
337	763	776	789	802	81$\bar{5}$	827	840	853	866	879	7 · 9.1
338	892	90$\bar{5}$	917	930	943	956	969	982	994	53 007	8 · 10.4
339	53 020	53 033	53 046	53 058	53 071	53 084	53 097	53 110	53 122	135	9 · 11.7
340	53 148	53 161	53 173	53 186	53 199	53 212	53 224	53 237	53 250	53 263	**12**
341	275	288	301	314	326	339	352	364	377	390	1 · 1.2
342	403	415	428	441	453	466	479	491	504	517	2 · 2.4
343	529	542	555	567	580	593	605	618	631	643	3 · 3.6
344	656	668	681	694	706	719	732	744	757	769	4 · 4.8
345	782	794	807	820	832	84$\bar{5}$	857	870	882	895	5 · 6.0
346	908	920	933	945	958	970	983	995	54 008	54 020	6 · 7.2
347	54 033	54 045	54 058	54 070	54 083	54 095	54 108	54 120	133	145	7 · 8.4
348	158	170	183	195	208	220	233	245	258	270	8 · 9.6
349	283	29$\bar{5}$	307	320	332	34$\bar{5}$	357	370	382	394	9 · 10.8
350	54 407	54 419	54 432	54 444	54 456	54 469	54 481	54 494	54 506	54 518	
N	**0**	**1**	**2**	**3**	**4**	**5**	**6**	**7**	**8**	**9**	

Logarithms of Numbers

N	0	1	2	3	4	5	6	7	8	9	P.P.
350	54 407	54 419	54 432	54 444	54 456	54 469	54 481	54 494	54 506	54 518	**13**
351	531	543	555	568	580	593	60$\overline{5}$	617	630	642	
352	654	667	679	691	704	716	728	741	753	765	1 1.3
353	777	790	802	814	827	839	851	864	876	888	2 2.6
354	900	913	92$\overline{5}$	937	949	962	974	986	998	55 011	3 3.9
355	55 023	55 035	55 047	55 060	55 072	55 084	55 096	55 108	55 121	133	4 5.2
356	14$\overline{5}$	157	169	182	194	206	218	230	242	25$\overline{5}$	5 6.5
357	267	279	291	303	315	328	340	352	364	376	6 7.8
358	388	400	413	42$\overline{5}$	437	449	461	473	485	497	7 9.1
359	509	522	534	546	558	570	582	594	606	618	8 10.4
											9 11.7
360	55 630	55 642	55 654	55 666	55 678	55 691	55 703	55 715	55 727	55 739	**12**
361	751	763	77$\overline{5}$	787	799	811	823	83$\overline{5}$	847	859	
362	871	883	89$\overline{5}$	907	919	931	943	95$\overline{5}$	967	979	1 1.2
363	991	56 003	56 015	56 027	56 038	56 050	56 062	56 074	56 086	56 098	2 2.4
364	56 110	122	134	146	158	170	182	194	205	217	3 3.6
365	229	241	253	26$\overline{5}$	277	289	301	312	324	336	4 4.8
366	348	360	372	384	396	407	419	431	443	45$\overline{5}$	5 6.0
367	46$\overline{7}$	478	490	502	514	526	538	549	561	573	6 7.2
368	58$\overline{5}$	597	608	620	632	644	656	66$\overline{7}$	679	691	7 8.4
369	703	714	726	738	750	761	773	78$\overline{5}$	797	808	8 9.6
											9 10.8
370	56 820	56 832	56 844	56 855	56 867	56 879	56 891	56 902	56 914	56 926	
371	937	949	961	972	984	996	57 008	57 019	57 031	57 043	
372	57 054	57 066	57 078	57 089	57 101	57 113	124	136	148	159	
373	171	183	194	206	217	229	241	252	264	276	
374	287	29$\overline{9}$	310	322	334	345	357	368	380	392	
375	403	41$\overline{5}$	426	438	449	461	473	484	496	507	
376	519	530	542	553	56$\overline{5}$	576	588	600	611	623	
377	634	646	657	669	680	692	703	71$\overline{5}$	726	738	
378	749	761	772	784	795	807	818	830	841	852	
379	864	875	887	898	910	921	933	944	955	967	
380	57 978	57 990	58 001	58 013	58 024	58 035	58 047	58 058	58 070	58 081	**11**
381	58 092	58 104	115	127	138	149	161	172	184	19$\overline{5}$	
382	206	218	229	240	252	263	274	286	297	309	1 1.1
383	320	331	343	354	365	377	388	399	410	422	2 2.2
384	433	444	456	467	478	490	501	512	524	53$\overline{5}$	3 3.3
385	546	557	569	580	591	602	614	62$\overline{5}$	636	647	4 4.4
386	659	670	681	692	704	71$\overline{5}$	726	737	749	760	5 5.5
387	771	782	794	80$\overline{5}$	816	827	838	850	861	872	6 6.6
388	883	894	906	917	928	939	950	961	973	984	7 7.7
389	99$\overline{5}$	59 006	59 017	59 028	59 040	59 051	59 062	59 073	59 084	59 095	8 8.8
											9 9.9
390	59 106	59 118	59 129	59 140	59 151	59 162	59 173	59 184	59 195	59 207	**10**
391	218	229	240	251	262	273	284	295	306	318	
392	329	340	351	362	373	384	395	406	417	428	1 1.0
393	439	450	461	472	483	494	506	517	528	539	2 2.0
394	550	561	572	583	594	60$\overline{5}$	616	627	638	649	3 3.0
395	660	671	682	693	704	71$\overline{5}$	726	737	748	759	4 4.0
396	770	780	791	802	813	824	835	846	857	868	5 5.0
397	879	890	901	912	923	934	94$\overline{5}$	956	966	977	6 6.0
398	988	999	60 010	60 021	60 032	60 043	60 054	60 065	60 076	60 086	7 7.0
399	60 097	60 108	119	130	141	152	163	173	184	195	8 8.0
400	60 206	60 217	60 228	60 239	60 249	60 260	60 271	60 282	60 293	60 304	9 9.0
N	0	1	2	3	4	5	6	7	8	9	

Numbers 350–400   Logs 54407–60304

Numbers 400–450   Logs 60206–65408

N	0	1	2	3	4	5	6	7	8	9
400	60 206	60 217	60 228	60 239	60 249	60 260	60 271	60 282	60 293	60 304
401	314	325	336	347	358	369	379	390	401	412
402	423	433	444	455	466	477	487	498	509	520
403	531	541	552	563	574	584	595	606	617	627
404	638	649	660	670	681	692	703	713	724	735̄
405	746	756	767	778	788	799	810	821	831	842
406	853	863	874	885̄	895	906	917	927	938	949
407	959	970	981	991	61 002	61 013	61 023	61 034	61 045̄	61 055
408	61 066	61 077	61 087	61 098	109	119	130	140	151	162
409	172	183	194	204	215̄	225	236	247	257	268
410	61 278	61 289	61 300	61 310	61 321	61 331	61 342	61 352	61 363	61 374
411	384	395̄	405	416	426	437	448	458	469	479
412	490	500	511	521	532	542	553	563	574	584
413	595	606	616	627	637	648	658	669	679	690
414	700	711	721	731	742	752	763	773	784	794
415	805̄	815	826	836	847	857	868	878	888	899
416	909	920	930	941	951	962	972	982	993	62 003
417	62 014	62 024	62 034	62 045̄	62 055	62 066	62 076	62 086	62 097	107
418	118	128	138	149	159	170	180	190	201	211̄
419	221	232	242	252	263	273	284	294	304	315̄
420	62 325̄	62 335	62 346	62 356	62 366	62 377	62 387	62 397	62 408	62 418
421	428	439	449	459	469	480	490	500	511	521
422	531	542	552	562	572	583	593	603	613	624
423	634	644	655̄	665̄	675	685	696	706	716	726
424	737	747	757	767	778	788	798	808	818	829
425	839	849	859	870	880	890	900	910	921	931
426	941	951	961	972	982	992	63 002	63 012	63 022	63 033
427	63 043	63 053	63 063	63 073̄	63 083̄	63 094	104	114	124	134
428	144	155̄	165	175̄	185̄	195	205	215	225	236
429	246	256	266	276	286	296	306	317	327	337
430	63 347	63 357	63 367	63 377	63 387	63 397	63 407	63 417	63 428	63 438
431	448	458	468	478	488	498	508	518	528	538
432	548	558	568	579	589	599	609	619	629	639
433	649	659	669	679	689	699	709	719	729	739
434	749	759	769	779	789	799	809	819	829	839
435	849	859	869	879	889	899	909	919	929	939
436	949	959	969	979	988	998	64 008	64 018	64 028	64 038
437	64 048	64 058	64 068	64 078	64 088	64 098	108	118	128	137
438	147	157	167	177	187	197	207	217	227	237
439	246	256	266	276	286	296	306	316	326	335
440	64 345	64 355	64 365	64 375̄	64 385	64 395̄	64 404	64 414	64 424	64 434
441	444	454	464	473	483	493	503	513	523	532
442	542	552	562	572	582	591	601	611	621	631
443	640	650	660	670	680	689	699	709	719	729
444	738	748	758	768	777	787	797	807	816	826
445	836	846	856	865	875	885̄	895	904	914	924
446	933	943	953	963	972	982	992	65 002	65 011	65 021
447	65 031	65 040	65 050	65 060	65 070	65 079	65 089	099	108	118
448	128	137	147	157	167	176	186	196	205	215̄
449	225̄	234	244	254	263	273	283	292	302	312
450	65 321	65 331	65 341	65 350	65 360	65 369	65 379	65 389	65 398	65 408
N	0	1	2	3	4	5	6	7	8	9

P.P.

11		10		9	
1	1.1	1	1.0	1	.9
2	2.2	2	2.0	2	1.8
3	3.3	3	3.0	3	2.7
4	4.4	4	4.0	4	3.6
5	5.5	5	5.0	5	4.5
6	6.6	6	6.0	6	5.4
7	7.7	7	7.0	7	6.3
8	8.8	8	8.0	8	7.2
9	9.9	9	9.0	9	8.1

Numbers 450–500   Logs 65321–69975

N	0	1	2	3	4	5	6	7	8	9	P.P.
450	65 321	65 331	65 341	65 350	65 360	65 369	65 379	65 389	65 398	65 408	**10**
451	418	427	437	447	456	466	475	485	495	504	1 1.0
452	514	523	533	543	552	562	571	581	591	600	2 2.0
453	610	619	629	639	648	658	667	677	686	696	3 3.0
454	706	715	725	734	744	753	763	772	782	792	4 4.0
455	801	811	820	830	839	849	858	868	877	887	5 5.0
456	896	906	916	925	935	944	954	963	973	982	6 6.0
457	992	66 001	66 011	66 020	66 030	66 039	66 049	66 058	66 068	66 077	7 7.0
458	66 087	096	106	115	124	134	143	153	162	172	8 8.0
459	181	191	200	210	219	229	238	247	257	266	9 9.0
460	66 276	66 285	66 295	66 304	66 314	66 323	66 332	66 342	66 351	66 361	
461	370	380	389	398	408	417	427	436	445	455	
462	464	474	483	492	502	511	521	530	539	549	
463	558	567	577	586	596	605	614	624	633	642	
464	652	661	671	680	689	699	708	717	727	736	
465	745	755	764	773	783	792	801	811	820	829	
466	839	848	857	867	876	885	894	904	913	922	
467	932	941	950	960	969	978	987	997	67 006	67 015	
468	67 025	67 034	67 043	67 052	67 062	67 071	67 080	67 089	099	108	
469	117	127	136	145	154	164	173	182	191	201	
470	67 210	67 219	67 228	67 237	67 247	67 256	67 265	67 274	67 284	67 293	**9**
471	302	311	321	330	339	348	357	367	376	385	1 0.9
472	394	403	413	422	431	440	449	459	468	477	2 1.8
473	486	495	504	514	523	532	541	550	560	569	3 2.7
474	578	587	596	605	614	624	633	642	651	660	4 3.6
475	669	679	688	697	706	715	724	733	742	752	5 4.5
476	761	770	779	788	797	806	815	825	834	843	6 5.4
477	852	861	870	879	888	897	906	916	925	934	7 6.3
478	943	952	961	970	979	988	997	68 006	68 015	68 024	8 7.2
479	68 034	68 043	68 052	68 061	68 070	68 079	68 088	097	106	115	9 8.1
480	68 124	68 133	68 142	68 151	68 160	68 169	68 178	68 187	68 196	68 205	
481	215	224	233	242	251	260	269	278	287	296	
482	305	314	323	332	341	350	359	368	377	386	
483	395	404	413	422	431	440	449	458	467	476	
484	485	494	502	511	520	529	538	547	556	565	
485	574	583	592	601	610	619	628	637	646	655	
486	664	673	681	690	699	708	717	726	735	744	
487	753	762	771	780	789	797	806	815	824	833	
488	842	851	860	869	878	886	895	904	913	922	
489	931	940	949	958	966	975	984	993	69 002	69 011	
490	69 020	69 028	69 037	69 046	69 055	69 064	69 073	69 082	69 090	69 099	**8**
491	108	117	126	135	144	152	161	170	179	188	1 0.8
492	197	205	214	223	232	241	249	258	267	276	2 1.6
493	285	294	302	311	320	329	338	346	355	364	3 2.4
494	373	381	390	399	408	417	425	434	443	452	4 3.2
495	461	469	478	487	496	504	513	522	531	539	5 4.0
496	548	557	566	574	583	592	601	609	618	627	6 4.8
497	636	644	653	662	671	679	688	697	705	714	7 5.6
498	723	732	740	749	758	767	775	784	793	801	8 6.4
499	810	819	827	836	845	854	862	871	880	888	9 7.2
500	69 897	69 906	69 914	69 923	69 932	69 940	69 949	69 958	69 966	69 975	
N	0	1	2	3	4	5	6	7	8	9	

Numbers 500–550   Logs 69897–74107

N	0	1	2	3	4	5	6	7	8	9
500	69 897	69 906	69 914	69 923	69 932	69 940	69 949	69 958	69 966	69 975
501	984	992	70 001	70 010	70 018	70 027	70 036	70 044	70 053	70 062
502	70 070	70 079	088	096	105	114	122	131	140	148
503	157	165	174	183	191	200	209	217	226	234
504	243	252	260	269	278	286	295	303	312	321
505	329	338	346	355	364	372	381	389	398	406
506	415	424	432	441	449	458	467	475	484	492
507	501	509	518	526	535	544	552	561	569	578
508	586	595	603	612	621	629	638	646	655	663
509	672	680	689	697	706	714	723	731	740	749
510	70 757	70 766	70 774	70 783	70 791	70 800	70 808	70 817	70 825	70 834
511	842	851	859	868	876	885	893	902	910	919
512	927	935	944	952	961	969	978	986	995	71 003
513	71 012	71 020	71 029	71 037	71 046	71 054	71 063	71 071	71 079	088
514	096	105	113	122	130	139	147	155	164	172
515	181	189	198	206	214	223	231	240	248	257
516	265	273	282	290	299	307	315	324	332	341
517	349	357	366	374	383	391	399	408	416	425
518	433	441	450	458	466	475	483	492	500	508
519	517	525	533	542	550	559	567	575	584	592
520	71 600	71 609	71 617	71 625	71 634	71 642	71 650	71 659	71 667	71 675
521	684	692	700	709	717	725	734	742	750	759
522	767	775	784	792	800	809	817	825	834	842
523	850	858	867	875	883	892	900	908	917	925
524	933	941	950	958	966	975	983	991	999	72 008
525	72 016	72 024	72 032	72 041	72 049	72 057	72 066	72 074	72 082	090
526	099	107	115	123	132	140	148	156	165	173
527	181	189	198	206	214	222	230	239	247	255
528	263	272	280	288	296	304	313	321	329	337
529	346	354	362	370	378	387	395	403	411	419
530	72 428	72 436	72 444	72 452	72 460	72 469	72 477	72 485	72 493	72 501
531	509	518	526	534	542	550	558	567	575	583
532	591	599	607	616	624	632	640	648	656	665
533	673	681	689	697	705	713	722	730	738	746
534	754	762	770	779	787	795	803	811	819	827
535	835	843	852	860	868	876	884	892	900	908
536	916	925	933	941	949	957	965	973	981	989
537	997	73 006	73 014	73 022	73 030	73 038	73 046	73 054	73 062	73 070
538	73 078	086	094	102	111	119	127	135	143	151
539	159	167	175	183	191	199	207	215	223	231
540	73 239	73 247	73 255	73 263	73 272	73 280	73 288	73 296	73 304	73 312
541	320	328	336	344	352	360	368	376	384	392
542	400	408	416	424	432	440	448	456	464	472
543	480	488	496	504	512	520	528	536	544	552
544	560	568	576	584	592	600	608	616	624	632
545	640	648	656	664	672	679	687	695	703	711
546	719	727	735	743	751	759	767	775	783	791
547	799	807	815	823	830	838	846	854	862	870
548	878	886	894	902	910	918	926	933	941	949
549	957	965	973	981	989	997	74 005	74 013	74 020	74 028
550	74 036	74 044	74 052	74 060	74 068	74 076	74 084	74 092	74 099	74 107
N	0	1	2	3	4	5	6	7	8	9

P.P.

9		8		7	
1	0.9	1	0.8	1	0.7
2	1.8	2	1.6	2	1.4
3	2.7	3	2.4	3	2.1
4	3.6	4	3.2	4	2.8
5	4.5	5	4.0	5	3.5
6	5.4	6	4.8	6	4.2
7	6.3	7	5.6	7	4.9
8	7.2	8	6.4	8	5.6
9	8.1	9	7.2	9	6.3

Numbers 550–600 Logs 74036–77880

N	0	1	2	3	4	5	6	7	8	9
550	74036	74044	74052	74060	74068	74076	74084	74092	74099	74107
551	115	123	131	139	147	155	162	170	178	186
552	194	202	210	218	225	233	241	249	257	265
553	273	280	288	296	304	312	320	327	335	343
554	351	359	367	374	382	390	398	406	414	421
555	429	437	445	453	461	468	476	484	492	500
556	507	515	523	531	539	547	554	562	570	578
557	586	593	601	609	617	624	632	640	648	656
558	663	671	679	687	695	702	710	718	726	733
559	741	749	757	764	772	780	788	796	803	811
560	74819	74827	74834	74842	74850	74858	74865	74873	74881	74889
561	896	904	912	920	927	935	943	950	958	966
562	974	981	989	997	75005	75012	75020	75028	75035	75043
563	75051	75059	75066	75074	082	089	097	105	113	120
564	128	136	143	151	159	166	174	182	189	197
565	205	213	220	228	236	243	251	259	266	274
566	282	289	297	305	312	320	328	335	343	351
567	358	366	374	381	389	397	404	412	420	427
568	435	442	450	458	465	473	481	488	496	504
569	511	519	526	534	542	549	557	565	572	580
570	75587	75595	75603	75610	75618	75626	75633	75641	75648	75656
571	664	671	679	686	694	702	709	717	724	732
572	740	747	755	762	770	778	785	793	800	808
573	815	823	831	838	846	853	861	868	876	884
574	891	899	906	914	921	929	937	944	952	959
575	967	974	982	989	997	76005	76012	76020	76027	76035
576	76042	76050	76057	76065	76072	080	087	095	103	110
577	118	125	133	140	148	155	163	170	178	185
578	193	200	208	215	223	230	238	245	253	260
579	268	275	283	290	298	305	313	320	328	335
580	76343	76350	76358	76365	76373	76380	76388	76395	76403	76410
581	418	425	433	440	448	455	462	470	477	485
582	492	500	507	515	522	530	537	545	552	559
583	567	574	582	589	597	604	612	619	626	634
584	641	649	656	664	671	678	686	693	701	708
585	716	723	730	738	745	753	760	768	775	782
586	790	797	805	812	819	827	834	842	849	856
587	864	871	879	886	893	901	908	916	923	930
588	938	945	953	960	967	975	982	989	997	77004
589	77012	77019	77026	77034	77041	77048	77056	77063	77070	078
590	77085	77093	77100	77107	77115	77122	77129	77137	77144	77151
591	159	166	173	181	188	195	203	210	217	225
592	232	240	247	254	262	269	276	283	291	298
593	305	313	320	327	335	342	349	357	364	371
594	379	386	393	401	408	415	422	430	437	444
595	452	459	466	474	481	488	495	503	510	517
596	525	532	539	546	554	561	568	576	583	590
597	597	605	612	619	627	634	641	648	656	663
598	670	677	685	692	699	706	714	721	728	735
599	743	750	757	764	772	779	786	793	801	808
600	77815	77822	77830	77837	77844	77851	77859	77866	77873	77880
N	0	1	2	3	4	5	6	7	8	9

P.P.

8
1	0.8
2	1.6
3	2.4
4	3.2
5	4.0
6	4.8
7	5.6
8	6.4
9	7.2

7
1	0.7
2	1.4
3	2.1
4	2.8
5	3.5
6	4.2
7	4.9
8	5.6
9	6.3

Numbers 600–650   Logs 77815–81351

N	0	1	2	3	4	5	6	7	8	9
600	77 815	77 822	77 830	77 837	77 844	77 851	77 859	77 866	77 873	77 880
601	887	895	902	909	916	924	931	938	945	952
602	960	967	974	981	988	996	78 003	78 010	78 017	78 025
603	78 032	78 039	78 046	78 053	78 061	78 068	075	082	089	097
604	104	111	118	125	132	140	147	154	161	168
605	176	183	190	197	204	211	219	226	233	240
606	247	254	262	269	276	283	290	297	305	312
607	319	326	333	340	347	355	362	369	376	383
608	390	398	405	412	419	426	433	440	447	455
609	462	469	476	483	490	497	504	512	519	526
610	78 533	78 540	78 547	78 554	78 561	78 569	78 576	78 583	78 590	78 597
611	604	611	618	625	633	640	647	654	661	668
612	675	682	689	696	704	711	718	725	732	739
613	746	753	760	767	774	781	789	796	803	810
614	817	824	831	838	845	852	859	866	873	880
615	888	895	902	909	916	923	930	937	944	951
616	958	965	972	979	986	993	79 000	79 007	79 014	79 021
617	79 029	79 036	79 043	79 050	79 057	79 064	071	078	085	092
618	099	106	113	120	127	134	141	148	155	162
619	169	176	183	190	197	204	211	218	225	232
620	79 239	79 246	79 253	79 260	79 267	79 274	79 281	79 288	79·295	79 302
621	309	316	323	330	337	344	351	358	365	372
622	379	386	393	400	407	414	421	428	435	442
623	449	456	463	470	477	484	491	498	505	511
624	518	525	532	539	546	553	560	567	574	581
625	588	595	602	609	616	623	630	637	644	650
626	657	664	671	678	685	692	699	706	713	720
627	727	734	741	748	754	761	768	775	782	789
628	796	803	810	817	824	831	837	844	851	858
629	865	872	879	886	893	900	906	913	920	927
630	79 934	79 941	79 948	79 955	79 962	79 969	79 975	79 982	79 989	79 996
631	80 003	80 010	80 017	80 024	80 030	80 037	80 044	80 051	80 058	80 065
632	072	079	085	092	099	106	113	120	127	134
633	140	147	154	161	168	175	182	188	195	202
634	209	216	223	229	236	243	250	257	264	271
635	277	284	291	298	305	312	318	325	332	339
636	346	353	359	366	373	380	387	393	400	407
637	414	421	428	434	441	448	455	462	468	475
638	482	489	496	502	509	516	523	530	536	543
639	550	557	564	570	577	584	591	598	604	611
640	80 618	80 625	80 632	80 638	80 645	80 652	80 659	80 665	80 672	80 679
641	686	693	699	706	713	720	726	733	740	747
642	754	760	767	774	781	787	794	801	808	814
643	821	828	835	841	848	855	862	868	875	882
644	889	895	902	909	916	922	929	936	943	949
645	956	963	969	976	983	990	996	81 003	81 010	81 017
646	81 023	81 030	81 037	81 043	81 050	81 057	81 064	070	077	084
647	090	097	104	111	117	124	131	137	144	151
648	158	164	171	178	184	191	198	204	211	218
649	224	231	238	245	251	258	265	271	278	285
650	81 291	81 298	81 305	81 311	81 318	81 325	81 331	81 338	81 345	81 351
N	0	1	2	3	4	5	6	7	8	9

P.P.

8		7		6	
1	0.8	1	0.7	1	0.6
2	1.6	2	1.4	2	1.2
3	2.4	3	2.1	3	1.8
4	3.2	4	2.8	4	2.4
5	4.0	5	3.5	5	3.0
6	4.8	6	4.2	6	3.6
7	5.6	7	4.9	7	4.2
8	6.4	8	5.6	8	4.8
9	7.2	9	6.3	9	5.4

Numbers 650–700   Logs 81291–84566

N	0	1	2	3	4	5	6	7	8	9
650	81 291	81 298	81 305	81 311	81 318	81 325	81 331	81 338	81 345	81 351
651	358	365	371	378	385	391	398	405	411	418
652	425	431	438	445	451	458	465	471	478	485
653	491	498	505	511	518	525	531	538	544	551
654	558	564	571	578	584	591	598	604	611	617
655	624	631	637	644	651	657	664	671	677	684
656	690	697	704	710	717	723	730	737	743	750
657	757	763	770	776	783	790	796	803	809	816
658	823	829	836	842	849	856	862	869	875	882
659	889	895	902	908	915	921	928	935	941	948
660	81 954	81 961	81 968	81 974	81 981	81 987	81 994	82 000	82 007	82 014
661	82 020	82 027	82 033	82 040	82 046	82 053	82 060	066	073	079
662	086	092	099	105	112	119	125	132	138	145
663	151	158	164	171	178	184	191	197	204	210
664	217	223	230	236	243	249	256	263	269	276
665	282	289	295	302	308	315	321	328	334	341
666	347	354	360	367	373	380	387	393	400	406
667	413	419	426	432	439	445	452	458	465	471
668	478	484	491	497	504	510	517	523	530	536
669	543	549	556	562	569	575	582	588	595	601
670	82 607	82 614	82 620	82 627	82 633	82 640	82 646	82 653	82 659	82 666
671	672	679	685	692	698	705	711	718	724	730
672	737	743	750	756	763	769	776	782	789	795
673	802	808	814	821	827	834	840	847	853	860
674	866	872	879	885	892	898	905	911	918	924
675	930	937	943	950	956	963	969	975	982	988
676	995	83 001	83 008	83 014	83 020	83 027	83 033	83 040	83 046	83 052
677	83 059	065	072	078	085	091	097	104	110	117
678	123	129	136	142	149	155	161	168	174	181
679	187	193	200	206	213	219	225	232	238	245
680	83 251	83 257	83 264	83 270	83 276	83 283	83 289	83 296	83 302	83 308
681	315	321	327	334	340	347	353	359	366	372
682	378	385	391	398	404	410	417	423	429	436
683	442	448	455	461	467	474	480	487	493	499
684	506	512	518	525	531	537	544	550	556	563
685	569	575	582	588	594	601	607	613	620	626
686	632	639	645	651	658	664	670	677	683	689
687	696	702	708	715	721	727	734	740	746	753
688	759	765	771	778	784	790	797	803	809	816
689	822	828	835	841	847	853	860	866	872	879
690	83 885	83 891	83 897	83 904	83 910	83 916	83 923	83 929	83 935	83 942
691	948	954	960	967	973	979	985	992	998	84 004
692	84 011	84 017	84 023	84 029	84 036	84 042	84 048	84 055	84 061	067
693	073	080	086	092	098	105	111	117	123	130
694	136	142	148	155	161	167	173	180	186	192
695	198	205	211	217	223	230	236	242	248	255
696	261	267	273	280	286	292	298	305	311	317
697	323	330	336	342	348	354	361	367	373	379
698	386	392	398	404	410	417	423	429	435	442
699	448	454	460	466	473	479	485	491	497	504
700	84 510	84 516	84 522	84 528	84 535	84 541	84 547	84 553	84 559	84 566
N	0	1	2	3	4	5	6	7	8	9

P.P.

7		6	
1	0.7	1	0.6
2	1.4	2	1.2
3	2.1	3	1.8
4	2.8	4	2.4
5	3.5	5	3.0
6	4.2	6	3.6
7	4.9	7	4.2
8	5.6	8	4.8
9	6.3	9	5.4

Numbers 700–750   Logs 84510–87558

N	0	1	2	3	4	5	6	7	8	9
700	84 510	84 516	84 522	84 528	84 535	84 541	84 547	84 553	84 559	84 566
701	572	578	584	590	597	603	609	615	621	628
702	634	640	646	652	658	665	671	677	683	689
703	696	702	708	714	720	726	733	739	745	751
704	757	763	770	776	782	788	794	800	807	813
705	819	825	831	837	844	850	856	862	868	874
706	880	887	893	899	905	911	917	924	930	936
707	942	948	954	960	967	973	979	985	991	997
708	85 003	85 009	85 016	85 022	85 028	85 034	85 040	85 046	85 052	85 058
709	065	071	077	083	089	095	101	107	114	120
710	85 126	85 132	85 138	85 144	85 150	85 156	85 163	85 169	85 175	85 181
711	187	193	199	205	211	217	224	230	236	242
712	248	254	260	266	272	278	285	291	297	303
713	309	315	321	327	333	339	345	352	358	364
714	370	376	382	388	394	400	406	412	418	425
715	431	437	443	449	455	461	467	473	479	485
716	491	497	503	509	516	522	528	534	540	546
717	552	558	564	570	576	582	588	594	600	606
718	612	618	625	631	637	643	649	655	661	667
719	673	679	685	691	697	703	709	715	721	727
720	85 733	85 739	85 745	85 751	85 757	85 763	85 769	85 775	85 781	85 788
721	794	800	806	812	818	824	830	836	842	848
722	854	860	866	872	878	884	890	896	902	908
723	914	920	926	932	938	944	950	956	962	968
724	974	980	986	992	998	86 004	86 010	86 016	86 022	86 028
725	86 034	86 040	86 046	86 052	86 058	064	070	076	082	088
726	094	100	106	112	118	124	130	136	141	147
727	153	159	165	171	177	183	189	195	201	207
728	213	219	225	231	237	243	249	255	261	267
729	273	279	285	291	297	303	308	314	320	326
730	86 332	86 338	86 344	86 350	86 356	86 362	86 368	86 374	86 380	86 386
731	392	398	404	410	415	421	427	433	439	445
732	451	457	463	469	475	481	487	493	499	504
733	510	516	522	528	534	540	546	552	558	564
734	570	576	581	587	593	599	605	611	617	623
735	629	635	641	646	652	658	664	670	676	682
736	688	694	700	705	711	717	723	729	735	741
737	747	753	759	764	770	776	782	788	794	800
738	806	812	817	823	829	835	841	847	853	859
739	864	870	876	882	888	894	900	906	911	917
740	86 923	86 929	86 935	86 941	86 947	86 953	86 958	86 964	86 970	86 976
741	982	988	994	999	87 005	87 011	87 017	87 023	87 029	87 035
742	87 040	87 046	87 052	87 058	064	070	075	081	087	093
743	099	105	111	116	122	128	134	140	146	151
744	157	163	169	175	181	186	192	198	204	210
745	216	221	227	233	239	245	251	256	262	268
746	274	280	286	291	297	303	309	315	320	326
747	332	338	344	349	355	361	367	373	379	384
748	390	396	402	408	413	419	425	431	437	442
749	448	454	460	466	471	477	483	489	495	500
750	87 506	87 512	87 518	87 523	87 529	87 535	87 541	87 547	87 552	87 558
N	0	1	2	3	4	5	6	7	8	9

P.P.

7		6		5	
1	0.7	1	0.6	1	0.5
2	1.4	2	1.2	2	1.0
3	2.1	3	1.8	3	1.5
4	2.8	4	2.4	4	2.0
5	3.5	5	3.0	5	2.5
6	4.2	6	3.6	6	3.0
7	4.9	7	4.2	7	3.5
8	5.6	8	4.8	8	4.0
9	6.3	9	5.4	9	4.5

Numbers 750–800 Logs 87506–90358

N	0	1	2	3	4	5	6	7	8	9
750	87 506	87 512	87 518	87 523	87 529	87 535	87 541	87 547	87 552	87 558
751	564	570	576	581	587	593	599	604	610	616
752	622	628	633	639	645	651	656	662	668	674
753	679	685	691	697	703	708	714	720	726	731
754	737	743	749	754	760	766	772	777	783	789
755	795	800	806	812	818	823	829	835	841	846
756	852	858	864	869	875	881	887	892	898	904
757	910	915	921	927	933	938	944	950	955	961
758	967	973	978	984	990	996	88 001	88 007	88 013	88 018
759	88 024	88 030	88 036	88 041	88 047	88 053	058	064	070	076
760	88 081	88 087	88 093	88 098	88 104	88 110	88 116	88 121	88 127	88 133
761	138	144	150	156	161	167	173	178	184	190
762	195	201	207	213	218	224	230	235	241	247
763	252	258	264	270	275	281	287	292	298	304
764	309	315	321	326	332	338	343	349	355	360
765	366	372	377	383	389	395	400	406	412	417
766	423	429	434	440	446	451	457	463	468	474
767	480	485	491	497	502	508	513	519	525	530
768	536	542	547	553	559	564	570	576	581	587
769	593	598	604	610	615	621	627	632	638	643
770	88 649	88 655	88 660	88 666	88 672	88 677	88 683	88 689	88 694	88 700
771	705	711	717	722	728	734	739	745	750	756
772	762	767	773	779	784	790	795	801	807	812
773	818	824	829	835	840	846	852	857	863	868
774	874	880	885	891	897	902	908	913	919	925
775	930	936	941	947	953	958	964	969	975	981
776	986	992	997	89 003	89 009	89 014	89 020	89 025	89 031	89 037
777	89 042	89 048	89 053	059	064	070	076	081	087	092
778	098	104	109	115	120	126	131	137	143	148
779	154	159	165	170	176	182	187	193	198	204
780	89 209	89 215	89 221	89 226	89 232	89 237	89 243	89 248	89 254	89 260
781	265	271	276	282	287	293	298	304	310	315
782	321	326	332	337	343	348	354	360	365	371
783	376	382	387	393	398	404	409	415	421	426
784	432	437	443	448	454	459	465	470	476	481
785	487	492	498	504	509	515	520	526	531	537
786	542	548	553	559	564	570	575	581	586	592
787	597	603	609	614	620	625	631	636	642	647
788	653	658	664	669	675	680	686	691	697	702
789	708	713	719	724	730	735	741	746	752	757
790	89 763	89 768	89 774	89 779	89 785	89 790	89 796	89 801	89 807	89 812
791	818	823	829	834	840	845	851	856	862	867
792	873	878	883	889	894	900	905	911	916	922
793	927	933	938	944	949	955	960	966	971	977
794	982	988	993	998	90 004	90 009	90 015	90 020	90 026	90 031
795	90 037	90 042	90 048	90 053	059	064	069	075	080	086
796	091	097	102	108	113	119	124	129	135	140
797	146	151	157	162	168	173	179	184	189	195
798	200	206	211	217	222	227	233	238	244	249
799	255	260	266	271	276	282	287	293	298	304
800	90 309	90 314	90 320	90 325	90 331	90 336	90 342	90 347	90 352	90 358
N	0	1	2	3	4	5	6	7	8	9

P.P.

6	
1	0.6
2	1.2
3	1.8
4	2.4
5	3.0
6	3.6
7	4.2
8	4.8
9	5.4

5	
1	0.5
2	1.0
3	1.5
4	2.0
5	2.5
6	3.0
7	3.5
8	4.0
9	4.5

Logarithms of Numbers

Numbers 800–850   Logs 90309–92988

N	0	1	2	3	4	5	6	7	8	9	P.P.	
800	90 309	90 314	90 320	90 325	90 331	90 336	90 342	90 347	90 352	90 358	**6**	
801	363	369	374	380	385̄	390	396	401	407	412	1	0.6
802	417	423	428	434	439	445̄	450	455	461̲	466	2	1.2
803	472	477	482	488	493	499	504	509	515̄	520	3	1.8
804	526	531	536	542	547	553	558	563	569	574	4	2.4
805	580	585̄	590	596	601	607	612	617	623	628	5	3.0
806	634	639	644	650	655	660	666	671	677	682	6	3.6
807	687	693	698	703	709	714	720	725	730	736	7	4.2
808	741̲	747	752	757	763	768	773	779	784	789	8	4.8
809	795̄	800	806	811	816	822	827	832	838	843	9	5.4
810	90 849	90 854	90 859	90 865̄	90 870	90 875̄	90 881	90 886	90 891	90 897		
811	902	907	913	918	924	929	934	940	945̄	950		
812	956	961	966	972	977	982	988	993	998	91 004		
813	91 009	91 014	91 020	91 025	91 030	91 036	91 041	91 046	91 052	057		
814	062	068	073	078	084	089	094	100	105	110		
815	116	121	126	132	137	142	148	153	158	164		
816	169	174	180	185̄	190	196	201	206	212	217		
817	222	228	233	238	243	249	254	259	265̄	270		
818	275	281	286	291	297	302	307	312	318	323		
819	328	334	339	344	350	355̄	360	365	371	376		
820	91 381	91 387	91 392	91 397	91 403	91 408	91 413	91 418	91 424	91 429	**5**	
821	434	440	445̄	450	455	461	466	471	477	482̲	1	0.5
822	487	492	498	503	508	514	519	524	529	535̄	2	1.0
823	540	545	551	556	561	566	572	577	582	587	3	1.5
824	593	598	603	609	614	619	624	630	635̄	640	4	2.0
825	645	651	656	661	666	672	677	682	687	693	5	2.5
826	698	703	709	714	719	724	730	735̄	740	745	6	3.0
827	751	756	761	766	772	777	782	787	793̲	798	7	3.5
828	803	808	814	819	824	829	834	840	845̄	850	8	4.0
829	855	861	866	871	876	882	887	892	897	903	9	4.5
830	91 908	91 913	91 918	91 924	91 929	91 934	91 939	91 944	91 950	91 955̄		
831	960	965	971	976	981	986	991	997	92 002	92 007		
832	92 012	92 018	92 023	92 028	92 033	92 038	92 044	92 049	054	059		
833	065̄	070	075̄	080	085	091	096	101	106	111		
834	117	122	127	132	137	143̲	148	153	158	163		
835	169	174	179	184	189	195̄	200	205	210	215		
836	221	226	231	236	241	247	252	257	262	267		
837	273	278	283	288	293	298	304	309	314	319		
838	324	330	335̄	340	345	350	355	361	366	371		
839	376	381	387	392	397	402	407	412	418	423		
840	92 428	92 433	92 438	92 443	92 449	92 454	92 459	92 464	92 469	92 474		
841	480	485̄	490	495	500	505	511	516	521	526		
842	531	536	542	547	552	557	562	567	572	578		
843	583	588	593	598	603	609	614	619	624	629		
844	634	639	645̄	650	655̄	660	665	670	675	681		
845	686	691	696	701	706	711	716	722	727	732		
846	737	742	747	752	758	763	768	773	778	783		
847	788	793̲	799	804	809	814	819	824	829	834		
848	840	845̄	850	855̄	860	865	870	875	881	886		
849	891	896	901	906	911	916	921	927	932	937		
850	92 942	92 947	92 952	92 957	92 962	92 967	92 973	92 978	92 983	92 988		
N	0	1	2	3	4	5	6	7	8	9		

Numbers 850–900   Logs 92942–95468

N	0	1	2	3	4	5	6	7	8	9
850	92 942	92 947	92 952	92 957	92 962	92 967	92 973	92 978	92 983	92 988
851	993	998	93 003	93 008	93 013	93 018	93 024	93 029	93 034	93 039
852	93 044	93 049	054	059	064	069	075	080	085	090
853	095	100	105	110	115	120	125	131	136	141
854	146	151	156	161	166	171	176	181	186	192
855	197	202	207	212	217	222	227	232	237	242
856	247	252	258	263	268	273	278	283	288	293
857	298	303	308	313	318	323	328	334	339	344
858	349	354	359	364	369	374	379	384	389	394
859	399	404	409	414	420	425	430	435	440	445
860	93 450	93 455	93 460	93 465	93 470	93 475	93 480	93 485	93 490	93 495
861	500	505	510	515	520	526	531	536	541	546
862	551	556	561	566	571	576	581	586	591	596
863	601	606	611	616	621	626	631	636	641	646
864	651	656	661	666	671	676	682	687	692	697
865	702	707	712	717	722	727	732	737	742	747
866	752	757	762	767	772	777	782	787	792	797
867	802	807	812	817	822	827	832	837	842	847
868	852	857	862	867	872	877	882	887	892	897
869	902	907	912	917	922	927	932	937	942	947
870	93 952	93 957	93 962	93 967	93 972	93 977	93 982	93 987	93 992	93 997
871	94 002	94 007	94 012	94 017	94 022	94 027	94 032	94 037	94 042	94 047
872	052	057	062	067	072	077	082	086	091	096
873	101	106	111	116	121	126	131	136	141	146
874	151	156	161	166	171	176	181	186	191	196
875	201	206	211	216	221	226	231	236	240	245
876	250	255	260	265	270	275	280	285	290	295
877	300	305	310	315	320	325	330	335	340	345
878	349	354	359	364	369	374	379	384	389	394
879	399	404	409	414	419	424	429	433	438	443
880	94 448	94 453	94 458	94 463	94 468	94 473	94 478	94 483	94 488	94 493
881	498	503	507	512	517	522	527	532	537	542
882	547	552	557	562	567	571	576	581	586	591
883	596	601	606	611	616	621	626	630	635	640
884	645	650	655	660	665	670	675	680	685	689
885	694	699	704	709	714	719	724	729	734	738
886	743	748	753	758	763	768	773	778	783	787
887	792	797	802	807	812	817	822	827	832	836
888	841	846	851	856	861	866	871	876	880	885
889	890	895	900	905	910	915	919	924	929	934
890	94 939	94 944	94 949	94 954	94 959	94 963	94 968	94 973	94 978	94 983
891	988	993	998	95 002	95 007	95 012	95 017	95 022	95 027	95 032
892	95 036	95 041	95 046	051	056	061	066	071	075	080
893	085	090	095	100	105	109	114	119	124	129
894	134	139	143	148	153	158	163	168	173	177
895	182	187	192	197	202	207	211	216	221	226
896	231	236	240	245	250	255	260	265	270	274
897	279	284	289	294	299	303	308	313	318	323
898	328	332	337	342	347	352	357	361	366	371
899	376	381	386	390	395	400	405	410	415	419
900	95 424	95 429	95 434	95 439	95 444	95 448	95 453	95 458	95 463	95 468
N	0	1	2	3	4	5	6	7	8	9

P.P.

6		5		4	
1	0.6	1	0.5	1	0.4
2	1.2	2	1.0	2	0.8
3	1.8	3	1.5	3	1.2
4	2.4	4	2.0	4	1.6
5	3.0	5	2.5	5	2.0
6	3.6	6	3.0	6	2.4
7	4.2	7	3.5	7	2.8
8	4.8	8	4.0	8	3.2
9	5.4	9	4.5	9	3.6

Numbers 900–950			Logs 95424–97813							P.P.	
N	0	1	2	3	4	5	6	7	8	9	
900	95 424	95 429	95 434	95 439	95 444	95 448	95 453	95 458	95 463	95 468	**5**	
901	472	477	482	487	492	497	501	506	511	516	1	0.5
902	521	525	530	535	540	54$\bar{5}$	550	554	559	564	2	1.0
903	569	574	578	583	588	593	598	602	607	612	3	1.5
904	617	622	626	631	636	641	646	650	655	660	4	2.0
905	66$\bar{5}$	670	674	679	684	689	694	698	703	708	5	2.5
906	713	718	722	727	732	737	742	746	751	756	6	3.0
907	761	766	770	775	780	78$\bar{5}$	789	794	799	804	7	3.5
908	809	813	818	823	828	832	837	842	847	852	8	4.0
909	856	861	866	871	875	880	885	890	89$\bar{5}$	899	9	4.5
910	95 904	95 909	95 914	95 918	95 923	95 928	95 933	95 938	95 942	95 947		
911	952	957	961	966	971	976	980	985	990	99$\bar{5}$		
912	999	96 004	96 009	96 014	96 019	96 023	96 028	96 033	96 038	96 042		
913	96 047	052	057	061	066	071	076	080	085	090		
914	09$\bar{5}$	099	104	109	114	118	123	128	133	137		
915	142	147	152	156	161	166	171	175	180	18$\bar{5}$		
916	190	194	199	204	209	213	218	223	227	232		
917	237	242	246	251	256	261	265	270	27$\bar{5}$	280		
918	284	289	294	298	303	308	313	317	322	327		
919	332	336	341	346	350	355	360	36$\bar{5}$	369	374		
920	96 379	96 384	96 388	96 393	96 398	96 402	96 407	96 412	96 417	96 421	**4**	
921	426	431	435	440	44$\bar{5}$	450	454	459	464	468	1	0.4
922	473	478	483	487	492	497	501	506	511	515	2	0.8
923	520	52$\bar{5}$	530	534	539	544	548	553	558	562	3	1.2
924	567	572	577	581	586	591	595	600	60$\bar{5}$	609	4	1.6
925	614	619	624	628	633	63$\underline{8}$	642	647	652	656	5	2.0
926	661	666	670	675	680	685	689	694	699	703	6	2.4
927	70$\underline{8}$	713	717	722	727	731	736	741	745	750	7	2.8
928	75$\bar{5}$	759	764	769	774	77$\underline{8}$	783	788	792	797	8	3.2
929	802	806	811	816	820	82$\bar{5}$	830	834	839	844	9	3.6
930	96 848	96 853	96 858	96 862	96 867	96 872	96 876	96 881	96 886	96 890		
931	89$\bar{5}$	900	904	909	914	918	923	928	932	937		
932	942	946	951	956	960	96$\bar{5}$	970	974	979	984		
933	988	993	997	97 002	97 007	97 011	97 016	97 021	97 025	97 030		
934	97 03$\bar{5}$	97 039	97 044	049	053	058	063	067	072	077		
935	081	086	090	095	100	104	109	114	11$\underline{8}$	123		
936	128	132	137	142	146	151	155	160	16$\bar{5}$	169		
937	174	179	183	188	192	197	202	206	211	216		
938	220	22$\bar{5}$	230	234	239	243	248	253	257	262		
939	267	271	276	280	285	290	294	299	304	308		
940	97 313	97 317	97 322	97 327	97 331	97 336	97 340	97 345	97 350	97 354		
941	359	364	368	373	377	382	387	391	396	400		
942	405	410	414	419	424	428	433	437	442	447		
943	451	456	460	46$\bar{5}$	470	474	479	483	488	493		
944	497	502	506	511	516	520	52$\bar{5}$	529	534	539		
945	543	548	552	557	562	566	571	575	580	58$\bar{5}$		
946	589	594	598	603	607	612	617	621	626	630		
947	63$\bar{5}$	640	644	649	653	658	663	667	672	676		
948	681	685	690	69$\bar{5}$	699	704	708	713	717	722		
949	727	731	736	740	74$\bar{5}$	749	754	759	763	768		
950	97 772	97 777	97 782	97 786	97 791	97 795	97 800	97 804	97 809	97 813		
N	0	1	2	3	4	5	6	7	8	9		

Numbers 950–1000   Logs 97772–00039

N	0	1	2	3	4	5	6	7	8	9
950	97 772	97 777	97 782	97 786	97 791	97 795	97 800	97 804	97 809	97 813
951	818	823	827	832	836	841	845	850	85$\overline{5}$	859
952	864	868	873	877	882	886	891	896	900	90$\overline{5}$
953	909	914	918	923	928	932	937	941	946	950
954	95$\overline{5}$	959	964	968	973	978	982	987	991	996
955	98 000	98 00$\overline{5}$	98 009	98 014	98 019	98 023	98 028	98 032	98 037	98 041
956	046	050	05$\overline{5}$	059	064	068	073	078	082	087
957	091	096	100	10$\overline{5}$	109	114	118	123	127	132
958	137	141	146	150	15$\overline{5}$	159	164	168	173	177
959	182	186	191	195	200	204	209	214	218	223
960	98 227	98 232	98 236	98 241	98 245	98 250	98 254	98 259	98 263	98 268
961	272	277	281	286	290	29$\overline{5}$	299	304	308	313
962	318	322	327	331	336	340	34$\overline{5}$	349	354	358
963	363	367	372	376	381	385	390	394	399	403
964	408	412	417	421	426	430	43$\overline{5}$	439	444	448
965	453	457	462	466	471	475	480	484	489	493
966	498	502	507	511	516	520	52$\overline{5}$	529	534	538
967	543	547	552	556	561	565	570	574	579	583
968	588	592	597	601	605	610	614	619	623	628
969	632	637	641	646	650	65$\overline{5}$	659	664	668	673
970	98 677	98 682	98 686	98 691	98 695	98 700	98 704	98 709	98 713	98 717
971	722	726	731	735	740	744	749	753	758	762
972	767	771	776	780	784	789	793	798	802	807
973	811	816	820	82$\overline{5}$	829	834	838	843	847	851
974	856	860	86$\overline{5}$	869	874	878	883	887	892	896
975	900	90$\overline{5}$	909	914	918	923	927	932	936	941
976	94$\overline{5}$	949	954	958	963	967	972	976	981	985
977	989	994	998	99 003	99 007	99 012	99 016	99 021	99 025	99 029
978	99 034	99 038	99 043	047	052	056	061	06$\overline{5}$	069	074
979	078	083	087	092	096	100	10$\overline{5}$	109	114	118
980	99 123	99 127	99 131	99 136	99 140	99 14$\overline{5}$	99 149	99 154	99 158	99 162
981	167	171	176	180	18$\overline{5}$	189	193	198	202	207
982	211	216	220	224	229	233	238	242	247	251
983	255	260	264	269	273	277	282	286	291	295
984	300	304	308	313	317	322	326	330	33$\overline{5}$	339
985	344	348	352	357	361	366	370	374	379	383
986	388	392	396	401	405	410	414	419	423	427
987	432	436	441	44$\overline{5}$	449	454	458	463	467	471
988	476	480	484	489	493	498	502	506	511	515
989	520	524	528	533	537	542	546	550	55$\overline{5}$	559
990	99 564	99 568	99 572	99 577	99 581	99 585	99 590	99 594	99 599	99 603
991	607	612	616	621	62$\overline{5}$	629	634	638	642	647
992	651	656	660	664	669	673	677	682	686	691
993	69$\overline{5}$	699	704	708	712	717	721	726	730	734
994	739	743	747	752	756	760	76$\overline{5}$	769	774	778
995	782	787	79$\overline{1}$	795	800	804	808	813	817	822
996	826	830	83$\overline{5}$	839	843	848	852	856	861	865
997	870	874	878	883	887	891	896	900	904	909
998	913	917	922	926	930	93$\overline{5}$	939	944	948	952
999	957	961	965	970	974	978	983	987	991	996
1000	00 000	00 004	00 009	00 013	00 017	00 022	00 026	00 030	00 03$\overline{5}$	00 039
N	0	1	2	3	4	5	6	7	8	9

P.P.

5

1	0.5
2	1.0
3	1.5
4	2.0
5	2.5
6	3.0
7	3.5
8	4.0
9	4.5

4

1	0.4
2	0.8
3	1.2
4	1.6
5	2.0
6	2.4
7	2.8
8	3.2
9	3.6

Numbers 1000–1050   Logs 0000000–0215614

N	0	1	2	3	4	5	6	7	8	9
1000	000 0000	0434̅	0869	1303	1737	2171	2605̅	3039	3473	3907
01	4341	4775̅	5208	5642	6076	6510	6943	7377	7810	8244
02	8677	9111	9544	9977	*0411	*0844	*1277	*1710	*2143	*2576
03	001 3009	3442	3875	4308	4741	5174	5607	6039	6472	6905̅
04	7337	7770	8202	8635̅	9067	9499	9932	*0364̅	*0796	*1228
05	002 1661	2093	2525̅	2957	3389	3821	4253	4685̅	5116	5548
06	5980	6411	6843	7275̅	7706	8138	8569	9001	9432	9863
07	003 0295̅	0726	1157	1588	2019	2451	2882	3313	3744	4174
08	4605	5036	5467	5898	6328	6759	7190	7620	8051	8481
09	8912	9342	9772	*0203	*0633	*1063	*1493	*1924	*2354	*2784
1010	004 3214	3644̅	4074	4504	4933	5363	5793	6223	6652	7082
11	7512	7941	8371	8800	9229	9659	*0088	*0517	*0947	*1376
12	005 1805	2234	2663	3092	3521	3950	4379	4808	5237	5666
13	6094	6523	6952	7380	7809	8238	8666	9094	9523	9951
14	006 0380	0808	1236	1664	2092	2521	2949	3377	3805̅	4233
15	4660	5088	5516	5944	6372	6799	7227	7655̅	8082	8510
16	8937	9365	9792	*0219	*0647	*1074	*1501	*1928	*2355̅	*2782
17	007 3210	3637	4064	4490	4917	5344	5771	6198	6624	7051
18	7478	7904	8331	8757	9184	9610	*0037	*0463	*0889	*1316
19	008 1742	2168	2594	3020	3446	3872	4298	4724	5150	5576
1020	6002	6427	6853	7279	7704	8130	8556	8981	9407	9832
21	009 0257	0683	1108	1533	1959	2384	2809	3234	3659	4084
22	4509	4934	5359	5784	6208	6633	7058	7483	7907	8332
23	8756	9181	9605̅	*0030	*0454	*0878	*1303	*1727	*2151	*2575̅
24	010 3000	3424	3848	4272	4696	5120	5544	5967	6391	6815̅
25	7239	7662	8086	8510	8933	9357	9780	*0204	*0627	*1050
26	011 1474	1897	2320	2743	3166	3590	4013	4436	4859	5282
27	5704	6127	6550	6973	7396	7818	8241	8664	9086	9509
28	9931	*0354	*0776	*1198	*1621	*2043	*2465	*2887	*3310	*3732
29	012 4154	4576	4998	5420	5842	6264	6685	7107	7529	7951
1030	8372	8794	9215	9637	*0059	*0480	*0901	*1323	*1744	*2165
31	013 2587	3008	3429	3850	4271	4692	5113	5534	5955	6376
32	6797	7218	7639	8059	8480	8901	9321	9742	*0162	*0583
33	014 1003	1424	1844	2264	2685̅	3105̅	3525	3945	4365	4785
34	5205	5625	6045	6465	6885	7305̅	7725̅	8144	8564	8984
35	9403	9823	*0243	*0662	*1082	*1501	*1920	*2340	*2759	*3178
36	015 3598	4017	4436	4855̅	5274	5693	6112	6531	6950	7369
37	7788	8206	8625	9044	9462	9881	*0300	*0718	*1137	*1555
38	016 1974	2392	2810	3229	3647	4065	4483	4901	5319	5737
39	6155	6573	6991	7409	7827	8245	8663	9080	9498	9916
1040	017 0333	0751	1168	1586	2003	2421	2838	3256	3673	4090
41	4507	4924	5342	5759	6176	6593	7010	7427	7844	8260
42	8677	9094	9511	9927	*0344	*0761	*1177	*1594	*2010	*2427
43	018 2843	3259	3676	4092	4508	4925̅	5341	5757	6173	6589
44	7005̅	7421	7837	8253	8669	9084	9500	9916	*0332	*0747
45	019 1163	1578	1994	2410	2825̅	3240	3656	4071	4486	4902
46	5317	5732	6147	6562	6977	7392	7807	8222	8637	9052
47	9467	9882	*0296	*0711	*1126	*1540	*1955̅	*2369	*2784	*3198
48	020 3613	4027	4442	4856	5270	5684	6099	6513	6927	7341
49	7755̅	8169	8583	8997	9411	9824	*0238	*0652	*1066	*1479
1050	021 1893	2307	2720	3134	3547	3961	4374	4787	5201	5614
N	0	1	2	3	4	5	6	7	8	9

	Numbers 1050–1100 Logs 0211893–0417479									
N	0	1	2	3	4	5	6	7	8	9
1050	021 1893	2307	2720	3134	3547	3961	4374	4787	5201	5614
51	6027	6440	6854	7267	7680	8093	8506	8919	9332	9745
52	022 0157	0570	0983	1396	1808	2221	2634	3046	3459	3871
53	4284	4696	5109	5521	5933	6345	6758	7170	7582	7994
54	8406	8818	9230	9642	*0054	*0466	*0878	*1289	*1701	*2113
55	023 2525	2936	3348	3759	4171	4582	4994	5405	5817	6228
56	6639	7050	7462	7873	8284	8695	9106	9517	9928	*0339
57	024 0750	1161	1572	1982	2393	2804	3214	3625	4036	4446
58	4857	5267	5678	6088	6498	6909	7319	7729	8139	8549
59	8960	9370	9780	*0190	*0600	*1010	*1419	*1829	*2239	*2649
1060	025 3059	3468	3878	4288	4697	5107	5516	5926	6335	6744
61	7154	7563	7972	8382	8791	9200	9609	*0018	*0427	*0836
62	026 1245	1654	2063	2472	2881	3289	3698	4107	4515	4924
63	5333	5741	6150	6558	6967	7375	7783	8192	8600	9008
64	9416	9824	*0233	*0641	*1049	*1457	*1865	*2273	*2680	*3088
65	027 3496	3904	4312	4719	5127	5535	5942	6350	6757	7165
66	7572	7979	8387	8794	9201	9609	*0016	*0423	*0830	*1237
67	028 1644	2051	2458	2865	3272	3679	4086	4492	4899	5306
68	5713	6119	6526	6932	7339	7745	8152	8558	8964	9371
69	9777	*0183	*0590	*0996	*1402	*1808	*2214	*2620	*3026	*3432
1070	029 3838	4244	4649	5055	5461	5867	6272	6678	7084	7489
71	7895	8300	8706	9111	9516	9922	*0327	*0732	*1138	*1543
72	030 1948	2353	2758	3163	3568	3973	4378	4783	5188	5592
73	5997	6402	6807	7211	7616	8020	8425	8830	9234	9638
74	031 0043	0447	0851	1256	1660	2064	2468	2872	3277	3681
75	4085	4489	4893	5296	5700	6104	6508	6912	7315	7719
76	8123	8526	8930	9333	9737	*0140	*0544	*0947	*1350	*1754
77	032 2157	2560	2963	3367	3770	4173	4576	4979	5382	5785
78	6188	6590	6993	7396	7799	8201	8604	9007	9409	9812
79	033 0214	0617	1019	1422	1824	2226	2629	3031	3433	3835
1080	4238	4640	5042	5444	5846	6248	6650	7052	7453	7855
81	8257	8659	9060	9462	9864	*0265	*0667	*1068	*1470	*1871
82	034 2273	2674	3075	3477	3878	4279	4680	5081	5482	5884
83	6285	6686	7087	7487	7888	8289	8690	9091	9491	9892
84	035 0293	0693	1094	1495	1895	2296	2696	3096	3497	3897
85	4297	4698	5098	5498	5898	6298	6698	7098	7498	7898
86	8298	8698	9098	9498	9898	*0297	*0697	*1097	*1496	*1896
87	036 2295	2695	3094	3494	3893	4293	4692	5091	5491	5890
88	6289	6688	7087	7486	7885	8284	8683	9082	9481	9880
89	037 0279	0678	1076	1475	1874	2272	2671	3070	3468	3867
1090	4265	4663	5062	5460	5858	6257	6655	7053	7451	7849
91	8248	8646	9044	9442	9839	*0237	*0635	*1033	*1431	*1829
92	038 2226	2624	3022	3419	3817	4214	4612	5009	5407	5804
93	6202	6599	6996	7393	7791	8188	8585	8982	9379	9776
94	039 0173	0570	0967	1364	1761	2158	2554	2951	3348	3745
95	4141	4538	4934	5331	5727	6124	6520	6917	7313	7709
96	8106	8502	8898	9294	9690	*0086	*0482	*0878	*1274	*1670
97	040 2066	2462	2858	3254	3650	4045	4441	4837	5232	5628
98	6023	6119	6814	7210	7605	8001	8396	8791	9187	9582
99	9977	*0372	*0767	*1162	*1557	*1952	*2347	*2742	*3137	*3532
1100	041 3927	4322	4716	5111	5506	5900	6295	6690	7084	7479
N	0	1	2	3	4	5	6	7	8	9

LOGARITHMS OF
TRIGONOMETRIC FUNCTIONS

′	L. Sin.	d.	L. Tang.	c. d.	L. Cotg.	L. Cos.	′
0	......		......		......	10.00 000	60
1	6.46 373		6.46 373		3.53 627	000	59
2	6.76 476	30103	6.76 476	30103	3.23 524	000	58
3	6.94 085	17609	6.94 085	17609	3.05 915	000	57
4	7.06 579	12494	7.06 579	12494	2.93 421	000	56
5	7.16 270	9691	7.16 270	9691	2.83 730	000	55
6	7.24 188	7918	7.24 188	7918	2.75 812	000	54
7	7.30 882	6694	7.30 882	6694	2.69 118	000	53
8	7.36 682	5800	7.36 682	5800	2.63 318	000	52
9	7.41 797	5115	7.41 797	5115	2.58 203	000	51
10	7.46 373	4576	7.46 373	4576	2.53 627	10.00 000	50
11	7.50 512	4139	7.50 512	4139	2.49 488	000	49
12	7.54 291	3779	7.54 291	3779	2.45 709	000	48
13	7.57 767	3476	7.57 767	3476	2.42 233	000	47
14	7.60 985	3218	7.60 986	3219	2.39 014	000	46
15	7.63 982	2997	7.63 982	2996	2.36 018	000	45
16	7.66 784	2802	7.66 785	2803	2.33 215	000	44
17	7.69 417	2633	7.69 418	2633	2.30 582	9.99 999	43
18	7.71 900	2483	7.71 900	2482	2.28 100	999	42
19	7.74 248	2348	7.74 248	2348	2.25 752	999	41
20	7.76 475	2227	7.76 476	2228	2.23 524	9.99 999	40
21	7.78 594	2119	7.78 595	2119	2.21 405	999	39
22	7.80 615	2021	7.80 615	2020	2.19 385	999	38
23	7.82 545	1930	7.82 546	1931	2.17 454	999	37
24	7.84 393	1848	7.84 394	1848	2.15 606	999	36
25	7.86 166	1773	7.86 167	1773	2.13 833	999	35
26	7.87 870	1704	7.87 871	1704	2.12 129	999	34
27	7.89 509	1639	7.89 510	1639	2.10 490	999	33
28	7.91 088	1579	7.91 089	1579	2.08 911	999	32
29	7.92 612	1524	7.92 613	1524	2.07 387	998	31
30	7.94 084	1472	7.94 086	1473	2.05 914	9.99 998	30
31	7.95 508	1424	7.95 510	1424	2.04 490	998	29
32	7.96 887	1379	7.96 889	1379	2.03 111	998	28
33	7.98 223	1336	7.98 225	1336	2.01 775	998	27
34	7.99 520	1297	7.99 522	1297	2.00 478	998	26
35	8.00 779	1259	8.00 781	1259	1.99 219	998	25
36	8.02 002	1223	8.02 004	1223	1.97 996	998	24
37	8.03 192	1190	8.03 194	1190	1.96 806	997	23
38	8.04 350	1158	8.04 353	1159	1.95 647	997	22
39	8.05 478	1128	8.05 481	1128	1.94 519	997	21
40	8.06 578	1100	8.06 581	1100	1.93 419	9.99 997	20
41	8.07 650	1072	8.07 653	1072	1.92 347	997	19
42	8.08 696	1046	8.08 700	1047	1.91 300	997	18
43	8.09 718	1022	8.09 722	1022	1.90 278	997	17
44	8.10 717	999	8.10 720	998	1.89 280	996	16
45	8.11 693	976	8.11 696	976	1.88 304	996	15
46	8.12 647	954	8.12 651	955	1.87 349	996	14
47	8.13 581	934	8.13 585	934	1.86 415	996	13
48	8.14 495	914	8.14 500	915	1.85 500	996	12
49	8.15 391	896	8.15 395	895	1.84 605	996	11
50	8.16 268	877	8.16 273	878	1.83 727	9.99 995	10
51	8.17 128	860	8.17 133	860	1.82 867	995	9
52	8.17 971	843	8.17 976	843	1.82 024	995	8
53	8.18 798	827	8.18 804	828	1.81 196	995	7
54	8.19 610	812	8.19 616	812	1.80 384	995	6
55	8.20 407	797	8.20 413	797	1.79 587	994	5
56	8.21 189	782	8.21 195	782	1.78 805	994	4
57	8.21 958	769	8.21 964	769	1.78 036	994	3
58	8.22 713	755	8.22 720	756	1.77 280	994	2
59	8.23 456	743	8.23 462	742	1.76 538	994	1
60	8.24 186	730	8.24 192	730	1.75 808	9.99 993	0
′	L. Cos.	d.	L. Cotg.	c. d.	L. Tang.	L. Sin.	′

P. P.

1′	5800	4576	3779
10″	967	763	630
20″	1933	1525	1260
30″	2900	2288	1890
40″	3867	3051	2519
50″	4833	3813	3149
1′	3218	2802	2483
10″	536	467	414
20″	1073	934	828
30″	1609	1401	1242
40″	2145	1868	1655
50″	2682	2335	2069
1′	2227	2021	1848
10″	371	337	308
20″	742	674	616
30″	1114	1011	924
40″	1485	1347	1232
50″	1856	1684	1540
1′	1704	1579	1472
10″	284	263	245
20″	568	526	491
30″	852	790	736
40″	1136	1053	981
50″	1420	1316	1227
1′	1379	1297	1223
10″	230	216	204
20″	460	432	408
30″	690	649	612
40″	919	865	815
50″	1149	1081	1019
1′	1158	1100	1046
10″	193	183	174
20″	386	367	349
30″	579	550	523
40″	772	733	697
50″	965	917	872
1′	999	954	914
10″	167	159	152
20″	333	318	305
30″	500	477	457
40″	666	636	609
50″	833	795	762
1′	877	843	812
10″	146	141	135
20″	292	281	271
30″	439	422	406
40″	585	562	541
50″	731	703	677
1′	782	755	730
10″	130	126	122
20″	261	252	243
30″	391	378	365
40″	521	503	487
50″	652	629	608

′	L. Sin.	d.	L. Tang.	c. d.	L. Cotg.	L. Cos.	′
0	8.24 186	717	8.24 192	718	1.75 808	9.99 993	60
1	903	706	910	706	090	993	59
2	8.25 609	695	8.25 616	696	1.74 384	993	58
3	8.26 304	684	8.26 312	684	1.73 688	993	57
4	988	673	996	673	004	992	56
5	8.27 661	663	8.27 669	663	1.72 331	992	55
6	8.28 324	653	8.28 332	654	1.71 668	992	54
7	977	644	986	643	•014	992	53
8	8.29 621	634	8.29 629	634	1.70 371	992	52
9	8.30 255	624	8.30 263	625	1.69 737	991	51
10	8.30 879	616	8.30 888	617	1.69 112	9.99 991	50
11	8.31 495	608	8.31 505	607	1.68 495	991	49
12	8.32 103	599	8.32 112	599	1.67 888	990	48
13	702	590	711	591	289	990	47
14	8.33 292	583	8.33 302	584	1.66 698	990	46
15	875	575	886	575	114	990	45
16	8.34 450	568	8.34 461	568	1.65 539	989	44
17	8.35 018	560	8.35 029	561	1.64 971	989	43
18	578	553	590	553	410	989	42
19	8.36 131	547	8.36 143	546	1.63 857	989	41
20	8.36 678	539	8.36 689	540	1.63 311	9.99 988	40
21	8.37 217	533	8.37 229	533	1.62 771	988	39
22	750	526	762	527	238	988	38
23	8.38 276	520	8.38 289	520	1.61 711	987	37
24	796	514	809	514	191	987	36
25	8.39 310	508	8.39 323	509	1.60 677	987	35
26	818	502	832	502	168	986	34
27	8.40 320	496	8.40 334	496	1.59 666	986	33
28	816	491	830	491	170	986	32
29	8.41 307	485	8.41 321	486	1.58 679	985	31
30	8.41 792	480	8.41 807	480	1.58 193	9.99 985	30
31	8.42 272	474	8.42 287	475	1.57 713	985	29
32	746	470	762	470	238	984	28
33	8.43 216	464	8.43 232	464	1.56 768	984	27
34	680	459	696	460	304	984	26
35	8.44 139	455	8.44 156	455	1.55 844	983	25
36	594	450	611	450	389	983	24
37	8.45 044	445	8.45 061	446	1.54 939	983	23
38	489	441	507	441	493	982	22
39	930	436	948	437	052	982	21
40	8.46 366	433	8.46 385	432	1.53 615	9.99 982	20
41	799	427	817	428	183	981	19
42	8.47 226	424	8.47 245	424	1.52 755	981	18
43	650	419	669	420	331	981	17
44	8.48 069	416	8.48 089	416	1.51 911	980	16
45	485	411	505	412	495	980	15
46	896	408	917	408	083	979	14
47	8.49 304	404	8.49 325	404	1.50 675	979	13
48	708	400	729	401	271	979	12
49	8.50 108	396	8.50 130	397	1.49 870	978	11
50	8.50 504	393	8.50 527	393	1.49 473	9.99 978	10
51	897	390	920	390	080	977	9
52	8.51 287	386	8.51 310	386	1.48 690	977	8
53	673	382	696	383	304	977	7
54	8.52 055	379	8.52 079	380	1.47 921	976	6
55	434	376	459	376	541	976	5
56	810	373	835	373	165	975	4
57	8.53 183	369	8.53 208	370	1.46 792	975	3
58	552	367	578	367	422	974	2
59	919	363	945	363	055	974	1
60	8.54 282		8.54 308		1.45 692	9.99 974	0
′	L. Cos.	d.	L. Cotg.	c. d.	L. Tang.	L. Sin.	′

P. P.

1′	717	673	644
10″	120	112	107
20″	239	224	215
30″	359	337	322
40″	478	449	429
50″	598	561	537
1′	616	590	568
10″	103	98	95
20″	205	197	189
30″	308	295	284
40″	411	393	379
50″	513	492	473
1′	547	533	520
10″	91	89	87
20″	182	178	173
30″	274	267	260
40″	365	355	347
50″	456	444	433
1′	508	496	485
10″	85	83	81
20″	169	165	162
30″	254	248	243
40″	339	331	323
50″	423	413	404
1′	474	464	455
10″	79	77	76
20″	158	155	152
30″	237	232	228
40″	316	309	303
50″	395	387	379
1′	445	436	427
10″	74	73	71
20″	148	145	142
30″	223	218	214
40″	297	291	285
50″	371	363	356
1′	419	411	404
10″	70	69	67
20″	140	137	135
30″	210	206	202
40″	279	274	269
50″	349	343	337
1′	396	390	382
10″	66	65	64
20″	132	130	127
30″	198	195	191
40″	264	260	255
50″	330	325	318
1′	376	369	363
10″	63	62	61
20″	125	123	121
30″	188	185	182
40″	251	246	242
50″	313	308	303

′	L. Sin.	d.	L. Tang.	c. d.	L. Cotg.	L. Cos.	′
0	8.54 282	360	8.54 308	361	1.45 692	9.99 974	60
1	642	357	669	358	331	973	59
2	999	355	8.55 027	355	1.44 973	973	58
3	8.55 354	351	382	352	618	972	57
4	705	349	734	349	266	972	56
5	8.56 054	346	8.56 083	346	1.43 917	971	55
6	400	343	429	344	571	971	54
7	743	341	773	341	227	970	53
8	8.57 084	337	8.57 114	338	1.42 886	970	52
9	421	336	452	336	548	969	51
10	8.57 757	332	8.57 788	333	1.42 212	9.99 969	50
11	8.58 089	330	8.58 121	330	1.41 879	968	49
12	419	328	451	328	549	968	48
13	747	325	779	326	221	967	47
14	8.59 072	323	8.59 105	323	1.40 895	967	46
15	395̄	320	428	321	572	967	45
16	715	318	749	319	251	966	44
17	8.60 033	316	8.60 068	316	1.39 932	966	43
18	349	313	384	314	616	965	42
19	662	311	698	311	302	964	41
20	8.60 973	309	8.61 009	310	1.38 991	9.99 964	40
21	8.61 282	307	319	307	681	963	39
22	589	305	626	305	374	963	38
23	894	302	931	303	069	962	37
24	8.62 196	301	8.62 234	301	1.37 766	962	36
25	497	298	535	299	465̄	961	35
26	795̄	296	834	297	166	961	34
27	8.63 091	294	8.63 131	295	1.36 869	960	33
28	385	293	426	292	574	960	32
29	678	290	718	291	282	959	31
30	8.63 968	288	8.64 009	289	1.35 991	9.99 959	30
31	8.64 256	287	298	287	702	958	29
32	543	284	585	285	415̄	958	28
33	827	283	870	284	130	957	27
34	8.65 110	281	8.65 154	281	1.34 846	956	26
35	391	279	435	280	565̄	956	25
36	670	277	715̄	278	285	955	24
37	947	276	993	276	007	955̄	23
38	8.66 223	274	8.66 269	274	1.33 731	954	22
39	497	272	543	273	457	954	21
40	8.66 769	270	8.66 816	271	1.33 184	9.99 953	20
41	8.67 039	269	8.67 087	269	1.32 913	952	19
42	308	267	356	268	644	952	18
43	575	266	624	266	376	951	17
44	841	263	890	264	110	951	16
45	8.68 104	263	8.68 154	263	1.31 846	950	15
46	367	260	417	261	583	949	14
47	627	259	678	260	322	949	13
48	886	258	938	258	062	948	12
49	8.69 144	256	8.69 196	257	1.30 804	948	11
50	8.69 400	254	8.69 453	255	1.30 547	9.99 947	10
51	654	253	708	254	292	946	9
52	907	252	962	252	038	946	8
53	8.70 159	250	8.70 214̄	251	1.29 786	945̄	7
54	409	249	465	249	535	944	6
55	658	247	714	248	286	944	5
56	905̄	246	962	246	038	943	4
57	8.71 151	244	8.71 208	245	1.28 792	942	3
58	395	243	453	244	547	942	2
59	638	242	697	243	303	941	1
60	8.71 880		8.71 940		1.28 060	9.99 940	0
′	L. Cos.	d.	L. Cotg.	c. d.	L. Tang.	L. Sin.	′

P. P.

1′	360	350	340
1″	6.0	5.8	5.7
2″	12.0	11.7	11.3
3″	18.0	17.5	17.0
4″	24.0	23.3	22.7
5″	30.0	29.2	28.3
6″	36.0	35.0	34.0
7″	42.0	40.8	39.7
8″	48.0	46.7	45.3
9″	54.0	52.5	51.0

1′	330	320	310
1″	5.5	5.3	5.2
2″	11.0	10.7	10.3
3″	16.5	16.0	15.5
4″	22.0	21.3	20.7
5″	27.5	26.7	25.8
6″	33.0	32.0	31.0
7″	38.5	37.3	36.2
8″	44.0	42.7	41.3
9″	49.5	48.0	46.5

1′	300	290	285
1″	5.0	4.8	4.8
2″	10.0	9.7	9.5
3″	15.0	14.5	14.3
4″	20.0	19.3	19.0
5″	25.0	24.2	23.8
6″	30.0	29.0	28.5
7″	35.0	33.8	33.3
8″	40.0	38.7	38.0
9″	45.0	43.5	42.8

1′	280	275	270
1″	4.7	4.6	4.5
2″	9.3	9.2	9.0
3″	14.0	13.8	13.5
4″	18.7	18.3	18.0
5″	23.3	22.9	22.5
6″	28.0	27.5	27.0
7″	32.7	32.1	31.5
8″	37.3	36.7	36.0
9″	42.0	41.3	40.5

1′	265	260	255
1″	4.4	4.3	4.3
2″	8.8	8.7	8.5
3″	13.3	13.0	12.8
4″	17.7	17.3	17.0
5″	22.1	21.7	21.3
6″	26.5	26.0	25.5
7″	30.9	30.3	29.8
8″	35.3	34.7	34.0
9″	39.8	39.0	38.3

1′	250	245	240
1″	4.2	4.1	4.0
2″	8.3	8.2	8.0
3″	12.5	12.3	12.0
4″	16.7	16.3	16.0
5″	20.8	20.4	20.0
6″	25.0	24.5	24.0
7″	29.2	28.6	28.0
8″	33.3	32.7	32.0
9″	37.5	36.8	36.0

Logarithmic Functions

3°

′	L. Sin.	d.	L. Tang.	c. d.	L. Cotg.	L. Cos.	′
0	8.71 880	240	8.71 940	241	1.28 060	9.99 940	60
1	8.72 120	239	8.72 181	239	1.27 819	940	59
2	359	238	420	239	580	939	58
3	597	237	659	237	341	938	57
4	834	235	896	236	104	938	56
5	8.73 069	234	8.73 132	234	1.26 868	937	55
6	303	232	366	234	634	936	54
7	535	232	600	232	400	936	53
8	767	230	832	231	168	935	52
9	997	229	8.74 063	229	1.25 937	934	51
10	8.74 226	228	8.74 292	229	1.25 708	9.99 934	50
11	454	226	521	227	479	933	49
12	680	226	748	226	252	932	48
13	906	224	974	225	026	932	47
14	8.75 130	223	8.75 199	224	1.24 801	931	46
15	353	222	423	224	577	930	45
16	575̅	220	645	222	355̅	929	44
17	795	220	867	222	133	929	43
18	8.76 015	219	8.76 087	220	1.23 913	928	42
19	234	217	306	219	694	927	41
20	8.76 451	216	8.76 525	219	1.23 475	9.99 926	40
21	667	216	742	217	258	926	39
22	883	214	958	216	042	925̅	38
23	8.77 097	213	8.77 173	215	1.22 827	924	37
24	310	212	387	214	613	923	36
25	522	211	600	213	400	923	35
26	733	210	811	211	189	922	34
27	943	209	8.78 022	211	1.21 978	921	33
28	8.78 152	208	232	210	768	920	32
29	360	208	441	209	559	920	31
30	8.78 568	206	8.78 649	208	1.21 351	9.99 919	30
31	774	205	855	206	145̅	918	29
32	979	204	8.79 061	206	1.20 939	917	28
33	8.79 183	203	266	205	734	917	27
34	386	202	470	204	530	916	26
35	588	201	673	203	327	915	25
36	789	201	875	202	125̅	914	24
37	990	199	8.80 076	201	1.19 924	913	23
38	8.80 189	199	277	201	723	913	22
39	388	197	476	199	524	912	21
40	8.80 585	197	8.80 674	198	1.19 326	9.99 911	20
41	782	196	872	198	128	910	19
42	978	195	8.81 068	196	1.18 932	909	18
43	8.81 173	194	264	196	736	909	17
44	367	193	459	195	541	908	16
45	560	192	653	194	347	907	15
46	752	192	846	193	154	906	14
47	944	190	8.82 038	192	1.17 962	905	13
48	8.82 131	190	230	192	770	904	12
49	324	189	420	190	580	904	11
50	8.82 513	188	8.82 610	190	1.17 390	9.99 903	10
51	701	187	799	189	201	902	9
52	888	187	987	188	013	901	8
53	8.83 075̅	186	8.83 175	188	1.16 825	900	7
54	261	185	361	186	639	899	6
55	446	185	547	186	453	898	5
56	630	184	732	185	268	898	4
57	813	183	916	184	084	897	3
58	996	183	8.84 100	184	1.15 900	896	2
59	8.84 177	181	282	182	718	895	1
60	8.84 358	181	8.84 464	182	1.15 536	9.99 894	0
′	L. Cos.	d.	L. Cotg.	c. d.	L. Tang.	L. Sin.	′

P. P.

1′	241	237	233
1″	4.0	4.0	3.9
2″	8.0	7.9	7.8
3″	12.1	11.9	11.7
4″	16.1	15.8	15.5
5″	20.1	19.8	19.4
6″	24.1	23.7	23.3
7″	28.1	27.7	27.2
8″	32.1	31.6	31.1
9″	36.2	35.6	35.0

1′	229	225	221
1″	3.8	3.8	3.7
2″	7.6	7.5	7.4
3″	11.5	11.3	11.1
4″	15.3	15.0	14.7
5″	19.1	18.8	18.4
6″	22.9	22.5	22.1
7″	26.7	26.3	25.8
8″	30.5	30.0	29.5
9″	34.4	33.8	33.2

1′	217	213	209
1″	3.6	3.6	3.5
2″	7.2	7.1	7.0
3″	10.9	10.7	10.5
4″	14.5	14.2	13.9
5″	18.1	17.8	17.4
6″	21.7	21.3	20.9
7″	25.3	24.9	24.4
8″	28.9	28.4	27.9
9″	32.6	32.0	31.4

1′	205	202	199
1″	3.4	3.4	3.3
2″	6.8	6.7	6.6
3″	10.3	10.1	10.0
4″	13.7	13.5	13.3
5″	17.1	16.8	16.6
6″	20.5	20.2	19.9.
7″	23.9	23.6	23.2
8″	27.3	26.9	26.5
9″	30.8	30.3	29.9

1′	196	193	190
1″	3.3	3.2	3.2
2″	6.5	6.4	6.3
3″	9.8	9.7	9.5
4″	13.1	12.9	12.7
5″	16.3	16.1	15.8
6″	19.6	19.3	19.0
7″	22.9	22.5	22.2
8″	26.1	25.7	25.3
9″	29.4	29.0	28.5

1′	187	184	181
1″	3.1	3.1	3.0
2″	6.2	6.1	6.0
3″	9.4	9.2	9.1
4″	12.5	12.3	12.1
5″	15.6	15.3	15.1
6″	18.7	18.4	18.1
7″	21.8	21.5	21.1
8″	24.9	24.5	24.1
9″	28.1	27.6	27.2

86°

′	L. Sin.	d.	L. Tang.	c. d.	L. Cotg.	L. Cos.	′		P. P.		
0	8.84 358	181	8.84 464	182	1.15 536	9.99 894	60	1′	181	178	175
1	539	179	646	180	354	893	59	1″	3.0	3.0	2.9
2	718	179	826	180	174	892	58	2″	6.0	5.9	5.8
3	897	178	8.85 006	179	1.14 994	891	57	3″	9.1	8.9	8.8
4	8.85 075	177	185	178	815	891	56	4″	12.1	11.9	11.7
5	252	177	363	178	637	890	55	5″	15.1	14.8	14.6
6	429	176	540	177	460	889	54	6″	18.1	17.8	17.5
7	605	175	717	177	283	888	53	7″	21.1	20.8	20.4
8	780	175	893	176	107	887	52	8″	24.1	23.7	23.3
9	955	173	8.86 069	176	1.13 931	886	51	9″	27.2	26.7	26.3
10	8.86 128	173	8.86 243	174	1 13 757	9.99 885	50	1′	173	171	169
11	301	173	417	174	583	884	49	1″	2.9	2.9	2.8
12	474	171	591	172	409	883	48	2″	5.8	5.7	5.6
13	645	171	763	172	237	882	47	3″	8.7	8.6	8.5
14	816	171	935	171	065	881	46	4″	11.5	11.4	11.3
15	987	169	8.87 106	171	1.12 894	880	45	5″	14.4	14.3	14.1
16	8.87 156	169	277	170	723	879	44	6″	17.3	17.1	16.9
17	325	169	447	169	553	879	43	7″	20.2	20.0	19.7
18	494	167	616	169	384	878	42	8″	23.1	22.8	22.5
19	661	168	785	168	215	877	41	9″	26.0	25.7	25.4
20	8.87 829	166	8.87 953	167	1.12 047	9.99 876	40	1′	167	165	163
21	995	166	8.88 120	167	1.11 880	875	39	1″	2.8	2.8	2.7
22	8.88 161	165	287	166	713	874	38	2″	5.6	5.5	5.4
23	326	164	453	165	547	873	37	3″	8.4	8.3	8.2
24	490	164	618	165	382	872	36	4″	11.1	11.0	10.9
25	654	163	783	165	217	871	35	5″	13 9	13.8	13.6
26	817	163	948	163	052	870	34	6″	16.7	16.5	16.3
27	980	162	8.89 111	163	1.10 889	869	33	7″	19.5	19.3	19.0
28	8.89 142	162	274	163	726	868	32	8″	22.3	22.0	21.7
29	304	160	437	161	563	867	31	9″	25.1	24.8	24.5
30	8.89 464	161	8.89 598	162	1.10 402	9.99 866	30	1′	161	159	157
31	625	159	760	160	240	865	29	1″	2.7	2.7	2.6
32	784	159	920	160	080	864	28	2″	5.4	5.3	5.2
33	943	159	8.90 080	160	1.09 920	863	27	3″	8.1	8.0	7.9
34	8.90 102	158	240	159	760	862	26	4″	10.7	10.6	10.5
35	260	157	399	158	601	861	25	5″	13.4	13.3	13.1
36	417	157	557	158	443	860	24	6″	16.1	15.9	15.7
37	574	156	715	157	285	859	23	7″	18.8	18.6	18.3
38	730	155	872	157	128	858	22	8″	21.5	21.2	20.9
39	885	155	8.91 029	156	1.08 971	857	21	9″	24.2	23.9	23.6
40	8.91 040	155	8.91 185	156	1.08 815	9.99 856	20	1′	155	153	151
41	195	154	340	155	660	855	19	1″	2.6	2.6	2.5
42	349	153	495	155	505	854	18	2″	5.2	5.1	5.0
43	502	153	650	153	350	853	17	3″	7.8	7.7	7.6
44	655	152	803	154	197	852	16	4″	10.3	10.2	10.1
45	807	152	957	153	043	851	15	5″	12.9	12.8	12.6
46	959	151	8.92 110	152	1.07 890	850	14	6″	15.5	15.3	15.1
47	8.92 110	151	262	152	738	848	13	7″	18.1	17.9	17.6
48	261	150	414	151	586	847	12	8″	20.7	20.4	20.1
49	411	150	565	151	435	846	11	9″	23.3	23.0	22.7
50	8.92 561	149	8.92 716	151	1.07 284	9.99 845	10	1′	149	147	145
51	710	149	866	150	134	844	9	1″	2.5	2.5	2.4
52	859	148	8.93 016	149	1.06 984	843	8	2″	5.0	4.9	4.8
53	8.93 007	147	165	148	835	842	7	3″	7.5	7.4	7.3
54	154	147	313	149	687	841	6	4″	9.9	9.8	9.7
55	301	147	462	147	538	840	5	5″	12.4	12.3	12.1
56	448	146	609	147	391	839	4	6″	14.9	14.7	14.5
57	594	146	756	147	244	838	3	7″	17.4	17.2	16.9
58	740	145	903	146	097	837	2	8″	19.9	19.6	19.3
59	885	145	8.94 049	146	1.05 951	836	1	9″	22.4	22.1	21.8
60	8.94 030		8.94 195		1.05 805	9.99 834	0				
′	L. Cos.	d.	L. Cotg.	c. d.	L. Tang.	L. Sin.	′				

′	L. Sin.	d.	L. Tang.	c. d.	L. Cotg.	L. Cos.	′
0	8.94 030	144	8.94 195	145	1.05 805̄	9.99 834	60
1	174	143	340	145	660	833	59
2	317	144	485	145	515̄	832	58
3	461	142	630	143	370	831	57
4	603	143	773	144	227	830	56
5	746	141	917	143	083	829	55
6	887	142	8.95 060	142	1.04 940	828	54
7	8.95 029	141	202	142	798	827	53
8	170	140	344	142	656	825	52
9	310	140	486	141	514	824	51
10	8.95 450	139	8.95 627	140	1.04 373	9.99 823	50
11	589	139	767	141	233	822	49
12	728	139	908	139	092	821	48
13	867	138	8.96 047	140	1.03 953	820	47
14	8.96 005	138	187	138	813	819	46
15	143	137	325	139	675̄	817	45
16	280	137	464	138	536	816	44
17	417	136	602	137	398	815	43
18	553	136	739	138	261	814	42
19	689	136	877	136	123	813	41
20	8.96 825̄	135	8.97 013	137	1.02 987	9.99 812	40
21	960	135	150	135	850	810	39
22	8.97 095̄	134	285	136	715̄	809	38
23	229	134	421	135	579	808	37
24	363	133	556	135	444	807	36
25	496	133	691	134	309	806	35
26	629	133	825̄	134	175	804	34
27	762	132	959	133	041	803	33
28	894	132	8.98 092	133	1.01 908	802	32
29	8.98 026	131	225	133	775̄	801	31
30	8.98 157	131	8.98 358	132	1.01 642	9.99 800	30
31	288	131	490	132	510	798	29
32	419	130	622	131	378	797	28
33	549	130	753	131	247	796̄	27
34	679	129	884	131	116	795̄	26
35	808	129	8.99 015	130	1.00 985	793	25
36	937	129	145	130	855̄	792	24
37	8.99 066	128	275̄	130	725̄	791	23
38	194	128	405	129	595	790	22
39	322	128	534	128	466	788	21
40	8.99 450	127	8.99 662	129	1.00 338	9.99 787	20
41	577	127	791	128	209	786	19
42	704	126	919	127	081	785̄	18
43	830	126	9.00 046	128	0.99 954	783	17
44	956	126	174	127	826	782	16
45	9.00 082	125	301	126	699	781	15
46	207	125	427	126	573	780	14
47	332	124	553	126	447	778	13
48	456	125	679	126	321	777	12
49	581	123	805	125	195	776	11
50	9.00 704	124	9.00 930	125	0.99 070	9.99 775̄	10
51	828	123	9.01 055̄	124	0.98 945	773	9
52	951	123	179	124	821	772	8
53	9.01 074	122	303	124	697	771	7
54	196	122	427	123	573	769	6
55	318	122	550	123	450	768	5
56	440	121	673	123	327	767	4
57	561	121	796	122	204	765̄	3
58	682	121	918	122	082	764	2
59	803	120	9.02 040	122	0.97 960	763	1
60	9.01 923		9.02 162		0.97 838	9.99 761	0
′	L. Cos.	d.	L. Cotg.	c. d.	L. Tang.	L. Sin.	′

P. P.

1′	145	143	141
1″	2.4	2.4	2.4
2″	4.8	4.8	4.7
3″	7.3	7.2	7.1
4″	9.7	9.5	9.4
5″	12.1	11.9	11.8
6″	14.5	14.3	14.1
7″	16.9	16.7	16.5
8″	19.3	19.1	18.8
9″	21.8	21.5	21.2
1′	139	137	135
1″	2.3	2.3	2.3
2″	4.6	4.6	4.5
3″	7.0	6.9	6.8
4″	9.3	9.1	9.0
5″	11.6	11.4	11.3
6″	13.9	13.7	13.5
7″	16.2	16.0	15.8
8″	18.5	18.3	18.0
9″	20.9	20.6	20.3
1′	133	131	129
1″	2.2	2.2	2.2
2″	4.4	4.4	4.3
3″	6.7	6.6	6.5
4″	8.9	8.7	8.6
5″	11.1	10.9	10.8
6″	13.3	13.1	12.9
7″	15.5	15.3	15.1
8″	17.7	17.5	17.2
9″	20.0	19.7	19.4
1′	128	127	126
1″	2.1	2.1	2.1
2″	4.3	4.2	4.2
3″	6.4	6.4	6.3
4″	8.5	8.5	8.4
5″	10.7	10.6	10.5
6″	12.8	12.7	12.6
7″	14.9	14.8	14.7
8″	17.1	16.9	16.8
9″	19.2	19.1	18.9
1′	125	124	123
1″	2.1	2.1	2.1
2″	4.2	4.1	4.1
3″	6.3	6.2	6.2
4″	8.3	8.3	8.2
5″	10.4	10.3	10.3
6″	12.5	12.4	12.3
7″	14.6	14.5	14.4
8″	16.7	16.5	16.4
9″	18.8	18.6	18.5
1′	122	121	120
1″	2.0	2.0	2.0
2″	4.1	4.0	4.0
3″	6.1	6.1	6.0
4″	8.1	8.1	8.0
5″	10.2	10.1	10.0
6″	12.2	12.1	12.0
7″	14.2	14.1	14.0
8″	16.3	16.1	16.0
9″	18.3	18.2	18.0

′	L. Sin.	d.	L. Tang.	c. d.	L. Cotg.	L. Cos.	′	P. P.		
0	9.01 923	120	9.02 162	121	0.97 838	9.99 761	60	1′	120	119	118
1	9.02 043	120	283	121	717	760	59	1″	2.0	2.0	2.0
2	163	120	404	121	596	759	58	2″	4.0	4.0	3.9
3	283	119	525	120	475̄	757	57	3″	6.0	6.0	5.9
4	402	118	645	121	355̄	756	56	4″	8.0	7.9	7.9
5	520	119	766	119	234	755̄	55	5″	10.0	9.9	9.8
6	639	118	885	120	115̄	753	54	6″	12.0	11.9	11.8
7	757	117	9.03 005̄	119	0.96 995	752	53	7″	14.0	13.9	13.8
8	874	118	124	118	876	751	52	8″	16.0	15.9	15.7
9	992	117	242	119	758	749	51	9″	18.0	17.9	17.7
10	9.03 109	117	9.03 361	118	0.96 639	9.99 748	50	1′	117	116	115
11	226	116	479	118	521	747	49	1″	2.0	1.9	1.9
12	342	116	597	117	403	745	48	2″	3.9	3.9	3.8
13	458	116	714	118	286	744	47	3″	5.9	5.8	5.8
14	574	116	832	116	168	742	46	4″	7.8	7.7	7.7
15	690	115	948	117	052	741	45	5″	9.8	9.7	9.6
16	805̄	115	9.04 065	116	0.95 935̄	740	44	6″	11.7	11.6	11.5
17	920	114	181	116	819	738	43	7″	13.7	13.5	13.4
18	9.04 034	115	297	116	703	737	42	8″	15.6	15.5	15.3
19	149	113	413	115	587	736	41	9″	17.6	17.4	17.3
20	9.04 262	114	9.04 528	115	0.95 472	9.99 734	40	1′	114	113	112
21	376	114	643	115	357	733	39	1″	1.9	1.9	1.9
22	490	113	758	115	242	731	38	2″	3.8	3.8	3.7
23	603	112	873	114	127	730	37	3″	5.7	5.7	5.6
24	715	113	987	114	013	728	36	4″	7.6	7.5	7.5
25	828	112	9.05 101	113	0.94 899	727	35	5″	9.5	9.4	9.3
26	940	112	214	114	786	726	34	6″	11.4	11.3	11.2
27	9.05 052	112	328	113	672	724	33	7″	13.3	13.2	13.1
28	164	111	441	112	559	723	32	8″	15.2	15.1	14.9
29	275̄	111	553	113	447	721	31	9″	17.1	17.0	16.8
30	9.05 386	111	9.05 666	112	0.94 334	9.99 720	30	1′	111	110	109
31	497	110	778	112	222	718	29	1″	1.9	1.8	1.8
32	607	110	890	112	110	717	28	2″	3.7	3.7	3.6
33	717	110	9.06 002	111	0.93 998	716	27	3″	5.6	5.5	5.5
34	827	110	113	111	887	714	26	4″	7.4	7.3	7.3
35	937	109	224	111	776	713	25	5″	9.3	9.2	9.1
36	9.06 046	109	335̄	110	665	711	24	6″	11.1	11.0	10.9
37	155	109	445	111	555̄	710	23	7″	13.0	12.8	12.7
38	264	108	556	110	444	708	22	8″	14.8	14.7	14.5
39	372	109	666	109	334̄	707	21	9″	16.7	16.5	16.4
40	9.06 481	108	9.06 775	110	0.93 225̄	9.99 705	20	1′	108	107	106
41	589	107	885̄	109	115	704	19	1″	1.8	1.8	1.8
42	696	108	994	109	006	702	18	2″	3.6	3.6	3.5
43	804	107	9.07 103	108	0.92 897	701	17	3″	5.4	5.4	5.3
44	911	107	211	109	789	699	16	4″	7.2	7.1	7.1
45	9.07 018	106	320	198	680	698	15	5″	9.0	8.9	8.8
46	124	107	428	108	572	696	14	6″	10.8	10.7	10.6
47	231	106	536	107	464	695̄	13	7″	12.6	12.5	12.4
48	337	105	643	108	357	693	12	8″	14.4	14.3	14.1
49	442	106	751	107	249	692	11	9″	16.2	16.1	15.9
50	9.07 548	105	9.07 858	106	0.92 142	9.99 690	10	1′	105	104	103
51	653	105	964	107	036	689	9	1″	1.8	1.7	1.7
52	758	105	9.08 071	106	0.91 929	687	8	2″	3.5	3.5	3.4
53	863	105	177	106	823	686	7	3″	5.3	5.2	5.2
54	968	104	283	106	717	684	6	4″	7.0	6.9	6.9
55	9.08 072	104	389	106	611	683	5	5″	8.8	8.7	8.6
56	176	104	495̄	105	505	681	4	6″	10.5	10.4	10.3
57	280	103	600	105	400	680	3	7″	12.3	12.1	12.0
58	383	103	705	105	295̄	678	2	8″	14.0	13.9	13.7
59	486	103	810	104	190	677	1	9″	15.8	15.6	15.5
60	9.08 589		9.08 914		0.91 086	9.99 675	0				
′	L. Cos.	d.	L. Cotg.	c. d.	L. Tang.	L. Sin.	′			

′	L. Sin.	d.	L. Tang.	c. d.	L. Cotg.	L. Cos.	′	P. P.		
0	9.08 589	103	9.08 914	105	0.91 086	9.99 675	60	1′	105	104	103
1	692	103	9.09 019	104	0.90 981	674	59	1″	1.8	1.7	1.7
2	795	102	123	104	877	672	58	2″	3.5	3.5	3.4
3	897	102	227	103	773	670	57	3″	5.3	5.2	5.2
4	999	102	330	104	670	669	56	4″	7.0	6.9	6.9
5	9.09 101	101	434	103	566	667	55	5″	8.8	8.7	8.6
6	202	102	537	103	463	666	54	6″	10.5	10.4	10.3
7	304	101	640	102	360	664	53	7″	12.3	12.1	12.0
8	405	101	742	103	258	663	52	8″	14.0	13.9	13.7
9	506	100	845	102	155	661	51	9″	15.8	15.6	15.5
10	9.09 606	101	9.09 947	102	0.90 053	9.99 659	50	1′	102	101	100
11	707	100	9.10 049	101	0.89 951	658	49	1″	1.7	1.7	1.7
12	807	100	150	102	850	656	48	2″	3.4	3.4	3.3
13	907	99	252	101	748	655	47	3″	5.1	5.1	5.0
14	9.10 006	100	353	101	647	653	46	4″	6.8	6.7	6.7
15	106	99	454	101	546	651	45	5″	8.5	8.4	8.3
16	205	99	555	101	445	650	44	6″	10.2	10.1	10.0
17	304	98	656	100	344	648	43	7″	11.9	11.8	11.7
18	402	99	756	100	244	647	42	8″	13.6	13.5	13.3
19	501	98	856	100	144	645	41	9″	15.3	15.2	15.0
20	9.10 599	98	9.10 956	100	0.89 044	9.99 643	40	1′	99	98	97
21	697	98	9.11 056	99	0.88 944	642	39	1″	1.7	1.6	1.6
22	795	98	155	99	845	640	38	2″	3.3	3.3	3.2
23	893	97	254	99	746	638	37	3″	5.0	4.9	4.9
24	990	97	353	99	647	637	36	4″	6.6	6.5	6.5
25	9.11 087	97	452	99	548	635	35	5″	8.3	8.2	8.1
26	184	97	551	98	449	633	34	6″	9.9	9.8	9.7
27	281	96	649	98	351	632	33	7″	11.6	11.4	11.3
28	377	97	747	98	253	630	32	8″	13.2	13.1	12.9
29	474	96	845	98	155	629	31	9″	14.9	14.7	14.6
30	9.11 570	96	9.11 943	97	0.88 057	9.99 627	30	1′	96	95	94
31	666	95	9.12 040	98	0.87 960	625	29	1″	1.6	1.6	1.6
32	761	96	138	97	862	624	28	2″	3.2	3.2	3.1
33	857	95	235	97	765	622	27	3″	4.8	4.8	4.7
34	952	95	332	96	668	620	26	4″	6.4	6.3	6.3
35	9.12 047	95	428	97	572	618	25	5″	8.0	7.9	7.8
36	142	94	525	96	475	617	24	6″	9.6	9.5	9.4
37	236	95	621	96	379	615	23	7″	11.2	11.1	11.0
38	331	94	717	96	283	613	22	8″	12.8	12.7	12.5
39	425	94	813	96	187	612	21	9″	14.4	14.3	14.1
40	9.12 519	93	9.12 909	95	0.87 091	9.99 610	20	1′	93	92	91
41	612	94	9.13 004	95	0.86 996	608	19	1″	1.6	1.5	1.5
42	706	93	099	95	901	607	18	2″	3.1	3.1	3.0
43	799	93	194	95	806	605	17	3″	4.7	4.6	4.6
44	892	93	289	95	711	603	16	4″	6.2	6.1	6.1
45	985	93	384	94	616	601	15	5″	7.8	7.7	7.6
46	9.13 078	93	478	95	522	600	14	6″	9.3	9.2	9.1
47	171	92	573	94	427	598	13	7″	10.9	10.7	10.6
48	263	92	667	94	333	596	12	8″	12.4	12.3	12.1
49	355	92	761	93	239	595	11	9″	14.0	13.8	13.7
50	9.13 447	92	9.13 854	94	0.86 146	9.99 593	10	1′	90	1	2
51	539	91	948	93	052	591	9	1″	1.5	0.02	0.03
52	630	92	9.14 041	93	0.85 959	589	8	2″	3.0	0.03	0.07
53	722	91	134	93	866	588	7	3″	4.5	0.05	0.10
54	813	91	227	93	773	586	6	4″	6.0	0.07	0.13
55	904	90	320	92	680	584	5	5″	7.5	0.08	0.17
56	994	91	412	92	588	582	4	6″	9.0	0.10	0.20
57	9.14 085	90	504	93	496	581	3	7″	10.5	0.12	0.23
58	175	91	597	91	403	579	2	8″	12.0	0.13	0.27
59	266	90	688	92	312	577	1	9″	13.5	0.15	0.30
60	9.14 356		9.14 780		0.85 220	9.99 575	0				
′	L. Cos.	d.	L. Cotg.	c. d.	L. Tang.	L. Sin.	′			

'	L. Sin.	d.	L. Tang.	c.d.	L. Cotg.	L. Cos.	d.	'
0	9.14 356	89	9.14 780	92	0.85 220	9.99 575	1	60
1	445	90	872	91	128	574	2	59
2	535	89	963	91	037	572	2	58
3	624	90	9.15 054	91	0.84 946	570	2	57
4	714	89	145	91	855	568	2	56
5	803	88	236	91	764	566	1	55
6	891	89	327	90	673	565	2	54
7	980	89	417	91	583	563	2	53
8	9.15 069	88	508	90	492	561	2	52
9	157	88	598	90	402	559	2	51
10	9.15 245	88	9.15 688	90	0.84 312	9.99 557	1	50
11	333	88	777	90	223	556	2	49
12	421	87	867	89	133	554	2	48
13	508	88	956	90	044	552	2	47
14	596	87	9.16 046	89	0.83 954	550	2	46
15	683	87	135	89	865	548	2	45
16	770	87	224	88	776	546	1	44
17	857	87	312	89	688	545	2	43
18	944	86	401	88	599	543	2	42
19	9.16 030	86	489	88	511	541	2	41
20	9.16 116	87	9.16 577	88	0.83 423	9.99 539	2	40
21	203	86	665	88	335	537	2	39
22	289	85	753	88	247	535	2	38
23	374	86	841	87	159	533	1	37
24	460	85	928	88	072	532	2	36
25	545	86	9.17 016	87	0.82 984	530	2	35
26	631	85	103	87	897	528	2	34
27	716	85	190	87	810	526	2	33
28	801	85	277	86	723	524	2	32
29	886	84	363	87	637	522	2	31
30	9.16 970	85	9.17 450	86	0.82 550	9.99 520	2	30
31	9.17 055	85	536	86	464	518	1	29
32	139	84	622	86	378	517	2	28
33	223	84	708	86	292	515	2	27
34	307	84	794	86	206	513	2	26
35	391	84	880	85	120	511	2	25
36	474	83	965	86	035	509	2	24
37	558	84	9.18 051	85	0.81 949	507	2	23
38	641	83	136	85	864	505	2	22
39	724	83	221	85	779	503	2	21
40	9.17 807	83	9.18 306	85	0.81 694	9.99 501	2	20
41	890	83	391	85	609	499	2	19
42	973	82	475	85	525	497	2	18
43	9 18 055	82	560	84	440	495	1	17
44	137	83	644	84	356	494	2	16
45	220	82	728	84	272	492	2	15
46	302	81	812	84	188	490	2	14
47	383	82	896	83	104	488	2	13
48	465	82	979	84	021	486	2	12
49	547	81	9.19 063	83	0.80 937	484	2	11
50	9.18 628	81	9.19 146	83	0.80 854	9.99 482	2	10
51	709	81	229	83	771	480	2	9
52	790	81	312	83	688	478	2	8
53	871	81	395	83	605	476	2	7
54	952	81	478	83	522	474	2	6
55	9.19 033	80	561	82	439	472	2	5
56	113	80	643	82	357	470	2	4
57	193	80	725	82	275	468	2	3
58	273	80	807	82	193	466	2	2
59	353	80	889	82	111	464	2	1
60	9.19 433		9.19 971		0 80 029	9 99 462		0
'	L. Cos.	d.	L. Cotg.	c.d.	L. Tang.	L. Sin.	d.	'

P. P.

1'	92	91	90
1"	1.5	1.5	1.5
2"	3.1	3.0	3.0
3"	4.6	4.6	4.5
4"	6.1	6.1	6.0
5"	7.7	7.6	7.5
6"	9.2	9.1	9.0
7"	10.7	10.6	10.5
8"	12.3	12.1	12.0
9"	13.8	13.7	13.5

1'	89	88	87
1"	1.5	1.5	1.5
2"	3.0	2.9	2.9
3"	4.5	4.4	4.4
4"	5.9	5.9	5.8
5"	7.4	7.3	7.3
6"	8.9	8.8	8.7
7"	10.4	10.3	10.2
8"	11.9	11.7	11.6
9"	13.4	13.2	13.1

1'	86	85
1"	1.4	1.4
2"	2.9	2.8
3"	4.3	4.3
4"	5.7	5.7
5"	7.2	7.1
6"	8.6	8.5
7"	10.0	9.9
8"	11.5	11.3
9"	12.9	12.8

1'	84	83
1"	1.4	1.4
2"	2.8	2.8
3"	4.2	4.2
4"	5.6	5.5
5"	7.0	6.9
6"	8.4	8.3
7"	9.8	9.7
8"	11.2	11.1
9"	12.6	12.5

1'	82	81
1"	1.4	1.4
2"	2.7	2.7
3"	4.1	4.1
4"	5.5	5.4
5"	6.8	6.8
6"	8.2	8.1
7"	9.6	9.5
8"	10.9	10.8
9"	12.3	12.2

1'	1	2	80
1"	0.02	0.03	1.3
2"	0.03	0.07	2.7
3"	0.05	0.10	4.0
4"	0.07	0.13	5.3
5"	0.08	0.17	6.7
6"	0.10	0.20	8.0
7"	0.12	0.23	9.3
8"	0.13	0.27	10.7
9"	0.15	0.30	12.0

′	L. Sin.	d.	L. Tang.	c.d.	L. Cotg.	L. Cos.	d.	′
0	9.19 433	80	9.19 971	82	0.80 029	9.99 462	2	60
1	513	79	9.20 053	81	0.79 947	460	2	59
2	592	80	134	82	866	458	2	58
3	672	79	216	81	784	456	2	57
4	751	79	297	81	703	454	2	56
5	830	79	378	81	622	452	2	55
6	909	79	459	81	541	450	2	54
7	988	79	540	81	460	448	2	53
8	9.20 067	78	621	80	379	446	2	52
9	145	78	701	81	299	444	2	51
10	9.20 223	79	9.20 782	80	0.79 218	9.99 442	2	50
11	302	78	862	80	138	440	2	49
12	380	78	942	80	058	438	2	48
13	458	77	9.21 022	80	0.78 978	436	2	47
14	535	78	102	80	898	434	2	46
15	613	78	182	79	818	432	3	45
16	691	77	261	80	739	429	2	44
17	768	77	341	79	659	427	2	43
18	845	77	420	79	580	425	2	42
19	922	77	499	79	501	423	2	41
20	9.20 999	77	9.21 578	79	0.78 422	9.99 421	2	40
21	9.21 076	77	657	79	343	419	2	39
22	153	76	736	78	264	417	2	38
23	229	77	814	79	186	415	2	37
24	306	76	893	78	107	413	2	36
25	382	76	971	78	029	411	2	35
26	458	76	9.22 049	78	0.77 951	409	2	34
27	534	76	127	78	873	407	3	33
28	610	75	205	78	795	404	2	32
29	685	76	283	78	717	402	2	31
30	9.21 761	75	9.22 361	77	0.77 639	9.99 400	2	30
31	836	76	438	78	562	398	2	29
32	912	75	516	77	484	396	2	28
33	987	75	593	77	407	394	2	27
34	9.22 062	75	670	77	330	392	2	26
35	137	74	747	77	253	390	2	25
36	211	75	824	77	176	388	3	24
37	286	75	901	76	099	385	2	23
38	361	74	977	76	023	383	2	22
39	435	74	9.23 054	76	0.76 946	381	2	21
40	9.22 509	74	9.23 130	76	0.76 870	9.99 379	2	20
41	583	74	206	77	794	377	2	19
42	657	74	283	76	717	375	3	18
43	731	74	359	76	641	372	2	17
44	805	73	435	75	565	370	2	16
45	878	74	510	76	490	368	2	15
46	952	73	586	75	414	366	2	14
47	9.23 025	73	661	75	339	364	2	13
48	098	73	737	75	263	362	3	12
49	171	73	812	75	188	359	2	11
50	9.23 244	73	9.23 887	75	0.76 113	9.99 357	2	10
51	317	73	962	75	038	355	2	9
52	390	72	9.24 037	75	0.75 963	353	2	8
53	462	73	112	74	888	351	3	7
54	535	72	186	75	814	348	2	6
55	607	72	261	74	739	346	2	5
56	679	73	335	75	665	344	2	4
57	752	71	410	74	590	342	2	3
58	823	72	484	74	516	340	3	2
59	895	72	558	74	442	337	2	1
60	9.23 967		9.24 632		0.75 368	9.99 335		0

′	L. Cos.	d.	L. Cotg.	c.d.	L. Tang.	L. Sin.	d.	′

P. P.

1′	82	81	80
1″	1.4	1.4	1.3
2″	2.7	2.7	2.7
3″	4.1	4.1	4.0
4″	5.5	5.4	5.3
5″	6.8	6.8	6.7
6″	8.2	8.1	8.0
7″	9.6	9.5	9.3
8″	10.9	10.8	10.7
9″	12.3	12.2	12.0

1′	79	78	77
1″	1.3	1.3	1.3
2″	2.6	2.6	2.6
3″	4.0	3.9	3.9
4″	5.3	5.2	5.1
5″	6.6	6.5	6.4
6″	7.9	7.8	7.7
7″	9.2	9.1	9.0
8″	10.5	10.4	10.3
9″	11.9	11.7	11.6

1′	76	75
1″	1.3	1.3
2″	2.5	2.5
3″	3.8	3.8
4″	5.1	5.0
5″	6.3	6.3
6″	7.6	7.5
7″	8.9	8.8
8″	10.1	10.0
9″	11.4	11.3

1′	74	73
1″	1.2	1.2
2″	2.5	2.4
3″	3.7	3.7
4″	4.9	4.9
5″	6.2	6.1
6″	7.4	7.3
7″	8.6	8.5
8″	9.9	9.7
9″	11.1	11.0

1′	72	71
1″	1.2	1.2
2″	2.4	2.4
3″	3.6	3.6
4″	4.8	4.7
5″	6.0	5.9
6″	7.2	7.1
7″	8.4	8.3
8″	9.6	9.5
9″	10.8	10.7

1′	2	3
1″	0.03	0.05
2″	0.07	0.10
3″	0.10	0.15
4″	0.13	0.20
5″	0.17	0.25
6″	0.20	0.30
7″	0.23	0.35
8″	0.27	0.40
9″	0.30	0.45

′	L. Sin.	d.	L. Tang.	c.d.	L. Cotg.	L. Cos.	d.	′
0	9.23 967	72	9.24 632	74	0.75 368	9.99 335	2	60
1	9.24 039	71	706	73	294	333	2	59
2	110	71	779	74	221	331	3	58
3	181	71	853	73	147	328	2	57
4	253	71	926	74	074	326	2	56
5	324	71	9.25 000	73	000	324	2	55
6	395̄	71	073	73	0.74 927	322	3	54
7	466	70	146	73	854	319	2	53
8	536	71	219	73	781	317	2	52
9	607	70	292	73	708	315̄	2	51
10	9.24 677	71	9.25 365̄	72	0.74 635	9.99 313	3	50
11	748	71	437	73	563	310	2	49
12	818	70	510	72	490	308	2	48
13	888	70	582	73	418	306	2	47
14	958	70	655̄	72	345	304	3	46
15	9.25 028	70	727	72	273	301	2	45
16	098	70	799	72	201	299	2	44
17	168	69	871	72	129	297	3	43
18	237	70	943	72	057	294	2	42
19	307	69	9.26 015	71	0.73 985	292	2	41
20	9.25 376	69	9.26 086	72	0.73 914	9.99 290	2	40
21	445	69	158	71	842	288	3	39
22	514	69	229	72	771	285	2	38
23	583	69	301	71	699	283	2	37
24	652	69	372	71	628	281	3	36
25	721	69	443	71	557	278	2	35
26	790	68	514	71	486	276	2	34
27	858	68	585̄	70	415	274	3	33
28	927	68	655	71	345̄	271	2	32
29	995	68	726	71	274	269	2	31
30	9.26 063	68	9.26 797	70	0.73 203	9.99 267	3	30
31	131	68	867	70	133	264	2	29
32	199	68	937	71	063	262	2	28
33	267	68	9.27 008	70	0.72 992	260	3	27
34	335	68	078	70	922	257̄	2	26
35	403	68	148	70	852	255̄	3	25
36	470	68	218	70	782	252	2	24
37	538	67	288	69	712	250	2	23
38	605	67	357	70	643	248	3	22
39	672	67	427	69	573	245	2	21
40	9.26 739	67	9.27 496	70	0.72 504	9.99 243	2	20
41	806	67	566	69	434̄	241	3	19
42	873	67	635	69	365̄	238	2	18
43	940	67	704	69	296	236	2	17
44	9.27 007	66	773	69	227	233	3	16
45	073	67	842	69	158	231	2	15
46	140	66	911	69	089	229	3	14
47	206	66	980	69	020	226	2	13
48	273	66	9.28 049	68	0.71 951	224	3	12
49	339	66	117	69	883	221	2	11
50	9.27 405̄	66	9.28 186	68	0.71 814	9.99 219	2	10
51	471	66	254	69	746	217	2	9
52	537	65	323	68	677	214	2	8
53	602	66	391	68	609	212	3	7
54	668	66	459	68	541	209	2	6
55	734	65	527	68	473	207	2	5
56	799	65	595̄	67	405	204	3	4
57	864	66	662	68	338	202	2	3
58	930	65	730	68	270	200	3	2
59	995	65	798	67	202	197	2	1
60	9.28 060		9.28 865		0.71 135	9.99 195		0

′	L. Cos.	d.	L. Cotg.	c.d.	L. Tang.	L. Sin.	d.	′

P. P.

1′	74	73
1″	1.2	1.2
2″	2.5	2.4
3″	3.7	3.7
4″	4.9	4.9
5″	6.2	6.1
6″	7.4	7.3
7″	8.6	8.5
8″	9.9	9.7
9″	11.1	11.0

1′	72	71
1″	1.2	1.2
2″	2.4	2.4
3″	3.6	3.6
4″	4.8	4.7
5″	6.0	5.9
6″	7.2	7.1
7″	8.4	8.3
8″	9.6	9.5
9″	10.8	10.7

1′	70	69
1″	1.2	1.2
2″	2.3	2.3
3″	3.5	3.5
4″	4.7	4.6
5″	5.8	5.8
6″	7.0	6.9
7″	8.2	8.1
8″	9.3	9.2
9″	10.5	10.4

1′	68	67
1″	1.1	1.1
2″	2.3	2.2
3″	3.4	3.4
4″	4.5	4.5
5″	5.7	5.6
6″	6.8	6.7
7″	7.9	7.8
8″	9.1	8.9
9″	10.2	10.1

1′	66	65
1″	1.1	1.1
2″	2.2	2.2
3″	3.3	3.3
4″	4.4	4.3
5″	5.5	5.4
6″	6.6	6.5
7″	7.7	7.6
8″	8.8	8.7
9″	9.9	9.8

1′	2	3
1″	0.03	0.05
2″	0.07	0 10
3″	0.10	0.15
4″	0.13	0.20
5″	0.17	0.25
6″	0.20	0.30
7″	0.23	0.35
8″	0.27	0.40
9″	0.30	0.45

′	L. Sin.	d.	L. Tang.	c.d.	L. Cotg.	L. Cos.	d.	′
0	9.28 060	65	9.28 865	68	0.71 135	9.99 195	3	60
1	125	65	933	67	067	192	2	59
2	190	64	9.29 000	67	000	190	3	58
3	254	65	067	67	0.70 933	187	2	57
4	319	65	134	67	866	185	3	56
5	384	64	201	67	799	182	2	55
6	448	64	268	67	732	180	3	54
7	512	65	335	67	665	177	2	53
8	577	64	402	66	598	175	3	52
9	641	64	468	67	532	172	2	51
10	9.28 705	64	9.29 535	66	0.70 465	9.99 170	3	50
11	769	64	601	67	399	167	2	49
12	833	63	668	66	332	165	3	48
13	896	64	734	66	266	162	2	47
14	960	64	800	66	200	160	3	46
15	9.29 024	63	866	66	134	157	2	45
16	087	63	932	66	068	155	3	44
17	150	64	998	65	002	152	2	43
18	214	63	9.30 064	66	0.69 936	150	3	42
19	277	63	130	66	870	147	2	41
20	9.29 340	63	9.30 195	65	0.69 805	9.99 145	3	40
21	403	63	261	66	739	142	2	39
22	466	63	326	65	674	140	3	38
23	529	62	391	65	609	137	2	37
24	591	63	457	66	543	135	3	36
25	654	62	522	65	478	132	2	35
26	716	63	587	65	413	130	3	34
27	779	62	652	65	348	127	3	33
28	841	62	717	65	283	124	2	32
29	903	63	782	64	218	122	3	31
30	9.29 966	62	9.30 846	65	0.69 154	9.99 119	2	30
31	9.30 028	62	911	64	089	117	3	29
32	090	61	975	65	025	114	2	28
33	151	62	9.31 040	64	0.68 960	112	3	27
34	213	62	104	64	896	109	3	26
35	275	61	168	65	832	106	2	25
36	336	62	233	64	767	104	3	24
37	398	61	297	64	703	101	2	23
38	459	62	361	64	639	099	3	22
39	521	61	425	64	575	096	3	21
40	9.30 582	61	9.31 489	63	0.68 511	9.99 093	2	20
41	643	61	552	64	448	091	3	19
42	704	61	616	63	384	088	2	18
43	765	61	679	64	321	086	3	17
44	826	61	743	63	257	083	3	16
45	887	60	806	64	194	080	3	15
46	947	61	870	63	130	078	2	14
47	9.31 008	60	933	63	067	075	3	13
48	068	61	996	63	004	072	2	12
49	129	60	9.32 059	63	0.67 941	070	3	11
50	9.31 189	61	9.32 122	63	0.67 878	9.99 067	3	10
51	250	60	185	63	815	064	3	9
52	310	60	248	63	752	062	3	8
53	370	60	311	62	689	059	3	7
54	430	60	373	63	627	056	?	6
55	490	59	436	62	561	054	3	5
56	549	60	498	63	502	051	3	4
57	609	60	561	62	439	048	2	3
58	669	59	623	62	377	046	3	2
59	728	60	685	62	315	043	3	1
60	9.31 788		9.32 747		0.67 253	9.99 040		0
′	L. Cos.	d.	L. Cotg.	c.d.	L. Tang.	L. Sin.	d.	′

P. P.

1′	68	67
1″	1.1	1.1
2″	2.3	2.2
3″	3.4	3.4
4″	4.5	4.5
5″	5.7	5.6
6″	6.8	6.7
7″	7.9	7.8
8″	9.1	8.9
9″	10.2	10.1

1′	66	65
1″	1.1	1.1
2″	2.2	2.2
3″	3.3	3.3
4″	4.4	4.3
5″	5.5	5.4
6″	6.6	6.5
7″	7.7	7.6
8″	8.8	8.7
9″	9.9	9.8

1′	64	63
1″	1.1	1.1
2″	2.1	2.1
3″	3.2	3.2
4″	4.3	4.2
5″	5.3	5.3
6″	6.4	6.3
7″	7.5	7.4
8″	8.5	8.4
9″	9.6	9.5

1′	62	61
1″	1.0	1.0
2″	2.1	2.0
3″	3.1	3.1
4″	4.1	4.1
5″	5.2	5.1
6″	6.2	6.1
7″	7.2	7.1
8″	8.3	8.1
9″	9.3	9.2

1′	60	59
1″	1.0	1.0
2″	2.0	2.0
3″	3.0	3.0
4″	4.0	3.9
5″	5.0	4.9
6″	6.0	5.9
7″	7.0	6.9
8″	8.0	7.9
9″	9.0	8.9

1′	2	3
1″	0.03	0.05
2″	0.07	0.10
3″	0.10	0.15
4″	0.13	0.20
5″	0.17	0.25
6″	0.20	0.30
7″	0.23	0.35
8″	0.27	0.40
9″	0.30	0.45

'	L. Sin.	d.	L. Tang.	c.d.	L. Cotg.	L. Cos.	d.	'
0	9.31 788	59	9.32 747	63	0.67 253	9.99 040	2	60
1	847	60	810	62	190	038	3	59
2	907	59	872	61	128	035	3	58
3	966	59	933	62	067	032	2	57
4	9.32 025	59	995	62	005	030	3	56
5	084	59	9.33 057	62	0.66 943	027	3	55
6	143	59	119	61	881	024	2	54
7	202	59	180	62	820	022	3	53
8	261	58	242	61	758	019	3	52
9	319	59	303	62	697	016	3	51
10	9.32 378	59	9.33 365	61	0.66 635	9.99 013	2	50
11	437	58	426	61	574	011	3	49
12	495	58	487	61	513	008	3	48
13	553	59	548	61	452	005	3	47
14	612	58	609	61	391	002	2	46
15	670	58	670	61	330	000	3	45
16	728	58	731	61	269	9.98 997	3	44
17	786	58	792	61	208	994	3	43
18	844	58	853	60	147	991	2	42
19	902	58	913	61	087	989	3	41
20	9.32 960	58	9.33 974	60	0.66 026	9.98 986	3	40
21	9.33 018	57	9.34 034	61	0.65 966	983	3	39
22	075	58	095	60	905	980	2	38
23	133	57	155	60	845	978	3	37
24	190	58	215	61	785	975	3	36
25	248	57	276	60	724	972	3	35
26	305	57	336	60	664	969	2	34
27	362	58	396	60	604	967	3	33
28	420	57	456	60	544	964	3	32
29	477	57	516	60	484	961	3	31
30	9.33 534	57	9.34 576	59	0.65 424	9.98 958	3	30
31	591	56	635	60	365	955	2	29
32	647	57	695	60	305	953	3	28
33	704	57	755	59	245	950	3	27
34	761	57	814	60	186	947	3	26
35	818	56	874	59	126	944	3	25
36	874	57	933	59	067	941	3	24
37	931	56	992	59	008	938	2	23
38	987	56	9.35 051	60	0.64 949	936	3	22
39	9.34 043	57	111	59	889	933	3	21
40	9.34 100	56	9.35 170	59	0.64 830	9.98 930	3	20
41	156	56	229	59	771	927	3	19
42	212	56	288	59	712	924	3	18
43	268	56	347	58	653	921	2	17
44	324	56	405	59	595	919	3	16
45	380	56	464	59	536	916	3	15
46	436	55	523	58	477	913	3	14
47	491	56	581	59	419	910	3	13
48	547	55	640	58	360	907	3	12
49	602	56	698	59	302	904	3	11
50	9.34 658	55	9.35 757	58	0.64 243	9.98 901	3	10
51	713	56	815	58	185	898	2	9
52	769	55	873	58	127	896	3	8
53	824	55	931	58	069	893	3	7
54	879	55	989	58	011	890	3	6
55	934	55	9.36 047	58	0.63 953	887	3	5
56	989	55	105	58	895	884	3	4
57	9.35 044	55	163	58	837	881	3	3
58	099	55	221	58	779	878	3	2
59	154	55	279	57	721	875	3	1
60	9.35 209		9.36 336		0.63 664	9.98 872		0
'	L. Cos.	d.	L. Cotg.	c.d.	L. Tang.	L. Sin.	d.	'

P. P.

1'	63	62
1"	1.1	1.0
2"	2.1	2.1
3"	3.2	3.1
4"	4.2	4.1
5"	5.3	5.2
6"	6.3	6.2
7"	7.4	7.2
8"	8.4	8.3
9"	9.5	9 3

1'	61	60
1"	1.0	1.0
2"	2.0	2.0
3"	3.1	3.0
4"	4.1	4.0
5"	5.1	5.0
6"	6.1	6.0
7"	7.1	7.0
8"	8.1	8.0
9"	9.2	9.0

1'	59	58
1"	1.0	1.0
2"	2.0	1.9
3"	3.0	2.9
4"	3.9	3.9
5"	4.9	4.8
6"	5.9	5.8
7"	6.9	6.8
8"	7.9	7.7
9"	8.9	8.7

1'	57	56
1"	1.0	0.9
2"	1.9	1.9
3"	2.9	2.8
4"	3.8	3.7
5"	4.8	4.7
6"	5.7	5.6
7"	6.7	6.5
8"	7.6	7.5
9"	8.6	8.4

1'	55
1"	0.9
2"	1.8
3"	2.8
4"	3.7
5"	4.6
6"	5.5
7"	6.4
8"	7.3
9"	8.3

1'	2	3
1"	0.03	0.05
2"	0.07	0.10
3"	0.10	0.15
4"	0.13	0.20
5"	0.17	0.25
6"	0.20	0.30
7"	0.23	0.35
8"	0.27	0.40
9"	0.30	0.45

′	L. Sin.	d.	L. Tang.	c.d.	L. Cotg.	L. Cos.	d.	′
0	9.35 209	54	9.36 336	58	0.63 664	9.98 872	3	60
1	263	55	394	58	606	869	2	59
2	318	55	452	57	548	867	3	58
3	373	54	509	57	491	864	3	57
4	427	54	566	58	434	861	3	56
5	481	55	624	57	376	858	3	55
6	536	54	681	57	319	855̄	3	54
7	590	54	738	57	262	852	3	53
8	644	54	795	57	205	849	3	52
9	698	54	852	57	148	846	3	51
10	9.35 752	54	9.36 909	57	0.63 091	9.98 843	3	50
11	806	54	966	57	034	840	3	49
12	860	54	9.37 023	57	0.62 977	837	3	48
13	914	54	080	57	920	834	3	47
14	968	54	137	56	863	831	3	46
15	9.36 022	53	193	57	807	828	3	45
16	075	54	250	56	750	825	3	44
17	129	53	306	57	694	822	3	43
18	182	54	363	56	637	819	3	42
19	236	53	419	57	581	816	3	41
20	9.36 289	53	9.37 476	56	0.62 524	9.98 813	3	40
21	342	53	532	56	468	810	3	39
22	395	54	588	56	412	807	3	38
23	449	53	644	56	356	804	3	37
24	502	53	700	56	300	801	3	36
25	555̄	53	756	56	244	798	3	35
26	608	52	812	56	188	795	3	34
27	660	53	868	56	132	792	3	33
28	713	53	924	56	076	789	3	32
29	766	53	980	55	020̄	786	3	31
30	9.36 819	52	9.38 035	56	0.61 965	9.98 783	3	30
31	871	53	091	56	909	780	3	29
32	924	52	147	55	853	777	3	28
33	976	52	202	55	798	774	3	27
34	9.37 028	53	257	56	743	771	3	26
35	081	52	313	55	687	768	3	25
36	133	52	368	55	632	765̄	3	24
37	185	52	423	56	577	762	3	23
38	237	52	479	55	521	759	3	22
39	289	52	534	55	466	756	3	21
40	9.37 341	52	9.38 589	55	0.61 411	9.98 753	3	20
41	393	52	644	55	356	750	4	19
42	445	52	699	55	301	746	3	18
43	497	52	754	54	246	743	3	17
44	549	51	808	55	192	740	3	16
45	600	52	863	55	137	737	3	15
46	652	51	918	54	082	734	3	14
47	703	52	972	55	028	731	3	13
48	755̄	51	9.39 027	55	0.60 973	728	3	12
49	806	52	082	54	918	725̄	3	11
50	9.37 858	51	9.39 136	54	0.60 864	9.98 722	3	10
51	909	51	190	55	810	719	4	9
52	960	51	245̄	54	755	715	3	8
53	9.38 011	51	299	54	701	712	3	7
54	062	51	353	54	647	709	3	6
55	113	51	407	54	593	706	3	5
56	164	51	461	54	539	703	3	4
57	215	51	515	54	485	700	3	3
58	266	51	569	54	431	697	3	2
59	317	51	623	54	377	694	4	1
60	9.38 368		9.39 677		0.60 323	9.98 690		0
′	L. Cos.	d.	L. Cotg.	c.d.	L. Tang.	L. Sin.	d.	′

P. P.

1′	58	57
1″	1.0	1.0
2″	1.9	1.9
3″	2.9	2.9
4″	3.9	3.8
5″	4.8	4.8
6″	5.8	5.7
7″	6.8	6.7
8″	7.7	7.6
9″	8.7	8.6

1′	56	55
1″	0.9	0.9
2″	1.9	1.8
3″	2.8	2.8
4″	3.7	3.7
5″	4.7	4.6
6″	5.6	5.5
7″	6.5	6.4
8″	7.5	7.3
9″	8.4	8.3

1′	54	53
1″	0.9	0.9
2″	1.8	1.8
3″	2.7	2.7
4″	3.6	3.5
5″	4.5	4.4
6″	5.4	5.3
7″	6.3	6.2
8″	7.2	7.1
9″	8.1	8.0

1′	52	51
1″	0.9	0.9
2″	1.7	1.7
3″	2.6	2.6
4″	3.5	3.4
5″	4.3	4.3
6″	5.2	5.1
7″	6.1	6.0
8″	6.9	6.8
9″	7.8	7.7

1′	2	
1″	0.03	
2″	0.07	
3″	0.10	
4″	0.13	
5″	0.17	
6″	0.20	
7″	0.23	
8″	0.27	
9″	0.30	

1′	3	4
1″	0.05	0.07
2″	0.10	0.13
3″	0.15	0.20
4″	0.20	0.27
5″	0.25	0.33
6″	0.30	0.40
7″	0.35	0.47
8″	0.40	0.53
9″	0.45	0.60

'	L. Sin.	d.	L. Tang.	c.d.	L. Cotg.	L. Cos.	d.	'
0	9.38 368	50	9.39 677	54	0.60 323	9.98 690	3	60
1	418	51	731¹	54	269	687	3	59
2	469	50	785	53	215	684	3	58
3	519	51	838	54	162	681	3	57
4	570	50	892	53	108	678	3	56
5	620	50	945	54	055	675	4	55
6	670	50	999	53	001	671	3	54
7	721	51	9.40 052	54	0.59 948	668	3	53
8	771	50	106	53	894	665	3	52
9	821	50	159	53	841	662	3	51
10	9.38 871	50	9.40 212	54	0.59 788	9.98 659	3	50
11	921	50	266	53	734	656	4	49
12	971	50	319	53	681	652	3	48
13	9.39 021	50	372	53	628	649	3	47
14	071	50	425	53	575	646	3	46
15	121	49	478	53	522	643	3	45
16	170	50	531	53	469	640	4	44
17	220	50	584	52	416	636	3	43
18	270	49	636	53	364	633	3	42
19	319	50	689	53	311	630	3	41
20	9.39 369	49	9.40 742	53	0.59 258	9.98 627	4	40
21	418	49	795	52	205	623	3	39
22	467	50	847	53	153	620	3	38
23	517	49	900	52	100	617	3	37
24	566	49	952	53	048	614	4	36
25	615	49	9.41 005	52	0.58 995	610	3	35
26	664	49	057	52	943	607	3	34
27	713	49	109	52	891	604	3	33
28	762	49	161	53	839	601	4	32
29	811	49	214	52	786	597	3	31
30	9.39 860	49	9.41 266	52	0.58 734	9.98 594	3	30
31	909	49	318	52	682	591	3	29
32	958	48	370	52	630	588	4	28
33	9.40 006	49	422	52	578	584	3	27
34	055	48	474	52	526	581	3	26
35	103	49	526	52	474	578	4	25
36	152	48	578	51	422	574	3	24
37	200	49	629	52	371	571	3	23
38	249	48	681	52	319	568	3	22
39	297	49	733	51	267	565	4	21
40	9.40 346	48	9.41 784	52	0.58 216	9.98 561	3	20
41	394	48	836	51	164	558	3	19
42	442	48	887	52	113	555	4	18
43	490	48	939	51	061	551	3	17
44	538	48	990	51	010	548	3	16
45	586	48	9.42 041	52	0.57 959	545	4	15
46	634	48	093	51	907	541	3	14
47	682	48	144	51	856	538	3	13
48	730	48	195	51	805	535	4	12
49	778	47	246	51	754	531	3	11
50	9.40 825	48	9.42 297	51	0.57 703	9.98 528	3	10
51	873	48	348	51	652	525	3	9
52	921	47	399	51	601	521	3	8
53	968	48	450	51	550	518	3	7
54	9.41 016	47	501	51	499	515	4	6
55	063	48	552	51	448	511	3	5
56	111	47	603	50	397	508	3	4
57	158	47	653	51	347	505	4	3
58	205	47	704	51	296	501	3	2
59	252	48	755	50	245	498	4	1
60	9.41 300		9.42 805		0 57 195	9 98 494		0
'	L. Cos.	d.	L. Cotg.	c.d.	L. Tang.	L. Sin.	d.	'

P. P.

1'	54	53
1"	0.9	0.9
2"	1.8	1.8
3"	2.7	2.7
4"	3.6	3.5
5"	4.5	4.4
6"	5.4	5.3
7"	6.3	6.2
8"	7.2	7.1
9"	8.1	8.0

1'	52	51
1"	0.9	0.9
2"	1.7	1.7
3"	2.6	2.6
4"	3.5	3.4
5"	4.3	4.3
6"	5.2	5.1
7"	6.1	6.0
8"	6.9	6.8
9"	7.8	7.7

1'	50	49
1"	0.8	0.8
2"	1.7	1.6
3"	2.5	2.5
4"	3.3	3.3
5"	4.2	4.1
6"	5.0	4.9
7"	5.8	5.7
8"	6.7	6.5
9"	7.5	7.4

1'	48
1"	0.8
2"	1.6
3"	2.4
4"	3.2
5"	4.0
6"	4.8
7"	5.6
8"	6.4
9"	7.2

1'	47
1"	0.8
2"	1.6
3"	2.4
4"	3.1
5"	3.9
6"	4.7
7"	5.5
8"	6.3
9"	7 1

1'	3	4
1"	0.05	0.07
2"	0.10	0 13
3"	0.15	0.20
4"	0.20	0.27
5"	0.25	0.33
6"	0.30	0.40
7"	0.35	0.47
8"	0.40	0.53
9"	0.45	0.60

′	L. Sin.	d.	L. Tang.	c.d.	L. Cotg.	L. Cos.	d.	′
0	9.41 300	47	9.42 805	51	0.57 195	9.98 494	3	60
1	347	47	856	50	144	491	3	59
2	394	47	906	51	094	488	4	58
3	441	47	957	50	043	484	3	57
4	488	47	9.43 007	50	0.56 993	481	4	56
5	535	47	057	51	943	477	3	55
6	582	46	108	50	892	474	3	54
7	628	47	158	50	842	471	4	53
8	675	47	208	50	792	467	3	52
9	722	46	258	50	742	464	4	51
10	9.41 768	47	9.43 308	50	0.56 692	9.98 460	3	50
11	815	46	358	50	642	457	4	49
12	861	47	408	50	592	453	3	48
13	908	46	458	50	542	450	3	47
14	954	47	508	50	492	447	4	46
15	9.42 001	46	558	49	442	443	3	45
16	047	46	607	50	393	440	4	44
17	093	47	657	50	343	436	3	43
18	140	46	707	49	293	433	4	42
19	186	46	756	50	244	429	3	41
20	9.42 232	46	9.43 806	49	0.56 194	9.98 426	4	40
21	278	46	855	50	145	422	3	39
22	324	46	905	50	095	419	4	38
23	370	46	954	50	046	415	3	37
24	416	45	9.44 004	49	0.55 996	412	3	36
25	461	46	053	49	947	409	4	35
26	507	46	102	49	898	405	3	34
27	553	46	151	50	849	402	4	33
28	599	45	201	49	799	398	3	32
29	644	46	250	49	750	395	4	31
30	9.42 690	45	9.44 299	49	0.55 701	9.98 391	3	30
31	735	46	348	49	652	388	4	29
32	781	45	397	49	603	384	3	28
33	826	46	446	49	554	381	4	27
34	872	45	495	49	505	377	4	26
35	917	45	544	48	456	373	3	25
36	962	46	592	49	408	370	4	24
37	9.43 008	45	641	49	359	366	3	23
38	053	45	690	48	310	363	4	22
39	098	45	738	49	262	359	3	21
40	9.43 143	45	9.44 787	49	0.55 213	9.98 356	4	20
41	188	45	836	48	164	352	3	19
42	233	45	884	49	116	349	4	18
43	278	45	933	48	067	345	3	17
44	323	44	981	48	019	342	4	16
45	367	45	9.45 029	49	0.54 971	338	4	15
46	412	45	078	48	922	334	3	14
47	457	45	126	48	874	331	4	13
48	502	44	174	48	826	327	3	12
49	546	45	222	49	778	324	4	11
50	9.43 591	44	9.45 271	48	0.54 729	9.98 320	3	10
51	635	45	319	48	681	317	4	9
52	680	44	367	48	633	313	4	8
53	724	45	415	48	585	309	3	7
54	769	44	463	48	537	306	4	6
55	813	44	511	48	489	302	3	5
56	857	44	559	47	441	299	4	4
57	901	45	606	48	394	295	4	3
58	946	44	654	48	346	291	3	2
59	990	44	702	48	298	288	4	1
60	9.44 034		9.45 750		0.54 250	9.98 284		0

′	L. Cos.	d.	L. Cotg.	c.d.	L. Tang.	L. Sin.	d.	′

P. P.

1′	51	50
1″	0.9	0.8
2″	1.7	1.7
3″	2.6	2.5
4″	3.4	3.3
5″	4.3	4.2
6″	5.1	5.0
7″	6.0	5.8
8″	6.8	6.7
9″	7.7	7.5

1′	49	48
1″	0.8	0.8
2″	1.6	1.6
3″	2.5	2.4
4″	3.3	3.2
5″	4.1	4.0
6″	4.9	4.8
7″	5.7	5.6
8″	6.5	6.4
9″	7.4	7.2

1′	47	46
1″	0.8	0.8
2″	1.6	1.5
3″	2.4	2.3
4″	3.1	3.1
5″	3.9	3.8
6″	4.7	4.6
7″	5.5	5.4
8″	6.3	6.1
9″	7.1	6.9

1′	45
1″	0.8
2″	1.5
3″	2.3
4″	3.0
5″	3.8
6″	4.5
7″	5.3
8″	6.0
9″	6.8

1′	44
1″	0.7
2″	1.5
3″	2.2
4″	2.9
5″	3.7
6″	4.4
7″	5.1
8″	5.9
9″	6.6

1′	3	4
1″	0.05	0.07
2″	0,10	0 13
3″	0.15	0.20
4″	0.20	0.27
5″	0.25	0.33
6″	0.30	0.40
7″	0.35	0.47
8″	0.40	0.53
9″	0.45	0.60

′	L. Sin.	d.	L. Tang.	c.d.	L. Cotg.	L. Cos.	d.	′		P. P.	
0	9.44 034	44	9.45 750	47	0.54 250	9.98 284	3	60	1′	48	47
1	078	44	797	48	203	281	4	59	1″	0.8	0.8
2	122	44	845	47	155	277	4	58	2″	1.6	1.6
3	.166	44	892	48	108	273	3	57	3″	2.4	2.4
4	210	43	940	47	060	270	4	56	4″	3.2	3.1
5	253	44	987	48	013	266	4	55	5″	4.0	3.9
6	297	44	9.46 035	47	0.53 965	262	3	54	6″	4.8	4.7
7	341	44	082	48	918	259	4	53	7″	5.6	5.5
8	385	43	130	47	870	255	4	52	8″	6.4	6.3
9	428	44	177	47	823	251	3	51	9″	7.2	7.1
10	9.44 472	44	9.46 224	47	0.53 776	9.98 248	4	50	1′	46	45
11	516	43	271	48	729	244	4	49	1″	0.8	0.8
12	559	43	319	47	681	240	3	48	2″	1.5	1.5
13	602	44	366	47	634	237	4	47	3″	2.3	2.3
14	646	43	413	47	587	233	4	46	4″	3.1	3.0
15	689	44	460	47	540	229	3	45	5″	3.8	3.8
16	733	43	507	47	493	226	4	44	6″	4.6	4.5
17	776	43	554	47	446	222	4	43	7″	5.4	5.3
18	819	43	601	47	399	218	3	42	8″	6.1	6.0
19	862	43	648	46	352	215	4	41	9″	6.9	6.8
20	9.44 905	43	9.46 694	47	0.53 306	9.98 211	4	40	1′	44	43
21	948	44	741	47	259	207	3	39	1″	0.7	0.7
22	992	43	788	47	212	204	4	38	2″	1.5	1.4
23	9.45 035	42	835	46	165	200	4	37	3″	2.2	2.2
24	077	43	881	47	119	196	4	36	4″	2.9	2.9
25	120	43	928	47	072	192	3	35	5″	3.7	3.6
26	163	43	975	46	025	189	4	34	6″	4.4	4.3
27	206	43	9.47 021	47	0.52 979	185	4	33	7″	5.1	5.0
28	249	43	068	46	932	181	4	32	8″	5.9	5.7
29	292	42	114	46	886	177	3	31	9″	6.6	6.5
30	9.45 334	43	9.47 160	47	0.52 840	9.98 174	4	30			
31	377	42	207	46	793	170	4	29	1′	42	
32	419	43	253	46	747	166	4	28	1″	0.7	
33	462	42	299	47	701	162	3	27	2″	1.4	
34	504	43	346	46	654	159	4	26	3″	2.1	
35	547	42	392	46	608	155	4	25	4″	2.8	
36	589	43	438	46	562	151	4	24	5″	3.5	
37	632	42	484	46	516	147	3	23	6″	4.2	
38	674	42	530	46	470	144	4	22	7″	4.9	
39	716	42	576	46	424	140	4	21	8″	5.6	
40	9.45 758	43	9.47 622	46	0.52 378	9.98 136	4	20	9″	6.3	
41	801	42	668	46	332	132	3	19	1′	41	
42	843	42	714	46	286	129	4	18	1″	0.7	
43	885	42	760	46	240	125	4	17	2″	1.4	
44	927	42	806	46	194	121	4	16	3″	2.1	
45	969	42	852	45	148	117	4	15	4″	2.7	
46	9.46 011	42	897	46	103	113	3	14	5″	3.4	
47	053	42	943	46	057	110	4	13	6″	4.1	
48	095	41	989	46	011	106	4	12	7″	4.8	
49	136	42	9.48 035	45	0.51 965	102	4	11	8″	5.5	
50	9.46 178	42	9.48 080	46	0.51 920	9.98 098	4	10	9″	6.2	
·51	220	42	126	45	874	094	4	9	1′	3	4
52	262	41	171	46	829	090	3	8	1″	0.05	0.07
53	303	42	217	45	783	087	4	7	2″	0.10	0.13
54	345	41	262	45	738	083	4	6	3″	0.15	0.20
55	386	42	307	46	693	079	4	5	4″	0.20	0.27
56	428	41	353	45	647	075	4	4	5″	0.25	0.33
57	469	42	398	45	602	071	4	3	6″	0.30	0.40
58	511	41	443	46	557	067	4	2	7″	0.35	0.47
59	552	42	489	45	511	063	3	1	8″	0.40	0.53
60	9.46 594		9.48 534		0.51 466	9 98 060		0	9″	0.45	0.60

| ′ | L. Cos. | d. | L. Cotg. | c.d. | L. Tang. | L. Sin. | d. | ′ | |

'	L. Sin.	d.	L. Tang.	c.d.	L. Cotg.	L. Cos.	d.	'
0	9.46 594	41	9.48 534	45	0.51 466	9.98 060	4	60
1	635	41	579	45	421	056	4	59
2	676	41	624	45	376	052	4	58
3	717	41	669	45	331	048	4	57
4	758	42	714	45	286	044	4	56
5	800	41	759	45	241	040	4	55
6	841	41	804	45	196	036	4	54
7	882	41	849	45	151	032	3	53
8	923	41	894	45	106	029	4	52
9	964	41	939	45	061	025	4	51
10	9.47 005	40	9.48 984	45	0.51 016	9.98 021	4	50
11	045	41	9.49 029	44	0.50 971	017	4	49
12	086	41	073	45	927	013	4	48
13	127	41	118	45	882	009	4	47
14	168	41	163	44	837	005	4	46
15	209	40	207	45	793	001	4	45
16	249	41	252	44	748	9.97 997	4	44
17	290	40	296	45	704	993	4	43
18	330	41	341	44	659	989	3	42
19	371	40	385	45	615	986	4	41
20	9.47 411	41	9.49 430	44	0.50 570	9.97 982	4	40
21	452	40	474	45	526	978	4	39
22	492	41	519	44	481	974	4	38
23	533	40	563	44	437	970	4	37
24	573	40	607	45	393	966	4	36
25	613	41	652	44	348	962	4	35
26	654	40	696	44	304	958	4	34
27	694	40	740	44	260	954	4	33
28	734	40	784	44	216	950	4	32
29	774	40	828	44	172	946	4	31
30	9.47 814	40	9.49 872	44	0.50 128	9.97 942	4	30
31	854	40	916	44	084	938	4	29
32	894	40	960	44	040	934	4	28
33	934	40	9.50 004	44	0.49 996	930	4	27
34	974	40	048	44	952	926	4	26
35	9.48 014	40	092	44	908	922	4	25
36	054	40	136	44	864	918	4	24
37	094	39	180	43	820	914	4	23
38	133	40	223	44	777	910	4	22
39	173	40	267	44	733	906	4	21
40	9.48 213	39	9.50 311	44	0.49 689	9.97 902	4	20
41	252	40	355	43	645	898	4	19
42	292	40	398	44	602	894	4	18
43	332	39	442	43	558	890	4	17
44	371	40	485	44	515	886	4	16
45	411	39	529	43	471	882	4	15
46	450	40	572	44	428	878	4	14
47	490	39	616	43	384	874	4	13
48	529	39	659	44	341	870	4	12
49	568	39	703	43	297	866	5	11
50	9.48 607	40	9.50 746	44	0.49 254	9.97 861	4	10
51	647	39	789	43	211	857	4	9
52	686	39	833	44	167	853	4	8
53	725	39	876	43	124	849	4	7
54	764	39	919	43	081	845	4	6
55	803	39	962	43	038	841	5	5
56	842	39	9.51 003	43	0.48 995	837	4	4
57	881	39	048	44	952	833	4	3
58	920	39	092	43	908	829	4	2
59	959	39	135	43	865	825	4	1
60	9.48 998		9.51 178		0.48 822	9.97 821		0

'	L. Cos.	d.	L. Cotg.	c.d.	L. Tang.	L. Sin.	d.	'

P. P.

1'	45	44
1"	0.8	0.7
2"	1.5	1.5
3"	2.3	2.2
4"	3.0	2.9
5"	3.8	3.7
6"	4.5	4.4
7"	5.3	5.1
8"	6.0	5.9
9"	6.8	6.6

1'	43	42
1"	0.7	0.7
2"	1.4	1.4
3"	2.2	2.1
4"	2.9	2.8
5"	3.6	3.5
6"	4.3	4.2
7"	5.0	4.9
8"	5.7	5.6
9"	6.5	6.3

1'	41	40
1"	0.7	0.7
2"	1.4	1.3
3"	2.1	2.0
4"	2.7	2.7
5"	3.4	3.3
6"	4.1	4.0
7"	4.8	4.7
8"	5.5	5.3
9"	6.2	6.0

1'	39
1"	0.7
2"	1.3
3"	2.0
4"	2.6
5"	3.3
6"	3.9
7"	4.6
8"	5.2
9"	5.9

1'	3
1"	0.05
2"	0.10
3"	0.15
4"	0.20
5"	0.25
6"	0.30
7"	0.35
8"	0.40
9"	0.45

1'	4	5
1"	0.07	0.08
2"	0.13	0.17
3"	0.20	0.25
4"	0.27	0.33
5"	0.33	0.42
6"	0.40	0.50
7"	0.47	0.58
8"	0.53	0.67
9"	0.60	0.75

′	L. Sin.	d.	L. Tang.	c. d.	L. Cotg.	L. Cos.	d.	′	P. P.		
0	9.48 998	39	9.51 178	43	0.48 822	9.97 821	4	**60**	**1′**	**43**	**42**
1	9.49 037	39	221	43	779	817	5	59	1″	0.7	0.7
2	076	39	264	42	736	812	4	58	2″	1.4	1.4
3	115	38	306	43	694	808	4	57	3″	2.2	2.1
4	153	39	349	43	651	804	4	56	4″	2.9	2.8
5	192	39	392	43	608	800	4	55	5″	3.6	3.5
6	231	38	435	43	565	796	4	54	6″	4.3	4.2
7	269	39	478	42	522	792	4	53	7″	5.0	4.9
8	308	39	520	43	480	788	4	52	8″	5.7	5.6
9	347	38	563	43	437	784	5	51	9″	6.5	6.3
10	9.49 385	39	9.51 606	42	0.48 394	9.97 779	4	**50**	**1′**	**41**	**39**
11	424	38	648	43	352	775	4	49	1″	0.7	0.7
12	462	38	691	43	309	771	4	48	2″	1.4	1.3
13	500	39	734	42	266	767	4	47	3″	2.1	2.0
14	539	38	776	43	224	763	4	46	4″	2.7	2.6
15	577	38	819	42	181	759	5	45	5″	3.4	3.3
16	615	39	861	42	139	754	4	44	6″	4.1	3.9
17	654	38	903	43	097	750	4	43	7″	4.8	4.6
18	692	38	946	42	054	746	4	42	8″	5.5	5.2
19	730	38	988	43	012	742	4	41	9″	6.2	5.9
20	9.49 768	38	9.52 031	42	0.47 969	9.97 738	4	**40**			
21	806	38	073	42	927	734	5	39	**1′**	**38**	
22	844	38	115	42	885	729	4	38	1″	0.6	
23	882	38	157	43	843	725	4	37	2″	1.3	
24	920	38	200	42	800	721	4	36	3″	1.9	
25	958	38	242	42	758	717	4	35	4″	2.5	
26	996	38	284	42	716	713	5	34	5″	3.2	
27	9.50 034	38	326	42	674	708	4	33	6″	3.8	
28	072	38	368	42	632	704	4	32	7″	4.4	
29	110	38	410	42	590	700	4	31	8″	5.1	
30	9.50 148	37	9.52 452	42	0.47 548	9.97 696	5	**30**	9″	5.7	
31	185	38	494	42	506	691	4	29	**1′**	**37**	
32	223	38	536	42	464	687	4	28	1″	0.6	
33	261	37	578	42	422	683	4	27	2″	1.2	
34	298	38	620	41	380	679	5	26	3″	1.9	
35	336	38	661	42	339	674	4	25	4″	2.5	
36	374	37	703	42	297	670	4	24	5″	3.1	
37	411	38	745	42	255	666	4	23	6″	3.7	
38	449	37	787	42	213	662	5	22	7″	4.3	
39	486	37	829	41	171	657	4	21	8″	4.9	
40	9.50 523	38	9.52 870	42	0.47 130	9.97 653	4	**20**	9″	5.6	
41	561	37	912	41	088	649	4	19	**1′**	**36**	
42	598	37	953	42	047	645	5	18	1″	0.6	
43	635	38	995	42	005	640	4	17	2″	1.2	
44	673	37	9.53 037	41	0.46 963	636	4	16	3″	1.8	
45	710	37	078	42	922	632	4	15	4″	2.4	
46	747	37	120	41	880	628	4	14	5″	3.0	
47	784	37	161	41	839	623	5	13	6″	3.6	
48	821	37	202	42	798	619	4	12	7″	4.2	
49	858	38	244	41	756	615	4	11	8″	4.8	
50	9.50 896	37	9.53 285	42	0.46 715	9.97 610	5	**10**	9″	5.4	
51	933	37	327	41	673	606	4	9	**1′**	**4**	**5**
52	970	37	368	41	632	602	4	8	1″	0.07	0.08
53	9.51 007	36	409	41	591	597	5	7	2″	0.13	0.17
54	043	37	450	42	550	593	4	6	3″	0.20	0.25
55	080	37	492	41	508	589	5	5	4″	0.27	0.33
56	117	37	533	41	467	584	4	4	5″	0.33	0.42
57	154	37	574	41	426	580	4	3	6″	0.40	0.50
58	191	36	615	41	385	576	5	2	7″	0.47	0.58
59	227	37	656	41	344	571	4	1	8″	0.53	0.67
60	9.51 264		9.53 697		0.46 303	9.97 567		**0**	9″	0.60	0.75
′	L. Cos.	d.	L. Cotg.	c.d.	L. Tang.	L. Sin.	d.	′			

′	L. Sin.	d.	L. Tang.	c. d.	L. Cotg.	L. Cos.	d.	′	P. P.		
0	9.51 264	37	9.53 697	41	0.46 303	9.97 567	4	60	1′	41	40
1	301	37	738	41	262	563	5	59	1″	0.7	0.7
2	338	36	779	41	221	558	4	58	2″	1.4	1.3
3	374	37	820	41	180	554	4	57	3″	2.1	2.0
4	411	36	861	41	139	550	5	56	4″	2.7	2.7
5	447	37	902	41	098	545	4	55	5″	3.4	3.3
6	484	36	943	41	057	541	5	54	6″	4.1	4.0
7	520	37	984	41	016	536	4	53	7″	4.8	4.7
8	557	36	9.54 025	40	0.45 975	532	4	52	8″	5.5	5.3
9	593	36	065	41	935	528	5	51	9″	6.2	6.0
10	9.51 629	37	9.54 106	41	0.45 894	9.97 523	4	50			
11	666	36	147	40	853	519	4	49			
12	702	36	187	41	813	515	5	48	1′	39	37
13	738	36	228	41	772	510	4	47	.1″	0.7	0.6
14	774	37	269	40	731	506	5	46	2″	1.3	1.2
15	811	36	309	41	691	501	4	45	3″	2.0	1.9
16	847	36	350	40	650	497	5	44	4″	2.6	2.5
17	883	36	390	41	610	492	4	43	5″	3.3	3.1
18	919	36	431	40	569	488	4	42	6″	3.9	3.7
19	955	36	471	41	529	484	5	41	7″	4.6	4.3
20	9.51 991	36	9.54 512	40	0.45 488	9.97 479	4	40	8″	5.2	4.9
21	9.52 027	36	552	41	448	475	5	39	9″	5.9	5.6
22	063	36	593	40	407	470	4	38			
23	099	36	633	40	367	466	5	37			
24	135	36	673	41	327	461	4	36			
25	171	36	714	40	286	457	4	35	1′	35	35
26	207	35	754	40	246	453	5	34	1″	0.6	0.6
27	242	36	794	41	206	448	4	33	2″	1.2	1.2
28	278	36	835	40	165	444	5	32	3″	1.8	1.8
29	314	36	875	40	125	439	4	31	4″	2.4	2.3
30	9.52 350	35	9.54 915	40	0.45 085	9.97 435	5	30	5″	3.0	2.9
31	385	36	955	40	045	430	4	29	6″	3.6	3.5
32	421	35	995	40	005	426	5	28	7″	4.2	4.1
33	456	36	9.55 035	40	0.44 965	421	4	27	8″	4.8	4.7
34	492	35	075	40	925	417	5	26	9″	5.4	5.3
35	527	36	115	40	885	412	4	25			
36	563	35	155	40	845	408	5	24			
37	598	36	195	40	805	403	4	23	1′	34	
38	634	35	235	40	765	399	5	22	1″	0.6	
39	669	36	275	40	725	394	4	21	2″	1.1	
40	9.52 705	35	9.55 315	40	0.44 685	9.97 390	5	20	3″	1.7	
41	740	35	355	40	645	385	4	19	4″	2.3	
42	775	36	395	39	605	381	5	18	5″	2.8	
43	811	35	434	40	566	376	4	17	6″	3.4	
44	846	35	474	40	526	372	5	16	7″	4.0	
45	881	35	514	40	486	367	4	15	8″	4.5	
46	916	35	554	40	446	363	5	14	9″	5.1	
47	951	35	593	39	407	358	5	13			
48	986	35	633	40	367	353	4	12			
49	9.53 021	35	673	40	327	349	5	11	1′	4	5
50	9.53 056	36	9.55 712	39	0.44 288	9.97 344	4	10	1″	0.07	0.08
51	092	34	752	39	248	340	5	9	2″	0.13	0.17
52	126	35	791	40	209	335	4	8	3″	0.20	0.25
53	161	35	831	39	169	331	5	7	4″	0.27	0.33
54	196	35	870	40	130	326	4	6	5″	0.33	0.42
55	231	35	910	39	090	322	5	5	6″	0.40	0.50
56	266	35	949	40	051	317	5	4	7″	0.47	0.58
57	301	35	989	39	011	312	4	3	8″	0.53	0.67
58	336	34	9.56 028	39	0.43 972	308	5	2	9″	0.60	0.75
59	370	35	067	40	933	303	4	1			
60	9.53 405		9.56 107		0.43 893	9.97 299		0			
′	L. Cos.	d.	L. Cotg.	c. d.	L. Tang.	L. Sin.	d.	′			

'	L. Sin.	d.	L. Tang.	c.d.	L. Cotg.	L. Cos.	d.	'
0	9.53 405	35	9.56 107	39	0.43 893	9.97 299	5	60
1	440	35	146	39	854	294	5	59
2	475	34	185	39	815̄	289	4	58
3	509	35	224	40	776	285	5	57
4	544	34	264	39	736	280	4	56
5	578	35	303	39	697	276	5	55
6	613	34	342	39	658	271	5	54
7	647	35	381	39	619	266	4	53
8	682	34	420	39	580	262	5	52
9	716	35	459	39	541	257	5	51
10	9.53 751	34	9.56 498	39	0.43 502	9.97 252	4	50
11	785	34	537	39	463	248	5	49
12	819	35	576	39	424	243	5	48
13	854	34	615	39	385	238	4	47
14	888	34	654	39	346	234	5	46
15	922	35	693	39	307	229	5	45
16	957	34	732	39	268	224	4	44
17	991	34	771	39	229	220	5	43
18	9.54 025̄	34	810	39	190	215	5	42
19	059	34	849	38	151	210	5	41
20	9.54 093	34	9.56 887	39	0.43 113	9.97 206	4	40
21	127	34	926	39	074	201	5	39
22	161	34	965̄	39	035	196	4	38
23	195	34	9.57 004	38	0.42 996	192	5	37
24	229	34	042	39	958	187	5	36
25	263	34	081	39	919	182	4	35
26	297	34	120	38	880	178	5	34
27	331	34	158	39	842	173	5	33
28	365̄	34	197	38	803	168	5	32
29	399	34	235	39	765̄	163	4	31
30	9.54 433	33	9.57 274	38	0.42 726	9.97 159	5	30
31	466	34	312	39	688	154	5	29
32	500	34	351	38	649	149̄	5	28
33	534	33	389	39	611	145̄	5	27
34	567	34	428	38	572	140	5	26
35	601	34	466	38	534	135	5	25
36	635̄	33	504	39	496	130	4	24
37	668	34	543	38	457	126	5	23
38	702	33	581	38	419	121	5	22
39	735	34	619	39	381	116	5	21
40	9.54 769	33	9.57 658	38	0.42 342	9.97 111	4	20
41	802	34	696	38	304	107	5	19
42	836	33	734	38	266	102	5	18
43	869	34	772	38	228	097	5	17
44	903	33	810	39	190	092	5	16
45	936	33	849	38	151	087	5	15
46	969	34	887	38	113	083	4	14
47	9.55 003	33	925̄	38	075	078	5	13
48	036	33	963	38	037	073	5	12
49	069	33	9.58 001	38	0.41 999	068	5	11
50	9.55 102	34	9.58 039	38	0.41 961	9.97 063	4	10
51	136	33	077	38	923	059	5	9
52	169	33	115̄	38	885	054	5	8
53	202	33	153	38	847	049	5	7
54	235̄	33	191	38	809	044	5	6
55	268	33	229	38	771	039	5	5
56	301	33	267	38	733	035̄	4	4
57	334	33	304	37	696	030	5	3
58	367	33	342	38	658	025̄	5	2
59	400	33	380	38	620	020	5	1
60	9.55 433		9.58 418		0.41 582	9.97 015		0
'	L. Cos.	d.	L. Cotg.	c.d.	L. Tang.	L. Sin.	d.	'

P. P.

1'	40	39
1"	0.7	0.7
2"	1.3	1.3
3"	2.0	2.0
4"	2.7	2.6
5"	3.3	3.3
6"	4.0	3.9
7"	4.7	4.6
8"	5.3	5.2
9"	6.0	5.9

1'	38	37
1"	0.6	0.6
2"	1.3	1.2
3"	1.9	1.9
4"	2.5	2.5
5"	3.2	3.1
6"	3.8	3.7
7"	4.4	4.3
8"	5.1	4.9
9"	5.7	5.6

1'	35
1"	0.6
2"	1.2
3"	1.8
4"	2.3
5"	2.9
6"	3.5
7"	4.1
8"	4.7
9"	5.3

1'	34
1"	0.6
2"	1.1
3"	1.7
4"	2.3
5"	2.8
6"	3.4
7"	4.0
8"	4.5
9"	5.1

1'	33
1"	0.6
2"	1.1
3"	1.7
4"	2.2
5"	2.8
6"	3.3
7"	3.9
8"	4.4
9"	5.0

1'	4	5
1"	0.07	0.08
2"	0.13	0.17
3"	0.20	0.25
4"	0.27	0.33
5"	0.33	0.42
6"	0.40	0.50
7"	0.47	0.58
8"	0.53	0.67
9"	0.60	0.75

′	L. Sin.	d.	L. Tang.	c. d.	L. Cotg.	L. Cos.	d.	′	P. P.		
0	9.55 433	33	9.58 418	37	0.41 582	9.97 015	5	60	1′	38	37
1	466	33	455	38	545	010	5	59	1″	0.6	0.6
2	499	33	493	38	507	005	4	58	2″	1.3	1.2
3	532	32	531	38	469	001	5	57	3″	1.9	1.9
4	564	33	569	37	431	9.96 996	5	56	4″	2.5	2.5
5	597	33	606	38	394	991	5	55	5″	3.2	3.1
6	630	33	644	37	356	986	5	54	6″	3.8	3.7
7	663	32	681	38	319	981	5	53	7″	4.4	4.3
8	695	33	719	38	281	976	5	52	8″	5.1	4.9
9	728	33	757	37	243	971	5	51	9″	5.7	5.6
10	9.55 761	32	9.58 794	38	0.41 206	9.96 966	4	50	1′	36	33
11	793	33	832	37	168	962	5	49	1″	0.6	0.6
12	826	32	869	38	131	957	5	48	2″	1.2	1.1
13	858	33	907	37	093	952	5	47	3″	1.8	1.7
14	891	32	944	37	056	947	5	46	4″	2.4	2.2
15	923	33	981	38	019	942	5	45	5″	3.0	2.8
16	956	32	9.59 019	37	0.40 981	937	5	44	6″	3.6	3.3
17	988	33	056	38	944	932	5	43	7″	4.2	3.9
18	9.56 021	32	094	37	906	927	5	42	8″	4.8	4.4
19	053	32	131	37	869	922	5	41	9″	5.4	5.0
20	9.56 085	33	9.59 168	37	0.40 832	9.96 917	5	40	1′	32	
21	118	32	205	38	795	912	5	39	1″	0.5	
22	150	32	243	37	757	907	4	38	2″	1.1	
23	182	33	280	37	720	903	5	37	3″	1.6	
24	215	32	317	37	683	898	5	36	4″	2.1	
25	247	32	354	37	646	893	5	35	5″	2.7	
26	279	32	391	38	609	888	5	34	6″	3.2	
27	311	32	429	37	571	883	5	33	7″	3.7	
28	343	32	466	37	534	878	5	32	8″	4.3	
29	375	33	503	37	497	873	5	31	9″	4.8	
30	9.56 408	32	9.59 540	37	0.40 460	9.96 868	5	30	1′	31	
31	440	32	577	37	423	863	5	29	1″	0.5	
32	472	32	614	37	386	858	5	28	2″	1.0	
33	504	32	651	37	349	853	5	27	3″	1.6	
34	536	32	688	37	312	848	5	26	4″	2.1	
35	568	31	725	37	275	843	5	25	5″	2.6	
36	599	32	762	37	238	838	5	24	6″	3.1	
37	631	32	799	36	201	833	5	23	7″	3.6	
38	663	32	835	37	165	828	5	22	8″	4.1	
39	695	32	872	37	128	823	5	21	9″	4.7	
40	9.56 727	32	9.59 909	37	0.40 091	9.96 818	5	20	1′	4	
41	759	31	946	37	054	813	5	19	1″	0.07	
42	790	32	983	36	017	808	5	18	2″	0.13	
43	822	32	9.60 019	37	0.39 981	803	5	17	3″	0.20	
44	854	32	056	37	944	798	5	16	4″	0.27	
45	886	31	093	37	907	793	5	15	5″	0.33	
46	917	32	130	36	870	788	5	14	6″	0.40	
47	949	31	166	37	834	783	5	13	7″	0.47	
48	980	32	203	37	797	778	6	12	8″	0.53	
49	9.57 012	32	240	36	760	772	5	11	9″	0.60	
50	9.57 044	31	9.60 276	37	0.39 724	9.96 767	5	10	1′	5	6
51	075	32	313	36	687	762	5	9	1″	0.08	0.10
52	107	31	349	37	651	757	5	8	2″	0.17	0.20
53	138	31	386	36	614	752	5	7	3″	0.25	0.30
54	169	32	422	37	578	747	5	6	4″	0.33	0.40
55	201	31	459	36	541	743	5	5	5″	0.42	0.50
56	232	32	495	37	505	737	5	4	6″	0.50	0.60
57	264	31	532	36	468	732	5	3	7″	0.58	0.70
58	295	31	568	37	432	727	5	2	8″	0.67	0.80
59	326	32	605	36	395	722	5	1	9″	0.75	0.90
60	9.57 358		9.60 641		0.39 359	9.96 717		0			
′	L. Cos.	d.	L. Cotg.	c. d.	L. Tang.	L. Sin.	d.	′			

′	L. Sin.	d.	L. Tang.	c.d.	L. Cotg.	L. Cos.	d.	′		P. P.	
0	9.57 358	31	9.60 641	36	0.39 359	9.96 717	6	60	1′	37	36
1	389	31	677	37	323	711	5	59	1″	0.6	0.6
2	420	31	714	36	286	706	5	58	2″	1.2	1.2
3	451	31	750	36	250	701	5	57	3″	1.9	1.8
4	482	32	786	37	214	696	5	56	4″	2.5	2.4
5	514	31	823	36	177	691	5	55	5″	3.1	3.0
6	545	31	859	36	141	686	5	54	6″	3.7	3.6
7	576	31	895	36	105	681	5	53	7″	4.3	4.2
8	607	31	931	36	069	676	6	52	8″	4.9	4.8
9	638	31	967	37	033	670	5	51	9″	5.6	5.4
10	9.57 669	31	9.61 004	36	0.38 996	9.96 665	5	50	1′	35	32
11	700	31	040	36	960	660	5	49	1″	0.6	0.5
12	731	31	076	36	924	655	5	48	2″	1.2	1.1
13	762	31	112	36	888	650	5	47	3″	1.8	1.6
14	793	31	148	36	852	645	5	46	4″	2.3	2.1
15	824	31	184	36	816	640	6	45	5″	2.9	2.7
16	855	30	220	36	780	634	5	44	6″	3.5	3.2
17	885	31	256	36	744	629	5	43	7″	4.1	3.7
18	916	31	292	36	708	624	5	42	8″	4.7	4.3
19	947	31	328	36	672	619	5	41	9″	5.3	4.8
20	9.57 978	30	9.61 364	36	0.38 636	9.96 614	6	40	1′	31	
21	9.58 008	31	400	36	600	608	5	39	1″	0.5	
22	039	31	436	36	564	603	5	38	2″	1.0	
23	070	31	472	36	528	598	5	37	3″	1.6	
24	101	30	508	36	492	593	5	36	4″	2.1	
25	131	31	544	35	456	588	6	35	5″	2.6	
26	162	30	579	36	421	582	5	34	6″	3.1	
27	192	31	615	36	385	577	5	33	7″	3.6	
28	223	30	651	36	349	572	5	32	8″	4.1	
29	253	31	687	35	313	567	5	31	9″	4.7	
30	9.58 284	30	9.61 722	36	0.38 278	9.96 562	6	30	1′	30	
31	314	31	758	36	242	556	5	29	1″	0.5	
32	345	30	794	36	206	551	5	28	2″	1.0	
33	375	31	830	35	170	546	5	27	3″	1.5	
34	406	30	865	36	135	541	6	26	4″	2.0	
35	436	31	901	35	099	535	5	25	5″	2.5	
36	467	30	936	36	064	530	5	24	6″	3.0	
37	497	30	972	36	028	525	5	23	7″	3.5	
38	527	30	9.62 008	35	0.37 992	520	6	22	8″	4.0	
39	557	31	043	36	957	514	5	21	9″	4.5	
40	9.58 588	30	9.62 079	35	0.37 921	9.96 509	5	20	1′	29	
41	618	30	114	36	886	504	6	19	1″	0.5	
42	648	30	150	35	850	498	5	18	2″	1.0	
43	678	31	185	36	815	493	5	17	3″	1.5	
44	709	30	221	35	779	488	5	16	4″	1.9	
45	739	30	256	36	744	483	6	15	5″	2.4	
46	769	30	292	35	708	477	5	14	6″	2.9	
47	799	30	327	35	673	472	5	13	7″	3.4	
48	829	30	362	36	638	467	6	12	8″	3.9	
49	859	30	398	35	602	461	5	11	9″	4.4	
50	9.58 889	30	9.62 433	35	0.37 567	9.96 456	5	10	1′	5	6
51	919	30	468	36	532	451	6	9	1″	0.08	0.10
52	949	30	504	35	496	445	5	8	2″	0.17	0.20
53	979	30	539	35	461	440	5	7	3″	0.25	0.30
54	9.59 009	30	574	35	426	435	6	6	4″	0.33	0.40
55	039	30	609	36	391	429	5	5	5″	0.42	0.50
56	069	29	645	35	355	424	5	4	6″	0.50	0.60
57	098	30	680	35	320	419	5	3	7″	0.58	0.70
58	128	30	715	35	285	413	6	2	8″	0.67	0.80
59	158	30	750	35	250	408	5	1	9″	0.75	0.90
60	9.59 188		9.62 785		0.37 215	9.96 403	5	0			
′	L. Cos.	d.	L. Cotg.	c.d.	L. Tang.	L. Sin.	d.	′			

′	L. Sin.	d.	L. Tang.	c.d.	L. Cotg.	L. Cos.	d.	′
0	9.59 188	30	9.62 785	35	0.37 215	9.96 403	6	60
1	218	29	820	35	180	397	5	59
2	247	30	855	35	145	392	5	58
3	277	30	890	36	110	387	6	57
4	307	29	926	35	074	381	5	56
5	336	30	961	35	039	376	5	55
6	366	30	996	35	004	370	6	54
7	396	29	9.63 031	35	0.36 969	365	5	53
8	425	30	066	35	934	360	5	52
9	455	29	101	34	899	354	6	51
10	9.59 484	30	9.63 135	35	0.36 865	9.96 349	5	50
11	514	29	170	35	830	343	6	49
12	543	30	205	35	795	338	5	48
13	573	29	240	35	760	333	5	47
14	602	30	275	35	725	327	6	46
15	632	29	310	35	690	322	5	45
16	661	29	345	34	655	316	6	44
17	690	30	379	35	621	311	5	43
18	720	29	414	35	586	305	6	42
19	749	29	449	35	551	300	5	41
20	9.59 778	30	9.63 484	35	0.36 516	9.96 294	6	40
21	808	29	519	34	481	289	5	39
22	837	29	553	35	447	284	5	38
23	866	29	588	35	412	278	6	37
24	895	29	623	34	377	273	5	36
25	924	30	657	35	343	267	6	35
26	954	29	692	34	308	262	5	34
27	983	29	726	35	274	256	6	33
28	9.60 012	29	761	35	239	251	5	32
29	041	29	796	34	204	245	5	31
30	9.60 070	29	9.63 830	35	0.36 170	9.96 240	5	30
31	099	29	865	34	135	234	6	29
32	128	29	899	35	101	229	5	28
33	157	29	934	34	066	223	5	27
34	186	29	968	35	032	218	5	26
35	215	29	9.64 003	34	0.35 997	212	6	25
36	244	29	037	35	963	207	5	24
37	273	29	072	34	928	201	5	23
38	302	29	106	34	894	196	6	22
39	331	28	140	35	860	190	5	21
40	9.60 359	29	9.64 175	34	0.35 825	9.96 185	6	20
41	388	29	209	34	791	179	5	19
42	417	29	243	35	757	174	6	18
43	446	28	278	34	722	168	6	17
44	474	29	312	34	688	162	5	16
45	503	29	346	35	654	157	6	15
46	532	29	381	34	619	151	5	14
47	561	28	415	34	585	146	6	13
48	589	29	449	34	551	140	5	12
49	618	28	483	34	516	135	6	11
50	9.60 646	29	9.64 517	35	0.35 483	9.96 129	6	10
51	675	29	552	34	448	123	5	9
52	704	28	586	34	414	118	5	8
53	732	29	620	34	380	112	6	7
54	761	28	654	34	346	107	6	6
55	789	29	688	34	313	101	6	5
56	818	28	722	34	278	095	6	4
57	846	29	756	34	244	090	6	3
58	875	28	790	34	210	084	5	2
59	903	28	824	34	176	079	6	1
60	9.60 931		9.64 858		0.35 142	9.96 073		0
′	L. Cos.	d.	L. Cotg.	c.d.	L. Tang.	L. Sin.	d.	′

P. P.

1′	36	35
1″	0.6	0.6
2″	1.2	1.2
3″	1.8	1.8
4″	2.4	2.3
5″	3.0	2.9
6″	3.6	3.5
7″	4.2	4.1
8″	4.8	4.7
9″	5.4	5.3

1′	34	30
1″	0.6	0.5
2″	1.1	1.0
3″	1.7	1.5
4″	2.3	2.0
5″	2.8	2.5
6″	3.4	3.0
7″	4.0	3.5
8″	4.5	4.0
9″	5.1	4.5

1′	29
1″	0.5
2″	1.0
3″	1.5
4″	1.9
5″	2.4
6″	2.9
7″	3.4
8″	3.9
9″	4.4

1′	28
1″	0.5
2″	0.9
3″	1.4
4″	1.9
5″	2.3
6″	2.8
7″	3.3
8″	3.7
9″	4.2

1′	5	6
1″	0.08	0.10
2″	0.17	0.20
3″	0.25	0.30
4″	0.33	0.40
5″	0.42	0.50
6″	0.50	0.60
7″	0.58	0.70
8″	0.67	0.80
9″	0.75	0.90

′	L. Sin.	d.	L. Tang.	c. d.	L. Cotg.	L. Cos.	d.	′	P. P.		
0	9.60 931	29	9.64 858	34	0.35 142	9.96 073	6	60	1′	34	33
1	960	28	892	34	108	067	5	59	1″	0.6	0.6
2	988	28	926	34	074	062	6	58	2″	1.1	1.1
3	9.61 016	29	960	34	040	056	6	57	3″	1.7	1.7
4	045̄	28	994	34	006	050	5	56	4″	2.3	2.2
5	073	28	9.65 028	34	0.34 972	045̄	5	55	5″	2.8	2.8
6	101̄	28	062	34	938	039	5	54	6″	3.4	3.3
7	129	29	096	34	904	034	6	53	7″	4.0	3.9
8	158	28	130	34	870	028	6	52	8″	4.5	4.4
9	186	28	164	33	836	022	5	51	9″	5.1	5.0
10	9.61 214	28	9.65 197	34	0.34 803	9.96 017	6	50			
11	242	28	231	34	769	011	6	49			
12	270	28	265	34	735̄	005	5	48	1′	29	
13	298	28	299	34	701	000	6	47	1″	0.5	
14	326	28	333	33	667	9.95 994	6	46	2″	1.0	
15	354	28	366	34	634	988	6	45	3″	1.5	
16	382	29	400	34	600	982	5	44	4″	1.9	
17	411	27	434	33	566	977	6	43	5″	2.4	
18	438	28	467	34	533	971	6	42	6″	2.9	
19	466	28	501	34	499	965	6	41	7″	3.4	
20	9.61 494	28	9.65 535̄	33	0.34 465	9.95 960	6	40	8″	3.9	
21	522	28	568	34	432	954	6	39	9″	4.4	
22	550	28	602	34	398	948	6	38			
23	578	28	636	33	364	942	5	37			
24	606	28	669	34	331	937	6	36	1′	28	
25	634	28	703	33	297	931	6	35	1″	0.5	
26	662	27	736	34	264	925	5	34	2″	0.9	
27	689	28	770	33	230	920	6	33	3″	1.4	
28	717	28	803	34	197	914	6	32	4″	1.9	
29	745̄	28	837	33	163	908	6	31	5″	2.3	
30	9.61 773	27	9.65 870	34	0.34 130	9.95 902	5	30	6″	2.8	
31	800	28	904	33	096	897	6	29	7″	3.3	
32	828	28	937	34	063	891	6	28	8″	3.7	
33	856	27	971	33	029	885̄	6	27	9″	4.2	
34	883	28	9.66 004	34	0.33 996	879	6	26			
35	911	28	038	33	962	873	5	25			
36	939	27	071	33	929	868	6	24	1′	27	
37	966	28	104	34	896	862	6	23	1″	0.5	
38	994	27	138	33	862	856	6	22	2″	0.9	
39	9.62 021	28	171	33	829	850	6	21	3″	1.4	
40	9.62 049	27	9.66 204	34	0.33 796	9.95 844	5	20	4″	1.8	
41	076	28	238	33	762	839	6	19	5″	2.3	
42	104	27	271	33	729	833	6	18	6″	2.7	
43	131	28	304	33	696	827	6	17	7″	3.2	
44	159	27	337	34	663	821	6	16	8″	3.6	
45	186	28	371	33	629	815	5	15	9″	4.1	
46	214	27	404	33	596	810	6	14			
47	241	27	437	33	563	804	6	13			
48	268	28	470	33	530	798	6	12			
49	296	27	503	34	497	792	6	11	1′	5	6
50	9.62 323	27	9.66 537	33	0.33 463	9.95 786	6	10	1″	0.08	0.10
51	350	27	570	33	430	780	5	9	2″	0.17	0.20
52	377	28	603	33	397	775̄	6	8	3″	0.25	0.30
53	405̄	27	636	33	364	769	6	7	4″	0.33	0.40
54	432	27	669	33	331	763̄	6	6	5″	0.42	0.50
55	459	27	702	33	298	757	6	5	6″	0.50	0.60
56	486	27	735	33	265̄	751	6	4	7″	0.58	0.70
57	513	28	768	33	232	745	6	3	8″	0.67	0.80
58	541	27	801	33	199	739	6	2	9″	0.75	0.90
59	568	27	834	33	166	733̄	5	1			
60	9.62 595̄		9.66 867		0.33 133	9.95 728		0			
′	L. Cos.	d.	L. Cotg.	c. d.	L. Tang.	L. Sin.	d.	′			

′	L. Sin.	d.	L. Tang.	c. d.	L. Cotg.	L. Cos.	d.	′		P. P.	
0	9.62 595	27	9.66 867	33	0.33 133	9.95 728	6	60	1′	33	32
1	622	27	900	33	100	722	6	59	1″	0.6	0.5
2	649	27	933	33	067	716	6	58	2″	1.1	1.1
3	676	27	966	33	034	710	6	57	3″	1.7	1.6
4	703	27	999	33	001	704	6	56	4″	2.2	2.1
5	730	27	9.67 032	33	0.32 968	698	6	55	5″	2.8	2 7
6	757	27	065	33	935	692	6	54	6″	3.3	3.2
7	784	27	098	33	902	686	6	53	7″	3.9	3.7
8	811	27	131	32	869	680	6	52	8″	4.4	4.3
9	838	27	163	33	837	674	6	51	9″	5.0	4.8
10	9.62 865	27	9.67 196	33	0.32 804	9.95 668	5	50			
11	892	26	229	33	771	663	6	49			
12	918	27	262	33	738	657	6	48	1′	27	
13	945	27	295	32	705	651	6	47	1″	0.5	
14	972	27	327	33	673	645	6	46	2″	0.9	
15	999	27	360	33	640	639	6	45	3″	1.4	
16	9.63 026	26	393	33	607	633	6	44	4″	1.8	
17	052	27	426	32	574	627	6	43	5″	2.3	
18	079	27	458	33	542	621	6	42	6″	2.7	
19	106	27	491	33	509	615	6	41	7″	3.2	
20	9.63 133	26	9.67 524	32	0.32 476	9.95 609	6	40	8″	3.6	
21	159	27	556	33	444	603	6	39	9″	4.1	
22	186	27	589	33	411	597	6	38			
23	213	26	622	32	378	591	6	37			
24	239	27	654	33	346	585	6	36	1′	26	
25	266	26	687	32	313	579	6	35	1″	0.4	
26	292	27	719	33	281	573	6	34	2″	0.9	
27	319	26	752	33	248	567	6	33	3″	1.3	
28	345	27	785	32	215	561	6	32	4″	1.7	
29	372	26	817	33	183	555	6	31	5″	2.2	
30	9.63 393	27	9.67 850	32	0.32 150	9.95 549	6	30	6″	2.6	
31	425	26	882	33	118	543	6	29	7″	3.0	
32	451	27	915	32	085	537	6	28	8″	3.5	
33	478	26	947	33	053	531	6	27	9″	3.9	
34	504	27	980	32	020	525	6	26			
35	531	26	9.68 012	32	0.31 988	519	6	25			
36	557	26	044	33	956	513	6	24			
37	583	27	077	32	923	507	7	23	1′	5	
38	610	26	109	33	891	500	6	22	1″	0.08	
39	636	26	142	32	858	494	6	21	2″	0.17	
40	9.63 662	27	9.68 174	32	0.31 826	9.95 488	6	20	3″	0.25	
41	689	26	206	33	794	482	6	19	4″	0.33	
42	715	26	239	32	761	476	6	18	5″	0.42	
43	741	26	271	32	729	470	6	17	6″	0.50	
44	767	27	303	33	697	464	6	16	7″	0.58	
45	794	26	336	32	664	458	6	15	8″	0.67	
46	820	26	368	32	632	452	6	14	9″	0.75	
47	846	26	400	32	600	446	6	13			
48	872	26	432	33	568	440	6	12			
49	898	26	465	32	535	434	7	11	1′	6	7
50	9.63 924	26	9.68 497	32	0.31 503	9.95 427	6	10	1″	0.10	0.12
51	950	26	529	32	471	421	6	9	2″	0.20	0.23
52	976	26	561	32	439	415	6	8	3″	0.30	0.35
53	9.64 002	26	593	33	407	409	6	7	4″	0.40	0.47
54	028	26	626	32	374	403	6	6	5″	0.50	0.58
55	054	26	658	32	342	397	6	5	6″	0.60	0.70
56	080	26	690	32	310	391	7	4	7″	0.70	0.82
57	106	26	722	32	278	384	6	3	8″	0.80	0.93
58	132	26	754	32	246	378	6	2	9″	0.90	1.05
59	158	26	786	32	214	372	6	1			
60	9.64 184		9.68 818		0.31 182	9.95 366		0			
′	L. Cos.	d.	L. Cotg.	c. d.	L. Tang.	L. Sin.	d.	′			

′	L. Sin.	d.	L. Tang.	c.d.	L. Cotg.	L. Cos.	d.	′
0	9.64 184	26	9.68 818	32	0.31 182	9.95 366	6	60
1	210	26	850	32	150	360	6	59
2	236	26	882	32	118	354	6	58
3	262	26	914	32	086	348	7	57
4	288	25	946	32	054	341	6	56
5	313	26	978	32	022	335	6	55
6	339	26	9.69 010	32	0.30 990	329	6	54
7	365	26	042	32	958	323	6	53
8	391	26	074	32	926	317	7	52
9	417	25	106	32	894	310	6	51
10	9.64 442	26	9.69 138	32	0.30 862	9.95 304	6	50
11	468	26	170	32	830	298	6	49
12	494	25	202	32	798	292	6	48
13	519	26	234	32	766	286	7	47
14	545	26	266	32	734	279	6	46
15	571	25	298	31	702	273	6	45
16	596	26	329	32	671	267	6	44
17	622	25	361	32	639	261	7	43
18	647	26	393	32	607	254	6	42
19	673	25	425̄	32	575	248	6	41
20	9.64 698	26	9.69 457	31	0.30 543	9.95 242	6	40
21	724	25	488	32	512	236	7	39
22	749	26	520	32	480	229	6	38
23	775̄	25	552	32	448	223	6	37
24	800	26	584	31	416	217	6	36
25	826	25	615	32	385	211	6	35
26	851	26	647	32	353	204	7	34
27	877	25	679	31	321	198	6	33
28	902	25	710	32	290	192	7	32
29	927	26	742	32	258	185	6	31
30	9.64 953	25	9.69 774	31	0.30 226	9.95 179	6	30
31	978	25	805	32	195̄	173	6	29
32	9.65 003	26	837	31	163	167	7	28
33	029	25	868	32	132	160	6	27
34	054	25	900	32	100	154	6	26
35	079	25	932	31	068	148	7	25
36	104	26	963	32	037	141	6	24
37	130	25	995̄	31	005	135̄	6	23
38	155̄	25	9.70 026	32	0.29 974	129	7	22
39	180	25	058	31	942	122	6	21
40	9.65 205	25	9.70 089	32	0.29 911	9.95 116	7	20
41	230	25	121	31	879	110	6	19
42	255	26	152	32	848	103	7	18
43	281	25	184	31	816̄	097	7	17
44	306	25	215	32	785̄	090	6	16
45	331	25	247	31	753	084	6	15
46	356	25	278	31	722	078	7	14
47	381	25	309	32	691	071̄	6	13
48	406	25	341	31	659	065	6	12
49	431	25	372	32	628	059	7	11
50	9.65 456	25	9.70 404	31	0.29 596	9.95 052	6	10
51	481	25	435̄	31	565	046	7	9
52	506	25	466	32	534	039	6	8
53	531	25	498	31	502	033	6	7
54	556	24	529	31	471	027	7	6
55	580	25	560	32	440	020	6	5
56	605	25	592	31	408	014	7	4
57	630	25	623	31	377	007	6	3
58	655	25	654	31	346	001	6	2
59	680	25	685	32	315	9.94 995	7	1
60	9.65 705̄		9.70 717		0.29 283	9.94 988		0
′	L. Cos.	d.	L. Cotg.	c.d.	L. Tang.	L. Sin.	d.	′

P. P.

1′	32	31
1″	0.5	0.5
2″	1.1	1.0
3″	1.6	1.6
4″	2.1	2.1
5″	2.7	2.6
6″	3.2	3.1
7″	3.7	3.6
8″	4.3	4.1
9″	4.8	4.7

1′	26
1″	0.4
2″	0.9
3″	1.3
4″	1.7
5″	2.2
6″	2.6
7″	3.0
8″	3.5
9″	3.9

1′	25
1″	0.4
2″	0.8
3″	1.3
4″	1.7
5″	2.1
6″	2.5
7″	2.9
8″	3.3
9″	3.8

1′	24
1″	0.4
2″	0.8
3″	1.2
4″	1.6
5″	2.0
6″	2.4
7″	2.8
8″	3.2
9″	3.6

1′	6	7
1″	0.10	0.12
2″	0.20	0.23
3″	0.30	0.35
4″	0.40	0.47
5″	0.50	0.58
6″	0.60	0.70
7″	0.70	0.82
8″	0.80	0.93
9″	0.90	1.05

′	L. Sin.	d.	L. Tang.	c. d.	L. Cotg.	L. Cos.	d.	′
0	9.65 705̄	24	9.70 717	31	0.29 283	9.94 988	6	60
1	729	25	748	31	252	982	7	59
2	754	25	779	31	221	975	6	58
3	779	25	810	31	190	969	7	57
4	804	24	841	32	159	962	6	56
5	828	25	873	31	127	956	7	55
6	853	25	904	31	096	949	7	54
7	878	24	935̄	31	065	943	7	53
8	902	25	966	31	034	936	6	52
9	927	25	997	31	003	930	7	51
10	9.65 952	24	9.71 028	31	0.28 972	9.94 923	6	50
11	976	25	059	31	941	917	6	49
12	9.66 001	24	090	31	910	911	7	48
13	025	25	121	32	879	904	6	47
14	050̄	25	153	31	847	898	7	46
15	075̄	24	184	31	816	891	6	45
16	099	25	215̄	31	785	885̄	7	44
17	124	24	246	31	754	878	7	43
18	148	25	277	31	723	871½	7	42
19	173	24	308	31	692	865̄	7	41
20	9.66 197	24	9.71 339	31	0.28 661	9.94 858	6	40
21	221	25	370	31	630	852	7	39
22	246	24	401	30	599	845	6	38
23	270	25	431	31	569	839	6	37
24	295̄	24	462	31	538	832	6	36
25	319	24	493	31	507	826	6	35
26	343	25	524	31	476̄	819	6	34
27	368	24	555	31	445	813	7	33
28	392	24	586	31	414	806	7	32
29	416	25	617	31	383	799	6	31
30	9.66 441	24	9.71 648	31	0.28 352	9.94 793	7	30
31	465̄	24	679	30	321	786	6	29
32	489	24	709	31	291	780	7	28
33	513	24	740	31	260	773	6	27
34	537	25	771	31	229	767	7	26
35	562	24	802	31	198	760	7	25
36	586	24	833	30	167	753	6	24
37	610	24	863	31	137	747	7	23
38	634	24	894	31	106	740	6	22
39	658	24	925̄	30	075	734	7	21
40	9.66 682	24	9.71 955	31	0.28 045	9.94 727	7	20
41	706	25	986	31	014	720	6	19
42	731	24	9.72 017	31	0.27 983	714	7	18
43	755̄	24	048	30	952	707	7	17
44	779	24	078	31	922	700	6	16
45	803	24	109	31	891	694	7	15
46	827	24	140	30	860	687	7	14
47	851½	24	170	31	830	680	6	13
48	875̄	24	201	30	799	674	7	12
49	899	23	231	31	769	667	7	11
50	9.66 922	24	9.72 262	31	0.27 738	9.94 660	6	10
51	946	24	293	30	707	654	7	9
52	970	24	323	31	677	647	7	8
53	994	24	354	30	646	640	6	7
54	9.67 018	24	384̄	31	616	634	7	6
55	042	24	415	30	585	627	7	5
56	066̄	24	445	31	555̄	620	6	4
57	090	23	476	30	524	614	7	3
58	113	24	506	31	494	607	7	2
59	137	24	537	30	463	600	7	1
60	9.67 161		9.72 567		0.27 433	9.94 593		0
′	L. Cos.	d.	L. Cotg.	c. d.	L. Tang.	L. Sin.	d.	′

P. P.

1′	32	31
1″	0.5	0.5
2″	1.1	1.0
3″	1.6	1.6
4″	2.1	2.1
5″	2.7	2.6
6″	3.2	3.1
7″	3.7	3.6
8″	4.3	4.1
9″	4.8	4.7

1′	30	25
1″	0.5	0.4
2″	1.0	0.8
3″	1.5	1.3
4″	2.0	1.7
5″	2.5	2.1
6″	3.0	2.5
7″	3.5	2.9
8″	4.0	3.3
9″	4.5	3.8

1′	24
1″	0.4
2″	0.8
3″	1.2
4″	1.6
5″	2.0
6″	2.4
7″	2.8
8″	3.2
9″	3.6

1′	23
1″	0.4
2″	0.8
3″	1.2
4″	1.5
5″	1.9
6″	2.3
7″	2.7
8″	3.1
9″	3.5

1′	6	7
1″	0.10	0.12
2″	0.20	0.23
3″	0.30	0.35
4″	0.40	0.47
5″	0.50	0.58
6″	0.60	0.70
7″	0.70	0.82
8″	0.80	0.93
9″	0.90	1.05

′	L. Sin.	d.	L. Tang.	c.d.	L. Cotg.	L. Cos.	d.	′
0	9.67 161	24	9.72 567	31	0.27 433	9.94 593	6	60
1	185̄	23	598	30	402	587	7	59
2	208	24	623	31	372	580	7	58
3	232	24	659	31	341	573̇	6	57
4	256	24	689	31	311	567	7	56
5	280	23	720	30	280	560	7	55
6	303	24	750	30	250	553	7	54
7	327	23	780	31	220	546	6	53
8	350	24	811	30	189	540	7	52
9	374	24	841	31	159	533	7	51
10	9.67 393	23	9.72 872	30	0.27 128	9.94 526	6	50
11	421	24	902	30	098	519	7	49
12	445̄	23	932	31	068	513	7	48
13	468	24	963	30	037	506	7	47
14	492	23	993	30	007	499	7	46
15	515	24	9.73 023	31	0.26 977	492	7	45
16	539	24	054	30	946	485	6	44
17	562	24	084	30	916	479	7	43
18	586	23	114	30	886	472	7	42
19	609	24	144	31	856	465	7	41
20	9.67 633	23	9.73 175	30	0.26 825	9.94 458	7	40
21	656	24	205	30	795	451	6	39
22	680	23	235	30	765̄	445̄	7	38
23	703	23	265	30	735̄	438	7	37
24	726	24	295	31	705̄	431	7	36
25	750	23	326	30	674	424	7	35
26	773	23	356	30	644	417	7	34
27	796	24	386	30	614	410	6	33
28	820	23	416	30	584	404	7	32
29	843	23	446	30	554	397	7	31
30	9.67 866	24	9.73 476	31	0.26 524	9.94 390	7	30
31	890	23	507	30	493	383	7	29
32	913	23	537	30	463	376	7	28
33	936	23	567	30	433	369	7	27
34	959	23	597	30	403	362	7	26
35	982	24	627	30	373	355	6	25
36	9.68 006	23	657	30	343	349	7	24
37	029	23	687	30	313	342	7	23
38	052	23	717	30	283	335	7	22
39	075	23	747	30	253	328	7	21
40	9.68 098	23	9.73 777	30	0.26 223	9.94 321	7	20
41	121	23	807	30	193	314	7	19
42	144	23	837	30	163	307	7	18
43	167	23	867	30	133	300	7	17
44	190	23	897	30	103	293	7	16
45	213	24	927	30	073	286	7	15
46	237	23	957	30	043	279	6	14
47	260	23	987	30	013	273	7	13
48	283	22	9.74 017	30	0.25 983	266	7	12
49	305	23	047	30	953	259	7	11
50	9.68 328	23	9.74 077	30	0.25 923	9.94 252	7	10
51	351	23	107	30	893	245̄	7	9
52	374	23	137	29	863	238	7	8
53	397	23	166	30	834	231	7	7
54	420	23	196	30	804	224	7	6
55	443	23	226	30	774	217	7	5
56	466	23	256	30	744	210	7	4
57	489	23	286	30	714	203	7	3
58	512	22	316	29	684	196	7	2
59	534	23	345	30	655̄	189	7	1
60	9.68 557		9.74 375		0.25 625̄	9.94 182		0
′	L. Cos.	d.	L. Cotg.	c.d.	L. Tang.	L. Sin.	d.	′

P. P.

1′	31	30
1″	0.5	0.5
2″	1.0	1.0
3″	1.6	1.5
4″	2.1	2.0
5″	2.6	2.5
6″	3.1	3.0
7″	3.6	3.5
8″	4.1	4.0
9″	4.7	4.5

1′	29	24
1″	0.5	0.4
2″	1.0	0.8
3″	1.5	1.2
4″	1.9	1.6
5″	2.4	2.0
6″	2.9	2.4
7″	3.4	2.8
8″	3.9	3.2
9″	4.4	3.6

1′	23
1″	0.4
2″	0.8
3″	1.2
4″	1.5
5″	1.9
6″	2.3
7″	2.7
8″	3.1
9″	3.5

1′	22
1″	0.4
2″	0.7
3″	1.1
4″	1.5
5″	1.8
6″	2.2
7″	2.6
8″	2.9
9″	3.3

1′	6	7
1″	0.10	0.12
2″	0.20	0.23
3″	0.30	0.35
4″	0.40	0.47
5″	0.50	0.58
6″	0.60	0.70
7″	0.70	0.82
8″	0.80	0.93
9″	0.90	1.05

′	L. Sin.	d.	L. Tang.	c.d.	L. Cotg.	L. Cos.	d.	′
0	9.68 557	23	9.74 375	30	0.25 625	9.94 182	7	60
1	580	23	405	30	595	175	7	59
2	603	22	435	30	565	163	7	58
3	625	23	465	29	535	161	7	57
4	648	23	494	30	506	154	7	56
5	671	23	524	30	476	147	7	55
6	694	22	554	29	446	140	7	54
7	716	23	583	30	417	133	7	53
8	739	23	613	30	387	126	7	52
9	762	22	643	30	357	119	7	51
10	9.68 784	23	9.74 673	29	0.25 327	9.94 112	7	50
11	807	22	702	30	298	105	7	49
12	829	23	732	30	268	093	8	48
13	852	23	762	29	238	090	7	47
14	875	22	791	30	209	083	7	46
15	897	23	821	30	179	076	7	45
16	920	22	851	29	149	069	7	44
17	942	23	880	30	120	062	7	43
18	965	22	910	29	090	055	7	42
19	987	23	939	30	061	048	7	41
20	9.69 010	22	9.74 969	29	0.25 031	9.94 041	7	40
21	032	23	998	30	002	034	7	39
22	055	22	9.75 028	30	0.24 972	027	7	38
23	077	23	058	29	942	020	8	37
24	100	22	087	30	913	012	7	36
25	122	22	117	29	883	005	7	35
26	144	23	146	30	854	9.93 998	7	34
27	167	22	176	30	824	991	7	33
28	189	23	205	29	795	984	7	32
29	212	22	235	29	765	977	7	31
30	9.69 234	22	9.75 264	30	0.24 736	9.93 970	7	30
31	256	23	294	29	706	963	8	29
32	279	22	323	30	677	955	7	28
33	301	22	353	29	647	948	7	27
34	323	22	382	29	618	941	7	26
35	345	23	411	30	589	934	7	25
36	368	22	441	29	559	927	7	24
37	390	22	470	30	530	920	8	23
38	412	22	500	30	500	912	7	22
39	434	22	529	29	471	905	7	21
40	9.69 456	23	9.75 558	30	0.24 442	9.93 898	7	20
41	479	22	588	29	412	891	7	19
42	501	22	617	30	383	884	8	18
43	523	22	647	29	353	876	7	17
44	545	22	676	29	324	869	7	16
45	567	22	705	30	295	862	7	15
46	589	22	735	29	265	855	8	14
47	611	22	764	29	236	847	7	13
48	633	22	793	29	207	840	7	12
49	655	22	822	30	178	833	7	11
50	9.69 677	22	9.75 852	29	0.24 148	9.93 826	7	10
51	699	22	881	29	119	819	8	9
52	721	22	910	29	090	811	7	8
53	743	22	939	30	061	804	7	7
54	765	22	969	29	031	797	8	6
55	787	22	998	29	002	789	7	5
56	809	22	9.76 027	29	0.23 973	782	7	4
57	831	22	056	30	944	775	7	3
58	853	22	086	29	914	768	8	2
59	875	22	115	29	885	760	7	1
60	9.69 897		9.76 144		0.23 856	9.93 753		0

′	L. Cos.	d.	L. Cotg.	c.d.	L. Tang.	L. Sin.	d.	′

P. P.

1′	30
1″	0.5
2″	1.0
3″	1.5
4″	2.0
5″	2.5
6″	3.0
7″	3.5
8″	4.0
9″	4.5

1′	29
1″	0.5
2″	1.0
3″	1.5
4″	1.9
5″	2.4
6″	2.9
7″	3.4
8″	3.9
9″	4.4

1′	23
1″	0.4
2″	0.8
3″	1.2
4″	1.5
5″	1.9
6″	2.3
7″	2.7
8″	3.1
9″	3.5

1′	22
1″	0.4
2″	0.7
3″	1.1
4″	1.5
5″	1.8
6″	2.2
7″	2.6
8″	2.9
9″	3.3

1′	7	8
1″	0.12	0.13
2″	0.23	0.27
3″	0.35	0.40
4″	0.47	0.53
5″	0.58	0.67
6″	0.70	0.80
7″	0.82	0.93
8″	0.93	1.07
9″	1.05	1.20

60°

'	L. Sin.	d.	L. Tang.	c.d.	L. Cotg.	L. Cos.	d.	'
0	9 69 897	22	9 76 144	29	0.23 856	9.93 753	7	60
1	919	22	173	29	827	746	8	59
2	941	22	202	29	798	738	7	58
3	963	21	231	30	769	731	7	57
4	984	22	261	29	739	724	7	56
5	9.70 006	22	290	29	710	717	8	55
6	028	22	319	29	681	709	7	54
7	050	22	348	29	652	702	7	53
8	072	21	377	29	623	695	8	52
9	093	22	406	29	594	687	7	51
10	9.70 115	22	9.76 435	29	0.23 565	9.93 680	7	50
11	137	22	464	29	536	673	8	49
12	159	21	493	29	507	665	7	48
13	180	22	522	29	478	658	8	47
14	202	22	551	29	449	650	7	46
15	224	21	580	29	420	643	7	45
16	245	22	609	30	391	636	8	44
17	267	21	639	29	361	628	7	43
18	288	22	668	29	332	621	7	42
19	310	22	697	28	303	614	8	41
20	9.70 332	21	9.76 725	29	0.23 275	9.93 606	7	40
21	353	22	754	29	246	599	8	39
22	375	21	783	29	217	591	7	38
23	396	22	812	29	188	584	7	37
24	418	21	841	29	159	577	8	36
25	439	22	870	29	130	569	7	35
26	461	21	899	29	101	562	7	34
27	482	22	928	29	072	554	7	33
28	504	21	957	29	043	547	8	32
29	525	22	986	29	014	539	7	31
30	9.70 547	21	9.77 015	29	0.22 985	9.93 532	7	30
31	568	22	044	29	956	525	8	29
32	590	21	073	28	927	517	7	28
33	611	22	101	29	899	510	8	27
34	633	21	130	29	870	502	7	26
35	654	21	159	29	841	495	8	25
36	675	22	188	29	812	487	7	24
37	697	21	217	29	783	480	8	23
38	718	21	246	28	754	472	7	22
39	739	22	274	29	726	465	8	21
40	9.70 761	21	9.77 303	29	0.22 697	9.93 457	7	20
41	782	21	332	29	668	450	8	19
42	803	21	361	28	639	442	7	18
43	824	22	390	28	610	435	8	17
44	846	21	418	29	582	427	7	16
45	867	21	447	29	553	420	8	15
46	888	21	476	29	524	412	7	14
47	909	22	505	28	495	405	8	13
48	931	21	533	29	467	397	7	12
49	952	21	562	29	438	390	8	11
50	9.70 973	21	9.77 591	28	0.22 409	9.93 382	7	10
51	994	21	619	29	381	375	8	9
52	9.71 015	21	648	29	352	367	7	8
53	036	22	677	29	323	360	8	7
54	058	21	706	28	294	352	8	6
55	079	21	734	29	266	344	7	5
56	100	21	763	28	237	337	8	4
57	121	21	791	29	209	329	7	3
58	142	21	820	29	180	322	8	2
59	163	21	849	28	151	314	7	1
60	9.71 184		9.77 877		0.22 123	9.93 307		0
'	L. Cos.	d.	L. Cotg.	c.d.	L. Tang.	L. Sin.	d.	'

P. P.

1'	30	29
1"	0.5	0.5
2"	1.0	1.0
3"	1.5	1.5
4"	2.0	1.9
5"	2.5	2.4
6"	3.0	2.9
7"	3.5	3.4
8"	4.0	3.9
9"	4.5	4.4

1'	28
1"	0.5
2"	0.9
3"	1.4
4"	1.9
5"	2.3
6"	2.8
7"	3.3
8"	3.7
9"	4.2

1'	22
1"	0.4
2"	0.7
3"	1.1
4"	1.5
5"	1.8
6"	2.2
7"	2.6
8"	2.9
9"	3.3

1'	21
1"	0.4
2"	0.7
3"	1.1
4"	1.4
5"	1.8
6"	2.1
7"	2.5
8"	2.8
9"	3.2

1'	7	8
1"	0.12	0.13
2"	0.23	0.27
3"	0.35	0.40
4"	0.47	0.53
5"	0.58	0.67
6"	0.70	0.80
7"	0.82	0.93
8"	0.93	1.07
9"	1.05	1.20

′	L. Sin.	d.	L. Tang.	c.d.	L. Cotg.	L. Cos.	d.	′
0	9.71 184	21	9.77 877	29	0.22 123	9.93 307	8	60
1	205	21	906	29	094	299	8	59
2	226	21	935	28	065	291	7	58
3	247	21	963	29	037	284	7	57
4	268	21	992	28	008	276	7	56
5	289	21	9.78 020	29	0.21 980	269	8	55
6	310	21	049	28	951	261	8	54
7	331	21	077	29	923	253	7	53
8	352	21	106	29	894	246	8	52
9	373	20	135	28	865	238	8	51
10	9.71 393	21	9.78 163	29	0.21 837	9.93 230	7	50
11	414	21	192	28	808	223	8	49
12	435	21	220	29	780	215	8	48
13	456	21	249	28	751	207	7	47
14	477	21	277	29	723	200	8	46
15	498	21	306	28	694	192	8	45
16	519	20	334	29	666	184	7	44
17	539	21	363	28	637	177	8	43
18	560	21	391	28	609	169	8	42
19	581	21	419	29	581	161	7	41
20	9.71 602	20	9.78 448	28	0.21 552	9.93 154	8	40
21	622	21	476	29	524	146	8	39
22	643	21	505	28	495	138	7	38
23	664	21	533	29	467	131	8	37
24	685	20	562	28	438	123	8	36
25	705	21	590	28	410	115	7	35
26	726	21	618	29	382	108	8	34
27	747	20	647	28	353	100	8	33
28	767	21	675	29	325	092	8	32
29	788	21	704	28	296	084	7	31
30	9.71 809	20	9.78 732	28	0.21 268	9.93 077	8	30
31	829	21	760	29	240	069	8	29
32	850	20	789	28	211	061	8	28
33	870	21	817	28	183	053	7	27
34	891	20	845	29	155	046	8	26
35	911	21	874	28	126	038	8	25
36	932	20	902	28	098	030	8	24
37	952	21	930	29	070	022	8	23
38	973	21	959	28	041	014	7	22
39	994	20	987	28	013	007	8	21
40	9.72 014	20	9.79 015	28	0.20 985	9.92 999	8	20
41	034	21	043	29	957	991	8	19
42	055	20	072	28	928	983	7	18
43	075	21	100	28	900	976	8	17
44	096	20	128	28	872	968	8	16
45	116	21	156	29	844	960	8	15
46	137	20	185	28	815	952	8	14
47	157	20	213	28	787	944	8	13
48	177	21	241	28	759	936	7	12
49	198	20	269	28	731	929	8	11
50	9.72 218	20	9.79 297	29	0.20 703	9.92 921	8	10
51	238	21	326	28	674	913	8	9
52	259	20	354	28	646	905	8	8
53	279	20	382	28	618	897	8	7
54	299	21	410	28	590	889	8	6
55	320	20	438	28	562	881	7	5
56	340	20	466	29	534	874	8	4
57	360	21	495	28	505	866	8	3
58	381	20	523	28	477	858	8	2
59	401	20	551	28	449	850	8	1
60	9.72 421		9.79 579		0.20 421	9.92 842		0
′	L. Cos.	d.	L. Cotg.	c.d.	L. Tang.	L. Sin.	d.	′

P. P.

	29
1″	0.5
2″	1.0
3″	1.5
4″	1.9
5″	2.4
6″	2.9
7″	3.4
8″	3.9
9″	4.4

	28
1″	0.5
2″	0.9
3″	1.4
4″	1.9
5″	2.3
6″	2.8
7″	3.3
8″	3.7
9″	4.2

	21
1″	0.4
2″	0.7
3″	1.1
4″	1.4
5″	1.8
6″	2.1
7″	2.5
8″	2.8
9″	3.2

	20
1″	0.3
2″	0.7
3″	1.0
4″	1.3
5″	1.7
6″	2.0
7″	2.3
8″	2.7
9″	3.0

	7	8
1″	0.12	0.13
2″	0.23	0.27
3″	0.35	0.40
4″	0.47	0.53
5″	0.58	0.67
6″	0.70	0.80
7″	0.82	0.93
8″	0.93	1.07
9″	1.05	1.20

′	L. Sin.	d.	L. Tang.	c. d.	L. Cotg.	L. Cos.	d.	′
0	9.72 421	20	9.79 579	28	0.20 421	9.92 842	8	60
1	441	20	607	28	393	834	8	59
2	461	21	635	28	365̄	826	8	58
3	482	20	663	28	337	818	8	57
4	502	20	691	28	309	810	7	56
5	522	20	719	28	281	803	8	55
6	542	20	747	29	253	795̄	8	54
7	562	20	776	28	224	787	8	53
8	582	20	804	28	196	779	8	52
9	602	20	832	28	168	771	8	51
10	9.72 622	21	9.79 860	28	0.20 140	9.92 763	8	50
11	643	20	888	28	112	755̄	8	49
12	663	20	916	28	084	747	8	48
13	683	20	944	28	056	739	8	47
14	703	20	972	28	028	731	8	46
15	723	20	9.80 000	28	000	723	8	45
16	743	20	028	28	0.19 972	715	8	44
17	763	20	056	28	944	707	8	43
18	783	20	084	28	916	699	8	42
19	803	20	112	28	888	691	8	41
20	9.72 823	20	9.80 140	28	0.19 860	9.92 683	8	40
21	843	20	168	27	832	675	8	39
22	863	20	195	28	805̄	667	8	38
23	883	19	223	28	777	659	8	37
24	902	20	251	28	749	651	8	36
25	922	20	279	28	721	643	8	35
26	942	20	307	28	693̄	635	8	34
27	962	20	335	28	665̄	627	8	33
28	982	20	363	28	637	619	8	32
29	9.73 002	20	391	28	609	611	8	31
30	9.73 022	19	9.80 419	28	0.19 581	9.92 603	8	30
31	041	20	447	27	553	595̄	8	29
32	061	20	474	28	526	587	8	28
33	081	20	502	28	498	579	8	27
34	101	20	530	28	470	571	8	26
35	121	19	558	28	442	563	8	25
36	140	20	586	28	414	555̄	9	24
37	160	20	614	28	386	546	8	23
38	180	20	642	27	358	538	8	22
39	200	19	669	28	331	530	8	21
40	9.73 219	20	9.80 697	28	0.19 303	9.92 522	8	20
41	239	20	725̄	28	275	514	8	19
42	259	19	753	28	247	506	8	18
43	278	20	781	27	219	498	8	17
44	298	20	808	28	192	490	8	16
45	318	19	836	28	164	482	9	15
46	337	20	864	28	136	473	8	14
47	357	20	892	27	108	465	8	13
48	377	19	919	28	081	457	8	12
49	396	20	947	28	053	449	8	11
50	9.73 416	19	9.80 975	28	0.19 025	9.92 441	8	10
51	435	20	9.81 003	27	0.18 997	433̄	9	9
52	455̄	19	030	28	970	425̄	8	8
53	474	20	058	28	942	416	9	7
54	494	19	086	27	914	408	8	6
55	513	20	113	28	887	400	8	5
56	533	19	141	28	859	392	8	4
57	552	20	169	27	831	384	8	3
58	572	19	196	28	804	376	9	2
59	591	20	224	28	776	367	8	1
60	9.73 611		9.81 252		0.18 748	9.92 359		0
′	L. Cos.	d.	L. Cotg.	c. d.	L. Tang.	L. Sin.	d.	′

P. P.

	29	28
1′		
1″	0.5	0.5
2″	1.0	0.9
3″	1.5	1.4
4″	1.9	1.9
5″	2.4	2.3
6″	2.9	2.8
7″	3.4	3.3
8″	3.9	3.7
9″	4.4	4.2

	27	21
1′		
1″	0.5	0.4
2″	0.9	0.7
3″	1.4	1.1
4″	1.8	1.4
5″	2.3	1.8
6″	2.7	2.1
7″	3.2	2.5
8″	3.6	2.8
9″	4.1	3.2

	20	19
1′		
1″	0.3	0.3
2″	0.7	0.6
3″	1.0	1.0
4″	1.3	1.3
5″	1.7	1.6
6″	2.0	1.9
7″	2.3	2.2
8″	2.7	2.5
9″	3.0	2.9

	7
1′	
1″	0.12
2″	0.23
3″	0.35
4″	0.47
5″	0.58
6″	0.70
7″	0.82
8″	0.93
9″	1.05

	8	9
1′		
1″	0.13	0.15
2″	0.27	0.30
3″	0.40	0.45
4″	0.53	0.60
5″	0.67	0.75
6″	0.80	0.90
7″	0.93	1.05
8″	1.07	1.20
9″	1.20	1.35

'	L. Sin.	d.	L. Tang.	c.d.	L. Cotg.	L. Cos.	d.	'
0	9.73 611	19	9.81 252	27	0.18 748	9.92 359	8	60
1	630	20	279	28	721	351	8	59
2	650	19	307	28	693	343	8	58
3	669	20	335	28	665	335	9	57
4	689	19	362	27	638	326	8	56
5	708	19	390	28	610	318	8	55
6	727	20	418	27	582	310	8	54
7	747	19	445	28	555	302	9	53
8	766	19	473	27	527	293	8	52
9	785	20	500	28	500	285	8	51
10	9.73 805	19	9.81 528	28	0.18 472	9.92 277	8	50
11	824	19	556	27	444	269	9	49
12	843	20	583	28	417	260	8	48
13	863	19	611	27	389	252	8	47
14	882	19	638	28	362	244	9	46
15	901	20	666	27	334	235	8	45
16	921	19	693	28	307	227	8	44
17	940	19	721	27	279	219	8	43
18	959	19	748	28	252	211	9	42
19	978	20	776	27	224	202	8	41
20	9.73 997	20	9.81 803	28	0.18 197	9.92 194	8	40
21	9.74 017	19	831	27	169	186	9	39
22	036	19	858	28	142	177	8	38
23	055	19	886	27	114	169	8	37
24	074	19	913	28	087	161	9	36
25	093	20	941	27	059	152	8	35
26	113	19	968	28	032	144	8	34
27	132	19	996	27	004	136	9	33
28	151	19	9.82 023	28	0.17 977	127	8	32
29	170	19	051	27	949	119	8	31
30	9.74 189	19	9.82 078	28	0.17 922	9.92 111	9	30
31	208	19	106	27	894	102	8	29
32	227	19	133	28	867	094	8	28
33	246	19	161	27	839	086	9	27
34	265	19	188	28	812	077	8	26
35	284	19	215	27	785	069	9	25
36	303	19	243	28	757	060	8	24
37	322	19	270	27	730	052	8	23
38	341	19	298	28	702	044	9	22
39	360	19	325	27	675	035	8	21
40	9.74 379	19	9.82 352	28	0.17 648	9.92 027	9	20
41	398	19	380	27	620	018	8	19
42	417	19	407	28	593	010	8	18
43	436	19	435	27	565	002	9	17
44	455	19	462	27	538	9.91 993	8	16
45	474	19	489	28	511	985	9	15
46	493	19	517	27	483	976	8	14
47	512	19	544	27	456	968	9	13
48	531	18	571	28	429	959	8	12
49	549	19	599	27	401	951	9	11
50	9.74 568	19	9.82 626	27	0.17 374	9.91 942	8	10
51	587	19	653	28	347	934	9	9
52	606	19	681	27	319	925	8	8
53	625	19	708	27	292	917	9	7
54	644	18	735	27	265	908	8	6
55	662	19	762	28	238	900	9	5
56	681	19	790	27	210	891	8	4
57	700	19	817	27	183	883	9	3
58	719	18	844	27	156	874	8	2
59	737	19	871	28	129	866	9	1
60	9.74 756		9.82 899		0.17 101	9.91 857		0
'	L. Cos.	d.	L. Cotg.	c.d.	L. Tang.	L. Sin.	d.	'

P. P.

1'	28	27
1"	0.5	0.5
2"	0.9	0.9
3"	1.4	1.4
4"	1.9	1.8
5"	2.3	2.3
6"	2.8	2.7
7"	3.3	3.2
8"	3.7	3.6
9"	4.2	4.1

1'	20
1"	0.3
2"	0.7
3"	1.0
4"	1.3
5"	1.7
6"	2.0
7"	2.3
8"	2.7
9"	3.0

1'	19
1"	0.3
2"	0.6
3"	1.0
4"	1.3
5"	1.6
6"	1.9
7"	2.2
8"	2.5
9"	2.9

1'	18
1"	0.3
2"	0.6
3"	0.9
4"	1.2
5"	1.5
6"	1.8
7"	2.1
8"	2.4
9"	2.7

1'	8	9
1"	0.13	0.15
2"	0.27	0.30
3"	0.40	0.45
4"	0.53	0.60
5"	0.67	0.75
6"	0.80	0.90
7"	0.93	1.05
8"	1.07	1.20
9"	1.20	1.35

'	L. Sin.	d.	L. Tang.	c.d.	L. Cotg.	L. Cos.	d.	'
0	9.74 756	19	9.82 899	27	0.17 101	9.91 857	8	60
1	775̄	19	926	27	074	849	9	59
2	794	18	953	27	047	840	8	58
3	812	19	980	28	020	832	8	57
4	831	19	9.83 008	27	0.16 992	823	8	56
5	850	18	035	27	965	815	9	55
6	868	19	062	27	938	806	8	54
7	887	19	089	28	911	798	8	53
8	906	18	117	27	883	789	8	52
9	924	19	144	27	856	781	8	51
10	9.74 943	18	9.83 171	27	0.16 829	9.91 772	9	50
11	961	19	198	27	802̄	763̄	8	49
12	980	19	225	27	775̄	755̄	9	48
13	999·	18	252	28	748	746	8	47
14	9.75 017	19	280	27	720	738	9	46
15	036	18	307	27	693	729	9	45
16	054	19	334	27	666	720	8	44
17	073	18	361	27	639	712	9	43
18	091	19	388	27	612	703	8	42
19	110	18	415	27	585̄	695	9	41
20	9.75 128	19	9.83 442	28	0.16 558	9.91 686	8	40
21	147	18	470	27	530	677	8	39
22	165	19	497	27	503	669	9	38
23	184	18	524	27	476	660	9	37
24	202	19	551	27	449	651	8	36
25	221	18	578	27	422	643	9	35
26	239	19	605	27	395̄	634	9	34
27	258	18	632	27	368	625	8	33
28	276	18	659	27	341	617	9	32
29	294	19	686	27	314	608	9	31
30	9.75 313	18	9.83 713	27	0.16 287	9.91 599	8	30
31	331	19	740	28	260	591	9	29
32	350	18	768	27	232	582	9	28
33	368	18	795	27	205	573	8	27
34	386	19	822	27	178	565̄	9	26
35	405	18	849	27	151	556	9	25
36	423	18	876	27	124	547	9	24
37	441	18	903	27	097	538	8	23
38	459	19	930	27	070	530	9	22
39	478	18	957	27	043	521	9	21
40	9.75 496	18	9.83 984	27	0.16 016	9.91 512	8	20
41	514	19	9.84 011	27	0.15 989	504	9	19
42	533	18	038	27	962	495̄	9	18
43	551	18	065	27	935	486	9	17
44	569	18	092	27	908	477	8	16
45	587	18	119	27	881	469	9	15
46	605	19	146	27	854	460	9	14
47	624	18	173	27	827	451	9	13
48	642	18	200	27	800	442	9	12
49	660	18	227	27	773	433	8	11
50	9.75 678	18	9.84 254	26	0.15 746	9.91 425̄	9	10
51	696	18	280	27	720	416	9	9
52	714	19	307	27	693	407	9	8
53	733	18	334	27	666	398	9	7
54	751	18	361	27	639	389	8	6
55	769	18	388	27	612	381	9	5
56	787	18	415	27	585̄	372	9	4
57	805̄	18	442	27	558	363	9	3
58	823	18	469	27	531	354	9	2
59	841	18	496	27	504	345	9	1
60	9.75 859		9.84 523		0.15 477	9.91 336		0
'	L. Cos.	d.	L. Cotg.	c.d.	L. Tang.	L. Sin.	d.	'

P. P.

	28	27
1'		
1"	0.5	0.5
2"	0.9	0.9
3"	1.4	1.4
4"	1.9	1.8
5"	2.3	2.3
6"	2.8	2.7
7"	3.3	3.2
8"	3.7	3.6
9"	4.2	4.1

	26
1'	
1"	0.4
2"	0.9
3"	1.3
4"	1.7
5"	2.2
6"	2.6
7"	3.0
8"	3.5
9"	3.9

	19
1'	
1"	0.3
2"	0.6
3"	1.0
4"	1.3
5"	1.6
6"	1.9
7"	2.2
8"	2.5
9"	2.9

	18
1'	
1"	0.3
2"	0.6
3"	0.9
4"	1.2
5"	1.5
6"	1.8
7"	2.1
8"	2.4
9"	2.7

	8	9
1'		
1"	0.13	0.15
2"	0.27	0.30
3"	0.40	0.45
4"	0.53	0.60
5"	0.67	0.75
6"	0.80	0.90
7"	0.93	1.05
8"	1.07	1.20
9"	1.20	1.35

'	L. Sin.	d.	L. Tang.	c. d.	L. Cotg.	L. Cos.	d.	'
0	9.75 859	18	9.84 523	27	0.15 477	9.91 336	8	60
1	877	18	550	26	450	328	9	59
2	895	18	576	27	424	319	9	58
3	913	18	603	27	397	310	9	57
4	931	18	630	27	370	301	9	56
5	949	18	657	27	343	292	9	55
6	967	18	684	27	316	283	9	54
7	985	18	711	27	289	274	8	53
8	9.76 003	18	738	26	262	266	9	52
9	021	18	764	27	236	257	9	51
10	9.76 039	18	9.84 791	27	0.15 209	9.91 248	9	50
11	057	18	818	27	182	239	9	49
12	075	18	845	27	155	230	9	48
13	093	18	872	27	128	221	9	47
14	111	18	899	26	101	212	9	46
15	129	17	925	27	075	203	9	45
16	146	18	952	27	048	194	9	44
17	164	18	979	27	021	185	9	43
18	182	18	9.85 006	27	0.14 994	176	9	42
19	200	18	033	26	967	167	9	41
20	9.76 218	18	9.85 059	27	0.14 941	9.91 158	9	40
21	236	17	086	27	914	149	8	39
22	253	18	113	27	887	141	9	38
23	271	18	140	26	860	132	9	37
24	289	18	166	27	834	123	9	36
25	307	17	193	27	807	114	9	35
26	324	18	220	27	780	105	9	34
27	342	18	247	26	753	096	9	33
28	360	18	273	27	727	087	9	32
29	378	17	300	27	700	078	9	31
30	9.76 395	18	9.85 327	27	0.14 673	9.91 069	9	30
31	413	18	354	26	646	060	9	29
32	431	17	380	27	620	051	9	28
33	448	18	407	27	593	042	9	27
34	466	18	434	26	566	033	10	26
35	484	17	460	27	540	023	9	25
36	501	18	487	27	513	014	9	24
37	519	18	514	26	486	005	9	23
38	537	17	540	27	460	9.90 996	9	22
39	554	18	567	27	433	9.90 987	9	21
40	9.76 572	18	9.85 594	26	0.14 406	9.90 978	9	20
41	590	17	620	27	380	969	9	19
42	607	18	647	27	353	960	9	18
43	625	17	674	26	326	951	9	17
44	642	18	700	27	300	942	9	16
45	660	17	727	27	273	933	9	15
46	677	18	754	26	246	924	9	14
47	695	17	780	27	220	915	9	13
48	712	18	807	27	193	906	10	12
49	730	17	834	26	166	896	9	11
50	9.76 747	18	9.85 860	27	0.14 140	9.90 887	9	10
51	765	17	887	26	113	878	9	9
52	782	18	913	27	087	869	9	8
53	800	17	940	27	060	860	9	7
54	817	18	967	26	033	851	9	6
55	835	17	993	27	007	842	10	5
56	852	18	9.86 020	26	0.13 980	832	9	4
57	870	17	046	27	954	823	9	3
58	887	17	073	27	927	814	9	2
59	904	18	100	26	900	805	9	1
60	9.76 922		9.86 126		0.13 874	9.90 796		0
'	L. Cos.	d.	L. Cotg.	c.d.	L. Tang.	L. Sin.	d.	'

P. P.

1'	27	26
1"	0.5	0.4
2"	0.9	0.9
3"	1.4	1.3
4"	1.8	1.7
5"	2.3	2.2
6"	2.7	2.6
7"	3.2	3.0
8"	3.6	3.5
9"	4.1	3.9

1'	18
1"	0.3
2"	0.6
3"	0.9
4"	1.2
5"	1.5
6"	1.8
7"	2.1
8"	2.4
9"	2.7

1'	17
1"	0.3
2"	0.6
3"	0.9
4"	1.1
5"	1.4
6"	1.7
7"	2.0
8"	2.3
9"	2.6

1'	8
1"	0.13
2"	0.27
3"	0.40
4"	0.53
5"	0.67
6"	0.80
7"	0.93
8"	1.07
9"	1.20

1'	9	10
1"	0.15	0.17
2"	0.30	0.33
3"	0.45	0.50
4"	0.60	0.67
5"	0.75	0.83
6"	0.90	1.00
7"	1.05	1.17
8"	1.20	1.33
9"	1.35	1.50

′	L. Sin.	d.	L. Tang.	c.d.	L. Cotg.	L. Cos.	d.	′
0	9.76 922	17	9.86 126	27	0.13 874	9.90 796	9	60
1	939	18	153	26	847	787	10	59
2	957	17	179	27	821	777	9	58
3	974	17	206	26	794	768	9	57
4	991	18	232	27	768	759	9	56
5	9.77 009	17	259	26	741	750	9	55
6	026	17	285	27	715̄	741	10	54
7	043	18	312	26	688	731	9	53
8	061	17	338	27	662̲	722	9	52
9	078	17	365	27	.635	713	9	51
10	9.77 095	17	9.86 392	26	0.13 608	9.90 704	10	50
11	112	18	418	27	582	694	9	49
12	130	17	445̄	26	555	685	9	48
13	147	17	471	27	529	676	9	47
14	164	17	498	26	502	667	10	46
15	181	18	524	27	476	657	9	45
16	199	17	551	26	449	648	9	44
17	216	17	577	26	423	639	9	43
18	233	17	603	27	397	630	10	42
19	250	18	630	26	370	620	9	41
20	9.77 268	17	9.86 656	27	0.13 344	9.90 611	9	40
21	285̄	17	683	26	317	602	10	39
22	302	17	709	27	291	592	9	38
23	319	17	736	26	264	583	9	37
24	336	17	762	27	238	574	9	36
25	353	17	789	26	211	565̄	10	35
26	370	17	815	27	185̄	555	9	34
27	387	18	842	26	158	546	9	33
28	405̄	17	868	26	132	537	10	32
29	422	17	894	27	106	527	9	31
30	9.77 439	17	9.86 921	26	0.13 079	9.90 518	9	30
31	456	17	947	27	053	509	10	29
32	473	17	974	26	026	499	9	28
33	490	17	9.87 000	27	000	490	10	27
34	507	17	027	26	0.12 973	480	9	26
35	524	17	053	27	947	471	9	25
36	541	17	079	26	921	462	10	24
37	558	17	106	26	894	452	9	23
38	575	17	132	26	868	443	9	22
39	592	17	158	27	842	434	10	21
40	9.77 609	17	9.87 185̄	26	0.12 815	9.90 424	9	20
41	626	17	211	27	789	415̄	10	19
42	643	17	238	26	762	405	10	18
43	660	17	264	27	736	396	10	17
44	677	17	290	26	710	386	10	16
45	694	17	317	26	683	377	9	·5
46	711	17	343	26	657	368	10	14
47	728	16	369	27	631	358	10	13
48	744	17	396	26	604	349	10	12
49	761	17	422	26	578	339	9	11
50	9.77 778	17	9.87 448	27	0.12 552	9.90 330	10	10
51	795	17	475̄	26	525	320	10	9
52	812	17	501	26	499	311	10	8
53	829	17	527	27	473	301	9	7
54	846	16	554	26	446	292	10	6
55	862	17	580	26	420	282	9	5
56	879	17	606	27	394	273	10	4
57	896	17	633	26	367	263	9	3
58	913	17	659	26	341̲	254	10	2
59	930	16	685	26	315̄	244̲	9	1
60	9.77 946		9.87 711		0.12 289	9.90 235		0
′	L. Cos.	d.	L. Cotg.	c.d.	L. Tang.	L. Sin.	d.	′

P. P.

	27	26
1′	27	26
1″	0.5	0.4
2″	0.9	0.9
3″	1.4	1.3
4″	1.8	1.7
5″	2.3	2.2
6″	2.7	2.6
7″	3 2	3.0
8″	3.6	3.5
9″	4.1	3.9

1′	18
1″	0.3
2″	0.6
3″	0.9
4″	1.2
5″	1.5
6″	1.8
7″	2.1
8″	2.4
9″	2.7

1′	17
1″	0.3
2″	0.6
3″	0.9
4″	1.1
5″	1.4
6″	1.7
7″	2.0
8″	2.3
9″	2.6

1′	16
1″	0.3
2″	0.5
3″	0.8
4″	1.1
5″	1.3
6″	1.6
7″	1.9
8″	2.1
9″	2.4

1′	9	10
1″	0.15	0.2
2″	0.30	0.3
3″	0.45	0.5
4″	0.60	0.7
5″	0.75	0.8
6″	0.90	1.0
7″	1.05	1.2
8″	1.20	1.3
9″	1.35	1.5

'	L. Sin.	d.	L. Tang.	c.d.	L. Cotg.	L. Cos.	d.	'
0	9.77 946	17	9.87 711	27	0.12 289	9.90 235̄	10	60
1	963	17	738	26	262	225	9	59
2	980	17	764	26	236	216	10	58
3	997	16	790	27	210	206	9	57
4	9.78 013	17	817	26	183	197	10	56
5	030	17	843	26	157	187	9	55
6	047	16	869	26	131̱	178	10	54
7	063	17	895	27	105̄	168	9	53
8	080	17	922	26	078	159	10	52
9	097	16	948	26	052	149	10	51
10	9.78 113	17	9.87 974	26	0.12 026	9.90 139	10	50
11	130	17	9.88 000	27	000	130	10	49
12	147	16	027	26	0.11 973	120	9	48
13	163	17	053	26	947	111	10	47
14	180	17	079	26	921	101	10	46
15	197	16	105	26	895̄	091	9	45
16	213	17	131	27	869	082	10	44
17	230	16	158	26	842	072	10	43
18	246	17	184	26	816	063	10	42
19	263	17	210	26	790	053	10	41
20	9.78 280	16	9.88 236	26	0.11 764	9.90 043	9	40
21	296	17	262	27	738	034	10	39
22	313	16	289	26	711	024	10	38
23	329	17	315̄	26	685	014̄	9	37
24	346	16	341	26	659	005̄	10	36
25	362	17	367	26	633	9.89 995	10	35
26	379	16	393	27	607	985	9	34
27	395	17	420	26	580	976	10	33
28	412	16	446	26	554	966	10	32
29	428	17	472	26	528	956	9	31
30	9.78 445̄	16	9.88 498	26	0.11 502	9.89 947	10	30
31	461	17	524	26	476	937	10	29
32	478	16	550	27	450	927	9	28
33	494	16	577	26	423	918	10	27
34	510	17	603	26	397	908	10	26
35	527	16	629	26	371	898	10	25
36	543	17	655̄	26	345	888	9	24
37	560	16	681	26	319	879	10	23
38	576	16	707	26	293	869	10	22
39	592	17	733	26	267	859	10	21
40	9.78 609	16	9.88 759	27	0.11 241	9.89 849	9	20
41	625	17	786	26	214	840	10	19
42	642	16	812	26	188	830	10	18
43	658	16	838	26	162	820	10	17
44	674	17	864	26	136	810	9	16
45	691	16	890	26	110	801	10	15
46	707	16	916	26	084	791	10	14
47	723	16	942	26	058	781	10	13
48	739	17	968	26	032	771	10	12
49	756	16	994	26	006	761	9	11
50	9.78 772	16	9.89 020	26	0.10 980	9.89 752	10	10
51	788	17	046	27	954	742	10	9
52	805	16	073	26	927	732	10	8
53	821	16	099	26	901	722	10	7
54	837	16	125	26	875	712̱	10	6
55	853	16	151	26	849	702	10	5
56	869	17	177	26	823	693	9	4
57	886	16	203	26	797	683	10	3
58	902	16	229	26	771	673	10	2
59	918	16	255̄	26	745	663	10	1
60	9.78 934		9.89 281		0.10 719	9.89 653		0
'	L. Cos.	d.	L. Cotg.	c.d.	L. Tang.	L. Sin.	d.	'

P. P.

1'	27
1"	0.5
2"	0.9
3"	1.4
4"	1.8
5"	2.3
6"	2.7
7"	3.2
8"	3.6
9"	4.1

1'	26
1"	0.4
2"	0.9
3"	1.3
4"	1.7
5"	2.2
6"	2.6
7"	3.0
8"	3.5
9"	3.9

1'	17
1"	0.3
2"	0.6
3"	0.9
4"	1.1
5"	1.4
6"	1.7
7"	2.0
8"	2.3
9"	2.6

1'	16
1"	0.3
2"	0.5
3"	0.8
4"	1.1
5"	1.3
6"	1.6
7"	1.9
8"	2.1
9"	2.4

1'	9	10
1"	0.15	0.2
2"	0.30	0.3
3"	0.45	0.5
4"	0.60	0.7
5"	0.75	0.8
6"	0.90	1.0
7"	1.05	1.2
8"	1.20	1.3
9"	1.35	1.5

′	L. Sin.	d.	L. Tang.	c.d.	L. Cotg.	L. Cos.	d.	′
0	9.78 934	16	9.89 281	26	0.10 719	9.89 653	10	60
1	950	17	307	26	693	643	10	59
2	967	16	333	26	667	633	9	58
3	983	16	359	26	641	624	10	57
4	999	16	385	26	615	614	10	56
5	9.79 015	16	411	26	589	604	10	55
6	031	16	437	26	563	594	10	54
7	047	16	463	26	537	584	10	53
8	063	16	489	26	511	574	10	52
9	079	16	515	26	485	564	10	51
10	9.79 095	16	9.89 541	26	0.10 459	9.89 554	10	50
11	111	17	567	26	433	544	10	49
12	128	16	593	26	407	534	10	48
13	144	16	619	26	381	524	10	47
14	160	16	645	26	355	514	10	46
15	176	16	671	26	329	504	9	45
16	192	16	697	26	303	495	10	44
17	208	16	723	26	277	485	10	43
18	224	16	749	26	251	475	10	42
19	240	16	775	26	225	465	10	41
20	9.79 256	16	9.89 801	26	0.10 199	9.89 455	10	40
21	272	16	827	26	173	445	10	39
22	288	16	853	26	147	435	10	38
23	304	15	879	26	121	425	10	37
24	319	16	905	26	095	415	10	36
25	335	16	931	26	069	405	10	35
26	351	16	957	26	043	395	10	34
27	367	16	983	26	017	385	10	33
28	383	16	9.90 009	26	0.09 991	375	11	32
29	399	16	035	26	965	364	10	31
30	9.79 415	16	9.90 061	25	0.09 939	9.89 354	10	30
31	431	16	086	26	914	344	10	29
32	447	16	112	26	888	334	10	28
33	463	15	138	26	862	324	10	27
34	478	16	164	26	836	314	10	26
35	494	16	190	26	810	304	10	25
36	510	16	216	26	784	294	10	24
37	526	16	242	26	758	284	10	23
38	542	16	268	26	732	274	10	22
39	558	15	294	26	706	264	10	21
40	9.79 573	16	9.90 320	26	0.09 680	9.89 254	11	20
41	589	16	346	25	654	244	10	19
42	605	16	371	26	629	233	10	18
43	621	15	397	26	603	223	10	17
44	636	16	423	26	577	213	10	16
45	652	16	449	26	551	203	10	15
46	668	16	475	26	525	193	10	14
47	684	15	501	26	499	183	10	13
48	699	16	527	26	473	173	11	12
49	715	16	553	25	447	162	10	11
50	9.79 731	15	9.90 578	26	0.09 422	9.89 152	10	10
51	746	16	604	26	396	142	10	9
52	762	16	630	26	370	132	10	8
53	778	15	656	26	344	122	10	7
54	793	16	682	26	318	112	11	6
55	809	16	708	26	292	101	10	5
56	825	15	734	25	266	091	10	4
57	840	16	759	26	241	081	10	3
58	856	16	785	26	215	071	11	2
59	872	15	811	26	189	060	10	1
60	9.79 887		9.90 837	26	0.09 163	9.89 050		0
′	L. Cos.	d.	L. Cotg.	c.d.	L. Tang.	L. Sin.	d.	′

P. P.

1′	26	25
1″	0.4	0.4
2″	0.9	0.8
3″	1.3	1.3
4″	1.7	1.7
5″	2.2	2.1
6″	2.6	2.5
7″	3.0	2.9
8″	3.5	3.3
9″	3.9	3.8

1′	17	16
1″	0.3	0.3
2″	0.6	0.5
3″	0.9	0.8
4″	1.1	1.1
5″	1.4	1.3
6″	1.7	1.6
7″	2.0	1.9
8″	2.3	2.1
9″	2.6	2.4

1′	15
1″	0.3
2″	0.5
3″	0.8
4″	1.0
5″	1.3
6″	1.5
7″	1.8
8″	2.0
9″	2.3

1′	9
1″	0.15
2″	0.30
3″	0.45
4″	0.60
5″	0.75
6″	0.90
7″	1.05
8″	1.20
9″	1.35

1′	10	11
1″	0.2	0.2
2″	0.3	0.4
3″	0.5	0.6
4″	0.7	0.7
5″	0.8	0.9
6″	1.0	1.1
7″	1.2	1.3
8″	1.3	1.5
9″	1.5	1.7

′	L. Sin.	d.	L. Tang.	c.d.	L. Cotg.	L. Cos.	d.	′
0	9.79 887	16	9.90 837	26	0.09 163	9.89 050	10	60
1	903	15	863	26	137	040	10	59
2	918	16	889	25	111	030	10	58
3	934	16	914	26	086	020	10	57
4	950	15	940	26	060	009	11	56
5	965	16	966	26	034	9.88 999	10	55
6	981	15	992	26	008	989	10	54
7	996	16	9.91 018	25	0.08 982	978	11	53
8	9.80 012	15	043	26	957	968	10	52
9	027	16	069	26	931	958	10	51
10	9.80 043	15	9.91 095	26	0.08 905	9.88 948	10	50
11	058	16	121	26	879	937	11	49
12	074	15	147	25	853	927	10	48
13	089	16	172	26	828	917	10	47
14	105	15	198	26	802	906	11	46
15	120	16	224	26	776	896	10	45
16	136	15	250	26	750	886	10	44
17	151	15	276	25	724	875	11	43
18	166	16	301	26	699	865	10	42
19	182	15	327	26	673	855	10	41
20	9.80 197	16	9.91 353	26	0.08 647	9.88 844	11	40
21	213	15	379	25	621	834	10	39
22	228	16	404	26	596	824	10	38
23	244	15	430	26	570	813	11	37
24	259	15	456	26	544	803	10	36
25	274	16	482	25	518	793	10	35
26	290	15	507	26	493	782	11	34
27	305	15	533	26	467	772	10	33
28	320	16	559	26	441	761	11	32
29	336	15	585	25	415	751	10	31
30	9.80 351	15	9.91 610	26	0.08 390	9.88 741	11	30
31	366	16	636	26	364	730	10	29
32	382	15	662	26	338	720	11	28
33	397	15	688	25	312	709	11	27
34	412	16	713	26	287	699	10	26
35	428	15	739	26	261	688	11	25
36	443	15	765	26	235	678	10	24
37	458	15	791	25	209	668	11	23
38	473	16	816	26	184	657	10	22
39	489	15	842	26	158	647	11	21
40	9.80 504	15	9.91 868	25	0.08 132	9.88 636	10	20
41	519	15	893	26	107	626	11	19
42	534	16	919	26	081	615	10	18
43	550	15	945	26	055	605	11	17
44	565	15	971	25	029	594	10	16
45	580	15	996	26	004	584	11	15
46	595	15	9.92 022	26	0.07 978	573	10	14
47	610	15	048	25	952	563	11	13
48	625	16	073	26	927	552	10	12
49	641	15	099	26	901	542	10	11
50	9.80 656	15	9.92 125	26	0.07 875	9.88 531	11	10
51	671	15	150	26	850	521	10	9
52	686	15	176	26	824	510	11	8
53	701	15	202	25	798	499	10	7
54	716	15	227	26	773	489	11	6
55	731	15	253	26	747	478	10	5
56	746	16	279	25	721	468	11	4
57	762	15	304	26	696	457	10	3
58	777	15	330	26	670	447	11	2
59	792	15	356	25	644	436	11	1
60	9.80 807		9.92 381		0.07 619	9.88 425		0
′	L. Cos.	d.	L. Cotg.	c.d.	L. Tang.	L. Sin.	d.	′

P. P.

1′	26
1″	0.4
2″	0.9
3″	1.3
4″	1.7
5″	2.2
6″	2.6
7″	3.0
8″	3.5
9″	3.9

1′	25
1″	0.4
2″	0.8
3″	1.3
4″	1.7
5″	2.1
6″	2.5
7″	2.9
8″	3.3
9″	3.8

1′	16
1″	0.3
2″	0.5
3″	0.8
4″	1.1
5″	1.3
6″	1.6
7″	1.9
8″	2.1
9″	2.4

1′	15
1″	0.3
2″	0.5
3″	0.8
4″	1.0
5″	1.3
6″	1.5
7″	1.8
8″	2.0
9″	2.3

1′	10	11
1″	0.2	0.2
2″	0.3	0.4
3″	0.5	0.6
4″	0.7	0.7
5″	0.8	0.9
6″	1.0	1.1
7″	1.2	1.3
8″	1.3	1.5
9″	1.5	1.7

′	L. Sin.	d.	L. Tang.	c. d.	L. Cotg.	L. Cos.	d.	′	P. P.		
0	9.80 807	15	9.92 381	26	0.07 619	9.88 425	10	60	1′	26	
1	822	15	407	26	593	415̄	11	59	1″	0.4	
2	837	15	433	25	567	404	10	58	2″	0.9	
3	852	15	458	26	542	394	11	57	3″	1.3	
4	867	15	484	26	516	383	11	56	4″	1.7	
5	882	15	510	25	490	372	10	55	5″	2.2	
6	897	15	535	26	465̄	362	11	54	6″	2.6	
7	912	15	561	26	439	351	11	53	7″	3.0	
8	927	15	587	25	413	340	10	52	8″	3.5	
9	942	15	612	26	388	330	11	51	9″	3.9	
10	9.80 957	15	9.92 638	25	0.07 362	9.88 319	11	50			
11	972	15	663	26	337	308	10	49			
12	987	15	689	26	311	298	11	48	1′	25	
13	9.81 002	15	715̄	25	285	287	11	47	1″	0.4	
14	017	15	740	26	260	276	10	46	2″	0.8	
15	032	15	766	26	234	266	11	45	3″	1.3	
16	047	14	792	25	208	255̄	11	44	4″	1.7	
17	061	15	817	26	183	244	10	43	5″	2.1	
18	076	15	843	25	157	234	11	42	6″	2.5	
19	091	15	868	26	132	223	11	41	7″	2.9	
20	9.81 106	15	9.92 894	26	0.07 106	9.88 212	11	40	8″	3.3	
21	121	15	920	25	080̄	201	10	39	9″	3.8	
22	136	15	945	26	055̄	191	11	38			
23	151	15	971	25	029	180	11	37			
24	166	14	996	26	004	169	11	36			
25	180	15	9.93 022	26	0.06 978	158	10	35	1′	15	
26	195	15	048	25	952	148	11	34	1″	0.3	
27	210	15	073	26	927	137	11	33	2″	0.5	
28	225̄	15	099	25	901	126	11	32	3″	0.8	
29	240	14	124	26	876	115	10	31	4″	1.0	
30	9.81 254	15	9.93 150	25	0.06 850	9.88 105	11	30	5″	1.3	
31	269	15	175	26	825̄	094	11	29	6″	1.5	
32	284	15	201	26	799	083	11	28	7″	1.8	
33	299	15	227	25	773	072	11	27	8″	2.0	
34	314	14	252	26	748	061	10	26	9″	2.3	
35	328	15	278	25	722	051	11	25			
36	343	15	303	26	697	040	11	24			
37	358	14	329	25	671	029	11	23	1′	14	
38	372	15	354	26	646	018	11	22	1″	0.2	
39	387	15	380	26	620	007	11	21	2″	0.5	
40	9.81 402	15	9.93 406	25	0.06 594	9.87 996	11	20	3″	0.7	
41	417	14	431	26	569	985	10	19	4″	0.9	
42	431	15	457	25	543	975̄	11	18	5″	1.2	
43	446	15	482	26	518	964	11	17	6″	1.4	
44	461	14	508	25	492	953	11	16	7″	1.6	
45	475̄	15	533	26	467	942	11	15	8″	1.9	
46	490	15	559	25	441	931	11	14	9″	2.1	
47	505̄	14	584	26	416	920	11	13			
48	519	15	610	26	390	909	11	12			
49	534	15	636	25	364	898	11	11	1′	10	11
50	9.81 549	14	9.93 661	26	0.06 339	9.87 887	10	10	1″	0.2	0.2
51	563	15	687	25	313	877	11	9	2″	0.3	0.4
52	578	14	712	26	288	866	11	8	3″	0.5	0.6
53	592	15	738	25	262	855̄	11	7	4″	0.7	0.7
54	607	15	763	26	237	844	11	6	5″	0.8	0.9
55	622	14	789	25	211	833	11	5	6″	1.0	1.1
56	636	15	814	26	186	822	11	4	7″	1.2	1.3
57	651	14	840	25	160	811	11	3	8″	1.3	1.5
58	665	15	865	26	135̄	800	11	2	9″	1.5	1.7
59	680	14	891	25	109	789	11	1			
60	9.81 694		9.93 916		0.06 084	9.87 778		0			

| ′ | L. Cos. | d. | L. Cotg. | c. d. | L. Tang. | L. Sin. | d. | ′ | |

′	L. Sin.	d.	L. Tang.	c.d.	L. Cotg.	L. Cos.	d.	′
0	9.81 694	15	9.93 916	26	0.06 084	9.87 778	11	60
1	709	14	942	25	058	767	11	59
2	723	15	967	26	033	756	11	58
3	738	14	993	25	007	745	11	57
4	752	15	9.94 018	26	0.05 982	734	11	56
5	767	14	044	25	956	723	11	55
6	781	15	069	26	931	712	11	54
7	796	14	095	25	905	701	11	53
8	810	15	120	26	880	690	11	52
9	825	14	146	25	854	679	11	51
10	9.81 839	15	9.94 171	26	0.05 829	9.87 668	11	50
11	854	14	197	25	803	657	11	49
12	868	14	222	26	778	646	11	48
13	882	15	248	25	752	635	11	47
14	897	14	273	26	727	624	11	46
15	911	15	299	25	701	613	11	45
16	926	14	324	26	676	601	12	44
17	940	15	350	25	650	590	11	43
18	955	14	375	26	625	579	11	42
19	969	14	401	25	599	568	11	41
20	9.81 983	15	9.94 426	26	0.05 574	9.87 557	11	40
21	998	14	452	25	548	546	11	39
22	9.82 012	14	477	26	523	535	11	38
23	026	15	503	25	497	524	11	37
24	041	14	528	26	472	513	12	36
25	055	14	554	25	446	501	11	35
26	069	15	579	25	421	490	11	34
27	084	14	604	26	396	479	11	33
28	098	14	630	25	370	468	11	32
29	112	14	655	26	345	457	11	31
30	9.82 126	15	9.94 681	25	0.05 319	9.87 446	12	30
31	141	14	706	26	294	434	11	29
32	155	14	732	25	268	423	11	28
33	169	15	757	26	243	412	11	27
34	184	14	783	25	217	401	11	26
35	198	14	808	26	192	390	12	25
36	212	14	834	25	166	378	11	24
37	226	14	859	25	141	367	11	23
38	240	15	884	26	116	356	11	22
39	255	14	910	25	090	345	11	21
40	9.82 269	14	9.94 935	26	0.05 065	9.87 334	12	20
41	283	14	961	25	039	322	11	19
42	297	14	986	26	014	311	11	18
43	311	15	9.95 012	25	0.04 988	300	12	17
44	326	14	037	25	963	288	11	16
45	340	14	062	26	938	277	11	15
46	354	14	088	25	912	266	11	14
47	368	14	113	26	887	255	12	13
48	382	14	139	25	861	243	11	12
49	396	14	164	26	836	232	11	11
50	9.82 410	14	9.95 190	25	0.04 810	9.87 221	12	10
51	424	15	215	25	785	209	11	9
52	439	14	240	26	760	198	11	8
53	453	14	266	25	734	187	12	7
54	467	14	291	26	709	175	11	6
55	481	14	317	25	683	164	11	5
56	495	14	342	26	658	153	12	4
57	509	14	368	25	632	141	11	3
58	523	14	393	25	607	130	12	2
59	537	14	418	26	582	119	12	1
60	9.82 551		9.95 444		0.04 556	9.87 107		0
′	L. Cos.	d.	L. Cotg.	c.d.	L. Tang.	L. Sin.	d.	′

P. P.

1′	26
1″	0.4
2″	0.9
3″	1.3
4″	1.7
5″	2.2
6″	2.6
7″	3.0
8″	3.5
9″	3.9

1′	25
1″	0.4
2″	0.8
3″	1.3
4″	1.7
5″	2.1
6″	2.5
7″	2.9
8″	3.3
9″	3.8

1′	15
1″	0.3
2″	0.5
3″	0.8
4″	1.0
5″	1.3
6″	1.5
7″	1.8
8″	2.0
9″	2.3

1′	14
1″	0.2
2″	0.5
3″	0.7
4″	0.9
5″	1.2
6″	1.4
7″	1.6
8″	1.9
9″	2.1

1′	11	12
1″	0.2	0.2
2″	0.4	0.4
3″	0.6	0.6
4″	0.7	0.8
5″	0.9	1.0
6″	1.1	1.2
7″	1.3	1.4
8″	1.5	1.6
9″	1.7	1.8

′	L. Sin.	d.	L. Tang.	c. d.	L. Cotg.	L. Cos.	d.	′	P. P.	
0	9.82 551	14	9.95 444	25	0.04 556	9.87 107	11	60	**1′**	**26**
1	565	14	469	26	531	096	11	59	1″	0.4
2	579	14	495	25	505	085	12	58	2″	0.9
3	593	14	520	25	480	073	11	57	3″	1.3
4	607	14	545	26	455	062	12	56	4″	1.7
5	621	14	571	25	429	050	11	55	5″	2.2
6	635	14	596	26	404	039	11	54	6″	2.6
7	649	14	622	25	378	028	12	53	7″	3.0
8	663	14	647	25	353	016	11	52	8″	3.5
9	677	14	672	26	328	005	12	51	9″	3.9
10	9.82 691	14	9.95 698	25	0.04 302	9.86 993	11	50		
11	705	14	723	25	277	982	12	49		
12	719	14	748	26	252	970	11	48	**1′**	**25**
13	733	14	774	25	226	959	12	47	1″	0.4
14	747	14	799	26	201	947	11	46	2″	0.8
15	761	14	825	25	175	936	11	45	3″	1.3
16	775	13	850	25	150	924	12	44	4″	1.7
17	788	14	875	26	125	913	11	43	5″	2.1
18	802	14	901	25	099	902	12	42	6″	2.5
19	816	14	926	26	074	890	11	41	7″	2.9
20	9.82 830	14	9.95 952	25	0.04 048	9.86 879	12	40	8″	3.3
21	844	14	977	25	023	867	12	39	9″	3.8
22	858	14	9.96 002	26	0.03 998	855	11	38		
23	872	13	028	25	972	844	12	37		
24	885	14	053	25	947	832	11	36	**1′**	**14**
25	899	14	078	26	922	821	12	35	1″	0.2
26	913	14	104	25	896	809	11	34	2″	0.5
27	927	14	129	26	871	798	12	33	3″	0.7
28	941	14	155	25	845	786	11	32	4″	0.9
29	955	13	180	25	820	775	12	31	5″	1.2
30	9.82 968	14	9.96 205	26	0.03 795	9.86 763	11	30	6″	1.4
31	982	14	231	25	769	752	12	29	7″	1.6
32	996	14	256	25	744	740	12	28	8″	1.9
33	9.83 010	13	281	26	719	728	11	27	9″	2.1
34	023	14	307	25	693	717	12	26		
35	037	14	332	25	668	705	11	25		
36	051	14	357	26	643	694	12	24	**1′**	**13**
37	065	13	383	25	617	682	12	23	1″	0.2
38	078	14	408	25	592	670	11	22	2″	0.4
39	092	14	433	26	567	659	12	21	3″	0.7
40	9.83 106	14	9.96 459	25	0.03 541	9.86 647	12	20	4″	0.9
41	120	13	484	26	516	635	11	19	5″	1.1
42	133	14	510	25	490	624	12	18	6″	1.3
43	147	14	535	25	465	612	12	17	7″	1.5
44	161	13	560	26	440	600	11	16	8″	1.7
45	174	14	586	25	414	589	12	15	9″	2.0
46	188	14	611	25	389	577	12	14		
47	202	13	636	26	364	565	11	13		
48	215	14	662	25	338	554	12	12			
49	229	13	687	25	313	542	12	11	**1′**	**12**	**11**
50	9.83 242	14	9.96 712	26	0.03 288	9.86 530	12	10	1″	0.2	0.2
51	256	14	738	25	262	518	12	9	2″	0.4	0.4
52	270	13	763	25	237	507	12	8	3″	0.6	0.6
53	283	14	788	26	212	495	11	7	4″	0.8	0.7
54	297	13	814	25	186	483	11	6	5″	1.0	0.9
55	310	14	839	25	161	472	12	5	6″	1.2	1.1
56	324	14	864	26	136	460	12	4	7″	1.4	1.3
57	338	13	890	25	110	448	12	3	8″	1.6	1.5
58	351	14	915	25	085	436	11	2	9″	1.8	1.7
59	365	13	940	26	060	425	12	1			
60	9.83 378	13	9.96 966		0.03 034	9.86 413		0			
′	L. Cos.	d.	L. Cotg.	c. d.	L. Tang.	L. Sin.	d.	′		

′	L. Sin.	d.	L. Tang.	c.d.	L. Cotg.	L. Cos.	d.	′
0	9.83 378	14	9.96 966	25	0.03 034	9.86 413	12	60
1	392	13	991	25	009	401	12	59
2	405	14	9.97 016	26	0.02 984	389	12	53
3	419	13	042	25	958	377	11	57
4	432	14	067	25	933	366	12	56
5	446	13	092	26	908	354	12	55
6	459	14	118	25	882	342	12	54
7	473	13	143	25	857	330	12	53
8	486	14	168	25	832	318	12	52
9	500	13	193	26	807	306	11	51
10	9.83 513	14	9.97 219	25	0.02 781	9.86 295	12	50
11	527	13	244	25	756	283	12	49
12	540	14	269	26	731	271	12	48
13	554	13	295	25	705	259	12	47
14	567	14	320	25	680	247	12	46
15	581	13	345	26	655	235	12	45
16	594	14	371	25	629	223	12	44
17	608	13	396	25	604	211	11	43
18	621	13	421	26	579	200	12	42
19	634	14	447	25	553	188	12	41
20	9.83 648	13	9.97 472	25	0.02 528	9.86 176	12	40
21	661	13	497	26	503	164	12	39
22	674	14	523	25	477	152	12	38
23	688	13	548	25	452	140	12	37
24	701	14	573	25	427	128	12	36
25	715	13	598	26	402	116	12	35
26	728	13	624	25	376	104	12	34
27	741	14	649	25	351	092	12	33
28	755	13	674	26	326	080	12	32
29	768	13	700	25	300	068	12	31
30	9.83 781	14	9.97 725	25	0.02 275	9.86 056	12	30
31	795	13	750	26	250	044	12	29
32	808	13	776	25	224	032	12	28
33	821	13	801	25	199	020	12	27
34	834	14	826	25	174	008	12	26
35	848	13	851	26	149	9.85 996	12	25
36	861	13	877	25	123	984	12	24
37	874	13	902	25	098	972	12	23
38	887	14	927	26	073	960	12	22
39	901	13	953	25	047	948	12	21
40	9.83 914	13	9.97 978	25	0.02 022	9.85 936	12	20
41	927	13	9.98 003	26	0.01 997	924	12	19
42	940	14	029	25	971	912	12	18
43	954	13	054	25	946	900	12	17
44	967	13	079	25	921	888	12	16
45	980	13	104	26	896	876	12	15
46	993	13	130	25	870	864	12	14
47	9.84 006	14	155	25	845	851	13	13
48	020	1?	180	26	820	839	12	12
49	033	13	206	25	794	827	12	11
50	9.84 046	13	9.98 231	25	0.01 769	9.85 815	12	10
51	059	13	256	25	744	803	12	9
52	072	13	281	26	719	791	12	8
53	085	13	307	25	693	779	13	7
54	098	14	332	25	668	766	12	6
55	112	13	357	26	643	754	12	5
56	125	13	383	25	617	742	12	4
57	138	13	408	25	592	730	12	3
58	151	13	433	26	567	718	12	2
59	164	13	458	26	542	706	13	1
60	9.84 177		9.98 484		0.01 516	9.85 693		0

| ′ | L. Cos. | d. | L. Cotg. | c.d. | L. Tang. | L. Sin. | d. | ′ |

P. P.

1′	26
1″	0.4
2″	0.9
3″	1.3
4″	1.7
5″	2.2
6″	2.6
7″	3.0
8″	3.5
9″	3.9

1′	25
1″	0.4
2″	0.8
3″	1.3
4″	1.7
5″	2.1
6″	2.5
7″	2.9
8″	3.3
9″	3.8

1′	11
1″	0.2
2″	0.5
3″	0.7
4″	0.9
5″	1.2
6″	1.4
7″	1.6
8″	1.9
9″	2.1

1′	13
1″	0.2
2″	0.4
3″	0.7
4″	0.9
5″	1.1
6″	1.3
7″	1.5
8″	1.7
9″	2.0

1′	12	11
1″	0.2	0.2
2″	0.4	0.4
3″	0.6	0.6
4″	0.8	0.7
5″	1.0	0.9
6″	1.2	1.1
7″	1.4	1.3
8″	1.6	1.5
9″	1.8	1.7

46°

Logarithmic Functions

44°

′	L. Sin.	d.	L. Tang.	c.d.	L. Cotg.	L. Cos.	d.	′	P. P.	
0	9.84 177	13	9.98 484	25	0.01 516	9.85 693	12	60	1′	26
1	190	13	509	25	491	681	12	59	1″	0.4
2	203	13	534	26	466	669	12	58	2″	0.9
3	216	13	560	25	440	657	12	57	3″	1.3
4	229	13	585̄	25	415	645̄	13	56	4″	1.7
5	242	13	610	25	390	632	12	55	5″	2.2
6	255	14	635	26	365̄	620	12	54	6″	2.6
7	269	13	661	25	339	608	12	53	7″	3.0
8	282̄	13	686	25	314	596	13	52	8″	3.5
9	295̄	13	711	26	289	583	12	51	9″	3.9
10	9.84 308	13	9.98 737	25	0.01 263	9.85 571	12	50		
11	321	13	762	25	238	559	12	49		
12	334	13	787	25	213	547	13	48	1′	25
13	347	13	812	26	188	534	12	47	1″	0.4
14	360	13	838	25	162	522	12	46	2″	0.8
15	373	12	863	25	137	510	13	45	3″	1.3
16	385	13	888	25	112	497	12	44	4″	1.7
17	398	13	913	26	087	485̄	12	43	5″	2.1
18	411	13	939	25	061	473	13	42	6″	2.5
19	424	13	964	25	036	460	12	41	7″	2.9
20	9.84 437	13	9.98 989	26	0.01 011	9.85 448	12	40	8″	3.3
21	450	13	9.99 015̄	25	0.00 985	436	13	39	9″	3.8
22	463	13	040	25	960	423	12	38		
23	476	13	065	25	935̄	411	12	37		
24	489	13	090	26	910	399	13	36	1′	14
25	502	13	116	25	884	386	12	35	1″	0.2
26	515̄	13	141	25	859	374	13	34	2″	0.5
27	528	12	166	25	834	361	12	33	3″	0.7
28	540	13	191	26	809	349	12	32	4″	0.9
29	553	13	217	25	783	337	13	31	5″	1.2
30	9.84 566	13	9.99 242	25	0.00 758	9.85 324	12	30	6″	1.4
31	579	13	267	26	733	312	13	29	7″	1.6
32	592̄	13	293	25	707	299	12	28	8″	1.9
33	605̄	13	318	25	682	287	13	27	9″	2.1
34	618	12	343	25	657	274	12	26		
35	630	13	368	26	632	262	12	25		
36	643	13	394	25	606	250	13	24	1′	13
37	656	13	419	25	581	237	12	23	1″	0.2
38	669	13	444	25	556	225̄	13	22	2″	0.4
39	682	12	469	26	531	212	12	21	3″	0.7
40	9.84 694	13	9.99 495	25	0.00 505	9.85 200	12	20	4″	0.9
41	707	13	520	25	480	187	12	19	5″	1.1
42	720	13	545	25	455̄	175̄	13	18	6″	1.3
43	733	12	570	26	430	162	12	17	7″	1.5
44	745	13	596	25	404	150	13	16	8″	1.7
45	758	13	621	25	379	137	12	15	9″	2.0
46	771	13	646	26	354	125̄	13	14		
47	784	12	672	25	328	112	13	13		
48	796	13	697	25	303	100	13	12		
49	809	13	722	25	278	087	13	11	1′	12
50	9.84 822	13	9.99 747	26	0.00 253	9.85 074	12	10	1″	0.2
51	835̄	12	773	25	227	062	13	9	2″	0.4
52	847	13	798	25	202	049	12	8	3″	0.6
53	860	13	823	25	177	037	13	7	4″	0.8
54	873	12	848	26	152	024	12	6	5″	1.0
55	885	13	874	25	126	012	13	5	6″	1.2
56	898	13	899	25	101	9.84 999	13	4	7″	1.4
57	911	12	924	25	076	986	12	3	8″	1.6
58	923	13	949	26	051	974	13	2	9″	1.8
59	936	13	975̄	25	025	961	12	1		
60	9.84 949		0.00 000		0.00 000	9.84 949		0		
′	L. Cos.	d.	L. Cotg.	c.d.	L. Tang.	L. Sin.	d.	′		

45°

NATURAL
TRIGONOMETRIC FUNCTIONS

′	0°		1°		2°		3°		4°		′
	N. sine	N. cos.	N. sine	N. cos.	N.sine	N.cos.	N.sine	N.cos.	N.sine	N.cos.	
0	.00000	1.00000	.01745	.99985	.03490	.99939	.05234	.99863	06976	.99756	60
1	029	000	774	984	519	938	263	861	07005	754	59
2	058	000	803	984	548	937	292	860	034	752	58
3	087	000	832	983	577	936	321	858	063	750	57
4	116	000	862	983	606	935	350	857	092	748	56
5	145	000	891	982	635	934	379	855	121	746	55
6	175	000	920	982	664	933	408	854	150	744	54
7	204	000	949	981	693	932	437	852	179	742	53
8	233	000	978	980	723	931	466	851	208	740	52
9	262	000	.02007	980	752	930	495	849	237	738	51
10	.00291	1.00000	.02036	.99979	.03781	.99929	.05524	.99847	07266	.99736	50
11	320	.99999	065	979	810	927	553	846	295	734	49
12	349	999	094	978	839	926	582	844	324	731	48
13	378	999	123	977	868	925	611	842	353	729	47
14	407	999	152	977	897	924	640	841	382	727	46
15	436	999	181	976	926	923	669	839	411	725	45
16	465	999	211	976	955	922	698	838	440	723	44
17	495	999	240	975	984	921	727	836	469	721	43
18	524	999	269	974	.04013	919	756	834	498	719	42
19	553	998	298	974	042	918	785	833	527	716	41
20	.00582	.99998	.02327	.99973	.04071	.99917	.05814	.99831	07556	.99714	40
21	611	998	356	972	100	916	844	829	585	712	39
22	640	998	385	972	129	915	873	827	614	710	38
23	669	998	414	971	159	913	902	826	643	708	37
24	698	998	443	970	188	912	931	824	672	705	36
25	727	997	472	969	217	911	960	822	701	703	35
26	756	997	501	969	246	910	989	821	730	701	34
27	785	997	530	968	275	909	.06018	819	759	699	33
28	814	997	560	967	304	907	047	817	788	696	32
29	844	996	589	966	333	906	076	815	817	694	31
30	.00873	.99996	.02618	.99966	.04362	.99905	.06105	.99813	07846	.99692	30
31	902	996	647	965	391	904	134	812	875	689	29
32	931	996	676	964	420	902	163	810	904	687	28
33	960	995	705	963	449	901	192	808	933	685	27
34	989	995	734	963	478	900	221	806	962	683	26
35	.01018	995	763	962	507	898	250	804	991	680	25
36	047	995	792	961	536	897	279	803	.08020	678	24
37	076	994	821	960	565	896	308	801	049	676	23
38	105	994	850	959	594	894	337	799	078	673	22
39	134	994	879	959	623	893	366	797	107	671	21
40	.01164	.99993	.02908	.99958	.04653	.99892	.06395	.99795	.08136	.99668	20
41	193	993	938	957	682	890	424	793	165	666	19
42	222	993	967	956	711	889	453	792	194	664	18
43	251	992	996	955	740	888	482	790	223	661	17
44	280	992	.03025	954	769	886	511	788	252	659	16
45	309	991	054	953	798	885	540	786	281	657	15
46	338	991	083	952	827	883	569	784	310	654	14
47	367	991	112	952	856	882	598	782	339	652	13
48	396	990	141	951	885	881	627	780	368	649	12
49	425	990	170	950	914	879	656	778	397	647	11
50	.01454	.99989	.03199	.99949	.04943	.99878	.06685	.99776	.08426	.99644	10
51	483	989	228	948	972	876	714	774	455	642	9
52	513	989	257	947	.05001	875	743	772	484	639	8
53	542	988	286	946	030	873	773	770	513	637	7
54	571	988	316	945	059	872	802	768	542	635	6
55	600	987	345	944	088	870	831	766	571	632	5
56	629	987	374	943	117	869	860	764	600	630	4
57	658	986	403	942	146	867	889	762	629	627	3
58	687	986	432	941	175	866	918	760	658	625	2
59	716	985	461	940	205	864	947	758	687	622	1
60	.01745	.99985	.03490	.99939	.05234	.99863	06976	.99756	.08716	.99619	0
	N. cos.	N. sine	N. cos.	N. sine	N.cos.	N.sine	N.cos.	N.sine	N.cos.	N.sine	
′	89°		88°		87°		86°		85°		′

′	0°		1°		2°		3°		4°		′
	Tang	Cotg	Tang	Cotg	Tang	Cotg	Tang	Cotg	Tang	Cotg	
0	.0000	Infinite	.0175	57.2900	.0349	28.6363	.0524	19.0811	.0699	14.3007	60
1	03	3437.75	77	56.3506	52	3994	27	18.9755	.0702	2411	59
2	06	1718.87	80	55.4415	55	1664	30	8711	05	1821	58
3	09	1145.92	83	54.5613	58	27.9372	33	7678	08	1235	57
4	12	859.436	86	53.7086	61	7117	36	6656	11	0655	56
5	15	687.549	89	52.8821	64	4899	39	5645	14	0079	55
6	17	572.957	92	0807	67	2715	42	4645	17	13.9507	54
7	20	491.106	95	51.3032	70	0566	44	3655	20	8940	53
8	23	429.718	98	50.5485	73	26.8450	47	2677	23	8378	52
9	26	381.971	.0201	49.8157	75	6367	50	1708	26	7821	51
10	.0029	343.774	.0204	49.1039	.0378	26.4316	.0553	18.0750	.0729	13.7267	50
11	32	312.521	07	48.4121	81	2296	56	17.9802	31	6719	49
12	35	286.478	09	47.7395	84	0307	59	8863	34	6174	48
13	38	264.441	12	0853	87	25.8348	62	7934	37	5634	47
14	41	245.552	15	46.4489	90	6418	65	7015	40	5098	46
15	44	229.182	18	45.8294	93	4517	68	6106	43	4566	45
16	47	214.858	21	2261	96	2644	71	5205	46	4039	44
17	49	202.219	24	44.6386	99	0798	74	4314	49	3515	43
18	52	190.984	27	0661	.0402	24.8978	77	3432	52	2996	42
19	55	180.932	30	43.5081	05	7185	80	2558	55	2480	41
20	.0058	171.885	.0233	42.9641	.0407	24.5418	.0582	17.1693	.0758	13.1969	40
21	61	163.700	36	4335	10	3675	85	0837	61	1461	39
22	64	156.259	39	41.9158	13	1957	88	16.9990	64	0958	38
23	67	149.465	41	4106	16	0263	91	9150	67	0458	37
24	70	143.237	44	40.9174	19	23.8593	94	8319	69	12.9962	36
25	73	137.507	47	4358	22	6945	97	7496	72	9469	35
26	76	132.219	50	39.9655	25	5321	.0600	6681	75	8981	34
27	79	127.321	53	5059	28	3718	03	5874	78	8496	33
28	81	122.774	56	0568	31	2137	06	5075	81	8014	32
29	84	118.540	59	38.6177	34	0577	09	4283	84	7536	31
30	.0087	114.589	.0262	38.1885	.0437	22.9038	.0612	16.3499	.0787	12.7062	30
31	90	110.892	65	37.7686	40	7519	15	2722	90	6591	29
32	93	107.426	68	3579	42	6020	17	1952	93	6124	28
33	96	104.171	71	36.9560	45	4541	20	1190	96	5660	27
34	99	101.107	74	5627	48	3081	23	0435	99	5199	26
35	.0102	98.2179	76	1776	51	1640	26	15.9687	.0802	4742	25
36	05	95.4895	79	35.8006	54	0217	29	8945	05	4288	24
37	08	92.9085	82	4313	57	21.8813	32	8211	08	3838	23
38	11	90.4633	85	0695	60	7426	35	7483	10	3390	22
39	13	88.1436	88	34.7151	63	6056	38	6762	13	2946	21
40	.0116	85.9398	.0291	34.3678	.0466	21.4704	.0641	15.6048	.0816	12.2505	20
41	19	83.8435	94	0273	69	3369	44	5340	19	2067	19
42	22	81.8470	97	33.6935	72	2049	47	4638	22	1632	18
43	25	79.9434	.0300	3662	75	0747	50	3943	25	1201	17
44	28	78.1263	03	0452	77	20.9460	53	3254	28	0772	16
45	31	76.3900	06	32.7303	80	8188	55	2571	31	0346	15
46	34	74.7292	08	4213	83	6932	58	1893	34	11.9923	14
47	37	73.1390	11	1181	86	5691	61	1222	37	9504	13
48	40	71.6151	14	31.8205	89	4465	64	0557	40	9087	12
49	43	70.1533	17	5284	92	3253	67	14.9898	43	8673	11
50	.0145	68.7501	.0320	31.2416	.0495	20.2056	.0670	14.9244	.0846	11.8262	10
51	48	67.4019	23	30.9599	98	0872	73	8596	49	7853	9
52	51	66.1055	26	6833	.0501	19.9702	76	7954	51	7448	8
53	54	64.8580	29	4116	04	8516	79	7317	54	7045	7
54	57	63.6567	32	1446	07	7403	82	6685	57	6645	6′
55	60	62.4992	35	29.8823	09	6273	85	6059	60	6248	5
56	63	61.3829	38	6245	12	5156	88	5438	63	5853	4
57	66	60.3058	40	3711	15	4051	90	4823	66	5461	3
58	69	59.2659	43	1220	18	2959	93	4212	69	5072	2
59	72	58.2612	46	28.8771	21	1879	96	3607	72	4685	1
60	.0175	57.2900	.0524	28.6363	.0524	19.0811	.0699	14.3007	.0875	11.4301	0
	Cotg	Tang	Cotg	Tang	Cotg	Tang	Cotg	Tang	Cotg	Tang	
′	89°		88°		87°		86°		85°		′

Natural Sines and Cosines

′	5°		6°		7°		8°		9°		′
	N.sine	N. cos.	N.sine	N. cos.	N.sine	N. cos.	N.sine	N. cos.	N.sine	N. cos.	
0	.08716	.99619	.10453	.99452	.12187	.99255	.13917	.99027	.15643	.98769	60
1	745	617	482	449	216	251	946	023	672	764	59
2	774	614	511	446	245	248	975	019	701	760	58
3	803	612	540	443	274	244	.14004	015	730	755	57
4	831	609	569	440	302	240	033	011	758	751	56
5	860	607	597	437	331	237	061	006	787	746	55
6	889	604	626	434	360	233	090	002	816	741	54
7	918	602	655	431	389	230	119	.98998	845	737	53
8	947	599	684	428	418	226	148	994	873	732	52
9	976	596	713	424	447	222	177	990	902	728	51
10	.09005	.99594	.10742	.99421	.12476	.99219	.14205	.98986	.15931	.98723	50
11	034	591	771	418	504	215	234	982	959	718	49
12	063	588	800	415	533	211	263	978	988	714	48
13	092	586	829	412	562	208	292	973	.16017	709	47
14	121	583	858	409	591	204	320	969	046	704	46
15	150	580	887	406	620	200	349	965	074	700	45
16	179	578	916	402	649	197	378	961	103	695	44
17	208	575	945	399	678	193	407	957	132	690	43
18	237	572	973	396	706	189	436	953	160	686	42
19	266	570	.11002	393	735	186	464	948	189	681	41
20	.09295	.99567	.11031	.99390	.12764	.99182	.14493	.98944	.16218	.98676	40
21	324	564	060	386	793	178	522	940	246	671	39
22	353	562	089	383	822	175	551	936	275	667	38
23	382	559	118	380	851	171	580	931	304	662	37
24	411	556	147	377	880	167	608	927	333	657	36
25	440	553	176	374	908	163	637	923	361	652	35
26	469	551	205	370	937	160	666	919	390	648	34
27	498	548	234	367	966	156	695	914	419	643	33
28	527	545	263	364	995	152	723	910	447	638	32
29	556	542	291	360	.13024	148	752	906	476	633	31
30	.09585	.99540	.11320	.99357	.13053	.99144	.14781	.98902	.16505	.98629	30
31	614	537	349	354	031	141	810	897	533	624	29
32	642	534	378	351	110	137	838	893	562	619	28
33	671	531	407	347	139	133	867	889	591	614	27
34	700	528	436	344	168	129	896	884	620	609	26
35	729	526	465	341	197	125	925	880	648	604	25
36	758	523	494	337	226	122	954	876	677	600	24
37	787	520	523	334	254	118	982	871	706	595	23
38	816	517	552	331	283	114	.15011	867	734	590	22
39	845	514	580	327	312	110	040	863	763	585	21
40	.09874	.99511	.11609	.99324	.13341	.99106	.15069	.98858	.16792	.98580	20
41	903	508	638	320	370	102	097	854	820	575	19
42	932	506	667	317	399	098	126	849	849	570	18
43	961	503	696	314	427	094	155	845	878	565	17
44	990	500	725	310	456	091	184	841	906	561	16
45	.10019	497	754	307	485	087	212	836	935	556	15
46	048	494	783	303	514	083	241	832	964	551	14
47	077	491	812	300	543	079	270	827	992	546	13
48	106	488	840	297	572	075	299	823	.17021	541	12
49	135	485	869	293	600	071	327	818	050	536	11
50	.10164	.99482	.11898	.99290	.13629	.99067	.15356	.98814	.17078	.98531	10
51	192	479	927	286	658	063	385	809	107	526	9
52	221	476	956	283	687	059	414	805	136	521	8
53	250	473	985	279	716	055	442	800	164	516	7
54	279	470	.12014	276	744	051	471	796	193	511	6
55	308	467	043	272	773	047	500	791	222	506	5
56	337	464	071	269	802	043	529	787	250	501	4
57	366	461	100	265	831	039	557	782	279	496	3
58	395	458	129	262	860	035	586	778	308	491	2
59	424	455	158	258	889	031	615	773	336	486	1
60	.10453	.99452	.12187	.99255	.13917	.99027	.15643	.98769	.17365	.98481	0
	N.cos.	N. sine	N.cos.	N. sine	N.cos.	N. sine	N.cos.	N. sine	N.cos.	N. sine	
′	84°		83°		82°		81°		80°		′

′	5° Tang.	5° Cotg.	6° Tang.	6° Cotg.	7° Tang.	7° Cotg.	8° Tang.	8° Cotg.	9° Tang.	9° Cotg.	′
0	.0875	11.4301	.1051	9.5144	.1228	8.1443	.1405	7.1154	.1584	6.3138	60
1	78	11.3919	54	9.4878	31	248	08	004	87	·019	59
2	81	540	57	614	34	054	11	7.0855	90	6.2901	58
3	84	163	60	352	37	8.0860	14	706	93	783	57
4	87	11.2789	63	090	40	667	17	558	96	666	56
5	90	417	66	9.3831	43	476	20	410	99	549	55
6	92	048	69	572	46	285	23	264	.1602	432	54
7	95	11.1681	72	315	49	095	26	117	05	316	53
8	98	316	75	060	51	7.9906	29	6.9972	08	200	52
9	.0901	11.0954	78	9.2806	54	718	32	827	11	085	51
10	.0904	11.0594	.1080	9.2553	.1257	7.9530	.1435	6.9682	.1614	6.1970	50
11	07	237	83	302	60	344	38	538	17	856	49
12	10	10.9882	86	052	63	158	41	395	20	742	48
13	13	529	89	9.1803	66	7.8973	44	252	23	628	47
14	16	178	92	555	69	789	47	110	26	515	46
15	19	10.8829	95	309	72	606	50	6.8969	29	402	45
16	22	483	98	065	75	424	53	828	32	290	44
17	25	139	.1101	9.0821	78	243	56	687	35	178	43
18	28	10.7797	04	579	81	062	59	548	38	066	42
19	31	457	07	338	84	7.7882	62	408	41	6.0955	41
20	.0934	10.7119	.1110	9.0098	.1287	7.7704	.1465	6.8269	.1644	6.0844	40
21	36	10.6783	13	8.9860	90	525	68	131	47	734	39
22	39	450	16	623	93	348	71	6.7994	50	624	38
23	42	118	19	387	96	171	74	856	53	514	37
24	45	10.5789	22	152	99	7.6996	77	720	55	405	36
25	48	462	25	8.8919	.1302	821	80	584	58	296	35
26	51	136	28	686	05	647	83	448	61	188	34
27	54	10.4813	31	455	08	473	86	313	64	080	33
28	57	491	33	225	11	301	89	179	67	5.9972	32
29	60	172	36	7.9996	14	129	92	045	70	865	31
30	.0963	10.3854	.1139	8.7769	.1317	7.5958	.1495	6.6912	.1673	5.9758	30
31	66	538	42	542	19	787	97	779	76	651	29
32	69	224	45	317	22	618	.1500	646	79	545	28
33	72	10.2913	48	093	25	449	03	514	82	439	27
34	75	602	51	8.6870	28	281	06	383	85	333	26
35	78	294	54	648	31	113	09	252	88	228	25
36	81	10.1988	57	427	34	7.4947	12	122	91	124	24
37	83	683	60	208	37	781	15	6.5992	94	019	23
38	86	381	63	8.5989	40	615	18	863	97	5.8915	22
39	89	080	66	772	43	451	21	734	.1700	811	21
40	.0992	10.0780	.1169	8.5555	.1346	7.4287	.1524	6.5606	.1703	5.8708	20
41	95	483	72	340	49	124	27	478	06	605	19
42	93	187	75	126	52	7.3962	30	350	09	502	18
43	.1001	9.9893	78	8.4913	55	800	33	223	12	400	17
44	04	601	81	701	58	639	36	097	15	298	16
45	07	310	84	490	61	479	39	6.4971	18	197	15
46	10	021	87	280	64	319	42	846	21	095	14
47	13	9.8734	89	071	67	160	45	721	24	5.7994	13
48	16	448	92	8.3863	70	002	48	596	27	894	12
49	19	164	95	656	73	7.2844	51	472	30	794	11
50	.1022	9.7882	.1198	8.3450	.1376	7.2687	.1554	6.4348	.1733	5.7694	10
51	25	601	.1201	245	79	531	57	225	36	594	9
52	28	322	04	041	82	375	60	103	39	495	8
53	30	044	07	8.2838	85	220	63	6.3980	42	396	7
54	33	9.6768	10	636	88	066	66	859	45	297	6
55	36	493	13	434	91	7.1912	69	737	48	199	5
56	39	220	16	234	94	759	72	617	51	101	4
57	42	9.5949	19	035	97	607	75	496	54	004	3
58	45	679	22	8.1837	99	455	78	376	57	5.6906	2
59	48	411	25	640	.1402	304	81	257	60	809	1
60	.1051	9.5144	.1228	8.1443	.1405	7.1154	.1584	6.3138	.1763	5.6713	0
	Cotg.	Tang.	Cotg.	Tang.	Cotg.	Tang.	Cotg.	Tang.	Cotg.	Tang.	
′	84°		83°		82°		81°		80°		′

′	10° N.sine	N. cos.	11° N.sine	N. cos.	12° N.sine	N. cos.	13° N.sine	N. cos.	14° N.sine	N. cos.	′
0	.17365	.98481	.19081	.98163	.20791	.97815	.22495	.97437	.24192	.97030	60
1	393	476	109	157	820	809	523	430	220	023	59
2	422	471	138	152	848	803	552	424	249	015	58
3	.451	466	167	146	·877	797	580	417	277	008	57
4	479	461	195	140	905	791	608	411	305	001	56
5	508	455	224	135	933	784	637	404	333	.96994	55
6	537	450	252	129	962	778	665	398	362	987	54
7	565	445	281	124	990	772	693	391	390	980	53
8	594	440	309	118	.21019	766	722	384	418	973	52
9	623	435	338	112	047	760	750	378	446	966	51
10	.17651	.98430	.19366	.98107	.21076	.97754	.22778	.97371	.24474	.96959	50
11	680	425	395	101	104	748	807	365	503	952	49
12	708	420	423	096	132	742	835	358	531	945	48
13	737	414	452	090	161	735	863	351	559	937	47
14	766	409	481	084	189	729	892	345	587	930	46
15	794	404	509	079	218	723	920	338	615	923	45
16	823	399	538	073	246	717	948	331	644	916	44
17	852	394·	566	067	275	711	977	325	672	909	43
18	880	389	595	061	303	705	.23005	318	700	902	42
19	909	383	623	056	331	698	033	311	728	894	41
20	.17937	.98378	.19652	.98050	.21360	.97692	.23062	.97304	.24756	.96887	40
21	966	373	680	044	388	686	090	298	784	880	39
22	995	368	709	039	417	680	118	291	813	873	38
23	.18023	362	737	033	445	673	146	284	841	866	37
24	052	357	766	027	474	667	175	278	869	858	36
25	081	352	794	021	502	661	203	271	897	851	35
26	109	347	823	016	530	655	231	264	925	844	34
27	138	341	851	010	559	648	260	257	954	837	33
28	166	336	880	004	587	642	288	251	982	829	32
29	195	331	908	.97998	616	636	316	244	.25010	822	31
30	.18224	.98325	.19937	.97992	.21644	.97630	.23345	.97237	.25038	.96815	30
31	252	320	965	987	672	623	373	230	066	807	29
32	281	315	994	981	701	617	401	223	094	800	28
33	309	310	.20022	975	729	611	429	217	122	793	27
34	338	304	051	969	758	604	458	210	151	786	26
35	367	299	079	963	786	598	486	203	179	778	25
36	395	294	108	958	814	592	514	196	207	771	24
37	424	288	136	952	843	585	542	189	235	764	23
38	452	283	165	946	871	579	571	182	263	756	22
39	481	277	193	940	899	573	599	176	291	749	21
40	.18509	.98272	.20222	.97934	.21928	.97566	.23627	.97169	.25320	.96742	20
41	538	267	250	928	956	560	656	162	348	734	19
42	567	261	279	922	985	553	684	155	376	727	18
43	595	256	307	916	.22013	547	712	148	404	719	17
44	624	250	336	910	041	541	740	141	432	712	16
45	652	245	364	905	070	534	769	134	460	705	15
46	681	240	393	899	098	528	797	127	488	697	14
47	710	234	421	893	126	521	825	120	516	690	13
48	738	229	450	887	155	515	853	113	545	682	12
49	767	223	478	881	183	508	882	106	573	675	11
50	.18795	.98218	.20507	.97875	.22212	.97502	.23910	.97100	.25601	.96667	10
51	824	212	535	869	240	496	938	093	629	660	9
52	852	207	563	863	268	489	966	086	657	653	8
53	881	201	592	857	297	483	995	079	685	645	7
54	910	196	620	851	325	476	.24023	072	713	638	6
55	938	190	649	845	353	470	051	065	741	630	5
56	967	185	677	839	382	463	079	058	769	623	4
57	995	179	706	833	410	457	108	051	798	615	3
58	19024	174	734	827	438	450	136	044	826	608	2
59	052	168	763	821	467	444	164	037	854	600	1
60	.19081	98163	20791	97815	.22495	.97437	.24192	.97030	.25882	.96593	0

	N.cos.	N. sine	N.cos.	N. sine	N.cos.	N. sine	N.cos.	N. sine	N.cos.	N. sine	
′	79°		78°		77°		76°		· 75°		′

′	10°		11°		12°		13°		14°		′
	Tang.	Cotg.	Tang.	Cotg.	Tang.	Cotg.	Tang.	Cotg.	Tang.	Cotg.	
0	.1763	5.6713	.1944	5.1446	.2126	4.7046	.2309	4.3315	.2493	4.0108	60
1	66	617	47	366	29	4.6979	12	257	96	058	59
2	69	521	50	286	32	912	15	200	99	009	58
3	72	425	53	207	35	845	18	143	.2503	3.9959	57
4	75	329	56	128	38	779	21	086	06	910	56
5	78	234	59	049	41	712	24	029	09	861	55
6	81	140	62	5.0970	44	646	27	4.2972	12	812	54
7	84	045	65	892	47	580	30	916	15	763	53
8	87	5.5951	68	814	50	514	33	859	18	714	52
9	90	857	71	736	53	448	36	803	21	665	51
10	.1793	5.5764	.1974	5.0658	.2156	4.6382	.2339	4.2747	.2524	3.9617	50
11	96	671	77	581	59	317	42	691	27	568	49
12	99	578	80	504	62	252	45	635	30	520	48
13	.1802	485	83	427	65	187	49	580	33	471	47
14	05	393	86	350	68	122	52	524	37	423	46
15	08	301	89	273	71	057	55	468	40	375	45
16	11	209	92	197	74	4.5993	58	413	43	327	44
17	14	118	95	121	77	928	61	358	46	279	43
18	17	026	98	045	80	864	64	303	49	232	42
19	20	5.4936	.2001	4.9969	83	800	67	248	52	184	41
20	.1823	5.4845	.2004	4.9894	.2186	4.5736	.2370	4.2193	.2555	3.9136	40
21	26	755	07	819	89	673	73	139	58	089	39
22	29	665	10	744	93	609	76	084	61	042	38
23	32	575	13	669	96	546	79	030	64	3.8995	37
24	35	486	16	594	99	483	82	4.1976	68	947	36
25	38	397	19	520	.2202	420	85	922	71	900	35
26	41	308	22	446	05	357	88	868	74	854	34
27	44	219	25	372	08	294	92	814	77	807	33
28	47	131	28	298	11	232	95	760	80	760	32
29	50	043	31	225	14	169	98	706	83	714	31
30	.1853	5.3955	.2035	4.9152	.2217	4.5107	.2401	4.1653	.2586	3.8667	30
31	56	868	38	078	20	045	04	690	89	621	29
32	59	781	41	006	23	4.4983	07	547	92	575	28
33	62	694	44	4.8933	26	922	10	493	95	528	27
34	65	607	47	860	29	860	13	441	99	482	26
35	68	521	50	788	32	799	16	388	.2602	436	25
36	71	435	53	716	35	737	19	335	05	391	24
37	74	349	56	644	38	676	22	282	08	345	23
38	77	263	59	573	41	615	25	230	11	299	22
39	80	178	62	501	44	555	28	178	14	254	21
40	.1883	5.3093	.2065	4.8430	.2247	4.4494	.2432	4.1126	.2617	3.8208	20
41	87	008	68	359	51	434	35	0/4	20	163	19
42	90	5.2924	71	288	54	374	38	022	23	118	18
43	93	839	74	218	57	313	41	4.0970	27	073	17
44	96	755	77	147	60	253	44	918	30	028	16
45	99	672	80	077	63	194	47	867	33	3.7983	15
46	.1902	588	83	007	66	134	50	815	36	938	14
47	05	505	86	4.7937	69	075	53	764	39	893	13
48	08	422	89	867	72	015	56	713	42	848	12
49	11	339	92	798	75	4.3956	59	662	45	804	11
50	.1914	5.2257	.2095	4.7729	.2278	4.3897	.2462	4.0611	.2648	3.7760	10
51	17	174	98	659	81	838	65	560	51	715	9
52	20	092	.2101	591	84	779	69	509	55	671	8
53	23	011	04	522	87	721	72	459	58	627	7
54	26	5.1929	07	453	90	662	75	408	61	583	6
55	29	848	10	385	93	604	78	358	64	539	5
56	32	767	13	317	96	546	81	308	67	495	4
57	35	686	16	249	99	488	84	257	70	451	3
58	38	606	19	181	.2303	430	87	207	73	408	2
59	41	526	23	113	06	372	90	158	76	364	1
60	.1944	5.1446	.2126	4.7046	.2309	4.3315	.2493	4.0108	.2679	3.7321	0
	Cotg.	Tang.	Cotg.	Tang.	Cotg.	Tang.	Cotg.	Tang.	Cotg.	Tang.	
′	79°		78°		77°		76°		75°		′

′	15°		16°		17°		18°		19°		′
	N.sine	N. cos.	N.sine	N. cos.	N.sine	N. cos.	N.sine	N. cos.	N.sine	N. cos.	
0	.25882	.96593	.27564	.96126	.29237	.95630	.30902	.95106	.32557	.94552	60
1	910	585	592	118	265	622	929	097	584	542	59
2	938	578	620	110	293	613	957	088	612	533	58
3	966	570	648	102	321	605	985	079	639	523	57
4	994	562	676	094	348	596	.31012	070	667	514	56
5	.26022	555	704	086	376	588	040	061	694	504	55
6	050	547	731	078	404	579	068	052	722	495	54
7	079	540	759	070	432	571	095	043	749	485	53
8	107	532	787	062	460	562	123	033	777	476	52
9	135	524	815	054	487	554	151	024	804	466	51
10	.26163	.96517	.27843	.96046	.29515	.95545	.31178	.95015	.32832	.94457	50
11	191	509	871	037	543	536	.206	006	859	447	49
12	219	502	899	029	571	528	233	.94997	887	438	48
13	247	494	927	021	599	519	261	988	914	428	47
14	275	486	955	013	626	511	289	979	942	418	46
15	303	479	983	005	654	502	316	970	969	409	45
16	331	471	.28011	.95997	682	493	344	961	997	399	44
17	359	463	039	989	710	485	372	952	.33024	390	43
18	387	456	067	981	737	476	399	943	051	380	42
19	415	448	095	972	765	467	427	933	079	370	41
20	.26443	.96440	.28123	.95964	.29793	.95459	.31454	.94924	.33106	.94361	40
21	471	433	150	956	821	450	482	915	134	351	39
22	500	425	178	948	849	441	510	906	161	342	38
23	528	417	206	940	876	433	537	897	189	332	37
24	556	410	234	931	904	424	565	888	216	322	36
25	584	402	262	923	932	415	593	878	244	313	35
26	612	394	290	915	960	407	620	869	271	303	34
27	640	386	318	907	987	393	648	860	298	293	33
28	668	379	346	898	.30015	389	675	851	326	284	32
29	696	371	374	890	043	380	703	842	353	274	31
30	.26724	.96363	.28402	.95882	.30071	.95372	.31730	.94832	.33381	.94264	30
31	752	355	429	874	098	363	758	823	408	254	29
32	780	347	457	865	126	354	786	814	436	245	28
33	808	340	485	857	154	345	813	805	463	235	27
34	836	332	513	849	182	337	841	795	490	225	26
35	864	324	541	841	209	328	868	786	518	215	25
36	892	316	569	832	237	319	896	777	545	206	24
37	920	308	597	824	265	310	923	768	573	196	23
38	948	301	625	816	292	301	951	758	600	186	22
39	976	293	652	807	320	293	979	749	627	176	21
40	.27004	.96285	.28680	.95799	.30348	.95284	.32006	.94740	.33655	.94167	20
41	.032	277	708	791	376	275	.034	730	632	157	19
42	060	269	736	782	403	266	061	721	710	147	18
43	088	261	764	774	431	257	089	712	737	137	17
44	116	253	792	766	459	248	116	702	764	127	16
45	144	246	820	757	486	240	144	693	792	118	15
46	172	238	847	749	514	231	171	684	819	108	14
47	200	230	875	740	542	222	199	674	846	098	13
48	228	222	903	732	570	213	227	665	874	088	12
49	256	214	931	724	597	204	254	656	901	078	11
50	.27284	.96206	.28959	.95715	.30625	.95195	.32282	.94646	.33929	.94068	10
51	312	198	987	707	653	186	309	637	956	058	9
52	340	190	.29015	698	680	177	337	627	983	049	8
53	368	182	042	690	708	168	364	618	.34011	039	7
54	396	174	070	681	736	159	392	609	038	029	6
55	424	166	098	673	763	150	419	599	065	019	5
56	452	158	126	664	791	142	447	590	093	009	4
57	480	150	154	656	819	133	474	580	120	.93999	3
58	508	142	182	647	846	124	502	571	147	989	2
59	536	134	209	639	874	115	529	561	175	979	1
60	.27564	.96126	.29237	.95630	.30902	.95106	.32557	.94552	.34202	.93969	0
	N.cos.	N. sine	N.cos.	N. sine	N.cos.	N. sine	N.cos.	N. sine	N.cos.	N. sine	
′	74°		73°		72°		71°		70°		′

′	15° Tang.	Cotg.	16° Tang.	Cotg.	17° Tang.	Cotg.	18° Tang.	Cotg.	19° Tang.	Cotg.	′
0	.2679	3.7321	.2867	3.4874	.3057	3.2709	.3249	3.0777	.3443	2.9042	60
1	83	277	71	836	60	675	52	746	47	015	59
2	86	234	74	798	64	641	56	716	50	2.8987	58
3	89	191	77	760	67	607	59	686	53	960	57
4	92	148	80	722	70	573	62	655	56	933	56
5	95	105	83	684	73	539	65	625	60	905	55
6	98	062	86	646	76	506	69	595	63	878	54
7	.2701	019	90	608	80	472	72	565	66	851	53
8	04	3.6976	93	570	83	438	75	535	69	824	52
9	08	933	96	533	86	405	78	505	73	797	51
10	.2711	3.6891	.2899	3.4495	.3089	3.2371	.3281	3.0475	.3476	2.8770	50
11	14	848	.2902	458	92	338	85	445	79	743	49
12	17	806	05	420	96	305	88	415	82	716	48
13	20	764	08	383	99	272	91	385	86	689	47
14	23	722	12	346	.3102	238	94	356	89	662	46
15	26	680	15	308	05	205	98	326	92	636	45
16	29	638	18	271	08	172	.3301	296	95	609	44
17	33	596	21	234	11	139	04	267	99	582	43
18	36	554	24	197	15	106	07	237	.3502	556	42
19	39	512	27	160	18	073	10	208	05	529	41
20	.2742	3.6470	.2931	3.4124	.3121	3.2041	.3314	3.0178	.3508	2.8502	40
21	45	429	34	087	24	008	17	149	12	476	39
22	48	387	37	050	27	3.1975	20	120	15	449	38
23	51	346	40	014	31	943	23	090	18	423	37
24	54	305	43	3.3977	34	910	27	061	22	397	36
25	58	264	46	941	37	878	30	032	25	370	35
26	61	222	49	904	40	845	33	003	28	344	34
27	64	181	53	868	43	813	36	2.9974	31	318	33
28	67	140	56	832	47	780	39	945	35	291	32
29	70	100	59	796	50	748	43	916	38	265	31
30	.2773	3.6059	.2962	3.3759	.3153	3.1716	.3346	2.9887	.3541	2.8239	30
31	76	018	65	723	56	684	49	858	44	213	29
32	80	3.5978	68	687	59	652	52	829	48	187	28
33	83	937	72	652	63	620	56	800	51	161	27
34	86	897	75	616	66	588	59	772	54	135	26
35	89	856	78	580	69	556	62	743	58	109	25
36	92	816	81	544	72	524	65	714	61	083	24
37	95	776	84	509	75	492	69	686	64	057	23
38	98	736	87	473	79	460	72	657	67	032	22
39	.2801	696	91	438	82	429	75	629	71	006	21
40	.2805	3.5656	.2994	3.3402	.3185	3.1397	.3378	2.9600	.3574	2.7980	20
41	08	616	97	367	88	366	82	572	77	955	19
42	11	576	.3000	332	91	334	85	544	81	929	18
43	14	536	03	297	95	303	88	515	84	903	17
44	17	497	06	261	98	271	91	487	87	878	16
45	20	457	10	226	.3201	240	95	459	90	852	15
46	23	418	13	191	04	209	98	431	94	827	14
47	27	379	16	156	07	178	.3401	403	97	801	13
48	30	339	19	122	11	146	04	375	.3600	776	12
49	33	300	22	087	14	115	08	347	04	751	11
50	.2836	3.5261	3026	3.3052	.3217	3.1084	.3411	2.9319	.3607	2.7725	10
51	39	222	29	017	20	053	14	291	10	700	9
52	42	183	32	3.2983	23	022	17	263	13	675	8
53	45	144	35	948	27	3.0991	21	235	17	650	7
54	49	105	38	914	30	961	24	208	20	625	6
55	52	067	41	879	33	930	27	180	23	600	5
56	55	028	45	845	36	899	30	152	27	575	4
57	58	3.4989	48	811	40	868	34	125	30	550	3
58	61	951	51	777	43	838	37	097	33	525	2
59	64	912	54	743	46	807	40	070	36	500	1
60	.2867	3.4874	.3057	3.2709	.3249	3.0777	.3443	2.9042	.3640	2.7475	0
′	Cotg.	Tang.	Cotg.	Tang.	Cotg.	Tang.	Cotg.	Tang.	Cotg.	Tang.	′
	74°		73°		72°		71°		70°		

82 Natural Sines and Cosines

'	20° N.sine	20° N. cos.	21° N.sine	21° N. cos.	22° N.sine	22° N. cos.	23° N.sine	23° N. cos.	24° N.sine	24° N. cos.	'
0	.34202	.93969	.35837	.93358	.37461	.92718	.39073	.92050	.40674	.91355	60
1	229	959	864	348	488	707	100	039	700	343	59
2	.257	949	891	337	515	697	127	028	727	331	58
3	284	939	918	327	542	686	153	016	753	319	57
4	311	929	945	316	569	675	180	005	780	307	56
5	339	919	973	306	595	664	207	.91994	806	295	55
6	366	909	.36000	295	622	653	234	982	833	283	54
7	393	899	027	285	649	642	260	971	860	272	53
8	421	889	054	274	676	.631	287	959	886	260	52
9	448	879	081	264	703	620	314	948	913	248	51
10	.34475	.93869	.36108	.93253	.37730	.92609	.39341	.91936	.40939	.91236	50
11	.503	859	135	243	757	598	367	925	966	224	49
12	530	849	162	232	784	587	394	914	992	212	48
13	557	839	190	222	811	576	421	902	.41019	200	47
14	584	829	217	211	838	565	448	891	045	188	46
15	612	819	244	201	865	554	474	879	072	176	45
16	639	809	271	190	892	543	501	868	098	164	44
17	666	799	298	180	919	532	528	856	125	152	43
18	694	789	325	169	946	521	555	845	151	140	42
19	721	779	352	159	973	510	581	833	178	128	41
20	.34748	.93769	.36379	.93148	.37999	.92499	.39608	.91822	.41204	.91116	40
21	775	759	406	137	.38026	488	635	810	231	104	39
22	803	748	434	127	053	477	661	799	257	092	38
23	830	738	461	116	080	466	688	787	284	080	37
24	857	728	488	106	107	455	715	775	310	068	36
25	884	718	515	095	134	444	741	764	337	056	35
26	912	708	542	084	161	432	768	752	363	044	34
27	939	698	569	074	188	421	795	741	390	032	33
28	966	688	596	063	215	410	822	729	416	020	32
29	993	677	623	052	241	399	848	718	443	008	31
30	.35021	.93667	.36650	.93042	.38268	.92388	.39875	.91706	.41469	.90996	30
31	048	657	677	031	295	377	902	694	496	984	29
32	075	647	704	020	322	366	928	683	522	972	28
33	102	637	731	010	349	355	955	671	549	960	27
34	130	626	758	.92999	376	343	982	660	575	948	26
35	157	616	785	988	403	332	.40008	648	602	936	25
36	184	606	812	978	430	321	035	636	628	924	24
37	211	596	839	967	456	310	062	625	655	911	23
38	239	585	867	956	483	299	088	613	681	899	22
39	266	575	894	945	510	287	115	601	707	887	21
40	.35293	.93565	.36921	.92935	.38537	.92276	.40141	.91590	.41734	.90875	20
41	320	555	948	924	564	265	168	578	760	863	19
42	347	544	975	913	591	254	195	566	787	851	18
43	375	534	.37002	902	617	243	221	555	813	839	17
44	402	524	029	892	644	231	248	543	840	826	16
45	429	514	056	881	671	220	275	531	866	814	15
46	456	503	083	870	698	209	301	519	892	802	14
47	484	493	110	859	725	198	328	508	919	790	13
48	511	483	137	849	752	186	355	496	945	778	12
49	538	472	164	833	778	175	381	484	972	766	11
50	.35565	.93462	.37191	.92827	.38805	.92164	.40408	.91472	.41998	.90753	10
51	592	452	218	816	832	152	434	461	.42024	741	9
52	619	441	245	805	859	141	461	449	051	729	8
53	647	431	272	794	886	130	488	437	077	717	7
54	674	420	299	784	912	119	514	425	104	704	6
55	701	410	326	773	939	107	541	414	130	692	5
56	728	400	353	762	966	096	567	402	156	680	4
57	755	390	380	751	993	035	594	390	183	668	3
58	782	379	407	740	.39020	073	621	378	209	655	2
59	810	368	434	729	046	062	647	366	235	643	1
60	.35837	.93358	.37461	.92718	.39073	.92050	.40674	.91355	.42262	.90631	0
	N.cos.	N. sine	N.cos.	N. sine	N.cos.	N. sine	N.cos.	N. sine	N.cos.	N. sine	
'	69°		68°		67°		66°		65°		'

'	20° Tang.	20° Cotg.	21° Tang.	21° Cotg.	22° Tang.	22° Cotg.	23° Tang.	23° Cotg.	24° Tang.	24° Cotg.	'
0	.3640	2.7475	.3839	2.6051	.4040	2.4751	.4245	2.3559	.4452	2.2460	60
1	43	50	42	28	44	30	48	39	56	43	59
2	46	25	45	06	47	09	52	20	59	25	58
3	50	00	49	2.5983	50	2.4689	55	01	63	08	57
4	53	2.7376	52	61	54	68	58	2.3483	66	2.2390	56
5	56	51	55	38	57	48	62	64	70	73	55
6	59	26	59	16	61	27	65	45	73	55	54
7	63	02	62	2.5893	64	06	69	26	77	38	53
8	66	2.7277	65	71	67	2.4586	72	07	80	20	52
9	69	53	69	48	71	66	76	2.3388	84	03	51
10	.3673	2.7228	.3872	2.5826	.4074	2.4545	.4279	2.3369	.4487	2.2286	50
11	76	04	75	04	78	25	83	51	91	68	49
12	79	2.7179	79	2.5782	81	04	86	32	94	51	48
13	83	55	82	59	84	2.4484	89	13	98	34	47
14	86	30	85	37	88	64	93	2.3294	.4501	16	46
15	89	06	89	15	91	43	96	76	05	2.2199	45
16	92	2.7082	92	2.5693	95	23	.4300	57	08	82	44
17	96	58	95	71	98	03	03	38	12	65	43
18	99	34	99	49	.4101	2.4383	07	20	15	48	42
19	.3702	09	.3902	27	05	62	10	01	19	30	41
20	.3706	2.6985	.3906	2.5605	.4108	2.4342	.4314	2.3183	.4522	2.2113	40
21	09	61	09	2.5583	11	22	17	64	26	2.2096	39
22	12	37	12	61	15	02	20	46	29	79	38
23	16	13	16	39	18	2.4282	24	27	33	62	37
24	19	2.6889	19	17	22	62	27	09	36	45	36
25	22	65	22	2.5495	25	42	31	2.3090	40	28	35
26	26	41	26	73	29	22	34	72	43	11	34
27	29	18	29	52	32	02	38	53	47	2.1994	33
28	32	2.6794	32	30	35	2.4182	41	35	50	77	32
29	36	70	36	08	39	62	45	17	54	60	31
30	.3739	2.6746	.3939	2.5386	.4142	2.4142	.4348	2.2998	.4557	2.1943	30
31	42	23	42	65	46	22	52	80	61	26	29
32	45	2.6699	46	43	49	02	55	62	64	09	28
33	49	75	49	22	52	2.4083	59	44	68	2.1892	27
34	52	52	53	00	56	63	62	25	71	76	26
35	55	28	56	2.5279	59	43	65	07	75	59	25
36	59	05	59	57	63	23	69	2.2889	78	42	24
37	62	2.6581	63	36	66	04	72	71	82	25	23
38	65	58	66	14	69	2.3984	76	53	85	08	22
39	69	34	69	2.5193	73	64	79	35	89	2.1792	21
40	.3772	2.6511	.3973	2.5172	.4176	2.3945	.4383	2.2817	.4592	2.1775	20
41	75	2.6488	76	50	80	25	86	2.2799	96	58	19
42	79	64	79	29	83	06	90	81	99	42	18
43	82	41	83	08	87	2.3886	93	63	.4603	25	17
44	85	18	86	2.5086	90	67	97	45	07	08	16
45	89	2.6395	90	65	93	47	.4400	27	10	2.1692	15
46	92	71	93	44	97	28	04	09	14	75	14
47	95	48	96	23	.4200	08	07	2.2691	17	59	13
48	99	25	.4000	02	04	2.3789	11	73	21	42	12
49	.3802	02	03	2.4981	07	70	14	55	24	25	11
50	.3805	2.6279	.4006	2.4960	.4210	2.3750	.4417	2.2637	.4628	2.1609	10
51	09	56	10	39	14	31	21	20	31	2.1592	9
52	12	33	13	18	17	12	24	02	35	76	8
53	15	10	17	2.4897	21	2.3693	28	2.2584	38	60	7
54	19	2.6187	20	76	24	73	31	66	42	43	6
55	22	65	23	55	28	54	35	49	45	27	5
56	25	42	27	34	31	35	38	31	49	10	4
57	29	19	30	13	34	16	42	13	52	2.1494	3
58	32	2.6096	33	2.4792	38	2.3597	45	2.2496	56	78	2
59	35	74	37	72	41	78	49	78	60	61	1
60	.3839	2.6051	.4040	2.4751	.4245	2.3559	.4452	2.2460	.4663	2.1445	0
'	Cotg.	Tang.	Cotg.	Tang.	Cotg.	Tang.	Cotg.	Tang.	Cotg.	Tang.	'
	69°		68°		67°		66°		65°		

′	25°		26°		27°		28°		29°		′
	N.sine	N. cos.	N.sine	N. cos.	N.sine	N. cos.	N.sine	N. cos.	N.sine	N. cos.	
0	.42262	.90631	.43837	.89879	.45399	.89101	.46947	.88295	.48481	.87462	60
1	288	618	863	867	425	087	973	281	506	448	59
2	315	606	889	854	451	074	999	267	532	434	58
3	341	594	916	841	477	061	.47024	254	557	420	57
4	367	582	942	828	503	048	050	240	583	406	56
5	394	569	968	816	529	035	076	226	608	391	55
6	420	557	994	803	554	021	101	213	634	377	54
7	446	545	.44020	790	580	008	127	199	659	363	53
8	473	532	046	777	606	.88995	153	185	684	349	52
9	499	520	072	764	632	981	178	172	710	335	51
10	.42525	.90507	.44098	.89752	.45658	.88968	.47204	.88158	.48735	.87321	50
11	552	495	124	739	684	955	229	144	761	306	49
12	578	483	151	726	710	942	255	130	786	292	48
13	604	470	177	713	736	928	281	117	811	278	47
14	631	458	203	700	762	915	306	103	837	264	46
15	657	446	229	687	787	902	332	089	862	250	45
16	683	433	255	674	813	888	358	075	888	235	44
17	709	421	281	662	839	875	383	062	913	221	43
18	736	408	307	649	865	862	409	048	938	207	42
19	762	396	333	636	891	848	434	034	964	193	41
20	.42788	.90383	.44359	.89623	.45917	.88835	.47460	.88020	.48989	.87178	40
21	815	371	385	610	942	822	486	006	.49014	164	39
22	841	358	411	597	968	808	511	.87993	040	150	38
23	867	346	437	584	994	795	537	979	065	136	37
24	894	334	464	571	.46020	782	562	965	090	121	36
25	920	321	490	558	046	768	588	951	116	107	35
26	946	309	516	545	072	755	614	937	141	093	34
27	972	296	542	532	097	741	639	923	166	079	33
28	999	284	568	519	123	728	665	909	192	064	32
29	.43025	271	594	506	149	715	690	896	217	050	31
30	.43051	.90259	.44620	.89493	.46175	.88701	.47716	.87882	.49242	.87036	30
31	077	246	646	480	201	688	741	868	268	021	29
32	104	233	672	467	226	674	767	854	293	007	28
33	130	221	698	454	252	661	793	840	318	.86993	27
34	156	208	724	441	278	647	818	826	344	978	26
35	182	196	750	428	304	634	844	812	369	964	25
36	209	183	776	415	330	620	869	798	394	949	24
37	235	171	802	402	355	607	895	784	419	935	23
38	261	158	828	389	381	593	920	770	445	921	22
39	287	146	854	376	407	580	946	756	470	906	21
40	.43313	.90133	.44880	.89363	.46433	.88566	.47971	.87743	.49495	.86892	20
41	340	120	906	350	458	553	997	729	521	878	19
42	366	108	932	337	484	539	.48022	715	546	863	18
43	392	095	958	324	510	526	048	701	571	849	17
44	418	082	984	311	536	512	073	687	596	834	16
45	445	070	.45010	298	561	499	099	673	622	820	15
46	471	057	036	285	587	485	124	659	647	805	14
47	497	045	062	272	613	472	150	645	672	791	13
48	523	032	088	259	639	458	175	631	697	777	12
49	549	019	114	245	664	445	201	617	723	762	11
50	.43575	.90007	.45140	.89232	.46690	.88431	.48226	.87603	.49748	.86748	10
51	602	.89994	166	219	716	417	252	589	773	733	9
52	628	981	192	206	742	404	277	575	798	719	8
53	654	968	218	193	767	390	303	561	824	704	7
54	680	956	243	180	793	377	328	546	849	690	6
55	706	943	269	167	819	363	354	532	874	675	5
56	733	930	295	153	844	349	379	518	899	661	4
57	759	918	321	140	870	336	405	504	924	646	3
58	785	905	347	127	896	322	430	490	950	632	2
59	811	892	373	114	921	308	456	476	975	617	1
60	.43837	.89879	.45399	.89101	.46947	.88295	.48481	.87462	.50000	.86603	0
	N.cos.	N. sine	N.cos.	N. sine	N.cos.	N. sine	N.cos.	N. sine	N.cos.	N. sine	
′	64°		63°		62°		61°		60°		′

′	25° Tang.	25° Cotg.	26° Tang.	26° Cotg.	27° Tang.	27° Cotg.	28° Tang.	28° Cotg.	29° Tang.	29° Cotg.	′
0	.4663	2.1445	.4877	2.0503	.5095	1.9626	.5317	1.8807	.5543	1.8040	60
1	67	29	81	2.0488	99	12	21	1.8794	47	28	59
2	70	13	85	73	.5103	1.9598	25	81	51	16	58
3	74	2.1396	88	58	06	84	28	68	55	03	57
4	77	80	92	43	10	70	32	55	58	1.7991	56
5	81	64	95	28	14	56	36	41	62	79	55
6	84	48	99	13	17	42	40	28	66	66	54
7	88	32	.4903	2.0398	21	28	43	15	70	54	53
8	91	15	06	83	25	14	47	02	74	42	52
9	95	2.1299	10	68	28	00	51	1.8689	77	30	51
10	.4699	2.1283	.4913	2.0353	.5132	1.9486	.5354	1.8676	.5581	1.7917	50
11	.4702	67	17	38	36	72	58	63	85	05	49
12	06	51	21	23	39	58	62	50	89	1.7893	48
13	09	35	24	08	43	44	66	37	93	81	47
14	13	19	28	2.0293	47	30	69	24	96	68	46
15	16	03	31	78	50	16	73	11	.5600	56	45
16	20	2.1187	35	63	54	02	77	1.8598	04	44	44
17	23	71	39	48	58	1.9388	81	85	08	32	43
18	27	55	42	33	61	75	84	72	12	20	42
19	31	39	46	19	65	61	88	59	16	08	41
20	.4734	2.1123	.4950	2.0204	.5169	1.9347	.5392	1.8546	.5619	1.7796	40
21	38	07	53	2.0189	72	33	96	33	23	83	39
22	41	2.1092	57	74	76	19	99	20	27	71	38
23	45	76	60	60	80	06	.5403	07	31	59	37
24	48	60	64	45	84	1.9292	07	1.8495	35	47	36
25	52	44	68	30	87	78	11	82	39	35	35
26	55	28	71	15	91	65	15	69	42	23	34
27	59	13	75	01	95	51	18	56	46	11	33
28	63	2.0997	79	2.0086	98	37	22	43	50	1.7699	32
29	66	81	82	72	.5202	23	26	30	54	87	31
30	.4770	2.0965	.4986	2.0057	.5206	1.9210	.5430	1.8418	.5658	1.7675	30
31	73	50	89	42	09	1.9196	33	05	62	63	29
32	77	34	93	28	13	83	37	1.8392	65	51	28
33	80	18	97	13	17	69	41	79	69	39	27
34	84	03	.5000	1.9999	20	55	45	67	73	27	26
35	88	2.0887	04	84	24	42	48	54	77	15	25
36	91	72	08	70	28	28	52	41	81	03	24
37	95	56	11	55	32	15	56	29	85	1.7591	23
38	98	40	15	41	35	01	60	16	88	79	22
39	.4802	25	19	26	39	1.9088	64	03	92	67	21
40	.4806	2.0809	.5022	1.9912	.5243	1.9074	.5467	1.8291	.5696	1.7556	20
41	09	2.0794	26	1.9897	46	61	71	78	.5700	44	19
42	13	78	29	83	50	47	75	65	04	32	18
43	16	63	33	68	54	34	79	53	08	20	17
44	20	48	37	54	58	20	82	40	12	08	16
45	23	32	40	40	61	07	86	28	15	1.7496	15
46	27	17	44	25	65	1.8993	90	15	19	85	14
47	31	01	48	11	69	80	94	02	23	73	13
48	34	2.0686	51	1.9797	72	67	98	1.8190	27	61	12
49	38	71	55	82	76	53	.5501	77	31	49	11
50	.4841	2.0655	.5059	1.9768	.5280	1.8940	.5505	1.8165	.5735	1.7437	10
51	45	40	62	54	84	27	09	52	39	26	9
52	49	25	66	40	87	13	13	40	43	14	8
53	52	09	70	25	91	00	17	27	46	02	7
54	56	2.0594	73	11	95	1.8887	20	15	50	1.7391	6
55	59	79	77	1.9697	98	73	24	03	54	79	5
56	63	64	81	83	.5302	60	28	1.8090	58	67	4
57	67	49	84	69	06	47	32	78	62	55	3
58	70	33	88	54	10	34	35	65	66	44	2
59	74	18	92	40	13	20	39	53	70	32	1
60	.4877	2.0503	.5095	1.9626	.5317	1.8807	.5543	1.8040	.5774	1.7321	0
′	Cotg.	Tang.	Cotg.	Tang.	Cotg.	Tang.	Cotg.	Tang.	Cotg.	Tang.	′
	64°		63°		62°		61°		60°		

′	30°		31°		32°		33°		34°		′
	N.sine	N. cos.	N.sine	N. cos.	N.sine	N. cos.	N.sine	N. cos.	N.sine	N. cos.	
0	50000	86603	51504	.85717	.52992	.84805	.54464	.83867	.55919	.82904	60
1	025	588	529	702	.53017	789	488	851	943	887	59
2	050	573	554	687	041	774	513	835	968	871	58
3	076	559	579	672	066	759	537	819	992	855	57
4	101	544	604	657	091	743	561	804	.56046	839	56
5	126	530	628	642	115	728	586	788	040	822	55
6	151	515	653	627	140	712	610	772	064	806	54
7	176	501	678	612	164	697	635	756	088	790	53
8	201	486	703	597	189	681	659	740	112	773	52
9	227	471	728	582	214	666	683	724	136	757	51
10	.50252	.86457	.51753	.85567	.53238	.84650	.54708	.83708	.56160	.82741	50
11	277	442	778	551	263	635	732	692	184	724	49
12	302	427	803	536	288	619	756	676	208	708	48
13	327	413	828	521	312	604	781	660	232	692	47
14	352	398	852	506	337	588	805	645	256	675	46
15	377	384	877	491	361	573	829	629	280	659	45
16	403	369	902	476	386	557	854	613	305	643	44
17	428	354	927	461	411	542	878	597	329	626	43
18	453	340	952	446	435	526	902	581	353	610	42
19	478	325	977	431	460	511	927	565	377	593	41
20	.50503	.86310	.52002	.85416	.53484	.84495	.54951	.83549	.56401	.82577	40
21	528	295	026	401	509	480	975	533	425	561	39
22	553	281	051	385	534	464	999	517	449	544	38
23	578	266	076	370	558	448	.55024	501	473	528	37
24	603	251	101	355	583	433	048	485	497	511	36
25	628	237	126	340	607	417	072	469	521	495	35
26	654	222	151	325	632	402	097	453	545	478	34
27	679	207	175	310	656	386	121	437	569	462	33
28	704	192	200	294	681	370	145	421	593	446	32
29	729	178	225	279	705	355	169	405	617	429	31
30	.50754	.86163	.52250	.85264	.53730	.84339	.55194	.83389	.56641	.82413	30
31	779	148	275	249	754	324	218	373	665	396	29
32	804	133	299	234	779	308	242	356	689	380	28
33	829	119	324	218	804	292	266	340	713	363	27
34	854	104	349	203	828	277	291	324	736	347	26
35	879	089	374	188	853	261	315	308	760	330	25
36	904	074	399	173	877	245	339	292	784	314	24
37	929	059	423	157	902	230	363	276	808	297	23
38	954	045	448	142	926	214	388	260	832	281	22
39	979	030	473	127	951	198	412	244	856	264	21
40	.51004	.86015	.52498	.85112	.53975	.84182	.55436	.83228	.56880	.82248	20
41	029	000	522	096	.54000	167	460	212	904	231	19
42	054	.85985	547	081	024	151	484	195	928	214	18
43	079	970	572	066	049	135	509	179	952	198	17
44	104	956	597	051	073	120	533	163	976	181	16
45	129	941	621	035	097	104	557	147	.57000	165	15
46	154	926	646	020	122	088	581	131	024	148	14
47	179	911	671	005	146	072	605	115	047	132	13
48	204	896	696	.84989	171	057	630	098	071	115	12
49	229	881	720	974	195	041	654	082	095	098	11
50	.51254	.85866	.52745	.84959	.54220	.84025	.55678	.83066	.57119	.82082	10
51	279	851	770	943	244	009	702	050	143	065	9
52	304	836	794	928	269	.83994	726	034	167	048	8
53	329	821	819	913	293	978	750	017	191	032	7
54	354	806	844	897	317	962	775	001	215	015	6
55	379	792	869	882	342	946	799	.82985	238	.81999	5
56	404	777	893	866	366	930	823	969	262	982	4
57	429	762	918	851	391	915	847	953	286	965	3
58	454	747	943	836	415	899	871	936	310	949	2
59	479	732	967	820	440	883	895	920	334	932	1
60	.51504	.85717	.52992	.84805	.54464	.83867	.55919	.82904	.57358	.81915	0
	N.cos.	N. sine	N.cos.	N. sine	N.cos.	N. sine	N.cos.	N. sine	N.cos.	N. sine	
′	59°		58°		57°		56°		55°		′

′	30° Tang.	30° Cotg.	31° Tang.	31° Cotg.	32° Tang.	32° Cotg.	33° Tang.	33° Cotg.	34° Tang.	34° Cotg.	′
0	.5774	1.7321	.6009	1.6643	.6249	1.6003	.6494	1.5399	.6745	1.4826	60
1	77	09	13	32	53	1.5993	98	89	49	16	59
2	81	1.7297	17	21	57	83	.6502	79	54	07	58
3	85	86	20	10	61	72	06	69	58	1.4798	57
4	89	74	24	1.6599	65	62	11	59	62	88	56
5	93	62	28	88	69	52	15	50	66	79	55
6	97	51	32	77	73	41	19	40	71	70	54
7	.5801	39	36	66	77	31	23	30	.75	61	53
8	05	28	40	55	81	21	27	20	79	51	52
9	08	16	44	45	85	11	31	11	83	42	51
10	.5812	1.7205	.6048	1.6534	.6289	1.5900	.6536	1.5301	.6787	1.4733	50
11	16	1.7193	52	23	93	1.5890	40	1.5291	92	24	49
12	20	82	56	12	97	80	44	82	96	15	48
13	24	70	60	01	.6301	69	48	72	.6800	05	47
14	28	59	64	1.6490	05	59	52	62	05	1.4696	46
15	32	47	68	79	10	49	56	53	09	87	45
16	36	36	72	69	14	39	60	43	13	78	44
17	40	24	76	58	18	29	65	33	17	69	43
18	44	13	80	47	22	18	69	24	22	1.4659	42
19	47	02	84	36	26	08	73	14	26	50	41
20	.5851	1.7090	.6088	1.6426	.6330	1.5798	.6577	1.5204	.6830	1.4641	40
21	55	79	92	15	34	88	·81	1.5195	34	32	39
22	59	67	96	04	38	78	85	85	39	23	38
23	63	56	.6100	1.6393	42	68	90	75	43	14	37
24	67	45	04	83	46	57	94	66	47	05	36
25	71	33	08	72	50	47	98	56	51	1.4596	35
26	75	22	12	61	54	37	.6602	47	56	86	34
27	79	11	16	51	58	27	06	37	60	77	33
28	83	1.6999	20	40	63	17	10	27	64	68	32
29	87	88	24	29	67	07	15	18	69	59	31
30	.5890	1.6977	.6128	1.6319	.6371	1.5697	.6619	1.5108	.6873	1.4550	30
31	94	65	32	08	75	87	23	1.5099	77	41	29
32	98	54	36	1.6297	79	77	27	89	81	32	28
33	.5902	43	40	87	83	67	31	80	86	23	27
34	06	32	44	76	87	57	36	70	90	14	26
35	10	20	48	65	91	47	40	61	94	05	25
36	14	09	52	55	95	37	44	51	99	1.4496	24
37	18	1.6898	56	44	99	27	48	42	.6903	87	23
38	22	87	60	34	.6403	17	52	32	07	78	22
39	26	75	64	23	08	07	57	23	11	69	21
40	.5930	1.6864	.6168	1.6212	.6412	1.5597	.6661	1.5013	.6916	1.4460	20
41	34	53	72	02	16	87	65	04	20	51	19
42	38	42	76	1.6191	20	77	69	1.4994	24	42	18
43	42	31	80	81	24	67	73	85	29	33	17
44	45	20	84	70	28	57	78	75	33	24	16
45	49	08	88	60	32	47	82	66	37	15	15
46	53	1.6797	92	49	36	37	86	57	42	06	14
47	57	86	96	39	40	27	90	47	46	1.4397	13
48	61	75	.6200	28	45	17	.94	38	50	88	12
49	65	64	04	18	49	07	99	28	54	79	11
50	.5969	1.6753	.6208	1.6107	.6453	1.5497	.6703	1.4919	.6959	1.4370	10
51	73	42	12	1.6097	57	87	07	10	63	61	9
52	77	31	16	87	61	77	11	00	67	52	8
53	81	20	20	76	65	68	15	1.4891	72	44	7
54	85	09	24	66	69	58	20	82	76	35	6
55	89	1.6698	28	55	73	48	24	72	80	26	5
56	93	87	33	45	78	38	28	03	85	17	4
57	97	76	37	34	82	28	32	54	89	08	3
58	.6001	65	41	24	86	18	37	44	93	1.4299	2
59	05	54	45	14	90	08	41	35	98	90	1
60	.6009	1.6643	.6249	1.6003	.6494	1.5399	.6745	1.4826	.7002	1.4281	0
	Cotg.	Tang.	Cotg.	Tang.	Cotg.	Tang.	Cotg.	Tang.	Cotg.	Tang.	
′	59°		58°		57°		56°		55°		′

′	35°		36°		37°		38°		39°		′
	N.sine	N. cos.	N.sine	N. cos.	N.sine	N. cos.	N.sine	N. cos.	N.sine	N. cos.	
0	.57358	.81915	.58779	.80902	.60182	.79864	.61566	.78801	.62932	.77715	60
1	381	899	802	885	205	846	589	783	955	696	59
2	405	882	826	867	228	829	612	765	977	678	58
3	429	865	849	850	251	811	635	747	.63000	660	57
4	453	848	873	833	274	793	658	729	022	641	56
5	477	832	896	816	298	776	681	711	045	623	55
6	501	815	920	799	321	758	704	694	068	605	54
7	524	798	943	782	344	741	726	676	090	586	53
8	548	782	967	765	367	723	749	658	113	568	52
9	572	765	990	748	390	706	772	640	135	550	51
10	57596	.81748	.59014	.80730	.60414	.79688	.61795	.78622	.63158	.77531	50
11	619	731	037	713	437	671	818	604	180	513	49
12	643	714	061	696	460	653	841	586	203	494	48
13	667	698	084	679	483	635	864	568	225	476	47
14	691	681	108	662	506	618	887	550	248	458	46
15	715	664	131	644	529	600	909	532	271	439	45
16	738	647	154	627	553	583	932	514	293	421	44
17	762	631	178	610	576	565	955	496	316	402	43
18	786	614	201	593	599	547	978	478	338	384	42
19	810	597	225	576	622	530	.62001	460	361	366	41
20	.57833	.81580	.59248	.80558	.60645	.79512	.62024	.78442	.63383	.77347	40
21	857	563	272	541	668	494	046	424	406	329	39
22	881	546	295	524	691	477	069	405	428	310	38
23	904	530	318	507	714	459	092	387	451	292	37
24	928	513	342	489	738	441	115	369	473	273	36
25	952	496	365	472	761	424	138	351	496	255	35
26	976	479	389	455	784	406	160	333	518	236	34
27	999	462	412	438	807	388	183	315	540	218	33
28	.58023	445	436	420	830	371	206	297	563	199	32
29	047	428	459	403	853	353	229	279	585	181	31
30	.58070	.81412	.59482	.80386	.60876	.79335	.62251	.78261	.63608	.77162	30
31	094	395	506	368	899	318	274	243	630	144	29
32	118	378	529	351	922	300	297	225	653	125	28
33	141	361	552	334	945	282	320	206	675	107	27
34	165	344	576	316	968	264	342	188	698	088	26
35	189	327	599	299	991	247	365	170	720	070	25
36	212	310	622	282	.61015	229	388	152	742	051	24
37	236	293	646	264	038	211	411	134	765	033	23
38	260	276	669	247	061	193	433	116	787	014	22
39	283	259	693	230	084	176	456	098	810	.76996	21
40	.58307	.81242	.59716	.80212	.61107	.79158	.62479	.78079	.63832	.76977	20
41	330	225	739	195	130	140	502	061	854	959	19
42	354	208	763	178	153	122	524	043	877	940	18
43	378	191	786	160	176	105	547	025	899	921	17
44	401	174	809	143	199	087	570	007	922	903	16
45	425	157	832	125	222	069	592	.77988	944	884	15
46	449	140	856	108	245	051	615	970	966	866	14
47	472	123	879	091	268	033	638	952	989	847	13
48	496	106	902	073	291	016	660	934	.64011	828	12
49	519	089	926	056	314	.78998	683	916	033	810	11
50	.58543	.81072	.59949	.80038	.61337	.78980	.62706	.77897	.64056	.76791	10
51	567	055	972	021	360	962	728	879	078	772	9
52	590	038	995	003	383	944	751	861	100	754	8
53	614	021	.60019	.79986	406	926	774	843	123	735	7
54	637	004	042	968	429	908	796	824	145	717	6
55	661	.80987	065	951	451	891	819	806	167	698	5
56	684	970	089	934	474	873	842	788	190	679	4
57	708	953	112	916	497	855	864	769	212	661	3
58	731	936	135	899	520	837	887	751	234	642	2
59	755	919	158	881	543	819	909	733	256	623	1
60	.58779	.80902	.60182	.79864	.61566	.78801	.62932	.77715	.64279	.76604	0
	N.cos.	N. sine	N.cos.	N. sine	N.cos.	N. sine	N.cos.	N. sine	N.cos.	N. sine	
′	54°		53°		52°		51°		50°		′

′	35°		36°		37°		38°		39°		′
	Tang.	Cotg.	Tang.	Cotg.	Tang.	Cotg.	Tang.	Cotg.	Tang.	Cotg.	
0	.7002	1.4281	.7265	1.3764	.7536	1.3270	.7813	1.2799	.8098	1.2349	60
1	06	73	70	55	40	62	18	92	.8103	42	59
2	11	64	74	47	45	54	22	84	07	34	58
3	15	55	79	39	49	46	27	76	12	27	57
4	19	46	83	30	54	38	32	69	17	20	56
5	24	37	88	22	58	30	36	61	22	12	55
6	28	29	92	13	63	22	41	53	27	05	54
7	32	20	97	05	68	14	46	46	32	1.2298	53
8	37	11	.7301	1.3697	72	06	50	38	36	90	52
9	41	02	06	88	77	1.3198	55	31	41	83	51
10	.7046	1.4193	.7310	1.3680	.7581	1.3190	.7860	1.2723	.8146	1.2276	50
11	50	85	14	72	86	82	65	15	51	68	49
12	54	76	19	63	90	75	69	08	56	61	48
13	59	67	23	55	95	67	74	00	61	54	47
14	63	58	28	47	.7600	59	79	1.2693	65	47	46
15	67	50	32	38	04	51	83	85	70	39	45
16	72	41	37	30	09	43	88	77	75	32	44
17	76	32	41	22	13	35	93	70	80	25	43
18	80	24	46	13	18	27	98	62	85	18	42
19	85	15	50	05	23	19	.7902	55	90	10	41
20	.7089	1.4106	.7355	1.3597	.7627	1.3111	.7907	1.2647	.8195	1.2203	40
21	94	1.4097	59	88	32	03	12	40	99	1.2196	39
22	98	89	64	80	36	1.3095	16	32	.8204	89	38
23	.7102	80	63	72	41	87	21	24	09	81	37
24	07	71	73	64	46	79	26	17	14	74	36
25	11	63	77	55	50	72	31	09	19	67	35
26	15	54	82	47	55	64	35	02	24	60	34
27	20	45	86	39	59	56	40	1.2594	29	53	33
28	24	37	91	31	64	48	45	87	34	45	32
29	29	23	95	22	69	40	50	79	38	38	31
30	.7133	1.4019	.7400	1.3514	.7673	1.3032	.7954	1.2572	.8243	1.2131	30
31	37	11	04	06	78	24	59	64	48	24	29
32	42	02	09	1.3498	83	17	64	57	53	17	28
33	46	1.3994	13	90	87	09	69	49	58	09	27
34	51	85	18	81	92	01	73	42	63	02	26
35	55	76	22	73	96	1.2993	78	34	68	1.2095	25
36	59	68	27	65	.7701	85	83	27	73	88	24
37	64	59	31	57	06	77	88	19	78	81	23
38	68	51	36	49	10	70	92	12	83	74	22
39	73	42	40	40	15	62	97	04	87	66	21
40	.7177	1.3934	.7445	1.3432	.7720	1.2954	.8002	1.2497	.8292	1.2059	20
41	81	25	49	24	24	46	07	89	97	52	19
42	86	16	54	16	29	38	12	82	.8302	45	18
43	90	08	58	08	34	31	16	75	07	38	17
44	95	1.3899	63	00	38	23	21	67	12	31	16
45	99	91	67	1.3392	43	15	26	60	17	24	15
46	.7203	82	72	84	47	07	31	52	22	17	14
47	08	74	76	75	52	00	35	45	27	09	13
48	12	65	81	67	57	1.2892	40	37	32	02	12
49	17	57	85	59	61	84	45	30	37	1.1995	11
50	.7221	1.3848	.7490	1.3351	.7766	1.2876	.8050	1.2423	.8342	1.1988	10
51	26	40	95	43	71	69	55	15	46	81	9
52	30	31	99	35	75	61	59	08	51	74	8
53	34	23	.7504	27	80	53	64	01	56	67	7
54	39	14	08	19	85	46	69	1.2393	61	60	6
55	43	06	13	11	89	38	74	86	66	53	5
56	48	1.3798	17	03	94	30	79	78	71	46	4
57	52	89	22	1.3295	99	22	83	71	76	39	3
58	57	81	26	87	.7803	15	88	64	81	32	2
59	61	72	31	78	07	07	93	56	86	25	1
60	.7265	1.3764	.7536	1.3270	.7813	1.2799	.8098	1.2349	.8391	1.1918	0
	Cotg.	Tang.	Cotg.	Tang.	Cotg.	Tang.	Cotg.	Tang.	Cotg.	Tang.	
′	54°		53°		52°		51°		50°		′

′	40°		41°		42°		43°		44°		′
	N.sine	N. cos.	N.sine	N. cos.	N.sine	N. cos.	N.sine	N. cos.	N.sine	N. cos.	
0	.64279	.76604	65606	.75471	66913	.74314	68200	.73135	.69466	.71934	60
1	301	586	628	452	935	295	221	116	487	914	59
2	323	567	650	433	956	276	242	096	508	894	58
3	346	548	672	414	978	256	264	076	529	873	57
4	368	530	694	395	999	237	285	056	549	853	56
5	390	511	716	375	.67021	217	306	036	570	833	55
6	412	492	738	356	043	198	327	016	591	813	54
7	435	473	759	337	064	178	349	.72996	612	792	53
8	457	455	781	318	086	159	370	976	633	772	52
9	479	436	803	299	107	139	391	957	654	752	51
10	.64501	.76417	.65825	.75280	.67129	.74120	.68412	.72937	69675	.71732	50
11	524	398	847	261	151	100	434	917	696	711	49
12	546	380	869	241	172	080	455	897	717	691	48
13	568	361	891	222	194	061	476	877	737	671	47
14	590	342	913	203	215	041	497	857	758	650	46
15	612	323	935	184	237	022	518	837	779	630	45
16	635	304	956	165	258	002	539	817	800	610	44
17	657	286	978	146	280	.73983	561	797	821	590	43
18	679	267	.66000	126	301	963	582	777	842	569	42
19	701	248	022	107	323	944	603	757	862	549	41
20	.64723	.76229	.66044	.75088	.67344	.73924	.68624	.72737	.69883	.71529	40
21	746	210	066	069	366	904	645	717	904	508	39
22	768	192	088	050	387	885	666	697	925	488	38
23	790	173	109	030	409	865	688	677	946	468	37
24	812	154	131	011	430	846	709	657	966	447	36
25	834	135	153	.74992	452	826	730	637	987	427	35
26	856	116	175	973	473	806	751	617	.70008	407	34
27	878	097	197	953	495	787	772	597	029	386	33
28	901	078	218	934	516	767	793	577	049	366	32
29	923	059	240	915	538	747	814	557	070	345	31
30	.64945	.76041	.66262	.74896	.67559	.73728	.68835	.72537	.70091	.71325	30
31	967	022	284	876	580	708	857	517	112	305	29
32	989	003	306	857	602	688	878	497	132	284	28
33	.65011	.75984	327	838	623	669	899	477	153	264	27
34	033	965	349	818	645	649	920	457	174	243	26
35	055	946	371	799	666	629	941	437	195	223	25
36	077	927	393	780	688	610	962	417	215	203	24
37	100	908	414	760	709	590	983	397	236	182	23
38	122	889	436	741	730	570	.69004	377	257	162	22
39	144	870	458	722	752	551	025	357	277	141	21
40	.65166	.75851	.66480	.74703	.67773	.73531	.69046	.72337	.70298	.71121	20
41	188	832	501	683	795	511	067	317	319	100	19
42	210	813	523	664	816	491	088	297	339	080	18
43	232	794	545	644	837	472	109	277	360	059	17
44	254	775	566	625	859	452	130	257	381	039	16
45	276	756	588	606	880	432	151	236	401	019	15
46	298	738	610	586	901	413	172	216	422	.70998	14
47	320	719	632	567	923	393	193	196	443	978	13
48	342	700	653	548	944	373	214	176	463	957	12
49	364	680	675	528	965	353	235	156	484	937	11
50	.65386	.75661	.66697	.74509	.67987	.73333	.69256	.72136	.70505	.70916	10
51	408	642	718	489	.68008	314	277	116	525	896	9
52	430	623	740	470	029	294	298	095	546	875	8
53	452	604	762	451	051	274	319	075	567	855	7
54	474	585	783	431	072	254	340	055	587	834	6
55	496	566	805	412	093	234	361	035	608	813	5
56	518	547	827	392	115	215	382	015	628	793	4
57	540	528	848	373	136	195	403	.71995	649	772	3
58	562	509	870	353	157	175	424	974	670	752	2
59	584	490	891	334	179	155	445	955	690	731	1
60	.65606	.75471	.66913	.74314	.68200	.73135	.69466	.71934	.70711	.70711	0
	N. cos.	N. sine	N.cos.	N. sine	N.cos.	N. sine	N.cos.	N. sine	N.cos.	N. sine	
′	49°		48°		47°		46°		45°		′

′	40° Tang.	40° Cotg.	41° Tang.	41° Cotg.	42° Tang.	42° Cotg.	43° Tang.	43° Cotg.	44° Tang.	44° Cotg.	′
0	.8391	1.1918	.8693	1.1504	.9004	1.1106	.9325	1.0724	.9657	1.0355	60
1	96	10	98	1.1497	09	00	31	17	63	49	59
2	.8401	03	.8703	90	15	1.1093	36	11	68	43	58
3	06	1.1896	08	83	20	87	41	05	74	37	57
4	11	89	13	77	25	80	47	1.0699	79	31	56
5	16	82	18	70	30	74	·52	92	85	25	55
6	21	75	24	63	36	67	58	86	91	19	54
7	26	68	29	56	41	61	63	80	96	13	53
8	31	61	34	50	46	54	69	74	.9702	07	52
9	36	54	39	43	52	48	74	68	08	01	51
10	.8441	1.1847	.8744	1.1436	.9057	1.1041	.9380	1.0661	.9713	1.0295	50
11	46	40	49	30	62	35	85	55	19	89	49
12	51	33	54	23	67	28	91	49	25	83	48
13	56	26	59	16	73	22	96	43	30	77	47
14	61	19	65	10	78	16	.9402	37	36	71	46
15	66	12	70	03	83	09	07	30	42	65	45
16	71	06	75	1.1396	89	03	13	24	47	59	44
17	76	1.1799	80	89	94	1.0996	18	18	53	53	43
18	81	92	85	83	99	90	24	12	59	47	42
19	86	85	90	76	.9105	83	29	06	64	41	41
20	.8491	1.1778	.8796	1.1369	.9110	1.0977	.9435	1.0599	.9770	1.0235	40
21	96	71	.8801	63	15	71	40	93	76	30	39
22	.8501	64	06	56	21	64	46	87	81	24	38
23	06	57	11	49	26	58	51	81	87	18	37
24	11	50	16	43	31	51	57	75	93	12	36
25	16	43	21	36	37	45	62	69	98	06	35
26	21	36	27	29	42	39	68	62	.9804	00	34
27	26	29	32	23	47	32	73	56	10	1.0194	33
28	31	22	37	16	53	26	79	50	16	88	32
29	36	15	42	10	58	19	84	44	21	82	31
30	.8541	1.1708	.8847	1.1303	.9163	1.0913	.9490	1.0538	.9827	1.0176	30
31	46	02	52	1.1296	69	0:	95	32	33	70	29
32	51	1.1695	58	90	74	00	.9501	26	38	64	28
33	56	88	63	83	79	1.0894	06	19	44	58	27
34	61	81	68	76	85	88	12	13	50	52	26
35	66	74	73	70	90	81	17	07	56	47	25
36	71	67	78	63	95	75	23	01	61	41	24
37	76	60	84	57	.9201	69	28	1.0495	67	35	23
38	81	53	89	50	06	62	34	89	73	29	22
39	86	47	94	43	12	56	40	83	79	23	21
40	.8591	1.1640	.8899	1.1237	.9217	1.0850	.9545	1.0477	.9884	1.0117	20
41	96	33	.8904	30	22	43	51	70	90	11	19
42	.8601	26	10	24	28	37	56	64	96	05	18
43	06	19	15	17	33	31	62	58	.9902	1.0099	17
44	11	12	20	11	39	24	67	52	07	94	16
45	17	06	25	04	44	18	73	46	13	88	15
46	22	1.1599	31	1.1197	49	12	78	40	19	82	14
47	27	92	36	91	55	05	84	34	25	76	13
48	32	85	41	84	60	1.0799	90	28	30	70	12
49	37	78	46	78	66	93	95	22	36	64	11
50	.8642	1.1571	.8952	1.1171	.9271	1.0786	.9601	1.0416	.9942	1.0058	10
51	47	65	57	65	76	80	06	10	48	52	9
52	52	58	62	58	82	74	12	04	54	47	8
53	57	51	67	52	87	68	18	1.0398	59	41	7
54	62	44	72	45	93	61	23	92	65	35	6
55	67	38	78	39	98	55	29	85	71	29	5
56	72	31	83	32	.9303	49	34	79	77	23	4
57	78	24	88	26	09	42	40	73	83	17	3
58	83	17	94	19	14	36	46	67	88	12	2
59	88	10	99	13	20	30	51	61	94	06	1
60	.8693	1.1504	.9004	1.1106	.9325	1.0724	.9657	1.0355	1.0000	1.0000	0
	Cotg.	Tang.	Cotg.	Tang.	Cotg.	Tang.	Cotg.	Tang.	Cotg.	Tang.	′
	49°		48°		47°		46°		45°		

NATURAL LOGARITHMS[1]

[1] From *Handbook of Chemistry and Physics*, 26th ed., Chemical Rubber Publishing Company.

Natural Logarithms

0.00–0.99

— 10 should be appended to each logarithm

N	.00	.01	.02	.03	.04	.05	.06	.07	.08	.09
0.0		5.39483	6.08798	6.49344	6.78112	7.00427	7.18659	7.34074	7.47427	7.59205
0.1	7.69741	7.79273	7.87974	7.95978	8.03389	8.10288	8.16742	8.22804	8.28520	8.33927
0.2	8.39056	8.43935	8.48587	8.53032	8.57288	8.61371	8.65293	8.69067	8.72703	8.76213
0.3	8.79603	8.82882	8.86057	8.89134	8.92119	8.95018	8.97835	9.00575	9.03242	9.05839
0.4	9.08371	9.10840	9.13250	9.15603	9.17902	9.20149	9.22347	9.24498	9.26603	9.28665
0.5	9.30685	9.32666	9.34607	9.36512	9.38381	9.40216	9.42018	9.43788	9.45527	9.47237
0.6	9.48917	9.50570	9.52196	9.53796	9.55371	9.56922	9.58448	9.59952	9.61434	9.62894
0.7	9.64333	9.65751	9.67150	9.68529	9.69889	9.71232	9.72556	9.73864	9.75154	9.76428
0.8	9.77686	9.78928	9.80155	9.81367	9.82565	9.83748	9.84918	9.86074	9.87217	9.88347
0.9	9.89464	9.90569	9.91662	9.92743	9.93812	9.94871	9.95918	9.96954	9.97980	9.98995

1.00–10.09

N	.00	.01	.02	.03	.04	.05	.06	.07	.08	.09
1.0	0.0 0000	0995	1980	2956	3922	4879	5827	6766	7696	8618
1.1	9531	*0436	*1333	*2222	*3103	*3976	*4842	*5700	*6551	*7395
1.2	0.1 8232	9062	9885	*0701	*1511	*2314	*3111	*3902	*4686	*5464
1.3	0.2 6236	7003	7763	8518	9267	*0010	*0748	*1481	*2208	*2930
1.4	0.3 3647	4359	5066	5767	6464	7156	7844	8526	9204	9878
1.5	0.4 0547	1211	1871	2527	3178	3825	4469	5108	5742	6373
1.6	7000	7623	8243	8858	9470	*0078	*0682	*1282	*1879	*2473
1.7	0.5 3063	3649	4232	4812	5389	5962	6531	7098	7661	8222
1.8	8779	9333	9884	*0432	*0977	*1519	*2058	*2594	*3127	*3658
1.9	0.6 4185	4710	5233	5752	6269	6783	7294	7803	8310	8813
2.0	9315	9813	*0310	*0804	*1295	*1784	*2271	*2755	*3237	*3716
2.1	0.7 4194	4669	5142	5612	6081	6547	7011	7473	7932	8390
2.2	8846	9299	9751	*0200	*0648	*1093	*1536	*1978	*2418	*2855
2.3	0.8 3291	3725	4157	4587	5015	5442	5866	6289	6710	7129
2.4	7547	7963	8377	8789	9200	9609	*0016	*0422	*0826	*1228
2.5	0.9 1629	2028	2426	2822	3216	3609	4001	4391	4779	5166
2.6	5551	5935	6317	6698	7078	7456	7833	8208	8582	8954
2.7	9325	9695	*0063	*0430	*0796	*1160	*1523	*1885	*2245	*2604
2.8	1 0 2962	3318	3674	4028	4380	4732	5082	5431	5779	6126
2.9	6471	6815	7158	7500	7841	8181	8519	8856	9192	9527
3.0	9861	*0194	*0526	*0856	*1186	*1514	*1841	*2168	*2493	*2817
3.1	1.1 3140	3462	3783	4103	4422	4740	5057	5373	5688	6002
3.2	6315	6627	6938	7248	7557	7865	8173	8479	8784	9089
3.3	9392	9695	9996	*0297	*0597	*0896	*1194	*1491	*1788	*2083
3.4	1.2 2378	2671	2964	3256	3547	3837	4127	4415	4703	4990
3.5	5276	5562	5846	6130	6413	6695	6976	7257	7536	7815
3.6	8093	8371	8647	8923	9198	9473	9746	*0019	*0291	*0563
3.7	1.3 0833	1103	1372	1641	1909	2176	2442	2708	2972	3237
3.8	3500	3763	4025	4286	4547	4807	5067	5325	5584	5841
3.9	6098	6354	6609	6864	7118	7372	7624	7877	8128	8379
4.0	8629	8879	9128	9377	9624	9872	*0118	*0364	*0610	*0854
4.1	1.4 1099	1342	1585	1828	2070	2311	2552	2792	3031	3270
4.2	3508	3746	3984	4220	4456	4692	4927	5161	5395	5629
4.3	5862	6094	6326	6557	6787	7018	7247	7476	7705	7933
4.4	8160	8387	8614	8840	9065	9290	9515	9739	9962	*0185
4.5	1.5 0408	0630	0851	1072	1293	1513	1732	1951	2170	2388
4.6	2606	2823	3039	3256	3471	3687	3902	4116	4330	4543
4.7	4756	4969	5181	5393	5604	5814	6025	6235	6444	6653
4.8	6862	7070	7277	7485	7691	7898	8104	8309	8515	8719
4.9	8924	9127	9331	9534	9737	9939	*0141	*0342	*0543	*0744
5.0	1.6 0944	1144	1343	1542	1741	1939	2137	2334	2531	2728
5.1	2924	3120	3315	3511	3705	3900	4094	4287	4481	4673
5.2	4866	5058	5250	5441	5632	5823	6013	6203	6393	6582
5.3	6771	6959	7147	7335	7523	7710	7896	8083	8269	8455
5.4	8640	8825	9010	9194	9378	9562	9745	9928	*0111	*0293

1.00–10.09 (Concluded)

N	.00	.01	.02	.03	.04	.05	.06	.07	.08	.09
5.5	1.7 0475	0656	0838	1019	1199	1380	1560	1740	1919	2098
5.6	2277	2455	2633	2811	2988	3166	3342	3519	3695	3871
5.7	4047	4222	4397	4572	4746	4920	5094	5267	5440	5613
5.8	5786	5958	6130	6302	6473	6644	6815	6985	7156	7326
5.9	7495	7665	7834	8002	8171	8339	8507	8675	8842	9009
6.0	9176	9342	9509	9675	9840	*0006	*0171	*0336	*0500	*0665
6.1	1.8 0829	0993	1156	1319	1482	1645	1808	1970	2132	2294
6.2	2455	2616	2777	2938	3098	3258	3418	3578	3737	3896
6.3	4055	4214	4372	4530	4688	4845	5003	5160	5317	5473
6.4	5630	5786	5942	6097	6253	6408	6563	6718	6872	7026
6.5	7180	7334	7487	7641	7794	7947	8099	8251	8403	8555
6.6	8707	8858	9010	9160	9311	9462	9612	9762	9912	*0061
6.7	1.9 0211	0360	0509	0658	0806	0954	1102	1250	1398	1545
6.8	1692	1839	1986	2132	2279	2425	2571	2716	2862	3007
6.9	3152	3297	3442	3586	3730	3874	4018	4162	4305	4448
7.0	4591	4734	4876	5019	5161	5303	5445	5586	5727	5869
7.1	6009	6150	6291	6431	6571	6711	6851	6991	7130	7269
7.2	7408	7547	7685	7824	7962	8100	8238	8376	8513	8650
7.3	8787	8924	9061	9198	9334	9470	9606	9742	9877	*0013
7.4	2.0 0148	0283	0418	0553	0687	0821	0956	1089	1223	1357
7.5	1490	1624	1757	1890	2022	2155	2287	2419	2551	2683
7.6	2815	2946	3078	3209	3340	3471	3601	3732	3862	3992
7.7	4122	4252	4381	4511	4640	4769	4898	5027	5156	5284
7.8	5412	5540	5668	5796	5924	6051	6179	6306	6433	6560
7.9	6686	6813	6939	7065	7191	7317	7443	7568	7694	7819
8.0	7944	8069	8194	8318	8443	8567	8691	8815	8939	9063
8.1	9186	9310	9433	9556	9679	9802	9924	*0047	*0169	*0291
8.2	2.1 0413	0535	0657	0779	0900	1021	1142	1263	1384	1505
8.3	1626	1746	1866	1986	2106	2226	2346	2465	2585	2704
8.4	2823	2942	3061	3180	3298	3417	3535	3653	3771	3889
8.5	4007	4124	4242	4359	4476	4593	4710	4827	4943	5060
8.6	5176	5292	5409	5524	5640	5756	5871	5987	6102	6217
8.7	6332	6447	6562	6677	6791	6905	7020	7134	7248	7361
8.8	7475	7589	7702	7816	7929	8042	8155	8267	8380	8493
8.9	8605	8717	8830	8942	9054	9165	9277	9389	9500	9611
9.0	9722	9834	9944	*0055	*0166	*0276	*0387	*0497	*0607	*0717
9.1	2.2 0827	0937	1047	1157	1266	1375	1485	1594	1703	1812
9.2	1920	2029	2138	2246	2354	2462	2570	2678	2786	2894
9.3	3001	3109	3216	3324	3431	3538	3645	3751	3858	3965
9.4	4071	4177	4284	4390	4496	4601	4707	4813	4918	5024
9.5	5129	5234	5339	5444	5549	5654	5759	5863	5968	6072
9.6	6176	6280	6384	6488	6592	6696	6799	6903	7006	7109
9.7	7213	7316	7419	7521	7624	7727	7829	7932	8034	8136
9.8	8238	8340	8442	8544	8646	8747	8849	8950	9051	9152
9.9	925?	9354	9455	9556	9657	9757	9858	9958	*0058	*0158
10.0	2.3 0259	0358	0458	0558	0658	0757	0857	0956	1055	1154

10–99

N	0	1	2	3	4	5	6	7	8	9
1	2.30259	39790	48491	56495	63906	70805	77259	83321	89037	94444
2	99573	*04452	*09104	*13549	*17805	*21888	*25810	*29584	*33220	*36730
3	3.40120	43399	46574	49651	52636	55535	58352	61092	63759	66356
4	68888	71357	73767	76120	78419	80666	82864	85015	87120	89182
5	91202	93183	95124	97029	98898	*00733	*02535	*04305	*06044	*07754
6	4.09434	11087	12713	14313	15888	17439	18965	20469	21951	23411
7	24850	26268	27667	29046	30407	31749	33073	34381	35671	36945
8	38203	39445	40672	41884	43082	44265	45435	46591	47734	48864
9	49981	51086	52179	53260	54329	55388	56435	57471	58497	59512

Natural Logarithms

100–1109

N	0	1	2	3	4	5	6	7	8	9
10	4.6 0517	1512	2497	3473	4439	5396	6344	7283	8213	9135
11	4.7 0048	0953	1850	2739	3620	4493	5359	6217	7068	7912
12	8749	9579	*0402	*1218	*2028	*2831	*3628	*4419	*5203	*5981
13	4.8 6753	7520	8280	9035	9784	*0527	*1265	*1998	*2725	*3447
14	4.9 4164	4876	5583	6284	6981	7673	8361	9043	9721	*0395
15	5.0 1064	1728	2388	3044	3695	4343	4986	5625	6260	6890
16	7517	8140	8760	9375	9987	*0595	*1199	*1799	*2396	*2990
17	5.1 3580	4166	4749	5329	5906	6479	7048	7615	8178	8739
18	9296	9850	*0401	*0949	*1494	*2036	*2575	*3111	*3644	*4175
19	5.2 4702	5227	5750	6269	6786	7300	7811	8320	8827	9330
20	9832	*0330	*0827	*1321	*1812	*2301	*2788	*3272	*3754	*4233
21	5.3 4711	5186	5659	6129	6598	7064	7528	7990	8450	8907
22	9363	9816	*0268	*0717	*1165	*1610	*2053	*2495	*2935	*3372
23	5.4 3808	4242	4674	5104	5532	5959	6383	6806	7227	7646
24	8064	8480	8894	9306	9717	*0126	*0533	*0939	*1343	*1745
25	5.5 2146	2545	2943	3339	3733	4126	4518	4908	5296	5683
26	6068	6452	6834	7215	7595	7973	8350	8725	9099	9471
27	9842	*0212	*0580	*0947	*1313	*1677	*2040	*2402	*2762	*3121
28	5.6 3479	3835	4191	4545	4897	5249	5599	5948	6296	6643
29	6988	7332	7675	8017	8358	8698	9036	9373	9709	*0044
30	5.7 0378	0711	1043	1373	1703	2031	2359	2685	3010	3334
31	3657	3979	4300	4620	4939	5257	5574	5890	6205	6519
32	6832	7144	7455	7765	8074	8383	8690	8996	9301	9606
33	9909	*0212	*0513	*0814	*1114	*1413	*1711	*2008	*2305	*2600
34	5.8 2895	3188	3481	3773	4064	4354	4644	4932	5220	5507
35	5793	6079	6363	6647	6930	7212	7493	7774	8053	8332
36	8610	8888	9164	9440	9715	9990	*0263	*0536	*0808	*1080
37	5.9 1350	1620	1889	2158	2426	2693	2959	3225	3489	3754
38	4017	4280	4542	4803	5064	5324	5584	5842	6101	6358
39	6615	6871	7126	7381	7635	7889	8141	8394	8645	8896
40	9146	9396	9645	9894	*0141	*0389	*0635	*0881	*1127	*1372
41	6.0 1616	1859	2102	2345	2587	2828	3069	3309	3548	3787
42	4025	4263	4501	4737	4973	5209	5444	5678	5912	6146
43	6379	6611	6843	7074	7304	7535	7764	7993	8222	8450
44	8677	8904	9131	9357	9582	9807	*0032	*0256	*0479	*0702
45	6.1 0925	1147	1368	1589	1810	2030	2249	2468	2687	2905
46	3123	3340	3556	3773	3988	4204	4419	4633	4847	5060
47	5273	5486	5698	5910	6121	6331	6542	6752	6961	7170
48	7379	7587	7794	8002	8208	8415	8621	8826	9032	9236
49	9441	9644	.9848	*0051	*0254	*0456	*0658	*0859	*1060	*1261
50	6.2 1461	1661	1860	2059	2258	2456	2654	2851	3048	3245
51	3441	3637	3832	4028	4222	4417	4611	4804	4998	5190
52	5383	5575	5767	5958	6149	6340	6530	6720	6910	7099
53	7288	7476	7664	7852	8040	8227	8413	8600	8786	8972
54	9157	9342	9527	9711	9895	*0079	*0262	*0445	*0628	*0810
55	6.3 0992	1173	1355	1536	1716	1897	2077	2257	2436	2615
56	2794	.2972	3150	3328	3505	3683	3859	4036	4212	4388
57	4564	4739	4914	5089	5263	5437	5611	5784	5957	6130
58	6303	6475	6647	6819	6990	7161	7332	7502	7673	7843
59	8012	8182	8351	8519	8688	8856	9024	9192	9359	9526
60	9693	9859	*0026	*0192	*0357	*0523	*0688	*0853	*1017	*1182
N	0	1	2	3	4	5	6	7	8	9

100–1109 (Concluded)

N	0	1	2	3	4	5	6	7	8	9
60	6.3 9693	9859	*0026	*0192	*0357	*0523	*0688	*0853	*1017	*1182
61	6.4 1346	1510	1673	1836	1999	2162	2325	2487	2649	2811
62	2972	3133	3294	3455	3615	3775	3935	4095	4254	4413
63	4572	4731	4889	5047	5205	5362	5520	5677	5834	5990
64	6147	6303	6459	6614	6770	6925	7080	7235	7389	7543
65	7697	7851	8004	8158	8311	8464	8616	8768	8920	9072
66	9224	9375	9527	9677	9828	9979	*0129	*0279	*0429	*0578
67	6.5 0728	0877	1026	1175	1323	1471	1619	1767	1915	2062
68	2209	2356	2503	2649	2796	2942	3088	3233	3379	3524
69	3669	3814	3959	4103	4247	4391	4535	4679	4822	4965
70	5108	5251	5393	5536	5678	5820	5962	6103	6244	6386
71	6526	6667	6808	6948	7088	7228	7368	7508	7647	7786
72	7925	8064	8203	8341	8479	8617	8755	8893	9030	9167
73	9304	9441	9578	9715	9851	9987	*0123	*0259	*0394	*0530
74	6.6 0665	0800	0935	1070	1204	1338	1473	1607	1740	1874
75	2007	2141	2274	2407	2539	2672	2804	2936	3068	3200
76	3332	3463	3595	3726	3857	3988	4118	4249	4379	4509
77	4639	4769	4898	5028	5157	5286	5415	5544	5673	5801
78	5929	6058	6185	6313	6441	6568	6696	6823	6950	7077
79	7203	7330	7456	7582	7708	7834	7960	8085	8211	8336
80	8461	8586	8711	8835	8960	9084	9208	9332	9456	9580
81	9703	9827	9950	*0073	*0196	*0319	*0441	*0564	*0686	*0808
82	6.7 0930	1052	1174	1296	1417	1538	1659	1780	1901	2022
83	2143	2263	2383	2503	2623	2743	2863	2982	3102	3221
84	3340	3459	3578	3697	3815	3934	4052	4170	4288	4406
85	4524	4641	4759	4876	4993	5110	5227	5344	5460	5577
86	5693	5809	5926	6041	6157	6273	6388	6504	6619	6734
87	6849	6964	7079	7194	7308	7422	7537	7651	7765	7878
88	7992	8106	8219	8333	8446	8559	8672	8784	8897	9010
89	9122	9234	9347	9459	9571	9682	9794	9906	*0017	*0128
90	6.8 0239	0351	0461	0572	0683	0793	0904	1014	1124	1235
91	1344	1454	1564	1674	1783	1892	2002	2111	2220	2329
92	2437	2546	2655	2763	2871	2979	3087	3195	3303	3411
93	3518	3626	3733	3841	3948	4055	4162	4268	4375	4482
94	4588	4694	4801	4907	5013	5118	5224	5330	5435	5541
95	5646	5751	5857	5961	6066	6171	6276	6380	6485	6589
96	6693	6797	6901	7005	7109	7213	7316	7420	7523	7626
97	7730	7833	7936	8038	8141	8244	8346	8449	8551	8653
98	8755	8857	8959	9061	9163	9264	9366	9467	9568	9669
99	9770	9871	9972	*0073	*0174	*0274	*0375	*0475	*0575	*0675
100	6.9 0776	0875	0975	1075	1175	1274	1374	1473	1572	1672
101	1771	1870	1968	2067	2166	2264	2363	2461	2560	2658
102	2756	2854	2952	3049	3147	3245	3342	3440	3537	3634
103	3731	3828	3925	4022	4119	4216	4312	4409	4505	4601
104	4698	4794	4890	4986	5081	5177	5273	5368	5464	5559
105	5655	5750	5845	5940	6035	6130	6224	6319	6414	6508
106	6602	6697	6791	6885	6979	7073	7167	7261	7354	7448
107	7541	7635	7728	7821	7915	8008	8101	8193	8286	8379
108	8472	8564	8657	8749	8841	8934	9026	9118	9210	9302
109	9393	9485	9577	9668	9760	9851	9942	*0033	*0125	*0216
110	7.0 0307	0397	0488	0579	0670	0760	0851	0941	1031	1121
N	0	1	2	3	4	5	6	7	8	9

CONVERSION
OF DEGREES TO RADIANS[1]

---

[1] From *Handbook of Chemistry and Physics*, 26th ed., Chemical Rubber Publishing Company.

Deg.	Radians	Deg.	Radians	Deg.	Radians	Deg.	Radians
0	0.00000	60	1.04720	120	2.09440	180	3.14159
1	0.01745	61	1.06465	121	2.11185	185	3.22886
2	0.03491	62	1.08210	122	2.12930	190	3.31613
3	0.05236	63	1.09956	123	2.14675	195	3.40339
4	0.06981	64	1.11701	124	2.16421	200	3.49066
5	0.08727	65	1.13446	125	2.18166	205	3.57792
6	0.10472	66	1.15192	126	2.19911	210	3.66519
7	0.12217	67	1.16937	127	2.21657	215	3.75246
8	0.13963	68	1.18682	128	2.23402	220	3.83972
9	0.15708	69	1.20428	129	2.25147	225	3.92699
10	0.17453	70	1.22173	130	2.26893	230	4.01426
11	0.19199	71	1.23918	131	2.28638	235	4.10152
12	0.20944	72	1.25664	132	2.30383	240	4.18879
13	0.22689	73	1.27409	133	2.32129	245	4.27606
14	0.24435	74	1.29154	134	2.33874	250	4.36332
15	0.26180	75	1.30900	135	2.35619	255	4.45059
16	0.27925	76	1.32645	136	2.37365	260	4.53786
17	0.29671	77	1.34390	137	2.39110	265	4.62512
18	0.31416	78	1.36136	138	2.40855	270	4.71239
19	0.33161	79	1.37881	139	2.42601	275	4.79966
20	0.34907	80	1.39626	140	2.44346	280	4.88692
21	0.36652	81	1.41372	141	2.46091	285	4.97419
22	0.38397	82	1.43117	142	2.47837	290	5.06145
23	0.40143	83	1.44862	143	2.49582	295	5.14872
24	0.41888	84	1.46608	144	2.51327	300	5.23599
25	0.43633	85	1.48353	145	2.53073	305	5.32325
26	0.45379	86	1.50098	146	2.54818	310	5.41052
27	0.47124	87	1.51844	147	2.56563	315	5.49779
28	0.48869	88	1.53589	148	2.58309	320	5.58505
29	0.50615	89	1.55334	149	2.60054	325	5.67232
30	0.52360	90	1.57080	150	2.61799	330	5.75959
31	0.54105	91	1.58825	151	2.63545	335	5.84685
32	0.55851	92	1.60570	152	2.65290	340	5.93412
33	0.57596	93	1.62316	153	2.67035	345	6.02139
34	0.59341	94	1.64061	154	2.68781	350	6.10865
35	0.61087	95	1.65806	155	2.70526	355	6.19592
36	0.62832	96	1.67552	156	2.72271	360	6.28319
37	0.64577	97	1.69297	157	2.74017	365	6.37045
38	0.66323	98	1.71042	158	2.75762	370	6.45772
39	0.68068	99	1.72788	159	2.77507	375	6.54498
40	0.69813	100	1.74533	160	2.79253	380	6.63225
41	0.71558	101	1.76278	161	2.80998	385	6.71952
42	0.73304	102	1.78024	162	2.82743	390	6.80678
43	0.75049	103	1.79769	163	2.84489	395	6.89405
44	0.76794	104	1.81514	164	2.86234	400	6.98132
45	0.78540	105	1.83260	165	2.87979	405	7.06858
46	0.80285	106	1.85005	166	2.89725	410	7.15585
47	0.82030	107	1.86750	167	2.91470	415	7.24312
48	0.83776	108	1.88496	168	2.93215	420	7.33038
49	0.85521	109	1.90241	169	2.94961	425	7.41765
50	0.87266	110	1.91986	170	2.96706	430	7.50492
51	0.89012	111	1.93732	171	2.98451	435	7.59218
52	0.90757	112	1.95477	172	3.00197	440	7.67945
53	0.92502	113	1.97222	173	3.01942	445	7.76672
54	0.94248	114	1.98968	174	3.03687	450	7.85398
55	0.95993	115	2.00713	175	3.05433	455	7.94125
56	0.97738	116	2.02458	176	3.07178	460	8.02851
57	0.99484	117	2.04204	177	3.08923	465	8.11578
58	1.01229	118	2.05949	178	3.10669	470	8.20305
59	1.02974	119	2.07694	179	3.12414	475	8.29031

Min.	Radians	Sec.	Radians
0	0.00000	0	0.00000
1	0.00029	1	0.00000
2	0.00058	2	0.00001
3	0.00087	3	0.00001
4	0.00116	4	0.00002
5	0.00145	5	0.00002
6	0.00175	6	0.00003
7	0.00204	7	0.00003
8	0.00233	8	0.00004
9	0.00262	9	0.00004
10	0.00291	10	0.00005
11	0.00320	11	0.00005
12	0.00349	12	0.00006
13	0.00378	13	0.00006
14	0.00407	14	0.00007
15	0.00436	15	0.00007
16	0.00465	16	0.00008
17	0.00495	17	0.00008
18	0.00524	18	0.00009
19	0.00553	19	0.00009
20	0.00582	20	0.00010
21	0.00611	21	0.00010
22	0.00640	22	0.00011
23	0.00669	23	0.00011
24	0.00698	24	0.00012
25	0.00727	25	0.00012
26	0.00756	26	0.00013
27	0.00785	27	0.00013
28	0.00814	28	0.00014
29	0.00844	29	0.00014
30	0.00873	30	0.00015
31	0.00902	31	0.00015
32	0.00931	32	0.00016
33	0.00960	33	0.00016
34	0.00989	34	0.00016
35	0.01018	35	0.00017
36	0.01047	36	0.00017
37	0.01076	37	0.00018
38	0.01105	38	0.00018
39	0.01134	39	0.00019
40	0.01164	40	0.00019
41	0.01193	41	0.00020
42	0.01222	42	0.00020
43	0.01251	43	0.00021
44	0.01280	44	0.00021
45	0.01309	45	0.00022
46	0.01338	46	0.00022
47	0.01367	47	0.00023
48	0.01396	48	0.00023
49	0.01425	49	0.00024
50	0.01454	50	0.00024
51	0.01484	51	0.00025
52	0.01513	52	0.00025
53	0.01542	53	0.00026
54	0.01571	54	0.00026
55	0.01600	55	0.00027
56	0.01629	56	0.00027
57	0.01658	57	0.00028
58	0.01687	58	0.00028
59	0.01716	59	0.00029
60	0.01745	60	0.00029

	Radians	Tenths	Hundredths	Thousandths	Ten-Thousandths
1	57°17'44.8"	5°43'46.5"	0°34'22.6"	0°03'26.3"	0°0'20.6"
2	114°35'29.6"	11°27'33.0"	1°08'45.3"	0°06'52.5"	0°0'41.3"
3	171°53'14.4"	17°11'19.4"	1°43'07.9"	0°10'18.8"	0°1'01.9"
4	229°10'59.2"	22°55'05.9"	2°17'30.6"	0°13'45.1"	0°1'22.5"
5	286°28'44.0"	28°38'52.4"	2°51'53.2"	0°17'11.3"	0°1'43.1"
6	343°46'28.8"	34°22'38.9"	3°26'15.9"	0°20'37.6"	0°2'03.8"
7	401°04'13.6"	40°06'25.4"	4°00'38.5"	0°24'03.9"	0°2'24.4"
8	458°21'58.4"	45°50'11.8"	4°35'01.2"	0°27'30.1"	0°2'45.0"
9	515°39'43.3"	51°33'58.3"	5°09'23.8"	0°30'56.4"	0°3'05.6"

SQUARES, CUBES, SQUARE ROOTS, AND CUBE ROOTS

n	n^2	n^3	$\sqrt{n}$	$\sqrt{10\,n}$	$\sqrt[3]{n}$	$\sqrt[3]{10\,n}$	$\sqrt[3]{100\,n}$
1	1	1	1.000 000	3.162 278	1.000 000	2.154 435	4.641 589
2	4	8	1.414 214	4.472 136	1.259 921	2.714 418	5.848 035
3	9	27	1.732 051	5.477 226	1.442 250	3.107 233	6.694 330
4	16	64	2.000 000	6.324 555	1.587 401	3.419 952	7.368 063
5	25	125	2.236 068	7.071 068	1.709 976	3.684 031	7.937 005
6	36	216	2.449 490	7.745 967	1.817 121	3.914 868	8.434 327
7	49	343	2.645 751	8.366 600	1.912 931	4.121 285	8.879 040
8	64	512	2.828 427	8.944 272	2.000 000	4.308 869	9.283 178
9	81	729	3.000 000	9.486 833	2.080 084	4.481 405	9.654 894
10	100	1 000	3.162 278	10.000 00	2.154 435	4.641 589	10.000 00
11	121	1 331	3.316 625	10.488 09	2.223 980	4.791 420	10.322 80
12	144	1 728	3.464 102	10.954 45	2.289 428	4.932 424	10.626 59
13	169	2 197	3.605 551	11.401 75	2.351 335	5.065 797	10.913 93
14	196	2 744	3.741 657	11.832 16	2.410 142	5.192 494	11.186 89
15	225	3 375	3.872 983	12.247 45	2.466 212	5.313 293	11.447 14
16	256	4 096	4.000 000	12.649 11	2.519 842	5.428 835	11.696 07
17	289	4 913	4.123 106	13.038 40	2.571 282	5.539 658	11.934 83
18	324	5 832	4.242 641	13.416 41	2.620 741	5.646 216	12.164 40
19	361	6 859	4.358 899	13.784 05	2.668 402	5.748 897	12.385 62
20	400	8 000	4.472 136	14.142 14	2.714 418	5.848 035	12.599 21
21	441	9 261	4.582 576	14.491 38	2.758 924	5.943 922	12.805 79
22	484	10 648	4.690 416	14.832 40	2.802 039	6.036 811	13.005 91
23	529	12 167	4.795 832	15.165 75	2.843 867	6.126 926	13.200 06
24	576	13 824	4.898 979	15.491 93	2.884 499	6.214 465	13.388 66
25	625	15 625	5.000 000	15.811 39	2.924 018	6.299 605	13.572 09
26	676	17 576	5.099 020	16.124 52	2.962 496	6.382 504	13.750 69
27	729	19 683	5.196 152	16.431 68	3.000 000	6.463 304	13.924 77
28	784	21 952	5.291 503	16.733 20	3.036 589	6.542 133	14.094 60
29	841	24 389	5.385 165	17.029 39	3.072 317	6.619 106	14.260 43
30	900	27 000	5.477 226	17.320 51	3.107 233	6.694 330	14.422 50
31	961	29 791	5.567 764	17.606 82	3.141 381	6.767 899	14.581 00
32	1 024	32 768	5.656 854	17.888 54	3.174 802	6.839 904	14.736 13
33	1 089	35 937	5.744 563	18.165 90	3.207 534	6.910 423	14.888 06
34	1 156	39 304	5.830 952	18.439 09	3.239 612	6.979 532	15.036 95
35	1 225	42 875	5.916 080	18.708 29	3.271 066	7.047 299	15.182 94
36	1 296	46 656	6.000 000	18.973 67	3.301 927	7.113 787	15.326 19
37	1 369	50 653	6.082 763	19.235 38	3.332 222	7.179 054	15.466 80
38	1 444	54 872	6.164 414	19.493 59	3.361 975	7.243 156	15.604 91
39	1 521	59 319	6.244 998	19.748 42	3.391 211	7.306 144	15.740 61
40	1 600	64 000	6.324 555	20.000 00	3.419 952	7.368 063	15.874 01
41	1 681	68 921	6.403 124	20.248 46	3.448 217	7.428 959	16.005 21
42	1 764	74 088	6.480 741	20.493 90	3.476 027	7.488 872	16.134 29
43	1 849	79 507	6.557 439	20.736 44	3.503 398	7.547 842	16.261 33
44	1 936	85 184	6.633 250	20.976 18	3.530 348	7.605 905	16.386 43
45	2 025	91 125	6.708 204	21.213 20	3.556 893	7.663 094	16.509 64
46	2 116	97 336	6.782 330	21.447 61	3.583 048	7.719 443	16.631 03
47	2 209	103 823	6.855 655	21.679 48	3.608 826	7.774 980	16.750 69
48	2 304	110 592	6.928 203	21.908 90	3.634 241	7.829 735	16.868 65
49	2 401	117 649	7.000 000	22.135 94	3.659 306	7.883 735	16.984 99
50	2 500	125 000	7.071 068	22.360 68	3.684 031	7.937 005	17.099 76
51	2 601	132 651	7.141 428	22.583 18	3.708 430	7.989 570	17.213 01
52	2 704	140 608	7.211 103	22.803 51	3.732 511	8.041 452	17.324 78
53	2 809	148 877	7.280 110	23.021 73	3.756 286	8.092 672	17.435 13
54	2 916	157 464	7.348 469	23.237 90	3.779 763	8.143 253	17.544 11
55	3 025	166 375	7.416 198	23.452 08	3.802 952	8.193 213	17.651 74
56	3 136	175 616	7.483 315	23.664 32	3.825 862	8.242 571	17.758 08
57	3 249	185 193	7.549 834	23.874 67	3.848 501	8.291 344	17.863 16
58	3 364	195 112	7.615 773	24.083 19	3.870 877	8.339 551	17.967 02
59	3 481	205 379	7.681 146	24.289 92	3.892 996	8.387 207	18.069 69
60	3 600	216 000	7.745 967	24.494 90	3.914 868	8.434 327	18.171 21

n	n^2	n^3	$\sqrt{n}$	$\sqrt{10\,n}$	$\sqrt[3]{n}$	$\sqrt[3]{10\,n}$	$\sqrt[3]{100\,n}$
61	3 721	226 981	7.810 250	24.698 18	3.936 497	8.480 926	18.271 60
62	3 844	238 328	7.874 008	24.899 80	3.957 892	8.527 019	18.370 91
63	3 969	250 047	7.937 254	25.099 80	3.979 057	8.572 619	18.469 15
64	4 096	262 144	8.000 000	25.298 22	4.000 000	8.617 739	18.566 36
65	4 225	274 625	8.062 258	25.495 10	4.020 726	8.662 391	18.662 56
66	4 356	287 496	8.124 038	25.690 47	4.041 240	8.706 588	18.757 77
67	4 489	300 763	8.185 353	25.884 36	4.061 548	8.750 340	18.852 04
68	4 624	314 432	8.246 211	26.076 81	4.081 655	8.793 659	18.945 36
69	4 761	328 509	8.306 624	26.267 85	4.101 566	8.836 556	19.037 78
70	4 900	343 000	8.366 600	26.457 51	4.121 285	8.879 040	19.129 31
71	5 041	357 911	8.426 150	26.645 83	4.140 818	8.921 121	19.219 97
72	5 184	373 248	8.485 281	26.832 82	4.160 168	8.962 809	19.309 79
73	5 329	389 017	8.544 004	27.018 51	4.179 339	9.004 113	19.398 77
74	5 476	405 224	8.602 325	27.202 94	4.198 336	9.045 042	19.486 95
75	5 625	421 875	8.660 254	27.386 13	4.217 163	9.085 603	19.574 34
76	5 776	438 976	8.717 798	27.568 10	4.235 824	9.125 805	19.660 95
77	5 929	456 533	8.774 964	27.748 87	4.254 321	9.165 656	19.746 81
78	6 084	474 552	8.831 761	27.928 48	4.272 659	9.205 164	19.831 92
79	6 241	493 039	8.888 194	28.106 94	4.290 840	9.244 335	19.916 32
80	6 400	512 000	8.944 272	28.284 27	4.308 869	9.283 178	20.000 00
81	6 561	531 441	9.000 000	28.460 50	4.326 749	9.321 698	20.082 99
82	6 724	551 368	9.055 385	28.635 64	4.344 481	9.359 902	20.165 30
83	6 889	571 787	9.110 434	28.809 72	4.362 071	9.397 796	20.246 94
84	7 056	592 704	9.165 151	28.982 75	4.379 519	9.435 388	20.327 93
85	7 225	614 125	9.219 544	29.154 76	4.396 830	9.472 682	20.408 28
86	7 396	636 056	9.273 618	29.325 76	4.414 005	9.509 685	20.488 00
87	7 569	658 503	9.327 379	29.495 76	4.431 048	9.546 403	20.567 10
88	7 744	681 472	9.380 832	29.664 79	4.447 960	9.582 840	20.645 60
89	7 921	704 969	9.433 981	29.832 87	4.464 745	9.619 002	20.723 51
90	8 100	729 000	9.486 833	30.000 00	4.481 405	9.654 894	20.800 84
91	8 281	753 571	9.539 392	30.166 21	4.497 941	9.690 521	20.877 59
92	8 464	778 688	9.591 663	30.331 50	4.514 357	9.725 888	20.953 79
93	8 649	804 357	9.643 651	30.495 90	4.530 655	9.761 000	21.029 44
94	8 836	830 584	9.695 360	30.659 42	4.546 836	9.795 861	21.104 54
95	9 025	857 375	9.746 794	30.822 07	4.562 903	9.830 476	21.179 12
96	9 216	884 736	9.797 959	30.983 87	4.578 857	9.864 848	21.253 17
97	9 409	912 673	9.848 858	31.144 82	4.594 701	9.898 983	21.326 71
98	9 604	941 192	9.899 495	31.304 95	4.610 436	9.932 884	21.399 75
99	9 801	970 299	9.949 874	31.464 27	4.626 065	9.966 555	21.472 29
100	10 000	1 000 000	10.000 00	31.622 78	4.641 589	10.000 00	21.544 35
101	10 201	1 030 301	10.049 88	31.780 50	4.657 010	10.033 22	21.615 92
102	10 404	1 061 208	10.099 50	31.937 44	4.672 329	10.066 23	21.687 03
103	10 609	1 092 727	10.148 89	32.093 61	4.687 548	10.099 02	21.757 67
104	10 816	1 124 864	10.198 04	32.249 03	4.702 669	10.131 59	21.827 86
105	11 025	1 157 625	10.246 95	32.403 70	4.717 694	10.163 96	21.897 60
106	11 236	1 191 016	10.295 63	32.557 64	4.732 623	10.196 13	21.966 89
107	11 449	1 225 043	10.344 08	32.710 85	4.747 459	10.228 09	22.035 75
108	11 664	1 259 712	10.392 30	32.863 35	4.762 203	10.259 86	22.104 19
109	11 881	1 295 029	10.440 31	33.015 15	4.776 856	10.291 42	22.172 20
110	12 100	1 331 000	10.488 09	33.166 25	4.791 420	10.322 80	22.239 80
111	12 321	1 367 631	10.535 65	33.316 66	4.805 896	10.353 99	22.306 99
112	12 544	1 404 928	10.583 01	33.466 40	4.820 285	10.384 99	22.373 78
113	12 769	1 442 897	10.630 15	33.615 47	4.834 588	10.415 80	22.440 17
114	12 996	1 481 544	10.677 08	33.763 89	4.848 808	10.446 44	22.506 17
115	13 225	1 520 875	10.723 81	33.911 65	4.862 944	10.476 90	22.571 79
116	13 456	1 560 896	10.770 33	34.058 77	4.876 999	10.507 18	22.637 02
117	13 689	1 601 613	10.816 65	34.205 26	4.890 973	10.537 28	22.701 89
118	13 924	1 643 032	10.862 78	34.351 13	4.904 868	10.567 22	22.766 38
119	14 161	1 685 159	10.908 71	34.496 38	4.918 685	10.596 99	22.830 51
120	14 400	1 728 000	10.954 45	34.641 02	4.932 424	10.626 59	22.894 28

n	n^2	n^3	$\sqrt{n}$	$\sqrt{10n}$	$\sqrt[3]{n}$	$\sqrt[3]{10n}$	$\sqrt[3]{100n}$
121	14 641	1 771 561	11.000 00	34.785 05	4.946 087	10.656 02	22.957 70
122	14 884	1 815 848	11.045 36	34.928 50	4.959 676	10.685 30	23.020 78
123	15 129	1 860 867	11.090 54	35.071 36	4.973 190	10.714 41	23.083 50
124	15 376	1 906 624	11.135 53	35.213 63	4.986 631	10.743 37	23.145 89
125	15 625	1 953 125	11.180 34	35.355 34	5.000 000	10.772 17	23.207 94
126	15 876	2 000 376	11.224 97	35.496 48	5.013 298	10.800 82	23.269 67
127	16 129	2 048 383	11.269 43	35.637 06	5.026 526	10.829 32	23.331 07
128	16 384	2 097 152	11.313 71	35.777 09	5.039 684	10.857 67	23.392 14
129	16 641	2 146 689	11.357 82	35.916 57	5.052 774	10.885 87	23.452 90
130	16 900	2 197 000	11.401 75	36.055 51	5.065 797	10.913 93	23.513 35
131	17 161	2 248 091	11.445 52	36.193 92	5.078 753	10.941 84	23.573 48
132	17 424	2 299 968	11.489 13	36.331 80	5.091 643	10.969 61	23.633 32
133	17 689	2 352 637	11.532 56	36.469 17	5.104 469	10.997 24	23.692 85
134	17 956	2 406 104	11.575 84	36.606 01	5.117 230	11.024 74	23.752 08
135	18 225	2 460 375	11.618 95	36.742 35	5.129 928	11.052 09	23.811 02
136	18 496	2 515 456	11.661 90	36.878 18	5.142 563	11.079 32	23.869 66
137	18 769	2 571 353	11.704 70	37.013 51	5.155 137	11.106 41	23.928 03
138	19 044	2 628 072	11.747 34	37.148 35	5.167 649	11.133 36	23.986 10
139	19 321	2 685 619	11.789 83	37.282 70	5.180 101	11.160 19	24.043 90
140	19 600	2 744 000	11.832 16	37.416 57	5.192 494	11.186 89	24.101 42
141	19 881	2 803 221	11.874 34	37.549 97	5.204 828	11.213 46	24.158 67
142	20 164	2 863 288	11.916 38	37.682 89	5.217 103	11.239 91	24.215 65
143	20 449	2 924 207	11.958 26	37.815 34	5.229 322	11.266 23	24.272 36
144	20 736	2 985 984	12.000 00	37.947 33	5.241 483	11.292 43	24.328 81
145	21 025	3 048 625	12.041 59	38.078 87	5.253 588	11.318 51	24.384 99
146	21 316	3 112 136	12.083 05	38.209 95	5.265 637	11.344 47	24.440 92
147	21 609	3 176 523	12.124 36	38.340 58	5.277 632	11.370 31	24.496 60
148	21 904	3 241 792	12.165 53	38.470 77	5.289 572	11.396 04	24.552 02
149	22 201	3 307 949	12.206 56	38.600 52	5.301 459	11.421 65	24.607 19
150	22 500	3 375 000	12.247 45	38.729 83	5.313 293	11.447 14	24.662 12
151	22 801	3 442 951	12.288 21	38.858 72	5.325 074	11.472 52	24.716 80
152	23 104	3 511 808	12.328 83	38.987 18	5.336 803	11.497 79	24.771 25
153	23 409	3 581 577	12.369 32	39.115 21	5.348 481	11.522 95	24.825 45
154	23 716	3 652 264	12.409 67	39.242 83	5.360 108	11.548 00	24.879 42
155	24 025	3 723 875	12.449 90	39.370 04	5.371 685	11.572 95	24.933 15
156	24 336	3 796 416	12.490 00	39.496 84	5.383 213	11.597 78	24.986 66
157	24 649	3 869 893	12.529 96	39.623 23	5.394 691	11.622 51	25.039 94
158	24 964	3 944 312	12.569 81	39.749 21	5.406 120	11.647 13	25.092 99
159	25 281	4 019 679	12.609 52	39.874 80	5.417 502	11.671 65	25.145 81
160	25 600	4 096 000	12.649 11	40.000 00	5.428 835	11.696 07	25.198 42
161	25 921	4 173 281	12.688 58	40.124 81	5.440 122	11.720 39	25.250 81
162	26 244	4 251 528	12.727 92	40.249 22	5.451 362	11.744 60	25.302 98
163	26 569	4 330 747	12.767 15	40.373 26	5.462 556	11.768 72	25.354 94
164	26 896	4 410 944	12.806 25	40.496 91	5.473 704	11.792 74	25.406 68
165	27 225	4 492 125	12.845 23	40.620 19	5.484 807	11.816 66	25.458 22
166	27 556	4 574 296	12.884 10	40.743 10	5.495 865	11.840 48	25.509 54
167	27 889	4 657 463	12.922 85	40.865 63	5.506 878	11.864 21	25.560 67
168	28 224	4 741 632	12.961 48	40.987 80	5.517 848	11.887 84	25.611 58
169	28 561	4 826 809	13.000 00	41.109 61	5.528 775	11.911 38	25.662 30
170	28 900	4 913 000	13.038 40	41.231 06	5.539 658	11.934 83	25.712 82
171	29 241	5 000 211	13.076 70	41.352 15	5.550 499	11.958 19	25.763 13
172	29 584	5 088 448	13.114 88	41.472 88	5.561 298	11.981 45	25.813 26
173	29 929	5 177 717	13.152 95	41.593 27	5.572 055	12.004 63	25.863 19
174	30 276	5 268 024	13.190 91	41.713 31	5.582 770	12.027 71	25.912 92
175	30 625	5 359 375	13.228 76	41.833 00	5.593 445	12.050 71	25.962 47
176	30 976	5 451 776	13.266 50	41.952 35	5.604 079	12.073 62	26.011 83
177	31 329	5 545 233	13.304 13	42.071 37	5.614 672	12.096 45	26.061 00
178	31 684	5 639 752	13.341 66	42.190 05	5.625 226	12.119 18	26.109 99
179	32 041	5 735 339	13.379 09	42.308 39	5.635 741	12.141 84	26.158 79
180	32 400	5 832 000	13.416 41	42.426 41	5.646 216	12.164 40	26.207 41

n	n^2	n^3	$\sqrt{n}$	$\sqrt{10\,n}$	$\sqrt[3]{n}$	$\sqrt[3]{10\,n}$	$\sqrt[3]{100\,n}$
181	32 761	5 929 741	13.453 62	42.544 09	5.656 653	12.186 89	26.255 86
182	33 124	6 028 568	13.490 74	42.661 46	5.667 051	12.209 29	26.304 12
183	33 489	6 128 487	13.527 75	42.778 50	5.677 411	12.231 61	26.352 21
184	33 856	6 229 504	13.564 66	42.895 22	5.687 734	12.253 85	26.400 12
185	34 225	6 331 625	13.601 47	43.011 63	5.698 019	12.276 01	26.447 86
186	34 596	6 434 856	13.638 18	43.127 72	5.708 267	12.298 09	26.495 43
187	34 969	6 539 203	13.674 79	43.243 50	5.718 479	12.320 09	26.542 83
188	35 344	6 644 672	13.711 31	43.358 97	5.728 654	12.342 01	26.590 06
189	35 721	6 751 269	13.747 73	43.474 13	5.738 794	12.363 86	26.637 12
190	36 100	6 859 000	13.784 05	43.588 99	5.748 897	12.385 62	26.684 02
191	36 481	6 967 871	13.820 27	43.703 55	5.758 965	12.407 31	26.730 75
192	36 864	7 077 888	13.856 41	43.817 80	5.768 998	12.428 93	26.777 32
193	37 249	7 189 057	13.892 44	43.931 77	5.778 997	12.450 47	26.823 73
194	37 636	7 301 384	13.928 39	44.045 43	5.788 960	12.471 94	26.869 97
195	38 025	7 414 875	13.964 24	44.158 80	5.798 890	12.493 33	26.916 06
196	38 416	7 529 536	14.000 00	44.271 89	5.808 786	12.514 65	26.961 99
197	38 809	7 645 373	14.035 67	44.384 68	5.818 648	12.535 90	27.007 77
198	39 204	7 762 392	14.071 25	44.497 19	5.828 477	12.557 07	27.053 39
199	39 601	7 880 599	14.106 74	44.609 42	5.838 272	12.578 18	27.098 86
200	40 000	8 000 000	14.142 14	44.721 36	5.848 035	12.599 21	27.144 18
201	40 401	8 120 601	14.177 45	44.833 02	5.857 766	12.620 17	27.189 34
202	40 804	8 242 408	14.212 67	44.944 41	5.867 464	12.641 07	27.234 36
203	41 209	8 365 427	14.247 81	45.055 52	5.877 131	12.661 89	27.279 22
204	41 616	8 489 664	14.282 86	45.166 36	5.886 765	12.682 65	27.323 94
205	42 025	8 615 125	14.317 82	45.276 93	5.896 369	12.703 34	27.368 52
206	42 436	8 741 816	14.352 70	45.387 22	5.905 941	12.723 96	27.412 95
207	42 849	8 869 743	14.387 49	45.497 25	5.915 482	12.744 52	27.457 23
208	43 264	8 998 912	14.422 21	45.607 02	5.924 992	12.765 01	27.501 38
209	43 681	9 129 329	14.456 83	45.716 52	5.934 472	12.785 43	27.545 38
210	44 100	9 261 000	14.491 38	45.825 76	5.943 922	12.805 79	27.589 24
211	44 521	9 393 931	14.525 84	45.934 74	5.953 342	12.826 09	27.632 96
212	44 944	9 528 128	14.560 22	46.043 46	5.962 732	12.846 32	27.676 55
213	45 369	9 663 597	14.594 52	46.151 92	5.972 093	12.866 48	27.720 00
214	45 796	9 800 344	14.628 74	46.260 13	5.981 424	12.886 59	27.763 31
215	46 225	9 938 375	14.662 88	46.368 09	5.990 726	12.906 63	27.806 49
216	46 656	10 077 696	14.696 94	46.475 80	6.000 000	12.926 61	27.849 53
217	47 089	10 218 313	14.730 92	46.583 26	6.009 245	12.946 53	27.892 44
218	47 524	10 360 232	14.764 82	46.690 47	6.018 462	12.966 38	27.935 22
219	47 961	10 503 459	14.798 65	46.797 44	6.027 650	12.986 18	27.977 87
220	48 400	10 648 000	14.832 40	46.904 16	6.036 811	13.005 91	28.020 39
221	48 841	10 793 861	14.866 07	47.010 64	6.045 944	13.025 59	28.062 78
222	49 284	10 941 048	14.899 66	47.116 88	6.055 049	13.045 21	28.105 05
223	49 729	11 089 567	14.933 18	47.222 88	6.064 127	13.064 77	28.147 18
224	50 176	11 239 424	14.966 63	47.328 64	6.073 178	13.084 27	28.189 19
225	50 625	11 390 625	15.000 00	47.434 16	6.082 202	13.103 71	28.231 08
226	51 076	11 543 176	15.033 30	47.539 46	6.091 199	13.123 09	28.272 84
227	51 529	11 697 083	15.066 52	47.644 52	6.100 170	13.142 42	28.314 48
228	51 984	11 852 352	15.099 67	47.749 35	6.109 115	13.161 69	28.356 00
229	52 441	12 008 989	15.132 75	47.853 94	6.118 033	13.180 90	28.397 39
230	52 900	12 167 000	15.165 75	47.958 32	6.126 926	13.200 06	28.438 67
231	53 361	12 326 391	15.198 68	48.062 46	6.135 792	13.219 16	28.479 83
232	53 824	12 487 168	15.231 55	48.166 38	6.144 634	13.238 21	28.520 86
233	54 289	12 649 337	15.264 34	48.270 07	6.153 449	13.257 21	28.561 78
234	54 756	12 812 904	15.297 06	48.373 55	6.162 240	13.276 14	28.602 59
235	55 225	12 977 875	15.329 71	48.476 80	6.171 006	13.295 03	28.643 27
236	55 696	13 144 256	15.362 29	48.579 83	6.179 747	13.313 86	28.683 84
237	56 169	13 312 053	15.394 80	48.682 65	6.188 463	13.332 64	28.724 30
238	56 644	13 481 272	15.427 25	48.785 24	6.197 154	13.351 36	28.764 64
239	57 121	13 651 919	15.459 62	48.887 63	6.205 822	13.370 04	28.804 87
240	57 600	13 824 000	15.491 93	48.989 79	6.214 465	13.388 66	28.844 99

n	n^2	n^3	$\sqrt{n}$	$\sqrt{10n}$	$\sqrt[3]{n}$	$\sqrt[3]{10n}$	$\sqrt[3]{100n}$
241	58 081	13 997 521	15.524 17	49.091 75	6.223 084	13.407 23	28.885 00
242	58 564	14 172 488	15.556 35	49.193 50	6.231 680	13.425 75	28.924 89
243	59 049	14 348 907	15.588 46	49.295 03	6.240 251	13.444 21	28.964 68
244	59 536	14 526 784	15.620 50	49.396 36	6.248 800	13.462 63	29.004 36
245	60 025	14 706 125	15.652 48	49.497 47	6.257 325	13.481 00	29.043 93
246	60 516	14 886 936	15.684 39	49.598 39	6.265 827	13.499 31	29.083 39
247	61 009	15 069 223	15.716 23	49.699 09	6.274 305	13.517 58	29.122 75
248	61 504	15 252 992	15.748 02	49.799 60	6.282 761	13.535 80	29.161 99
249	62 001	15 438 249	15.779 73	49.899 90	6.291 195	13.553 97	29.201 14
250	62 500	15 625 000	15.811 39	50.000 00	6.299 605	13.572 09	29.240 18
251	63 001	15 813 251	15.842 98	50.099 90	6.307 994	13.590 16	29.279 11
252	63 504	16 003 008	15.874 51	50.199 60	6.316 360	13.608 18	29.317 94
253	64 009	16 194 277	15.905 97	50.299 11	6.324 704	13.626 16	29.356 67
254	64 516	16 387 064	15.937 38	50.398 41	6.333 026	13.644 09	29.395 30
255	65 025	16 581 375	15.968 72	50.497 52	6.341 326	13.661 97	29.433 83
256	65 536	16 777 216	16.000 00	50.596 44	6.349 604	13.679 81	29.472 25
257	66 049	16 974 593	16.031 22	50.695 17	6.357 861	13.697 60	29.510 58
258	66 564	17 173 512	16.062 38	50.793 70	6.366 097	13.715 34	29.548 80
259	67 081	17 373 979	16.093 48	50.892 04	6.374 311	13.733 04	29.586 93
260	67 600	17 576 000	16.124 52	50.990 20	6.382 504	13.750 69	29.624 96
261	68 121	17 779 581	16.155 49	51.088 16	6.390 677	13.768 30	29.662 89
262	68 644	17 984 728	16.186 41	51.185 94	6.398 828	13.785 86	29.700 73
263	69 169	18 191 447	16.217 27	51.283 53	6.406 959	13.803 37	29.738 47
264	69 696	18 399 744	16.248 08	51.380 93	6.415 069	13.820 85	29.776 11
265	70 225	18 609 625	16.278 82	51.478 15	6.423 158	13.838 28	29.813 66
266	70 756	18 821 096	16.309 51	51.575 19	6.431 228	13.855 66	29.851 11
267	71 289	19 034 163	16.340 13	51.672 04	6.439 277	13.873 00	29.888 47
268	71 824	19 248 832	16.370 71	51.768 72	6.447 306	13.890 30	29.925 74
269	72 361	19 465 109	16.401 22	51.865 21	6.455 315	13.907 55	29.962 92
270	72 900	19 683 000	16.431 68	51.961 52	6.463 304	13.924 77	30.000 00
271	73 441	19 902 511	16.462 08	52.057 66	6.471 274	13.941 94	30.036 99
272	73 984	20 123 648	16.492 42	52.153 62	6.479 224	13.959 06	30.073 89
273	74 529	20 346 417	16.522 71	52.249 40	6.487 154	13.976 15	30.110 70
274	75 076	20 570 824	16.552 95	52.345 01	6.495 065	13.993 19	30.147 42
275	75 625	20 796 875	16.583 12	52.440 44	6.502 957	14.010 20	30.184 05
276	76 176	21 024 576	16.613 25	52.535 70	6.510 830	14.027 16	30.220 60
277	76 729	21 253 933	16.643 32	52.630 79	6.518 684	14.044 08	30.257 05
278	77 284	21 484 952	16.673 33	52.725 71	6.526 519	14.060 96	30.293 42
279	77 841	21 717 639	16.703 29	52.820 45	6.534 335	14.077 80	30.329 70
280	78 400	21 952 000	16.733 20	52.915 03	6.542 133	14.094 60	30.365 89
281	78 961	22 188 041	16.763 05	53.009 43	6.549 912	14.111 36	30.402 00
282	79 524	22 425 768	16.792 86	53.103 67	6.557 672	14.128 08	30.438 02
283	80 089	22 665 187	16.822 60	53.197 74	6.565 414	14.144 76	30.473 95
284	80 656	22 906 304	16.852 30	53.291 65	6.573 138	14.161 40	30.509 81
285	81 225	23 149 125	16.881 94	53.385 39	6.580 844	14.178 00	30.545 57
286	81 796	23 393 656	16.911 53	53.478 97	6.588 532	14.194 56	30.581 26
287	82 369	23 639 903	16.941 07	53.572 38	6.596 202	14.211 09	30.616 86
288	82 944	23 887 872	16.970 56	53.665 63	6.603 854	14.227 57	30.652 38
289	83 521	24 137 569	17.000 00	53.758 72	6.611 489	14.244 02	30.687 81
290	84 100	24 389 000	17.029 39	53.851 65	6.619 106	14.260 43	30.723 17
291	84 681	24 642 171	17.058 72	53.944 42	6.626 705	14.276 80	30.758 44
292	85 264	24 897 088	17.088 01	54.037 02	6.634 287	14.293 14	30.793 63
293	85 849	25 153 757	17.117 24	54.129 47	6.641 852	14.309 44	30.828 74
294	86 436	25 412 184	17.146 43	54.221 77	6.649 400	14.325 70	30.863 78
295	87 025	25 672 375	17.175 56	54.313 90	6.656 930	14.341 92	30.898 74
296	87 616	25 934 336	17.204 65	54.405 88	6.664 444	14.358 11	30.933 63
297	88 209	26 198 073	17.233 69	54.497 71	6.671 940	14.374 26	30.968 44
298	88 804	26 463 592	17.262 68	54.589 38	6.679 420	14.390 37	31.003 17
299	89 401	26 730 899	17.291 62	54.680 89	6.686 883	14.406 45	31.037 76
300	90 000	27 000 000	17.320 51	54.772 26	6.694 330	14.422 50	31.072 33

n	n^2	n^3	$\sqrt{n}$	$\sqrt{10n}$	$\sqrt[3]{n}$	$\sqrt[3]{10n}$	$\sqrt[3]{100n}$
301	90 601	27 270 901	17.349 35	54.863 47	6.701 759	14.438 50	31.106 81
302	91 204	27 543 608	17.378 15	54.954 53	6.709 173	14.454 47	31.141 22
303	91 809	27 818 127	17.406 90	55.045 44	6.716 570	14.470 41	31.175 56
304	92 416	28 094 464	17.435 60	55.136 20	6.723 951	14.486 31	31.209 82
305	93 025	28 372 625	17.464 25	55.226 81	6.731 315	14.502 18	31.244 00
306	93 636	28 652 616	17.492 86	55.317 27	6.738 664	14.518 01	31.278 11
307	94 249	28 934 443	17.521 42	55.407 58	6.745 997	14.533 81	31.312 14
308	94 864	29 218 112	17.549 93	55.497 75	6.753 313	14.549 57	31.346 10
309	95 481	29 503 629	17.578 40	55.587 77	6.760 614	14.565 30	31.379 99
310	96 100	29 791 000	17.606 82	55.677 64	6.767 899	14.581 00	31.413 81
311	96 721	30 080 231	17.635 19	55.767 37	6.775 169	14.596 66	31.447 55
312	97 344	30 371 328	17.663 52	55.856 96	6.782 423	14.612 29	31.481 22
313	97 969	30 664 297	17.691 81	55.946 40	6.789 661	14.627 88	31.514 82
314	98 596	30 959 144	17.720 05	56.035 70	6.796 884	14.643 44	31.548 34
315	99 225	31 255 875	17.748 24	56.124 86	6.804 092	14.658 97	31.581 80
316	99 856	31 554 496	17.776 39	56.213 88	6.811 285	14.674 47	31.615 18
317	100 489	31 855 013	17.804 49	56.302 75	6.818 462	14.689 93	31.648 50
318	101 124	32 157 432	17.832 55	56.391 49	6.825 624	14.705 36	31.681 74
319	101 761	32 461 759	17.860 57	56.480 08	6.832 771	14.720 76	31.714 92
320	102 400	32 768 000	17.888 54	56.568 54	6.839 904	14.736 13	31.748 02
321	103 041	33 076 161	17.916 47	56.656 86	6.847 021	14.751 46	31.781 06
322	103 684	33 386 248	17.944 36	56.745 04	6.854 124	14.766 76	31.814 03
323	104 329	33 698 267	17.972 20	56.833 09	6.861 212	14.782 03	31.846 93
324	104 976	34 012 224	18.000 00	56.921 00	6.868 285	14.797 27	31.879 76
325	105 625	34 328 125	18.027 76	57.008 77	6.875 344	14.812 48	31.912 52
326	106 276	34 645 976	18.055 47	57.096 41	6.882 389	14.827 66	31.945 22
327	106 929	34 965 783	18.083 14	57.183 91	6.889 419	14.842 80	31.977 85
328	107 584	35 287 552	18.110 77	57.271 28	6.896 434	14.857 92	32.010 41
329	108 241	35 611 289	18.138 36	57.358 52	6.903 436	14.873 00	32.042 91
330	108 900	35 937 000	18.165 90	57.445 63	6.910 423	14.888 06	32.075 34
331	109 561	36 264 691	18.193 41	57.532 60	6.917 396	14.903 08	32.107 71
332	110 224	36 594 368	18.220 87	57.619 44	6.924 356	14.918 07	32.140 01
333	110 889	36 926 037	18.248 29	57.706 15	6.931 301	14.933 03	32.172 25
334	111 556	37 259 704	18.275 67	57.792 73	6.938 232	14.947 97	32.204 42
335	112 225	37 595 375	18.303 01	57.879 18	6.945 150	14.962 87	32.236 53
336	112 896	37 933 056	18.330 30	57.965 51	6.952 053	14.977 74	32.268 57
337	113 569	38 272 753	18.357 56	58.051 70	6.958 943	14.992 59	32.300 55
338	114 244	38 614 472	18.384 78	58.137 77	6.965 820	15.007 40	32.332 47
339	114 921	38 958 219	18.411 95	58.223 71	6.972 683	15.022 19	32.364 33
340	115 600	39 304 000	18.439 09	58.309 52	6.979 532	15.036 95	32.396 12
341	116 281	39 651 821	18.466 19	58.395 21	6.986 368	15.051 67	32.427 85
342	116 964	40 001 688	18.493 24	58.480 77	6.993 191	15.066 37	32.459 52
343	117 649	40 353 607	18.520 26	58.566 20	7.000 000	15.081 04	32.491 12
344	118 336	40 707 584	18.547 24	58.651 51	7.006 796	15.095 68	32.522 67
345	119 025	41 063 625	18.574 18	58.736 70	7.013 579	15.110 30	32.554 15
346	119 716	41 421 736	18.601 08	58.821 76	7.020 349	15.124 88	32.585 57
347	120 409	41 781 923	18.627 94	58.906 71	7.027 106	15.139 44	32.616 94
348	121 104	42 144 192	18.654 76	58.991 52	7.033 850	15.153 97	32.648 24
349	121 801	42 508 549	18.681 54	59.076 22	7.040 581	15.168 47	32.679 48
350	122 500	42 875 000	18.708 29	59.160 80	7.047 299	15.182 94	32.710 66
351	123 201	43 243 551	18.734 99	59.245 25	7.054 004	15.197 39	32.741 79
352	123 904	43 614 208	18.761 66	59.329 59	7.060 697	15.211 81	32.772 85
353	124 609	43 986 977	18.788 29	59.413 80	7.067 377	15.226 20	32.803 86
354	125 316	44 361 864	18.814 89	59.497 90	7.074 044	15.240 57	32.834 80
355	126 025	44 738 875	18.841 44	59.581 88	7.080 699	15.254 90	32.865 69
356	126 736	45 118 016	18.867 96	59.665 74	7.087 341	15.269 21	32.896 52
357	127 449	45 499 293	18.894 44	59.749 48	7.093 971	15.283 50	32.927 30
358	128 164	45 882 712	18.920 89	59.833 10	7.100 588	15.297 75	32.958 01
359	128 881	46 268 279	18.947 30	59.916 61	7.017 194	15.311 98	32.988 67
360	129 600	46 656 000	18.973 67	60.000 00	7.113 787	15.326 19	33.019 27

n	n^2	n^3	$\sqrt{n}$	$\sqrt{10n}$	$\sqrt[3]{n}$	$\sqrt[3]{10n}$	$\sqrt[3]{100n}$
361	130 321	47 045 881	19.000 00	60.083 28	7.120 367	15.340 37	33.049 82
362	131 044	47 437 928	19.026 30	60.166 44	7.126 936	15.354 52	33.080 31
363	131 769	47 832 147	19.052 56	60.249 48	7.133 492	15.368 64	33.110 74
364	132 496	48 228 544	19.078 78	60.332 41	7.140 037	15.382 74	33.141 12
365	133 225	48 627 125	19.104 97	60.415 23	7.146 569	15.396 82	33.171 44
366	133 956	49 027 896	19.131 13	60.497 93	7.153 090	15.410 87	33.201 70
367	134 689	49 430 863	19.157 24	60.580 52	7.159 599	15.424 89	33.231 91
368	135 424	49 836 032	19.183 33	60.663 00	7.166 096	15.438 89	33.262 07
369	136 161	50 243 409	19.209 37	60.745 37	7.172 581	15.452 86	33.292 17
370	136 900	50 653 000	19.235 38	60.827 63	7.179 054	15.466 80	33.322 22
371	137 641	51 064 811	19.261 36	60.909 77	7.185 516	15.480 73	33.352 21
372	138 384	51 478 848	19.287 30	60.991 80	7.191 966	15.494 62	33.382 15
373	139 129	51 895 117	19.313 21	61.073 73	7.198 405	15.508 49	33.412 04
374	139 876	52 313 624	19.339 08	61.155 54	7.204 832	15.522 34	33.441 87
375	140 625	52 734 375	19.364 92	61.237 24	7.211 248	15.536 16	33.471 65
376	141 376	53 157 376	19.390 72	61.318 84	7.217 652	15.549 96	33.501 37
377	142 129	53 582 633	19.416 49	61.400 33	7.224 045	15.563 73	33.531 05
378	142 884	54 010 152	19.442 22	61.481 70	7.230 427	15.577 48	33.560 67
379	143 641	54 439 939	19.467 92	61.562 98	7.236 797	15.591 21	33.590 24
380	144 400	54 872 000	19.493 59	61.644 14	7.243 156	15.604 91	33.619 75
381	145 161	55 306 341	19.519 22	61.725 20	7.249 505	15.618 58	33.649 22
382	145 924	55 742 968	19.544 82	61.806 15	7.255 842	15.632 24	33.678 63
383	146 689	56 181 887	19.570 39	61.886 99	7.262 167	15.645 87	33.708 00
384	147 456	56 623 104	19.595 92	61.967 73	7.268 482	15.659 47	33.737 31
385	148 225	57 066 625	19.621 42	62.048 37	7.274 786	15.673 05	33.766 57
386	148 996	57 512 456	19.646 88	62.128 90	7.281 079	15.686 61	33.795 78
387	149 769	57 960 603	19.672 32	62.209 32	7.287 362	15.700 14	33.824 94
388	150 544	58 411 072	19.697 72	62.289 65	7.293 633	15.713 66	33.854 05
389	151 321	58 863 869	19.723 08	62.369 86	7.299 894	15.727 14	33.883 10
390	152 100	59 319 000	19.748 42	62.449 98	7.306 144	15.740 61	33.912 11
391	152 881	59 776 471	19.773 72	62.529 99	7.312 383	15.754 05	33.941 07
392	153 664	60 236 288	19.798 99	62.609 90	7.318 611	15.767 47	33.969 99
393	154 449	60 698 457	19.824 23	62.689 71	7.324 829	15.780 87	33.998 85
394	155 236	61 162 984	19.849 43	62.769 42	7.331 037	15.794 24	34.027 66
395	156 025	61 629 875	19.874 61	62.849 03	7.337 234	15.807 59	34.056 42
396	156 816	62 099 136	19.899 75	62.928 53	7.343 420	15.820 92	34.085 14
397	157 609	62 570 773	19.924 86	63.007 94	7.349 597	15.834 23	34.113 81
398	158 404	63 044 792	19.949 94	63.087 24	7.355 762	15.847 51	34.142 42
399	159 201	63 521 199	19.974 98	63.166 45	7.361 918	15.860 77	34.171 00
400	160 000	64 000 000	20.000 00	63.245 55	7.368 063	15.874 01	34.199 52
401	160 801	64 481 201	20.024 98	63.324 56	7.374 198	15.887 23	34.227 99
402	161 604	64 964 808	20.049 94	63.403 47	7.380 323	15.900 42	34.256 42
403	162 409	65 450 827	20.074 86	63.482 28	7.386 437	15.913 60	34.284 80
404	163 216	65 939 264	20.099 75	63.560 99	7.392 542	15.926 75	34.313 14
405	164 025	66 430 125	20.124 61	63.639 61	7.398 636	15.939 88	34.341 43
406	164 836	66 923 416	20.149 44	63.718 13	7.404 721	15.952 99	34.369 67
407	165 649	67 419 143	20.174 24	63.796 55	7.410 795	15.966 07	34.397 86
408	166 464	67 917 312	20.199 01	63.874 88	7.416 860	15.979 14	34.426 01
409	167 281	68 417 929	20.223 75	63.953 11	7.422 914	15.992 18	34.454 12
410	168 100	68 921 000	20.248 46	64.031 24	7.428 959	16.005 21	34.482 17
411	168 921	69 426 531	20.273 13	64.109 28	7.434 994	16.018 21	34.510 13
412	169 744	69 934 528	20.297 78	64.187 23	7.441 019	16.031 19	34.538 15
413	170 569	70 444 997	20.322 40	64.265 08	7.447 034	16.044 15	34.566 07
414	171 396	70 957 944	20.346 99	64.342 83	7.453 040	16.057 09	34.593 95
415	172 225	71 473 375	20.371 55	64.420 49	7.459 036	16.070 01	34.621 78
416	173 056	71 991 296	20.396 08	64.498 06	7.465 022	16.082 90	34.649 56
417	173 889	72 511 713	20.420 58	64.575 54	7.470 999	16.095 78	34.677 31
418	174 724	73 034 632	20.445 05	64.652 92	7.476 966	16.108 64	34.705 00
419	175 561	73 560 059	20.469 49	64.730 21	7.482 924	16.121 47	34.732 66
420	176 400	74 088 000	20.493 90	64.807 41	7.488 872	16.134 29	34.760 27

n	n^2	n^3	$\sqrt{n}$	$\sqrt{10\,n}$	$\sqrt[3]{n}$	$\sqrt[3]{10\,n}$	$\sqrt[3]{100\,n}$
421	177 241	74 618 461	20.518 28	64.884 51	7.494 811	16.147 08	34.787 83
422	178 084	75 151 448	20.542 64	64.961 53	7.500 741	16.159 86	34.815 35
423	178 929	75 686 967	20.566 96	65.038 45	7.506 661	16.172 61	34.842 83
424	179 776	76 225 024	20.591 26	65.115 28	7.512 572	16.185 34	34.870 27
425	180 625	76 765 625	20.615 53	65.192 02	7.518 473	16.198 06	34.897 66
426	181 476	77 308 776	20.639 77	65.268 68	7.524 365	16.210 75	34.925 01
427	182 329	77 854 483	20.663 98	65.345 24	7.530 248	16.223 43	34.952 32
428	183 184	78 402 752	20.688 16	65.421 71	7.536 122	16.236 08	34.979 58
429	184 041	78 953 589	20.712 32	65.498 09	7.541 987	16.248 72	35.006 80
430	184 900	79 507 000	20.736 44	65.574 39	7.547 842	16.261 33	35.033 98
431	185 761	80 062 991	20.760 54	65.650 59	7.553 689	16.273 93	35.061 12
432	186 624	80 621 568	20.784 61	65.726 71	7.559 526	16.286 51	35.088 21
433	187 489	81 182 737	20.808 65	65.802 74	7.565 355	16.299 06	35.115 27
434	188 356	81 746 504	20.832 67	65.878 68	7.571 174	16.311 60	35.142 28
435	189 225	82 312 875	20.856 65	65.954 53	7.576 985	16.324 12	35.169 25
436	190 096	82 881 856	20.880 61	66.030 30	7.582 787	16.336 62	35.196 18
437	190 969	83 453 453	20.904 54	66.105 98	7.588 579	16.349 10	35.223 07
438	191 844	84 027 672	20.928 45	66.181 57	7.594 363	16.361 56	35.249 91
439	192 721	84 604 519	20.952 33	66.257 08	7.600 139	16.374 00	35.276 72
440	193 600	85 184 000	20.976 18	66.332 50	7.605 905	16.386 43	35.303 48
441	194 481	85 766 121	21.000 00	66.407 83	7.611 663	16.398 83	35.330 21
442	195 364	86 350 888	21.023 80	66.483 08	7.617 412	16.411 22	35.356 89
443	196 249	86 938 307	21.047 57	66.558 25	7.623 152	16.423 58	35.383 54
444	197 136	87 528 384	21.071 31	66.633 32	7.628 884	16.435 93	35.410 14
445	198 025	88 121 125	21.095 02	66.708 32	7.634 607	16.448 26	35.436 71
446	198 916	88 716 536	21.118 71	66.783 23	7.640 321	16.460 57	35.463 23
447	199 809	89 314 623	21.142 37	66.858 06	7.646 027	16.472 87	35.489 71
448	200 704	89 915 392	21.166 01	66.932 80	7.651 725	16.485 14	35.516 16
449	201 601	90 518 849	21.189 62	67.007 46	7.657 414	16.497 40	35.542 57
450	202 500	91 125 000	21.213 20	67.082 04	7.663 094	16.509 64	35.568 93
451	203 401	91 733 851	21.236 76	67.156 53	7.668 766	16.521 86	35.595 26·
452	204 304	92 345 408	21.260 29	67.230 95	7.674 430	16.534 06	35.621 55
453	205 209	92 959 677	21.283 80	67.305 27	7.680 086	16.546 24	35.647 80
454	206 116	93 576 664	21.307 28	67.379 52	7.685 733	16.558 41	35.674 01
455	207 025	94 196 375	21.330 73	67.453 69	7.691 372	16.570 56	35.700 18
456	207 936	94 818 816	21.354 16	67.527 77	7.697 002	16.582 69	35.726 32
457	208 849	95 443 993	21.377 56	67.601 78	7.702 625	16.594 80	35.752 42
458	209 764	96 071 912	21.400 93	67.675 70	7.708 239	16.606 90	35.778 48
459	210 681	96 702 579	21.424 29	67.749 54	7.713 845	16.618 97	35.804 50
460	211 600	97 336 000	21.447 61	67.823 30	7.719 443	16.631 03	35.830 48
461	212 521	97 972 181	21.470 91	67.896 98	7.725 032	16.643 08	35.856 42
462	213 444	98 611 128	21.494 19	67.970 58	7.730 614	16.655 10	35.882 33
463	214 369	99 252 847	21.517 43	68.044 10	7.736 188	16.667 11	35.908 20
464	215 296	99 897 344	21.540 66	68.117 55	7.741 753	16.679 10	35.934 04
465	216 225	100 544 625	21.563 86	68.190 91	7.747 311	16.691 08	35.959 83
466	217 156	101 194 696	21.587 03	68.264 19	7.752 861	16.703 03	35.985 59
467	218 089	101 847 563	21.610 18	68.337 40	7.758 402	16.714 97	36.011 31
468	219 024	102 503 232	21.633 31	68.410 53	7.763 936	16.726 89	36.037 00
469	219 961	103 161 709	21.656 41	68.483 57	7.769 462	16.738 80	36.062 65
470	220 900	103 823 000	21.679 48	68.556 55	7.774 980	16.750 69	36.088 26
471	221 841	104 487 111	21.702 53	68.629 44	7.780 490	16.762 56	36.113 84
472	222 784	105 154 048	21.725 56	68.702 26	7.785 993	16.774 41	36.139 38
473	223 729	105 823 817	21.748 56	68.775 00	7.791 488	16.786 25	36.164 88
474	224 676	106 496 424	21.771 54	68.847 66	7.796 975	16.798 07	36.190 35
475	225 625	107 171 875	21.794 49	68.920 24	7.802 454	16.809 88	36.215 78
476	226 576	107 850 176	21.817 42	68.992 75	7.807 925	16.821 67	36.241 18
477	227 529	108 531 333	21.840 33	69.065 19	7.813 389	16.833 44	36.266 54
478	228 484	109 215 352	21.863 21	69.137 54	7.818 846	16.845 19	36.291 87
479	229 441	109 902 239	21.886 07	69.209 83	7.824 294	16.856 93	36.317 16
480	230 400	110 592 000	21.908 90	69.282 03	7.829 735	16.868 65	36.342 41

n	n^2	n^3	$\sqrt{n}$	$\sqrt{10n}$	$\sqrt[3]{n}$	$\sqrt[3]{10n}$	$\sqrt[3]{100n}$
481	231 361	111 284 641	21.931 71	69.354 16	7.835 169	16.880 36	36.367 63
482	232 324	111 980 168	21.954 50	69.426 22	7.840 595	16.892 05	36.392 82
483	233 289	112 678 587	21.977 26	69.498 20	7.846 013	16.903 72	36.417 97
484	234 256	113 379 904	22.000 00	69.570 11	7.851 424	16.915 38	36.443 08
485	235 225	114 084 125	22.022 72	69.641 94	7.856 828	16.927 02	36.468 17
486	236 196	114 791 256	22.045 41	69.713 70	7.862 224	16.938 65	36.493 21
487	237 169	115 501 303	22.068 08	69.785 39	7.867 613	16.950 26	36.518 22
488	238 144	116 214 272	22.090 72	69.857 00	7.872 994	16.961 85	36.543 20
489	239 121	116 930 169	22.113 34	69.928 53	7.878 368	16.973 43	36.568 15
490	240 100	117 649 000	22.135 94	70.000 00	7.883 735	16.984 99	36.593 06
491	241 081	118 370 771	22.158 52	70.071 39	7.889 095	16.996 54	36.617 93
492	242 064	119 095 488	22.181 07	70.142 71	7.894 447	17.008 07	36.642 78
493	243 049	119 823 157	22.203 60	70.213 96	7.899 792	17.019 59	36.667 58
494	244 036	120 553 784	22.226 11	70.285 13	7.905 129	17.031 08	36.692 36
495	245 025	121 287 375	22.248 60	70.356 24	7.910 460	17.042 57	36.717 10
496	246 016	122 023 936	22.271 06	70.427 27	7.915 783	17.054 04	36.741 81
497	247 009	122 763 473	22.293 50	70.498 23	7.921 099	17.065 49	36.766 49
498	248 004	123 505 992	22.315 91	70.569 12	7.926 408	17.076 93	36.791 13
499	249 001	124 251 499	22.338 31	70.639 93	7.931 710	17.088 35	36.815 74
500	250 000	125 000 000	22.360 68	70.710 68	7.937 005	17.099 76	36.840 31
501	251 001	125 751 501	22.383 03	70.781 35	7.942 293	17.111 15	36.864 86
502	252 004	126 506 008	22.405 36	70.851 96	7.947 574	17.122 53	36.889 37
503	253 009	127 263 527	22.427 66	70.922 49	7.952 848	17.133 89	36.913 85
504	254 016	128 024 064	22.449 94	70.992 96	7.958 114	17.145 24	36.938 30
505	255 025	128 787 625	22.472 21	71.063 35	7.963 374	17.156 57	36.962 71
506	256 036	129 554 216	22.494 44	71.133 68	7.968 627	17.167 89	36.987 09
507	257 049	130 323 843	22.516 66	71.203 93	7.973 873	17.179 19	37.011 44
508	258 064	131 096 512	22.538 86	71.274 12	7.979 112	17.190 48	37.035 76
509	259 081	131 872 229	22.561 03	71.344 24	7.984 344	17.201 75	37.060 04
510	260 100	132 651 000	22.583 18	71.414 28	7.989 570	17.213 01	37.084 30
511	261 121	133 432 831	22.605 31	71.484 26	7.994 788	17.224 25	37.108 52
512	262 144	134 217 728	22.627 42	71.554 18	8.000 000	17.235 48	37.132 71
513	263 169	135 005 697	22.649 50	71.624 02	8.005 205	17.246 69	37.156 87
514	264 196	135 796 744	22.671 57	71.693 79	8.010 403	17.257 89	37.181 00
515	265 225	136 590 875	22.693 61	71.763 50	8.015 595	17.269 08	37.205 09
516	266 256	137 388 096	22.715 63	71.833 14	8.020 779	17.280 25	37.229 16
517	267 289	138 188 413	22.737 63	71.902 71	8.025 957	17.291 40	37.253 19
518	268 324	138 991 832	22.759 61	71.972 22	8.031 129	17.302 54	37.277 20
519	269 361	139 798 359	22.781 57	72.041 65	8.036 293	17.313 67	37.301 17
520	270 400	140 608 000	22.803 51	72.111 03	8.041 452	17.324 78	37.325 11
521	271 441	141 420 761	22.825 42	72.180 33	8.046 603	17.335 88	37.349 03
522	272 484	142 236 648	22.847 32	72.249 57	8.051 748	17.346 96	37.372 90
523	273 529	143 055 667	22.869 19	72.318 74	8.056 886	17.358 04	37.396 75
524	274 576	143 877 824	22.891 05	72.387 84	8.062 018	17.369 09	37.420 57
525	275 625	144 703 125	22.912 88	72.456 88	8.067 143	17.380 13	37.444 36
526	276 676	145 531 576	22.934 69	72.525 86	8.072 262	17.391 16	37.468 13
527	277 729	146 363 183	22.956 48	72.594 77	8.077 374	17.402 18	37.491 85
528	278 784	147 197 952	22.978 25	72.663 61	8.082 480	17.413 18	37.515 55
529	279 841	148 035 889	23.000 00	72.732 39	8.087 579	17.424 16	37.539 22
530	280 900	148 877 000	23.021 73	72.801 10	8.092 672	17.435 13	37.562 86
531	281 961	149 721 291	23.043 44	72.869 75	8.097 759	17.446 09	37.586 47
532	283 024	150 568 768	23.065 13	72.938 33	8.102 839	17.457 04	37.610 05
533	284 089	151 419 437	23.086 79	73.006 85	8.107 913	17.467 97	37.633 60
534	285 156	152 273 304	23.108 44	73.075 30	8.112 980	17.478 89	37.657 12
535	286 225	153 130 375	23.130 07	73.143 69	8.118 041	17.489 79	37.680 62
536	287 296	153 990 656	23.151 67	73.212 02	8.123 096	17.500 68	37.704 09
537	288 369	154 854 153	23.173 26	73.280 28	8.128 145	17.511 56	37.727 53
538	289 444	155 720 872	23.194 83	73.348 48	8.133 187	17.522 42	37.750 94
539	290 521	156 590 819	23.216 37	73.416 62	8.138 223	17.533 27	37.774 24
540	291 600	157 464 000	23.237 90	73.484 69	8.143 253	17.544 11	37.797 6x

n	n^2	n^3	$\sqrt{n}$	$\sqrt{10n}$	$\sqrt[3]{n}$	$\sqrt[3]{10n}$	$\sqrt[3]{100n}$
541	292 681	158 340 421	23.259 41	73.552 70	8.148 276	17.554 93	37.820 95
542	293 764	159 220 088	23.280 89	73.620 65	8.153 294	17.565 74	37.844 24
543	294 849	160 103 007	23.302 36	73.688 53	8.158 305	17.576 54	37.867 50
544	295 936	160 989 184	23.323 81	73.756 36	8.163 310	17.587 32	37.890 73
545	297 025	161 878 625	23.345 24	73.824 12	8.168 309	17.598 09	37.913 93
546	298 116	162 771 336	23.366 64	73.891 81	8.173 302	17.608 85	37.937 11
547	299 209	163 667 323	23.388 03	73.959 45	8.178 289	17.619 59	37.960 25
548	300 304	164 566 592	23.409 40	74.027 02	8.183 269	17.630 32	37.983 37
549	301 401	165 469 149	23.430 75	74.094 53	8.188 244	17.641 04	38.006 46
550	302 500	166 375 000	23.452 08	74.161 98	8.193 213	17.651 74	38.029 52
551	303 601	167 284 151	23.473 39	74.229 37	8.198 175	17.662 43	38.052 56
552	304 704	168 196 608	23.494 68	74.296 70	8.203 132	17.673 11	38.075 57
553	305 809	169 112 377	23.515 95	74.363 97	8.208 082	17.683 78	38.098 54
554	306 916	170 031 464	23.537 20	74.431 18	8.213 027	17.694 43	38.121 49
555	308 025	170 953 875	23.558 44	74.498 32	8.217 966	17.705 07	38.144 42
556	309 136	171 879 616	23.579 65	74.565 41	8.222 899	17.715 70	38.167 31
557	310 249	172 808 693	23.600 85	74.632 43	8.227 825	17.726 31	38.190 18
558	311 364	173 741 112	23.622 02	74.699 40	8.232 746	17.736 91	38.213 02
559	312 481	174 676 879	23.643 18	74.766 30	8.237 661	17.747 50	38.235 84
560	313 600	175.616 000	23.664 32	74.833 15	8.242 571	17.758 08	38.258 62
561	314 721	176 558 481	23.685 44	74.899 93	8.247 474	17.768 64	38.281 38
562	315 844	177 504 328	23.706 54	74.966 66	8.252 372	17.779 20	38.304 12
563	316 969	178 453 547	23.727 62	75.033 33	8.257 263	17.789 73	38.326 82
564	318 096	179 406 144	23.748 68	75.099 93	8.262 149	17.800 26	38.349 50
565	319 225	180 362 125	23.769 73	75.166 48	8.267 029	17.810 77	38.372 15
566	320 356	181 321 496	23.790 75	75.232 97	8.271 904	17.821 28	38.394 78
567	321 489	182 284 263	23.811 76	75.299 40	8.276 773	17.831 77	38.417 37
568	322 624	183.250 432	23.832 75	75.365 77	8.281 635	17.842 24	38.439 95
569	323 761	184 220 009	23.853 72	75.432 09	8.286 493	17.852 71	38.462 49
570	324 900	185 193 000	23.874 67	75.498 34	8.291 344	17.863 16	38.485 01
571	326 041	186 169 411	23.895 61	75.564 54	8.296 190	17.873 60	38.507 50
572	327 184	187 149 248	23.916 52	75.630 68	8.301 031	17.884 03	38.529 97
573	328 329	188 132 517	23.937 42	75.696 76	8.305 865	17.894 44	38.552 41
574	329 476	189 119 224	23.958 30	75.762 79	8.310 694	17.904 85	38.574 82
575	330 625	190 109 375	23.979 16	75.828 75	8.315 517	17.915 24	38.597 21
576	331 776	191 102 976	24.000 00	75.894 66	8.320 335	17.925 62	38.619 58
577	332 929	192 100 033	24.020 82	75.960 52	8.325 148	17.935 99	38.641 91
578	334 084	193 100 552	24.041 63	76.026 31	8.329 954	17.946 34	38.664 22
579	335 241	194 104 539	24.062 42	76.092 05	8.334 755	17.956 69	38.686 51
580	336 400	195 112 000	24.083 19	76.157 73	8.339 551	17.967 02	38.708 77
581	337 561	196 122 941	24.103 94	76.223 36	8.344 341	17.977 34	38.731 00
582	338 724	197 137 368	24.124 68	76.288 92	8.349 126	17.987 65	38.753 21
583	339 889	198 155 287	24.145 39	76.354 44	8.353 905	17.997 94	38.775 39
584	341 056	199 176 704	24.166 09	76.419 89	8.358 678	18.008 23	38.797 55
585	342 225	200 201 625	24.186 77	76.485 29	8.363 447	18.018 50	38.819 68
586	343 396	201 230 056	24.207 44	76.550 64	8.368 209	18.028 76	38.841 79
587	344 569	202 262 003	24.228 08	76.615 93	8.372 967	18.039 01	38.863 87
588	345 744	203 297 472	24.248 71	76.681 16	8.377 719	18.049 25	38.885 93
589	346 921	204 336 469	24.269 32	76.746 34	8.382 465	18.059 47	38.907 96
590	348 100	205 379 000	24.289 92	76.811 46	8.387 207	18.069 69	38.929 96
591	349 281	206 425 071	24.310 49	76.876 52	8.391 942	18.079 89	38.951 95
592	350 464	207 474 688	24.331 05	76.941 54	8.396 673	18.090 08	38.973 90
593	351 649	208 527 857	24.351 59	77.006 49	8.401 398	18.100 26	38.995 84
594	352 836	209 584 584	24.372 12	77.071 40	8.406 118	18.110 43	39.017 74
595	354 025	210 644 875	24.392 62	77.136 24	8.410 833	18.120 59	39.039 63
596	355 216	211 708 736	24.413 11	77.201 04	8.415 542	18.130 74	39.061 49
597	356 409	212 776 173	24.433 58	77.265 78	8.420 246	18.140 87	39.083 32
598	357 604	213 847 192	24.454 04	77.330 46	8.424 945	18.150 99	39.105 13
599	358 801	214 921 799	24.474 48	77.395 09	8.429 638	18.161 11	39.126 92
600	360 000	216 000 000	24.494 90	77.459 67	8.434 327	18.171 21	39.148 68

n	n^2	n^3	$\sqrt{n}$	$\sqrt{10n}$	$\sqrt[3]{n}$	$\sqrt[3]{10n}$	$\sqrt[3]{100n}$
601	361 201	217 081 801	24.515 30	77.524 19	8.439 010	18.181 30	39.170 4?
602	362 404	218 167 208	24.535 69	77.588 66	8.443 688	18.191 37	39.192 1.
603	363 609	219 256 227	24.556 06	77.653 07	8.448 361	18.201 44	39.213 8.
604	364 816	220 348 864	24.576 41	77.717 44	8.453 028	18.211 50	39.235 48
605	366 025	221 445 125	24.596 75	77.781 75	8.457 691	18.221 54	39.257 1?
606	367 236	222 545 016	24.617 07	77.846 00	8.462 348	18.231 58	39.278 7?
607	368 449	223 648 543	24.637 37	77.910 20	8.467 000	18.241 60	39.300 3.
608	369 664	224 755 712	24.657 66	77.974 35	8.471 647	18.251 61	39.321 9?
609	370 881	225 866 529	24.677 93	78.038 45	8.476 289	18.261 61	39.343 4.
610	372 100	226 981 000	24.698 18	78.102 50	8.480 926	18.271 60	39.364 9
611	373 321	228 099 131	24.718 41	78.166 49	8.485 558	18.281 58	39.386 4
612	374 544	229 220 928	24.738 63	78.230 43	8.490 185	18.291 55	39.407 9.
613	375 769	230 346 397	24.758 84	78.294 32	8.494 807	18.301 51	39.429 4?
614	376 996	231 475 544	24.779 02	78.358 15	8.499 423	18.311 45	39.450 8.
615	378 225	232 608 375	24.799 19	78.421 94	8.504 035	18.321 39	39.472 2.
616	379 456	233 744 896	24.819 35	78.485 67	8.508 642	18.331 31	39.493 6.
617	380 689	234 885 113	24.839 48	78.549 35	8.513 243	18.341 23	39.514 9.
618	381 924	236 029 032	24.859 61	78.612 98	8.517 840	18.351 13	39.536 3
619	383 161	237 176 659	24.879 71	78.676 55	8.522 432	18.361 02	39.557 6.
620	384 400	238 328 000	24.899 80	78.740 08	8.527 019	18.370 91	39.578 9
621	385 641	239 483 061	24.919 87	78.803 55	8.531 601	18.380 78	39.600 1
622	386 884	240 641 848	24.939 93	78.866 98	8.536 178	18.390 64	39.621 4
623	388 129	241 804 367	24.959 97	78.930 35	8.540 750	18.400 49	39.642 6.
624	389 376	242 970 624	24.979 99	78.993 67	8.545 317	18.410 33	39.663 8.
625	390 625	244 140 625	25.000 00	79.056 94	8.549 880	18.420 16	39.685 0?
626	391 876	245 314 376	25.019 99	79.120 16	8.554 437	18.429 98	39.706 1.
627	393 129	246 491 883	25.039 97	79.183 33	8.558 990	18.439 78	39.727 3.
628	394 384	247 673 152	25.059 93	79.246 45	8.563 538	18.449 58	39.748 4.
629	395 641	248 858 189	25.079 87	79.309 52	8.568 081	18.459 37	39.769 5.
630	396 900	250 047 000	25.099 80	79.372 54	8.572 619	18.469 15	39.790 5
631	398 161	251 239 591	25.119 71	79.435 51	8.577 152	18.478 91	39.811 6.
632	399 424	252 435 968	25.139 61	79.498 43	8.581 681	18.488 67	39.832 6.
633	400 689	253 636 137	25.159 49	79.561 30	8.586 205	18.498 42	39.853 6.
634	401 956	254 840 104	25.179 36	79.624 12	8.590 724	18.508 15	39.874 6.
635	403 225	256 047 875	25.199 21	79.686 89	8.595 238	18.517 88	39.895 5.
636	404 496	257 259 456	25.219 04	79.749 61	8.599 748	18.527 59	39.916 4.
637	405 769	258 474 853	25.238 86	79.812 28	8.604 252	18.537 30	39.937 4.
638	407 044	259 694 072	25.258 66	79.874 90	8.608 753	18.547 00	39.958 2.
639	408 321	260 917 119	25.278 45	79.937 48	8.613 248	18.556 36	39.979 1.
640	409 600	262 144 000	25.298 22	80.000 00	8.617 739	18.566 36	40.000 0.
641	410 881	263 374 721	25.317 98	80.062 48	8.622 225	18.576 02	40.020 8.
642	412 164	264 609 288	25.337 72	80.124 90	8.626 706	18.585 68	40.041 6.
643	413 449	265 847 707	25.357 44	80.187 28	8.631 183	18.595 32	40.062 4.
644	414 736	267 089 984	25.377 16	80.249 61	8.635 655	18.604 95	40.083 1.
645	416 025	268 336 125	25.396 85	80.311 89	8.640 123	18.614 58	40.103 9.
646	417 316	269 586 136	25.416 53	80.374 13	8.644 585	18.624 19	40.124 6.
647	418 609	270 840 023	25.436 19	80.436 31	8.649 044	18.633 80	40.145 3.
648	419 904	272 097 792	25.455 84	80.498 45	8.653 497	18.643 40	40.165 9.
649	421 201	273 359 449	25.475 48	80.560 54	8.657 947	18.652 98	40.186 6.
650	422 500	274 625 000	25.495 10	80.622 58	8.662 391	18.662 56	40.207 2.
651	423 801	275 894 451	25.514 70	80.684 57	8.666 831	18.672 12	40.227 8.
652	425 104	277 167 808	25.534 29	80.746 52	8.671 266	18.681 68	40.248 4.
653	426 409	278 445 077	25.553 86	80.808 42	8.675 697	18.691 22	40.269 0.
654	427 716	279 726 264	25.573 42	80.870 27	8.680 124	18.700 76	40.289 5.
655	429 025	281 011 375	25.592 97	80.932 07	8.684 546	18.710 29	40.310 0.
656	430 336	282 300 416	25.612 50	80.993 83	8.688 963	18.719 80	40.330 5.
657	431 649	283 593 393	25.632 01	81.055 54	8.693 376	18.729 31	40.351 0.
658	432 964	284 890 312	25.651 51	81.117 20	8.697 784	18.738 81	40.371 4.
659	434 281	286 191 179	25.671 00	81.178 81	8.702 188	18.748 30	40.391 9.
660	435 600	287 496 000	25.690 47	81.240 38	8.706 588	18.757 77	40.412 .

n	n^2	n^3	$\sqrt{n}$	$\sqrt{10n}$	$\sqrt[3]{n}$	$\sqrt[3]{10n}$	$\sqrt[3]{100n}$
661	436 921	288 804 781	25.709 92	81.301 91	8.710 983	18.767 24	40.432 80
662	438 244	290 117 528	25.729 36	81.363 38	8.715 373	18.776 70	40.453 18
663	439 569	291 434 247	25.748 79	81.424 81	8.719 760	18.786 15	40.473 54
664	440 896	292 754 944	25.768 20	81.486 20	8.724 141	18.795 59	40.493 88
665	442 225	294 079 625	25.787 59	81.547 53	8.728 519	18.805 02	40.514 20
666	443 556	295 408 296	25.806 98	81.608 82	8.732 892	18.814 44	40.534 49
667	444 889	296 740 963	25.826 34	81.670 07	8.737 260	18.823 86	40.554 77
668	446 224	298 077 632	25.845 70	81.731 27	8.741 625	18.833 26	40.575 03
669	447 561	299 418 309	25.865 03	81.792 42	8.745 985	18.842 65	40.595 26
670	448 900	300 763 000	25.884 36	81.853 53	8.750 340	18.852 04	40.615 48
671	450 241	302 111 711	25.903 67	81.914 59	8.754 691	18.861 41	40.635 68
672	451 584	303 464 448	25.922 96	81.975 61	8.759 038	18.870 78	40.655 85
673	452 929	304 821 217	25.942 24	82.036 58	8.763 381	18.880 13	40.676 01
674	454 276	306 182 024	25.961 51	82.097 50	8.767 719	18.889 48	40.696 15
675	455 625	307 546 875	25.980 76	82.158 38	8.772 053	18.898 82	40.716 26
676	456 976	308 915 776	26.000 00	82.219 22	8.776 383	18.908 14	40.736 36
677	458 329	310 288 733	26.019 22	82.280 01	8.780 708	18.917 46	40.756 44
678	459 684	311 665 752	26.038 43	82.340 76	8.785 030	18.926 77	40.776 50
679	461 041	313 046 839	26.057 63	82.401 46	8.789 347	18.936 07	40.796 53
680	462 400	314 432 000	26.076 81	82.462 11	8.793 659	18.945 36	40.816 55
681	463 761	315 821 241	26.095 98	82.522 72	8.797 968	18.954 65	40.836 55
682	465 124	317 214 568	26.115 13	82.583 29	8.802 272	18.963 92	40.856 53
683	466 489	318 611 987	26.134 27	82.643 81	8.806 572	18.973 18	40.876 49
684	467 856	320 013 504	26.153 39	82.704 29	8.810 868	18.982 44	40.896 43
685	469 225	321 419 125	26.172 50	82.764 73	8.815 160	18.991 69	40.916 35
686	470 596	322 828 856	26.191 60	82.825 12	8.819 447	19.000 92	40.936 25
687	471 969	324 242 703	26.210 68	82.885 46	8.823 731	19.010 15	40.956 13
688	473 344	325 660 672	26.229 75	82.945 77	8.828 010	19.019 37	40.975 99
689	474 721	327 082 769	26.248 81	83.006 02	8.832 285	19.028 58	40.995 84
690	476 100	328 509 000	26.267 85	83.066 24	8.836 556	19.037 78	41.015 66
691	477 481	329 939 371	26.286 88	83.126 41	8.840 823	19.046 98	41.035 46
692	478 864	331 373 888	26.305 89	83.186 54	8.845 085	19.056 16	41.055 25
693	480 249	332 812 557	26.324 89	83.246 62	8.849 344	19.065 33	41.075 02
694	481 636	334 255 384	26.343 88	83.306 66	8.853 599	19.074 50	41.094 76
695	483 025	335 702 375	26.362 85	83.366 66	8.857 849	19.083 66	41.114 49
696	484 416	337 153 536	26.381 81	83.426 61	8.862 095	19.092 81	41.134 20
697	485 809	338 608 873	26.400 76	83.486 53	8.866 338	19.101 95	41.153 89
698	487 204	340 068 392	26.419 69	83.546 39	8.870 576	19.111 08	41.173 57
699	488 601	341 532 099	26.438 61	83.606 22	8.874 810	19.120 20	41.193 22
700	490 000	343 000 000	26.457 51	83.666 00	8.879 040	19.129 31	41.212 85
701	491 401	344 472 101	26.476 40	83.725 74	8.883 266	19.138 42	41.232 47
702	492 804	345 948 408	26.495 28	83.785 44	8.887 488	19.147 51	41.252 07
703	494 209	347 428 927	26.514 15	83.845 10	8.891 706	19.156 60	41.271 64
704	495 616	348 913 664	26.533 00	83.904 71	8.895 920	19.165 68	41.291 20
705	497 025	350 402 625	26.551 84	83.964 28	8.900 130	19.174 75	41.310 75
706	498 436	351 895 816	26.570 66	84.023 81	8.904 337	19.183 81	41.330 27
707	499 849	353 393 243	26.589 47	84.083 29	8.908 539	19.192 86	41.349 77
708	501 264	354 894 912	26.608 27	84.142 74	8.912 737	19.201 91	41.369 26
709	502 681	356 400 829	26.627 05	84.202 14	8.916 931	19.210 95	41.388 73
710	504 100	357 911 000	26.645 83	84.261 50	8.921 121	19.219 97	41.408 18
711	505 521	359 425 431	26.664 58	84.320 82	8.925 308	19.228 99	41.427 61
712	506 944	360 944 128	26.683 33	84.380 09	8.929 490	19.238 00	41.447 02
713	508 369	362 467 097	26.702 06	84.439 33	8.933 669	19.247 01	41.466 42
714	509 796	363 994 344	26.720 78	84.498 52	8.937 843	19.256 00	41.485 79
715	511 225	365 525 875	26.739 48	84.557 67	8.942 014	19.264 99	41.505 15
716	512 656	367 061 696	26.758 18	84.616 78	8.946 181	19.273 96	41.524 49
717	514 089	368 601 813	26.776 86	84.675 85	8.950 344	19.282 93	41.543 82
718	515 524	370 146 232	26.795 52	84.734 88	8.954 503	19.291 89	41.563 12
719	516 961	371 694 959	26.814 18	84.793 87	8.958 658	19.300 84	41.582 41
720	518 400	373 248 000	26.832 82	84.852 81	8.962 809	19.309 79	41.601 68

n	n^2	n^3	$\sqrt{n}$	$\sqrt{10n}$	$\sqrt[3]{n}$	$\sqrt[3]{10n}$	$\sqrt[3]{100n}$
721	519 841	374 805 361	26.851 44	84.911 72	8.966 957	19.318 72	41.620 9
722	521 284	376 367 048	26.870 06	84.970 58	8.971 101	19.327 65	41.640 1
723	522 729	377 933 067	26.888 66	85.029 41	8.975 241	19.336 57	41.659 3
724	524 176	379 503 424	26.907 25	85.088 19	8.979 377	19.345 48	41.678 5
725	525 625	381 078 125	26.925 82	85.146 93	8.983 509	19.354 38	41.697 7
726	527 076	382 657 176	26.944 39	85.205 63	8.987 637	19.363 28	41.716 9
727	528 529	384 240 583	26.962 94	85.264 29	8.991 762	19.372 16	41.736 0
728	529 984	385 828 352	26.981 48	85.322 92	8.995 883	19.381 04	41.755 1
729	531 441	387 420 489	27.000 00	85.381 50	9.000 000	19.389 91	41.774 3
730	532 900	389 017 000	27.018 51	85.440 04	9.004 113	19.398 77	41.793 3
731	534 361	390 617 891	27.037 01	85.498 54	9.008 223	19.407 63	41.812 4
732	535 824	392 223 168	27.055 50	85.557 00	9.012 329	19.416 47	41.831 5
733	537 289	393 832 837	27.073 97	85.615 42	9.016 431	19.425 31	41.850 5
734	538 756	395 446 904	27.092 43	85.673 80	9.020 529	19.434 14	41.869 5
735	540 225	397 065 375	27.110 88	85.732 14	9.024 624	19.442 96	41.888 5
736	541 696	398 688 256	27.129 32	85.790 44	9.028 715	19.451 78	41.907 5
737	543 169	400 315 553	27.147 74	85.848 70	9.032 802	19.460 58	41.926 5
738	544 644	401 947 272	27.166 16	85.906 93	9.036 886	19.469 38	41.945 5
739	546 121	403 583 419	27.184 55	85.965 11	9.040 966	19.478 17	41.464 4
740	547 600	405 224 000	27.202 94	86.023 25	9.045 042	19.486 95	41.983 3
741	549 081	406 869 021	27.221 32	86.081 36	9.049 114	19.495 73	42.002 2
742	550 564	408 518 488	27.239 68	86.139 42	9.053 183	19.504 49	42.021 1
743	552 049	410 172 407	27.258 03	86.197 45	9.057 248	19.513 25	42.040 0
744	553 536	411 830 784	27.276 36	86.255 43	9.061 310	19.522 00	42.058 8
745	555 025	413 493 625	27.294 69	86.313 38	9.065 368	19.530 74	42.077 7
746	556 516	415 160 936	27.313 00	86.371 29	9.069 422	19.539 48	42.096 5
747	558 009	416 832 723	27.331 30	86.429 16	9.073 473	19.548 20	42.115 3
748	559 504	418 508 992	27.349 59	86.486 99	9.077 520	19.556 92	42.134 1
749	561 001	420 189 749	27.367 86	86.544 79	9.081 563	19.565 63	42.152 8
750	562 500	421 875 000	27.386 13	86.602 54	9.085 603	19.574 34	42.171 6
751	564 001	423 564 751	27.404 38	86.660 26	9.089 639	19.583 03	42.190 3
752	565 504	425 259 008	27.422 62	86.717 93	9.093 672	19.591 72	42.209 0
753	567 009	426 957 777	27.440 85	86.775 57	9.097 701	19.600 40	42.227 7
754	568 516	428 661 064	27.459 06	86.833 17	9.101 727	19.609 08	42.246 4
755	570 025	430 368 875	27.477 26	86.890 74	9.105 748	19.617 74	42.265 1
756	571 536	432 081 216	27.495 45	86.948 26	9.109 767	19.626 40	42.283 7
757	573 049	433 798 093	27.513 63	87.005 75	9.113 782	19.635 05	42.302 4
758	574 564	435 519 512	27.531 80	87.063 20	9.117 793	19.643 69	42.321 0
759	576 081	437 245 479	27.549 95	87.120 61	9.121 801	19.652 32	42.339 6
760	577 600	438 976 000	27.568 10	87.177 98	9.125 805	19.660 95	42.358 2
761	579 121	440 711 081	27.586 23	87.235 31	9.129 806	19.669 57	42.376 8
762	580 644	442 450 728	27.604 35	87.292 61	9.133 803	19.678 18	42.395 3
763	582 169	444 194 947	27.622 45	87.349 87	9.137 797	19.686 79	42.413 9
764	583 696	445 943 744	27.640 55	87.407 09	9.141 787	19.695 38	42.432 4
765	585 225	447 697 125	27.658 63	87.464 28	9.145 774	19.703 97	42.450 9
766	586 756	449 455 096	27.676 71	87.521 43	9.149 758	19.712 56	42.469 4
767	588 289	451 217 663	27.694 76	87.578 54	9.153 738	19.721 13	42.487 8
768	589 824	452 984 832	27.712 81	87.635 61	9.157 714	19.729 70	42.506 3
769	591 361	454 756 609	27.730 85	87.692 65	9.161 687	19.738 26	42.524 7
770	592 900	456 533 000	27.748 87	87.749 64	9.165 656	19.746 81	42.543 2
771	594 441	458 314 011	27.766 89	87.806 61	9.169 623	19.755 35	42.561 6
772	595 984	460 099 648	27.784 89	87.863 53	9.173 585	19.763 89	42.580 0
773	597 529	461 889 917	27.802 88	87.920 42	9.177 544	19.772 42	42.598 3
774	599 076	463 684 824	27.820 86	87.977 27	9.181 500	19.780 94	42.616 7
775	600 625	465 484 375	27.838 82	88.034 08	9.185 453	19.789 46	42.635 0
776	602 176	467 288 576	27.856 78	88.090 86	9.189 402	19.797 97	42.653 4
777	603 729	469 097 433	27.874 72	88.147 60	9.193 347	19.806 47	42.671 7
778	605 284	470 910 952	27.892 65	88.204 31	9.197 290	19.814 96	42.690 0
779	606 841	472 729 139	27.910 57	88.260 98	9.201 229	19.823 45	42.708 3
780	608 400	474 552 000	27.928 48	88.317 61	9.205 164	19.831 92	42.726 5

n	n^2	n^3	$\sqrt{n}$	$\sqrt{10n}$	$\sqrt[3]{n}$	$\sqrt[3]{10n}$	$\sqrt[3]{100n}$
781	609 961	476 379 541	27.946 38	88.374 20	9.209 096	19.840 40	42.744 84
782	611 524	478 211 768	27.964 26	88.430 76	9.213 025	19.848 86	42.763 07
783	613 089	480 048 687	27.982 14	88.487 29	9.216 950	19.857 32	42.781 29
784	614 656	481 890 304	28.000 00	88.543 77	9.220 873	19.865 77	42.799 50
785	616 225	483 736 625	28.017 85	88.600 23	9.224 791	19.874 21	42.817 69
786	617 796	485 587 656	28.035 69	88.656 64	9.228 707	19.882 65	42.835 86
787	619 369	487 443 403	28.053 52	88.713 02	9.232 619	19.891 07	42.854 02
788	620 944	489 303 872	28.071 34	88.769 36	9.236 528	19.899 50	42.872 16
789	622 521	491 169 069	28.089 14	88.825 67	9.240 433	19.907 91	42.890 29
790	624 100	493 039 000	28.106 94	88.881 94	9.244 335	19.916 32	42.908 40
791	625 681	494 913 671	28.124 72	88.938 18	9.248 234	19.924 72	42.926 50
792	627 264	496 793 088	28.142 49	88.994 38	9.252 130	19.933 11	42.944 58
793	628 849	498 677 257	28.160 26	89.050 55	9.256 022	19.941 50	42.962 65
794	630 436	500 566 184	28.178 01	89.106 68	9.259 911	19.949 87	42.980 70
795	632 025	502 459 875	28.195 74	89.162 77	9.263 797	19.958 25	42.998 74
796	633 616	504 358 336	28.213 47	89.218 83	9.267 680	19.966 61	43.016 76
797	635 209	506 261 573	28.231 19	89.274 86	9.271 559	19.974 97	43.034 77
798	636 804	508 169 592	28.248 89	89.330 85	9.275 435	19.983 32	43.052 76
799	638 401	510 082 399	28.266 59	89.386 80	9.279 308	19.991 66	43.070 73
800	640 000	512 000 000	28.284 27	89.442 72	9.283 178	20.000 00	43.088 69
801	641 601	513 922 401	28.301 94	89.498 60	9.287 044	20.008 33	43.106 64
802	643 204	515 849 608	28.319 60	89.554 45	9.290 907	20.016 65	43.124 57
803	644 809	517 781 627	28.337 25	89.610 27	9.294 767	20.024 97	43.142 49
804	646 416	519 718 464	28.354 89	89.666 05	9.298 624	20.033 28	43.160 39
805	648 025	521 660 125	28.372 52	89.721 79	9.302 477	20.041 58	43.178 28
806	649 636	523 606 616	28.390 14	89.777 50	9.306 328	20.049 88	43.196 15
807	651 249	525 557 943	28.407 75	89.833 18	9.310 175	20.058 16	43.214 00
808	652 864	527 514 112	28.425 34	89.888 82	9.314 019	20.066 45	43.231 85
809	654 481	529 475 129	28.442 93	89.944 43	9.317 860	20.074 72	43.249 67
810	656 100	531 441 000	28.460 50	90.000 00	9.321 698	20.082 99	43.267 49
811	657 721	533 411 731	28.478 06	90.055 54	9.325 532	20.091 25	43.285 29
812	659 344	535 387 328	28.495 61	90.111 04	9.329 363	20.099 50	43.303 07
813	660 969	537 367 797	28.513 15	90.166 51	9.333 192	20.107 75	43.320 84
814	662 596	539 353 144	28.530 69	90.221 95	9.337 017	20.115 99	43.338 59
815	664 225	541 343 375	28.548 20	90.277 35	9.340 839	20.124 23	43.356 33
816	665 856	543 338 496	28.565 71	90.332 72	9.344 657	20.132 45	43.374 06
817	667 489	545 338 513	28.583 21	90.388 05	9.348 473	20.140 67	43.391 77
818	669 124	547 343 432	28.600 70	90.443 35	9.352 286	20.148 89	43.409 47
819	670 761	549 353 259	28.618 18	90.498 62	9.356 095	20.157 10	43.427 15
820	672 400	551 368 000	28.635 64	90.553 85	9.359 902	20.165 30	43.444 81
821	674 041	553 387 661	28.653 10	90.609 05	9.363 705	20.173 49	43.462 47
822	675 684	555 412 248	28.670 54	90.664 22	9.367 505	20.181 68	43.480 11
823	677 329	557 441 767	28.687 98	90.719 35	9.371 302	20.189 86	43.497 73
824	678 976	559 476 224	28.705 40	90.774 45	9.375 096	20.198 03	43.515 34
825	680 625	561 515 625	28.722 81	90.829 51	9.378 887	20.206 20	43.532 94
826	682 276	563 559 976	28.740 22	90.884 54	9.382 675	20.214 36	43.550 52
827	683 929	565 609 283	28.757 61	90.939 54	9.386 460	20.222 52	43.568 09
828	685 584	567 663 552	28.774 99	90.994 51	9.390 242	20.230 66	43.585 64
829	687 241	569 722 789	28.792 36	91.049 44	9.394 021	20.238 80	43.603 18
830	688 900	571 787 000	28.809 72	91.104 34	9.397 796	20.246 94	43.620 71
831	690 561	573 856 191	28.827 07	91.159 20	9.401 569	20.255 07	43.638 22
832	692 224	575 930 368	28.844 41	91.214 03	9.405 339	20.263 19	43.655 72
833	693 889	578 009 537	28.861 74	91.268 83	9.409 105	20.271 30	43.673 20
834	695 556	580 093 704	28.879 06	91.323 60	9.412 869	20.279 41	43.690 67
835	697 225	582 182 875	28.896 37	91.378 33	9.416 630	20.287 51	43.708 12
836	698 896	584 277 056	28.913 66	91.433 04	9.420 387	20.295 61	43.725 56
837	700 569	586 376 253	28.930 95	91.487 70	9.424 142	20.303 70	43.742 99
838	702 244	588 480 472	28.948 23	91.542 34	9.427 894	20.311 78	43.760 41
839	703 921	590 589 719	28.965 50	91.596 94	9.431 642	20.319 86	43.777 81
840	705 600	592 704 000	28.982 75	91.651 51	9.435 388	20.327 93	43.795 19

n	n^2	n^3	$\sqrt{n}$	$\sqrt{10n}$	$\sqrt[3]{n}$	$\sqrt[3]{10n}$	$\sqrt[3]{100n}$
841	707 281	594 823 321	29.000 00	91.706 05	9.439 131	20.335 99	43.812 5
842	708 964	596 947 688	29.017 24	91.760 56	9.442 870	20.344 05	43.829 9
843	710 649	599 077 107	29.034 46	91.815 03	9.446 607	20.352 10	43.847 2
844	712 336	601 211 584	29.051 68	91.869 47	9.450 341	20.360 14	43.864 6
845	714 025	603 351 125	29.068 88	91.923 88	9.454 072	20.368 18	43.881 9
846	715 716	605 495 736	29.086 08	91.978 26	9.457 800	20.376 21	43.899 2
847	717 409	607 645 423	29.103 26	92.032 60	9.461 525	20.384 24	43.916 5
848	719 104	609 800 192	29.120 44	92.086 92	9.465 247	20.392 26	43.933 7
849	720 801	611 960 049	29.137 60	92.141 20	9.468 966	20.400 27	43.951 0
850	722 500	614 125 000	29.154 76	92.195 44	9.472 682	20.408 28	43.968 3
851	724 201	616 295 051	29.171 90	92.249 66	9.476 396	20.416 28	43.985 5
852	725 904	618 470 208	29.189 04	92.303 85	9.480 106	20.424 27	44.002 7
853	727 609	620 650 477	29.206 16	92.358 00	9.483 814	20.432 26	44.019 9
854	729 316	622 835 864	29.223 28	92.412 12	9.487 518	20.440 24	44.037 1
855	731 025	625 026 375	29.240 38	92.466 21	9.491 220	20.448 21	44.054 3
856	732 736	627 222 016	29.257 48	92.520 27	9.494 919	20.456 18	44.071 5
857	734 449	629 422 793	29.274 56	92.574 29	9.498 615	20.464 15	44.088 6
858	736 164	631 628 712	29.291 64	92.628 29	9.502 308	20.472 10	44.105 8
859	737 881	633 839 779	29.308 70	92.682 25	9.505 998	20.480 05	44.122 9
860	739 600	636 056 000	29.325 76	92.736 18	9.509 685	20.488 00	44.140 0
861	741 321	638 277 381	29.342 80	92.790 09	9.513 370	20.495 93	44.157 1
862	743 044	640 503 928	29.359 84	92.843 96	9.517 052	20.503 87	44.174 2
863	744 769	642 735 647	29.376 86	92.897 79	9.520 730	20.511 79	44.191 3
864	746 496	644 972 544	29.393 88	92.951 60	9.524 406	20.519 71	44.208 3
865	748 225	647 214 625	29.410 88	93.005 38	9.528 079	20.527 62	44.225 4
866	749 956	649 461 896	29.427 88	93.059 12	9.531 750	20.535 53	44.242 4
867	751 689	651 714 363	29.444 86	93.112 83	9.535 417	20.543 43	44.259 4
868	753 424	653 972 032	29.461 84	93.166 52	9.539 082	20.551 33	44.276 5
869	755 161	656 234 909	29.478 81	93.220 17	9.542 744	20.559 22	44.293 4
870	756 900	658 503 000	29.495 76	93.273 79	9.546 403	20.567 10	44.310 4
871	758 641	660 776 311	29.512 71	93.327 38	9.550 059	20.574 98	44.327 4
872	760 384	663 054 848	29.529 65	93.380 94	9.553 712	20.582 85	44.344 4
873	762 129	665 338 617	29.546 57	93.434 47	9.557 363	20.590 71	44.361 3
874	763 876	667 627 624	29.563 49	93.487 97	9.561 011	20.598 57	44.378 2
875	765 625	669 921 875	29.580 40	93.541 43	9.564 656	20.606 43	44.395 2
876	767 376	672 221 376	29.597 30	93.594 87	9.568 298	20.614 27	44.412 1
877	769 129	674 526 133	29.614 19	93.648 28	9.571 938	20.622 11	44.429 0
878	770 884	676 836 152	29.631 06	93.701 65	9.575 574	20.629 95	44.445 8
879	772 641	679 151 439	29.647 93	93.755 00	9.579 208	20.637 78	44.462
880	774 400	681 472 000	29.664 79	93.808 32	9.582 840	20.645 60	44.479 0
881	776 161	683 797 841	29.681 64	93.861 60	9.586 468	20.653 42	44.496 4
882	777 924	686 128 968	29.698 48	93.914 86	9.590 094	20.661 23	44.513 2
883	779 689	688 465 387	29.715 32	93.968 08	9.593 717	20.669 04	44.530 0
884	781 456	690 807 104	29.732 14	94.021 27	9.597 337	20.676 84	44.546 8
885	783 225	693 154 125	29.748 95	94.074 44	9.600 955	20.684 63	44.563 6
886	784 996	695 506 456	29.765 75	94.127 57	9.604 570	20.692 42	44.580 4
887	786 769	697 864 103	29.782 55	94.180 68	9.608 182	20.700 20	44.597 2
888	788 544	700 227 072	29.799 33	94.233 75	9.611 791	20.707 98	44.613 9
889	790 321	702 595 369	29.816 10	94.286 80	9.615 398	20.715 75	44.630 7
890	792 100	704 969 000	29.832 87	94.339 81	9.619 002	20.723 51	44.647
891	793 881	707 347 971	29.849 62	94.392 80	9.622 603	20.731 27	44.664
892	795 664	709 732 288	29.866 37	94.445 75	9.626 202	20.739 02	44.680 8
893	797 449	712 121 957	29.883 11	94.498 68	9.629 797	20.746 77	44.697
894	799 236	714 516 984	29.899 83	94.551 57	9.633 391	20.754 51	44.714
895	801 025	716 917 375	29.916 55	94.604 44	9.636 981	20.762 25	44.730
896	802 816	719 323 136	29.933 26	94.657 28	9.640 569	20.769 98	44.747
897	804 609	721 734 273	29.949 96	94.710 08	9.644 154	20.777 70	44.764
898	806 404	724 150 792	29.966 65	94.762 86	9.647 737	20.785 42	44.780
899	808 201	726 572 699	29.983 33	94.815 61	9.651 317	20.793 13	44.797
900	810 000	729 000 000	30.000 00	94.868 33	9.654 894	20.800 84	44.814

n	n^2	n^3	$\sqrt{n}$	$\sqrt{10n}$	$\sqrt[3]{n}$	$\sqrt[3]{10n}$	$\sqrt[3]{100n}$
901	811 801	731 432 701	30.016 66	94.921 02	9.658 468	20.808 54	44.830 64
902	813 604	733 870 808	30.033 31	94.973 68	9.662 040	20.816 23	44.847 22
903	815 409	736 314 327	30.049 96	95.026 31	9.665 610	20.823 92	44.863 79
904	817 216	738 763 264	30.066 59	95.078 91	9.669 176	20.831 61	44.880 34
905	819 025	741 217 625	30.083 22	95.131 49	9.672 740	20.839 29	44.896 88
906	820 836	743 677 416	30.099 83	95.184 03	9.676 302	20.846 96	44.913 41
907	822 649	746 142 643	30.116 44	95.236 55	9.679 860	20.854 63	44.929 93
908	824 464	748 613 312	30.133 04	95.289 03	9.683 417	20.862 29	44.946 44
909	826 281	751 089 429	30.149 63	95.341 49	9.686 970	20.869 94	44.962 93
910	828 100	753 571 000	30.166 21	95.393 92	9.690 521	20.877 59	44.979 41
911	829 921	756 058 031	30.182 78	95.446 32	9.694 069	20.885 24	44.995 88
912	831 744	758 550 528	30.199 34	95.498 69	9.697 615	20.892 88	45.012 34
913	833 569	761 048 497	30.215 89	95.551 03	9.701 158	20.900 51	45.028 79
914	835 396	763 551 944	30.232 43	95.603 35	9.704 699	20.908 14	45.045 22
915	837 225	766 060 875	30.248 97	95.655 63	9.708 237	20.915 76	45.061 64
916	839 056	768 575 296	30.265 49	95.707 89	9.711 772	20.923 38	45.078 05
917	840 889	771 095 213	30.282 01	95.760 12	9.715 305	20.930 99	45.094 45
918	842 724	773 620 632	30.298 51	95.812 32	9.718 835	20.938 60	45.110 84
919	844 561	776 151 559	30.315 01	95.864 49	9.722 363	20.946 20	45.127 21
920	846 400	778 688 000	30.331 50	95.916 63	9.725 888	20.953 79	45.143 57
921	848 241	781 229 961	30.347 98	95.968 74	9.729 411	20.961 38	45.159 92
922	850 084	783 777 448	30.364 45	96.020 83	9.732 931	20.968 96	45.176 26
923	851 929	786 330 467	30.380 92	96.072 89	9.736 448	20.976 54	45.192 59
924	853 776	788 889 024	30.397 37	96.124 92	9.739 963	20.984 11	45.208 91
925	855 625	791 453 125	30.413 81	96.176 92	9.743 476	20.991 68	45.225 21
926	857 476	794 022 776	30.430 25	96.228 89	9.746 986	20.999 24	45.241 50
927	859 329	796 597 983	30.446 67	96.280 84	9.750 493	21.006 80	45.257 78
928	861 184	799 178 752	30.463 09	96.332 76	9.753 998	21.014 35	45.274 05
929	863 041	801 765 089	30.479 50	96.384 65	9.757 500	21.021 90	45.290 30
930	864 900	804 357 000	30.495 90	96.436 51	9.761 000	21.029 44	45.306 55
931	866 761	806 954 491	30.512 29	96.488 34	9.764 497	21.036 97	45.322 78
932	868 624	809 557 568	30.528 68	96.540 15	9.767 992	21.044 50	45.339 00
933	870 489	812 166 237	30.545 05	96.591 93	9.771 485	21.052 03	45.355 21
934	872 356	814 780 504	30.561 41	96.643 68	9.774 974	21.059 54	45.371 41
935	874 225	817 400 375	30.577 77	96.695 40	9.778 462	21.067 06	45.387 60
936	876 096	820 025 856	30.594 12	96.747 09	9.781 946	21.074 56	45.403 77
937	877 969	822 656 953	30.610 46	96.798 76	9.785 429	21.082 07	45.419 94
938	879 844	825 293 672	30.626 79	96.850 40	9.788 909	21.089 56	45.436 09
939	881 721	827 936 019	30.643 11	96.902 01	9.792 386	21.097 06	45.452 23
940	883 600	830 584 000	30.659 42	96.953 60	9.795 861	21.104 54	45.468 36
941	885 481	833 237 621	30.675 72	97.005 15	9.799 334	21.112 02	45.484 48
942	887 364	835 896 888	30.692 02	97.056 68	9.802 804	21.119 50	45.500 58
943	889 249	838 561 807	30.708 31	97.108 19	9.806 271	21.126 97	45.516 68
944	891 136	841 232 384	30.724 58	97.159 66	9.809 736	21.134 44	45.532 76
945	893 025	843 908 625	30.740 85	97.211 11	9.813 199	21.141 90	45.548 83
946	894 916	846 590 536	30.757 11	97.262 53	9.816 659	21.149 35	45.564 90
947	896 809	849 278 123	30.773 37	97.313 93	9.820 117	21.156 80	45.580 95
948	898 704	851 971 392	30.789 61	97.365 29	9.823 572	21.164 24	45.596 98
949	900 601	854 670 349	30.805 84	97.416 63	9.827 025	21.171 68	45.613 01
950	902 500	857 375 000	30.822 07	97.467 94	9.830 476	21.179 12	45.629 03
951	904 401	860 085 351	30.838 29	97.519 23	9.833 924	21.186 55	45.645 03
952	906 304	862 801 408	30.854 50	97.570 49	9.837 369	21.193 97	45.661 02
953	908 209	865 523 177	30.870 70	97.621 72	9.840 813	21.201 39	45.677 01
954	910 116	868 250 664	30.886 89	97.672 92	9.844 254	21.208 80	45.692 98
955	912 025	870 983 875	30.903 07	97.724 10	9.847 692	21.216 21	45.708 94
956	913 936	873 722 816	30.919 25	97.775 25	9.851 128	21.223 61	45.724 89
957	915 849	876 467 493	30.935 42	97.826 38	9.854 562	21.231 01	45.740 82
958	917 764	879 217 912	30.951 58	97.877 47	9.857 993	21.238 40	45.756 75
959	919 681	881 974 079	30.967 73	97.928 55	9.861 422	21.245 79	45.772 67
960	921 600	884 736 000	30.983 87	97.979 59	9.864 848	21.253 17	45.788 57

n	n^2	n^3	$\sqrt{n}$	$\sqrt{10n}$	$\sqrt[3]{n}$	$\sqrt[3]{10n}$	$\sqrt[3]{100n}$
961	923 521	887 503 681	31.000 00	98.030 61	9.868 272	21.260 55	45.804 46
962	925 444	890 277 128	31.016 12	98.081 60	9.871 694	21.267 92	45.820 35
963	927 369	893 056 347	31.032 24	98.132 56	9.875 113	21.275 29	45.836 22
964	929 296	895 841 344	31.048 35	98.183 50	9.878 530	21.282 65	45.852 08
965	931 225	898 632 125	31.064 45	98.234 41	9.881 945	21.290 01	45.867 93
966	933 156	901 428 696	31.080 54	98.285 30	9.885 357	21.297 36	45.883 76
967	935 089	904 231 063	31.096 62	98.336 16	9.888 767	21.304 70	45.899 59
968	937 024	907 039 232	31.112 70	98.386 99	9.892 175	21.312 04	45.915 41
969	938 961	909 853 209	31.128 76	98.437 80	9.895 580	21.319 38	45.931 21
970	940 900	912 673 000	31.144 82	98.488 58	9.898 983	21.326 71	45.947 01
971	942 841	915 498 611	31.160 87	98.539 33	9.902 384	21.334 04	45.962 79
972	944 784	918 330 048	31.176 91	98.590 06	9.905 782	21.341 36	45.978 57
973	946 729	921 167 317	31.192 95	98.640 76	9.909 178	21.348 68	45.994 33
974	948 676	924 010 424	31.208 97	98.691 44	9.912 571	21.355 99	46.010 08
975	950 625	926 859 375	31.224 99	98.742 09	9.915 962	21.363 29	46.025 82
976	952 576	929 714 176	31.241 00	98.792 71	9.919 351	21.370 59	46.041 55
977	954 529	932 574 833	31.257 00	98.843 31	9.922 738	21.377 89	46.057 27
978	956 484	935 441 352	31.272 99	98.893 88	9.926 122	21.385 18	46.072 98
979	958 441	938 313 739	31.288 98	98.944 43	9.929 504	21.392 47	46.088 68
980	960 400	941 192 000	31.304 95	98.994 95	9.932 884	21.399 75	46.104 36
981	962 361	944 076 141	31.320 92	99.045 44	9.936 261	21.407 03	46.120 04
982	964 324	946 966 168	31.336 88	99.095 91	9.939 636	21.414 30	46.135 71
983	966 289	949 862 087	31.352 83	99.146 36	9.943 009	21.421 56	46.151 36
984	968 256	952 763 904	31.368 77	99.196 77	9.946 380	21.428 83	46.167 00
985	970 225	955 671 625	31.384 71	99.247 17	9.949 748	21.436 08	46.182 64
986	972 196	958 585 256	31.400 64	99.297 53	9.953 114	21.443 33	46.198 26
987	974 169	961 504 803	31.416 56	99.347 87	9.956 478	21.450 58	46.213 87
988	976 144	964 430 272	31.432 47	99.398 19	9.959 839	21.457 82	46.229 48
989	978 121	967 361 669	31.448 37	99.448 48	9.963 198	21.465 06	46.245 07
990	980 100	970 299 000	31.464 27	99.498 74	9.966 555	21.472 29	46.260 65
991	982 081	973 242 271	31.480 15	99.548 98	9.969 910	21.479 52	46.276 22
992	984 064	976 191 488	31.496 03	99.599 20	9.973 262	21.486 74	46.291 78
993	986 049	979 146 657	31.511 90	99.649 39	9.976 612	21.493 96	46.307 33
994	988 036	982 107 784	31.527 77	99.699 55	9.979 960	21.501 17	46.322 87
995	990 025	985 074 875	31.543 62	99.749 69	9.983 305	21.508 38	46.338 40
996	992 016	988 047 936	31.559 47	99.799 80	9.986 649	21.515 58	46.353 92
997	994 009	991 026 973	31.575 31	99.849 89	9.989 990	21.522 78	46.369 43
998	996 004	994 011 992	31.591 14	99.899 95	9.993 329	21.529 97	46.384 92
999	998 001	997 002 999	31.606 96	99.949 99	9.996 666	21.537 16	46.400 41
1000	1000 000	1000 000 000	31.622 78	100.000 00	10.000 000	21.544 35	46.415 89

RECIPROCALS, CIRCUMFERENCES, AND AREAS OF CIRCLES

n	1000/n	Circum. of circle πn	Area of circle $\frac{1}{4}\pi n^2$	n	1000/n	Circum. of circle πn	Area af circle $\frac{1}{4}\pi n^2$
				50	20.000 00	157.079 6	1 963.495
1	1000.000	3.141 593	0.785 3982	51	19.607 84	160.221 2	2 042.821
2	500.000 0	6.283 185	3.141 593	52	19.230 77	163.362 8	2 123.717
3	333.333 3	9.424 778	7.068 583	53	18.867 92	166.504 4	2 206.183
4	250.000 0	12.566 37	12.566 37	54	18.518 52	169.646 0	2 290.221
5	200.000 0	15.707 96	19.634 95	55	18.181 82	172.787 6	2 375.829
6	166.666 7	18.849 56	28.274 33	56	17.857 14	175.929 2	2 463.009
7	142.857 1	21.991 15	38.484 51	57	17.543 86	179.070 8	2 551.759
8	125.000 0	25.132 74	50.265 48	58	17.241 38	182.212 4	2 642.079
9	111.111 1	28.274 33	63.617 25	59	16.949 15	185.354 0	2 733.971
10	100.000 0	31.415 93	78.539 82	60	16.666 67	188.495 6	2 827.433
11	90.909 09	34.557 52	95.033 18	61	16.393 44	191.637 2	2 922.467
12	83.333 33	37.699 11	113.097 3	62	16.129 03	194.778 7	3 019.071
13	76.923 08	40.840 70	132.732 3	63	15.873 02	197.920 3	3 117.245
14	71.428 57	43.982 30	153.938 0	64	15.625 00	201.061 9	3 216.991
15	66.666 67	47.123 89	176.714 6	65	15.384 62	204.203 5	3 318.307
16	62.500 00	50.265 48	201.061 9	66	15.151 52	207.345 1	3 421.194
17	58.823 53	53.407 08	226.980 1	67	14.925 37	210.486 7	3 525.652
18	55.555 56	56.548 67	254.469 0	68	14.705 88	213.628 3	3 631.681
19	52.631 58	59.690 26	283.528 7	69	14.492 75	216.769 9	3 739.281
20	50.000 00	62.831 85	314.159 3	70	14.285 71	219.911 5	3 848.451
21	47.619 05	65.973 45	346.360 6	71	14.084 51	223.053 1	3 959.192
22	45.454 55	69.115 04	380.132 7	72	13.888 89	226.194 7	4 071.504
23	43.478 26	72.256 63	415.475 6	73	13.698 63	229.336 3	4 185.387
24	41.666 67	75.398 22	452.389 3	74	13.513 51	232.477 9	4 300.840
25	40.000 00	78.539 82	490.873 9	75	13.333 33	235.619 4	4 417.865
26	38.461 54	81.681 41	530.929 2	76	13.157 89	238.761 0	4 536.460
27	37.037 04	84.823 00	572.555 3	77	12.987 01	241.902 6	4 656.626
28	35.714 29	87.964 59	615.752 2	78	12.820 51	245.044 2	4 778.362
29	34.482 76	91.106 19	660.519 9	79	12.658 23	248.185 8	4 901.670
30	33.333 33	94.247 78	706.858 3	80	12.500 00	251.327 4	5 026.548
31	32.258 06	97.389 37	754.767 6	81	12.345 68	254.469 0	5 152.997
32	31.250 00	100.531 0	804.247 7	82	12.195 12	257.610 6	5 281.017
33	30.303 03	103.672 6	855.298 6	83	12.048 19	260.752 2	5 410.608
34	29.411 76	106.814 2	907.920 3	84	11.904 76	263.893 8	5 541.769
35	28.571 43	109.955 7	962.112 8	85	11.764 71	267.035 4	5 674.502
36	27.777 78	113.097 3	1 017.876	86	11.627 91	270.177 0	5 808.805
37	27.027 03	116.238 9	1 075.210	87	11.494 25	273.318 6	5 944.679
38	26.315 79	119.380 5	1 134.115	88	11.363 64	276.460 2	6 082.123
39	25.641 03	122.522 1	1 194.591	89	11.235 96	279.601 7	6 221.139
40	25.000 00	125.663 7	1 256.637	90	11.111 11	282.743 3	6 361.725
41	24.390 24	128.805 3	1 320.254	91	10.989 01	285.884 9	6 503.882
42	23.809 52	131.946 9	1 385.442	92	10.869 57	289.026 5	6 647.610
43	23.255 81	135.088 5	1 452.201	93	10.752 69	292.168 1	6 792.909
44	22.727 27	138.230 1	1 520.531	94	10.638 30	295.309 7	6 939.778
45	22.222 22	141.371 7	1 590.431	95	10.526 32	298.451 3	7 088.218
46	21.739 13	144.513 3	1 661.903	96	10.416 67	301.592 9	7 238.229
47	21.276 60	147.654 9	1 734.945	97	10.309 28	304.734 5	7 389.811
48	20.833 33	150.796 4	1 809.557	98	10.204 08	307.876 1	7 542.964
49	20.408 16	153.938 0	1 885.741	99	10.101 01	311.017 7	7 697.687

n	1000/n	Circum. of circle πn	Area of circle $\frac{1}{4}\pi n^2$	n	1000/n	Circum. of circle πn	Area of circle $\frac{1}{4}\pi n^2$
100	10.000 000	314.159 3	7 853.982	150	6.666 667	471.238 9	17 671.46
101	9.900 990	317.300 9	8 011.847	151	6.622 517	474.380 5	17 907.86
102	9.803 922	320.442 5	8 171.282	152	6.578 947	477.522 1	18 145.84
103	9.708 738	323.584 0	8 332.289	153	6.535 948	480.663 7	18 385.39
104	9.615 385	326.725 6	8 494.867	154	6.493 506	483.805 3	18 626.50
105	9.523 810	329.867 2	8 659.015	155	6.451 613	486.946 9	18 869.19
106	9.433 962	333.008 8	8 824.734	156	6.410 256	490.088 5	19 113.45
107	9.345 794	336.150 4	8 992.024	157	6.369 427	493.230 0	19 359.28
108	9.259 259	339.292 0	9 160.884	158	6.329 114	496.371 6	19 606.68
109	9.174 312	342.433 6	9 331.316	159	6.289 308	499.513 2	19 855.65
110	9.090 909	345.575 2	9 503.318	160	6.250 000	502.654 8	20 106.19
111	9.009 009	348.716 8	9 676.891	161	6.211 180	505.796 4	20 358.31
112	8.928 571	351.858 4	9 852.035	162	6.172 840	508.938 0	20 611.99
113	8.849 558	355.000 0	10 028.75	163	6.134 969	512.079 6	20 867.24
114	8.771 930	358.141 6	10 207.03	164	6.097 561	515.221 2	21 124.07
115	8.695 652	361.283 2	10 386.89	165	6.060 606	518.362 8	21 382.46
116	8.620 690	364.424 7	10 568.32	166	6.024 096	521.504 4	21 642.43
117	8.547 009	367.566 3	10 751.32	167	5.988 024	524.646 0	21 903.97
118	8.474 576	370.707 9	10 935.88	168	5.952 381	527.787 6	22 167.08
119	8.403 361	373.849 5	11 122.02	169	5.917 160	530.929 2	22 431.76
120	8.333 333	376.991 1	11 309.73	170	5.882 353	534.070 8	22 698.01
121	8.264 463	380.132 7	11 499.01	171	5.847 953	537.212 3	22 965.83
122	8.196 721	383.274 3	11 689.87	172	5.813 953	540.353 9	23 235.22
123	8.130 081	386.415 9	11 882.29	173	5.780 347	543.495 5	23 506.18
124	8.064 516	389.557 5	12 076.28	174	5.747 126	546.637 1	23 778.71
125	8.000 000	392.699 1	12 271.85	175	5.714 286	549.778 7	24 052.82
126	7.936 508	395.840 7	12 468.98	176	5.681 818	552.920 3	24 328.49
127	7.874 016	398.982 3	12 667.69	177	5.649 718	556.061 9	24 605.74
128	7.812 500	402.123 9	12 867.96	178	5.617 978	559.203 5	24 884.56
129	7.751 938	405.265 5	13 069.81	179	5.586 592	562.345 1	25 164.94
130	7.692 308	408.407 0	13 273.23	180	5.555 556	565.486 7	25 446.90
131	7.633 588	411.548 6	13 478.22	181	5.524 862	568.628 3	25 730.43
132	7.575 758	414.690 2	13 684.78	182	5.494 505	571.769 9	26 015.53
133	7.518 797	417.831 8	13 892.91	183	5.464 481	574.911 5	26 302.20
134	7.462 687	420.973 4	14 102.61	184	5.434 783	578.053 0	26 590.44
135	7.407 407	424.115 0	14 313.88	185	5.405 405	581.194 6	26 880.25
136	7.352 941	427.256 6	14 526.72	186	5.376 344	584.336 2	27 171.63
137	7.299 270	430.398 2	14 741.14	187	5.347 594	587.477 8	27 464.59
138	7.246 377	433.539 8	14 957.12	188	5.319 149	590.619 4	27 759.11
139	7.194 245	436.681 4	15 174.68	189	5.291 005	593.761 0	28 055.21
140	7.142 857	439.823 0	15 393.80	190	5.263 158	596.902 6	28 351.87
141	7.092 199	442.964 6	15 614.50	191	5.235 602	600.044 2	28 652.11
142	7.042 254	446.106 2	15 836.77	192	5.208 333	603.185 8	28 952.92
143	6.993 007	449.247 7	16 060.61	193	5.181 347	606.327 4	29 255.30
144	6.944 444	452.389 3	16 286.02	194	5.154 639	609.469 0	29 559.25
145	6.896 552	455.530 9	16 513.00	195	5.128 205	612.610 6	29 864.77
146	6.849 315	458.672 5	16 741.55	196	5.102 041	615.752 2	30 171.86
147	6.802 721	461.814 1	16 971.67	197	5.076 142	618.893 8	30 480.52
148	6.756 757	464.955 7	17 203.36	198	5.050 505	622.035 3	30 790.75
149	6.711 409	468.097 3	17 436.62	199	5.025 126	625.176 9	31 102.55

n	1000/n	Circum. of circle πn	Area of circle $\frac{1}{4}\pi n^2$	n	1000/n	Circum. of circle πn	Area of circle $\frac{1}{4}\pi n^2$
200	5.000 000	628.318 5	31 415.93	250	4.000 000	785.398 2	49 087.39
201	4.975 124	631.460 1	31 730.87	251	3.984 064	788.539 8	49 480.87
202	4.950 495	634.601 7	32 047.39	252	3.968 254	791.681 3	49 875.92
203	4.926 108	637.743 3	32 365.47	253	3.952 569	794.822 9	50 272.55
204	4.901 961	640.884 9	32 685.13	254	3.937 008	797.964 5	50 670.75
205	4.878 049	644.026 5	33 006.36	255	3.921 569	801.106 1	51 070.52
206	4.854 369	647.168 1	33 329.16	256	3.906 250	804.247 7	51 471.85
207	4.830 918	650.309 7	33 653.53	257	3.891 051	807.389 3	51 874.76
208	4.807 692	653.451 3	33 979.47	258	3.875 969	810.530 9	52 279.24
209	4.784 689	656.592 9	34 306.98	259	3.861 004	813.672 5	52 685.29
210	4.761 905	659.734 5	34 636.06	260	3.846 154	816.814 1	53 092.92
211	4.739 336	662.876 0	34 966.71	261	3.831 418	819.955 7	53 502.11
212	4.716 981	666.017 6	35 298.94	262	3.816 794	823.097 3	53 912.87
213	4.694 836	669.159 2	35 632.73	263	3.802 281	826.238 9	54 325.21
214	4.672 897	672.300 8	35 968.09	264	3.787 879	829.380 5	54 739.11
215	4.651 163	675.442 4	36 305.03	265	3.773 585	832.522 1	55 154.59
216	4.629 630	678.584 0	36 643.54	266	3.759 398	835.663 6	55 571.63
217	4.608 295	681.725 6	36 983.61	267	3.745 318	838.805 2	55 990.25
218	4.587 156	684.867 2	37 325.26	268	3.731 343	841.946 8	56 410.44
219	4.566 210	688.008 8	37 668.48	269	3.717 472	845.088 4	56 832.20
220	4.545 455	691.150 4	38 013.27	270	3.703 704	848.230 0	57 255.53
221	4.524 887	694.292 0	38 359.63	271	3.690 037	851.371 6	57 680.43
222	4.504 505	697.433 6	38 707.56	272	3.676 471	854.513 2	58 106.90
223	4.484 305	700.575 2	39 057.07	273	3.663 004	857.654 8	58 534.94
224	4.464 286	703.716 8	39 408.14	274	3.649 635	860.796 4	58 964.55
225	4.444 444	706.858 3	39 760.78	275	3.636 364	863.938 0	59 395.74
226	4.424 779	709.999 9	40 115.00	276	3.623 188	867.079 6	59 828.49
227	4.405 286	713.141 5	40 470.78	277	3.610 108	870.221 2	60 262.82
228	4.385 965	716.283 1	40 828.14	278	3.597 122	873.362 8	60 698.71
229	4.366 812	719.424 7	41 187.07	279	3.584 229	876.504 4	61 136.18
230	4.347 826	722.566 3	41 547.56	280	3.571 429	879.645 9	61 575.22
231	4.329 004	725.707 9	41 909.63	281	3.558 719	882.787 5	62 015.82
232	4.310 345	728.849 5	42 273.27	282	3.546 099	885.929 1	62 458.00
233	4.291 845	731.991 1	42 638.48	283	3.533 569	889.070 7	62 901.75
234	4.273 504	735.132 7	43 005.26	284	3.521 127	892.212 3	63 347.07
235	4.255 319	738.274 3	43 373.61	285	3.508 772	895.353 9	63 793.97
236	4.237 288	741.415 9	43 743.54	286	3.496 503	898.495 5	64 242.43
237	4.219 409	744.557 5	44 115.03	287	3.484 321	901.637 1	64 692.46
238	4.201 681	747.699 1	44 488.09	288	3.472 222	904.778 7	65 144.07
239	4.184 100	750.840 6	44 862.73	289	3.460 208	907.920 3	65 597.24
240	4.166 667	753.982 2	45 238.93	290	3.448 276	911.061 9	66 051.99
241	4.149 378	757.123 8	45 616.71	291	3.436 426	914.203 5	66 508.30
242	4.132 231	760.265 4	45 996.06	292	3.424 658	917.345 1	66 966.19
243	4.115 226	763.407 0	46 376.98	293	3.412 969	920.486 6	67 425.65
244	4.098 361	766.548 6	46 759.47	294	3.401 361	923.628 2	67 886.68
245	4.081 633	769.690 2	47 143.52	295	3.389 831	926.769 8	68 349.28
246	4.065 041	772.831 8	47 529.16	296	3.378 378	929.911 4	68 813.45
247	4.048 583	775.973 4	47 916.36	297	3.367 003	933.053 0	69 279.19
248	4.032 258	779.115 0	48 305.13	298	3.355 705	936.194 6	69 746.50
249	4.016 064	782.256 6	48 695.47	299	3.344 482	939.336 2	70 215.38

n	1000/n	Circum. of circle πn	Area of circle $\frac{1}{4}\pi n^2$	n	1000/n	Circum. of circle πn	Area of circle $\frac{1}{4}\pi n^2$
300	3.333 333	942.477 8	70 685.83	350	2.857 143	1 099.557	96 211.28
301	3.322 259	945.619 4	71 157.86	351	2.849 003	1 102.699	96 761.84
302	3.311 258	948.761 0	71 631.45	352	2.840 909	1 105.841	97 313.97
303	3.300 330	951.902 6	72 106.62	353	2.832 861	1 108.982	97 867.68
304	3.289 474	955.044 2	72 583.36	354	2.824 859	1 112.124	98 422.96
305	3.278 689	958.185 8	73 061.66	355	2.816 901	1 115.265	98 979.80
306	3.267 974	961.327 4	73 541.54	356	2.808 989	1 118.407	99 538.22
307	3.257 329	964.468 9	74 022.99	357	2.801 120	1 121.549	100 098.2
308	3.246 753	967.610 5	74 506.01	358	2.793 296	1 124.690	100 659.8
309	3.236 246	970.752 1	74 990.60	359	2.785 515	1 127.832	101 222.9
310	3.225 806	973.893 7	75 476.76	360	2.777 778	1 130.973	101 787.6
311	3.215 434	977.035 3	75 964.50	361	2.770 083	1 134.115	102 353.9
312	3.205 128	980.176 9	76 453.80	362	2.762 431	1 137.257	102 921.7
313	3.194 888	983.318 5	76 944.67	363	2.754 821	1 140.398	103 491.1
314	3.184 713	986.460 1	77 437 12	364	2.747 253	1 143.540	104 062.1
315	3.174 603	989.601 7	77 931.13	365	2.739 726	1 146.681	104 634.7
316	3.164 557	992.743 3	78 426.72	366	2.732 240	1 149.823	105 208.8
317	3.154 574	995.884 9	78 923.88	367	2.724 796	1 152.965	105 784.5
318	3.144 654	999.026 5	79 422.60	368	2.717 391	1 156.106	106 361.8
319	3.134 796	1 002.168	79 922.90	369	2.710 027	1 159.248	106 940.6
320	3.125 000	1 005.310	80 424.77	370	2.702 703	1 162.389	107 521.0
321	3.115 265	1 008.451	80 928.21	371	2.695 418	1 165.531	108 103.0
322	3.105 590	1 011.593	81 433.22	372	2.688 172	1 168.672	108 686.5
323	3.095 975	1 014.734	81 939.80	373	2.680 965	1 171.814	109 271.7
324	3.086 420	1 017.876	82 447.96	374	2.673 797	1 174.956	109 858.4
325	3.076 923	1 021.018	82 957.68	375	2.666 667	1 178.097	110 446.6
326	3.067 485	1 024.159	83 468.97	376	2.659 574	1 181.239	111 036.5
327	3.058 104	1 027.301	83 981.84	377	2.652 520	1 184.380	111 627.9
328	3.048 780	1 030.442	84 496.28	378	2.645 503	1 187.522	112 220.8
329	3.039 514	1 033.584	85 012.28	379	2.638 522	1 190.664	112 815.4
330	3.030 303	1 036.726	85 529.86	380	2.631 579	1 193.805	113 411.5
331	3.021 148	1 039.867	86 049.01	381	2.624 672	1 196.947	114 009.2
332	3.012 048	1 043.009	86 569.73	382	2.617 801	1 200.088	114 608.4
333	3.003 003	1 046.150	87 092.02	383	2.610 966	1 203.230	115 209.3
334	2.994 012	1 049.292	87 615.88	384	2.604 167	1 206.372	115 811.7
335	2.985 075	1 052.434	88 141.31	385	2.597 403	1 209.513	116 415.6
336	2.976 190	1 055.575	88 668.31	386	2.590 674	1 212.655	117 021.2
337	2.967 359	1 058.717	89 196.88	387	2.583 979	1 215.796	117 628.3
338	2.958 580	1 061.858	89 727.03	388	2.577 320	1 218.938	118 237.0
339	2.949 853	1 065.000	90 258.74	389	2.570 694	1 222.080	118 847.2
340	2.941 176	1 068.142	90 792.03	390	2.564 103	1 225.221	119 459.1
341	2.932 551	1 071.283	91 326.88	391	2.557 545	1 228.363	120 072.5
342	2.923 977	1 074.425	91 863.31	392	2.551 020	1 231.504	120 687.4
343	2.915 452	1 077.566	92 401.31	393	2.544 529	1 234.646	121 304.0
344	2.906 977	1 080.708	92 940.88	394	2.538 071	1 237.788	121 922.1
345	2.898 551	1 083.849	93 482.02	395	2.531 646	1 240.929	122 541 7
346	2.890 173	1 086.991	94 024.73	396	2.525 253	1 244.071	123 163.0
347	2.881 844	1 090.133	94 569.01	397	2.518 892	1 247.212	123 785.8
348	2.873 563	1 093.274	95 114.86	398	2.512 563	1 250.354	124 410.2
349	2.865 330	1 096.416	95 662.28	399	2.506 266	1 253.495	125 036.2

n	1000/n	Circum. of circle πn	Area of circle ¼πn²	n	1000/n	Circum. of circle πn	Area of circle ¼πn²
400	2.500 000	1 256.637	125 663.7	450	2.222 222	1 413.717	159 043.1
401	2.493 766	1 259.779	126 292.8	451	2.217 295	1 416.858	159 750.8
402	2.487 562	1 262.920	126 923.5	452	2.212 389	1 420.000	160 460.0
403	2.481 390	1 266.062	127 555.7	453	2.207 506	1 423.141	161 170.8
404	2.475 248	1 269.203	128 189.5	454	2.202 643	1 426.283	161 883.1
405	2.469 136	1 272.345	128 824.9	455	2.197 802	1 429.425	162 597.1
406	2.463 054	1 275.487	129 461.9	456	2.192 982	1 432.566	163 312.6
407	2.457 002	1 278.628	130 100.4	457	2.188 184	1 435.708	164 029.6
408	2.450 980	1 281.770	130 740.5	458	2.183 406	1 438.849	164 748.3
409	2.444 988	1 284.911	131 382.2	459	2.178 649	1 441.991	165 468.5
410	2.439 024	1 288.053	132 025.4	460	2.173 913	1 445.133	166 190.3
411	2.433 090	1 291.195	132 670.2	461	2.169 197	1 448.274	166 913.6
412	2.427 184	1 294.336	133 316.6	462	2.164 502	1 451.416	167 638.5
413	2.421 308	1 297.478	133 964.6	463	2.159 827	1 454.557	168 365.0
414	2.415 459	1 300.619	134 614.1	464	2.155 172	1 457.699	169 093.1
415	2.409 639	1 303.761	135 265.2	465	2.150 538	1 460.841	169 822.7
416	2.403 846	1 306.903	135 917.9	466	2.145 923	1 463.982	170 553.9
417	2.398 082	1 310.044	136 572.1	467	2.141 328	1 467.124	171 286.7
418	2.392 344	1 313.186	137 227.9	468	2.136 752	1 470.265	172 021.0
419	2.386 635	1 316.327	137 885.3	469	2.132 196	1 473.407	172 757.0
420	2.380 952	1 319.469	138 544.2	470	2.127 660	1 476.549	173 494.5
421	2.375 297	1 322.611	139 204.8	471	2.123 142	1 479.690	174 233.5
422	2.369 668	1 325.752	139 866.8	472	2.118 644	1 482.832	174 974.1
423	2.364 066	1 328.894	140 530.5	473	2.114 165	1 485.973	175 716.3
424	2.358 491	1 332.035	141 195.7	474	2.109 705	1 489.115	176 460.1
425	2.352 941	1 335.177	141 862.5	475	2.105 263	1 492.257	177 205.5
426	2.347 418	1 338.318	142 530.9	476	2.100 840	1 495.398	177 952.4
427	2.341 920	1 341.460	143 200.9	477	2.096 436	1 498.540	178 700.9
428	2.336 449	1 344.602	143 872.4	478	2.092 050	1 501.681	179 450.9
429	2.331 002	1 347.743	144 545.5	479	2.087 683	1 504.823	180 202.5
430	2.325 581	1 350.885	145 220.1	480	2.083 333	1 507.964	180 955.7
431	2.320 186	1 354.026	145 896.3	481	2.079 002	1 511.106	181 710.5
432	2.314 815	1 357.168	146 574.1	482	2.074 689	1 514.248	182 466.8
433	2.309 469	1 360.310	147 253.5	483	2.070 393	1 517.389	183 224.8
434	2.304 147	1 363.451	147 934.5	484	2.066 116	1 520.531	183 984.2
435	2.298 851	1 366.593	148 617.0	485	2.061 856	1 523.672	184 745.3
436	2.293 578	1 369.734	149 301.0	486	2.057 613	1 526.814	185 507.9
437	2.288 330	1 372.876	149 986.7	487	2.053 388	1 529.956	186 272.1
438	2.283 105	1 376.018	150 673.9	488	2.049 180	1 533.097	187 037.9
439	2.277 904	1 379.159	151 362.7	489	2.044 990	1 536.239	187 805.2
440	2.272 727	1 382.301	152 053.1	490	2.040 816	1 539.380	188 574.1
441	2.267 574	1 385.442	152 745.0	491	2.036 660	1 542.522	189 344.6
442	2.262 443	1 388.584	153 438.5	492	2.032 520	1 545.664	190 116.6
443	2.257 336	1 391.726	154 133.6	493	2.028 398	1 548.805	190 890.2
444	2.252 252	1 394.867	154 830.3	494	2.024 291	1 551.947	191 665.4
445	2.247 191	1 398.009	155 528.5	495	2.020 202	1 555.088	192 442.2
446	2.242 152	1 401.150	156 228.3	496	2.016 129	1 558.230	193 220.5
447	2.237 136	1 404.292	156 929.6	497	2.012 072	1 561.372	194 000.4
448	2.232 143	1 407.434	157 632.6	498	2.008 032	1 564.513	194 781.9
449	2.227 171	1 410.575	158 337.1	499	2.004 008	1 567.655	195 564.9

n	1000/n	Circum. of circle πn	Area of circle $\frac{1}{4}\pi n^2$	n	1000/n	Circum. of circle πn	Area of circle $\frac{1}{4}\pi n^2$
500	2.000 000	1 570.796	196 349.5	550	1.818 182	1 727.876	237 582.9
501	1.996 008	1 573.938	197 135.7	551	1.814 882	1 731.018	238 447.7
502	1.992 032	1 577.080	197 923.5	552	1.811 594	1 734.159	239 314.0
503	1.988 072	1 580.221	198 712.8	553	1.808 318	1 737.301	240 181.8
504	1.984 127	1 583.363	199 503.7	554	1.805 054	1 740.442	241 051.3
505	1.980 198	1 586.504	200 296.2	555	1.801 802	1 743.584	241 922.3
506	1.976 285	1 589.646	201 090.2	556	1.798 561	1 746.726	242 794.8
507	1.972 387	1 592.787	201 885.8	557	1.795 332	1 749.867	243 669.0
508	1.968 504	1 595.929	202 683.0	558	1.792 115	1 753.009	244 544.7
509	1.964 637	1 599.071	203 481.7	559	1.788 909	1 756.150	245 422.0
510	1.960 784	1 602.212	204 282.1	560	1.785 714	1 759.292	246 300.9
511	1.956 947	1 605.354	205 084.0	561	1.782 531	1 762.433	247 181.3
512	1.953 125	1 608.495	205 887.4	562	1.779 359	1 765.575	248 063.3
513	1.949 318	1 611.637	206 692.4	563	1.776 199	1 768.717	248 946.9
514	1.945 525	1 614.779	207 499.1	564	1.773 050	1 771.858	249 832.0
515	1.941 748	1 617.920	208 307.2	565	1.769 912	1 775.000	250 718.7
516	1.937 984	1 621.062	209 117.0	566	1.766 784	1 778.141	251 607.0
517	1.934 236	1 624.203	209 928.3	567	1.763 668	1 781.283	252 496.9
518	1.930 502	1 627.345	210 741.2	568	1.760 563	1 784.425	253 388.3
519	1.926 782	1 630.487	211 555.6	569	1.757 469	1 787.566	254 281.3
520	1.923 077	1 633.628	212 371.7	570	1.754 386	1 790.708	255 175.9
521	1.919 386	1 636.770	213 189.3	571	1.751 313	1 793.849	256 072.0
522	1.915 709	1 639.911	214 008.4	572	1.748 252	1 796.991	256 969.7
523	1.912 046	1 643.053	214 829.2	573	1.745 201	1 800.133	257 869.0
524	1.908 397	1 646.195	215 651.5	574	1.742 160	1 803.274	258 769.8
525	1.904 762	1 649.336	216 475.4	575	1.739 130	1 806.416	259 672.3
526	1.901 141	1 652.478	217 300.8	576	1.736 111	1 809.557	260 576.3
527	1.897 533	1 655.619	218 127.8	577	1.733 102	1 812.699	261 481.8
528	1.893 939	1 658.761	218 956.4	578	1.730 104	1 815.841	262 389.0
529	1.890 359	1 661.903	219 786.6	579	1.727 116	1 818.982	263 297.7
530	1.886 792	1 665.044	220 618.3	580	1.724 138	1 822.124	264 207.9
531	1.883 239	1 668.186	221 451.7	581	1.721 170	1 825.265	265 119.8
532	1.879 699	1 671.327	222 286.5	582	1.718 213	1 828.407	266 033.2
533	1.876 173	1 674.469	223 123.0	583	1.715 266	1 831.549	266 948.2
534	1.872 659	1 677.610	223 961.0	584	1.712 329	1 834.690	267 864.8
535	1.869 159	1 680.752	224 800.6	585	1.709 402	1 837.832	268 782.9
536	1.865 672	1 683.894	225 641.8	586	1.706 485	1 840.973	269 702.6
537	1.862 197	1 687.035	226 484.5	587	1.703 578	1 844.115	270 623.9
538	1.858 736	1 690.177	227 328.8	588	1.700 680	1 847.256	271 546.7
539	1.855 288	1 693.318	228 174.7	589	1.697 793	1 850.398	272 471.1
540	1.851 852	1 696.460	229 022.1	590	1.694 915	1 853.540	273 397.1
541	1.848 429	1 699.602	229 871.1	591	1.692 047	1 856.681	274 324.7
542	1.845 018	1 702.743	230 721.7	592	1.689 189	1 859.823	275 253.8
543	1.841 621	1 705.885	231 573.9	593	1.686 341	1 862.964	276 184.5
544	1.838 235	1 709.026	232 427.6	594	1.683 502	1 866.106	277 116.7
545	1.834 862	1 712.168	233 282.9	595	1.680 672	1 869.248	278 050.0
546	1.831 502	1 715.310	234 139.8	596	1.677 852	1 872.389	278 986.0
547	1.828 154	1 718.451	234 998.2	597	1.675 042	1 875.531	279 923.0
548	1.824 818	1 721.593	235 858.2	598	1.672 241	1 878.672	280 861.5
549	1.821 494	1 724.734	236 719.8	599	1.669 449	1 781.814	281 801.6

n	1000/n	Circum. of circle πn	Area of circle ¼πn²	n	1000/n	Circum. of circle πn	Area of circle ¼πn²
600	1.666 667	1 884.956	282 743.3	650	1.538 462	2 042.035	331 830.7
601	1.663 894	1 888.097	283 686.6	651	1.536 098	2 045.177	332 852.5
602	1.661 130	1 891.239	284 631.4	652	1.533 742	2 048.318	333 875.9
603	1.658 375	1 894.380	285 577.8	653	1.531 394	2 051.460	334 900.8
604	1.655 629	1 897.522	286 525.8	654	1.529 052	2 054.602	335 927.4
605	1.652 893	1 900.664	287 475.4	655	1.526 718	2 057.743	336 955.4
606	1.650 165	1 903.805	288 426.5	656	1.524 390	2 060.885	337 985.1
607	1.647 446	1 906.947	289 379.2	657	1.522 070	2 064.026	339 016.3
608	1.644 737	1 910.088	290 333.4	658	1.519 757	2 067.168	340 049.1
609	1.642 036	1 913.230	291 289.3	659	1.517 451	2 070.310	341 083.5
610	1.639 344	1 916.372	292 246.7	660	1.515 152	2 073.451	342 119.4
611	1.636 661	1 919.513	293 205.6	661	1.512 859	2 076.593	343 157.0
612	1.633 987	1 922.655	294 166.2	662	1.510 574	2 079.734	344 196.0
613	1.631 321	1 925.796	295 128.3	663	1.508 296	2 082.876	345 236.7
614	1.628 664	1 928.938	296 092.0	664	1.506 024	2 086.018	346 278.9
615	1.626 016	1 932.079	297 057.2	665	1.503 759	2 089.159	347 322.7
616	1.623 377	1 935.221	298 024.0	666	1.501 502	2 092.301	348 368.1
617	1.620 746	1 938.363	298 992.4	667	1.499 250	2 095.442	349 415.0
618	1.618 123	1 941.504	299 962.4	668	1.497 006	2 098.584	350 463.5
619	1.615 509	1 944.646	300 933.9	669	1.494 768	2 101.725	351 513.6
620	1.612 903	1 947.787	301 907.1	670	1.492 537	2 104.867	352 565.2
621	1.610 306	1 950.929	302 881.7	671	1.490 313	2 108.009	353 618.5
622	1.607 717	1 954.071	303 858.0	672	1.488 095	2 111.150	354 673.2
623	1.605 136	1 957.212	304 835.8	673	1.485 884	2 114.292	355 729.6
624	1.602 564	1 960.354	305 815.2	674	1.483 680	2 117.433	356 787.5
625	1.600 000	1 963.495	306 796.2	675	1.481 481	2 120.575	357 847.0
626	1.597 444	1 966.637	307 778.7	676	1.479 290	2 123.717	358 908.1
627	1.594 896	1 969.779	308 762.8	677	1.477 105	2 126.858	359 970.8
628	1.592 357	1 972.920	309 748.5	678	1.474 926	2 130.000	361 035.0
629	1.589 825	1 976.062	310 735.7	679	1.472 754	2 133.141	362 100.8
630	1.587 302	1 979.203	311 724.5	680	1.470 588	2 136.283	363 168.1
631	1.584 786	1 982.345	312 714.9	681	1.468 429	2 139.425	364 237.0
632	1.582 278	1 985.487	313 706.9	682	1.466 276	2 142.566	365 307.5
633	1.579 779	1 988.628	314 700.4	683	1.464 129	2 145.708	366 379.6
634	1.577 287	1 991.770	315 695.5	684	1.461 988	2 148.849	367 453.2
635	1.574 803	1 994.911	316 692.2	685	1.459 854	2 151.991	368 528.5
636	1.572 327	1 998.053	317 690.4	686	1.457 726	2 155.133	369 605.2
637	1.569 859	2 001.195	318 690.2	687	1.455 604	2 158.274	370 683.6
638	1.567 398	2.004.336	319 691.6	688	1.453 488	2 161.416	371 763.5
639	1.564 945	2 007.478	320 694.6	689	1.451 379	2 164.557	372 845.0
640	1.562 500	2 010.619	321 699.1	690	1.449 275	2 167.699	373 928.1
641	1.560 062	2 013.761	322 705.2	691	1.447 178	2 170.841	375 012.7
642	1.557 632	2 016.902	323 712.8	692	1.445 087	2 173.982	376 098.9
643	1.555 210	2 020.044	324 722.1	693	1.443 001	2 177.124	377 186.7
644	1.552 795	2 023.186	325 732.9	694	1.440 922	2 180.265	378 276.0
645	1.550 388	2 026.327	326 745.3	695	1.438 849	2 183.407	379 366.9
646	1.547 988	2 029.469	327 759.2	696	1.436 782	2 186.548	380 459.4
647	1.545 595	2 032.610	328 774.7	697	1.434 720	2 189.690	381 553.5
648	1.543 210	2 035.752	329 791.8	698	1.432 665	2 192.832	382 649.1
649	1.540 832	2 038.894	330 810.5	699	1.430 615	2 195.973	383 746.3

n	1000/n	Circum. of circle πn	Area of circle ¼πn²	n	1000/n	Circum. of circle πn	Area of circle ¼πn²
700	1.428 571	2 199.115	384 845.1	750	1.333 333	2 356.194	441 786.5
701	1.426 534	2 202.256	385 945.4	751	1.331 558	2 359.336	442 965.3
702	1.424 501	2 205.398	387 047.4	752	1.329 787	2 362.478	444 145.8
703	1.422 475	2 208.540	388 150.8	753	1.328 021	2 365.619	445 327.8
704	1.420 455	2 211.681	389 255.9	754	1.326 260	2 368.761	446 511.4
705	1.418 440	2 214.823	390 362.5	755	1.324 503	2 371.902	447 696.6
706	1.416 431	2 217.964	391 470.7	756	1.322 751	2 375.044	448 883.3
707	1.414 427	2 221.106	392 580.5	757	1.321 004	2 378.186	450 071.6
708	1.412 429	2 224.248	393 691.8	758	1.319 261	2 381.327	451 261.5
709	1.410 437	2 227.389	394 804.7	759	1.317 523	2 384.469	452 453.0
710	1.408 451	2 230.531	395 919.2	760	1.315 789	2 387.610	453 646.0
711	1.406 470	2 233.672	397 035.3	761	1.314 060	2 390.752	454 840.6
712	1.404 494	2 236.814	398 152.9	762	1.312 336	2 393.894	456 036.7
713	1.402 525	2 239.956	399 272.1	763	1.310 616	2 397.035	457 234.5
714	1.400 560	2 243.097	400 392.8	764	1.308 901	2 400.177	458 433.8
715	1.398 601	2 246.239	401 515.2	765	1.307 190	2 403.318	459 634.6
716	1.396 648	2 249.380	402 639.1	766	1.305 483	2 406.460	460 837.1
717	1.394 700	2 252.522	403 764.6	767	1.303 781	2 409.602	462 041.1
718	1.392 758	2 255.664	404.891.6	768	1.302 083	2 412.743	463 246.7
719	1.390 821	2 258.805	406 020.2	769	1.300 390	2 415.885	464 453.8
720	1.388 889	2 261.947	407 150.4	770	1.298 701	2 419.026	465 662.6
721	1.386 963	2 265.088	408 282.2	771	1.297 017	2 422.168	466 872.9
722	1.385 042	2 268.230	409 415.5	772	1.295 337	2 425.310	468 084.7
723	1.383 126	2 271.371	410 550.4	773	1.293 661	2 428.451	469 298.2
724	1.381 215	2 274.513	411 686.9	774	1.291 990	2 431.593	470 513.2
725	1.379 310	2 277.655	412 824.9	775	1.290 323	2 434.734	471 729.8
726	1.377 410	2 280.796	413 964.5	776	1.288 660	2 437.876	472 947.9
727	1.375 516	2 283.938	415 105.7	777	1.287 001	2 441.017	474 167.6
728	1.373 626	2 287.079	416 248.5	778	1.285 347	2 444.159	475 388.9
729	1.371 742	2 290.221	417 392.8	779	1.283 697	2 447.301	476 611.8
730	1.369 863	2 293.363	418 538.7	780	1.282 051	2 450.442	477 836.2
731	1.367 989	2 296.504	419 686.1	781	1.280 410	2 453.584	479 062.2
732	1.366 120	2 299.646	420 835.2	782	1.278 772	2 456.725	480 289.8
733	1.364 256	2 302.787	421 985.8	783	1.277 139	2 459.867	481 519.0
734	1.362 398	2 305.929	423 138.0	784	1.275 510	2 463.009	482 749.7
735	1.360 544	2 309.071	424 291.7	785	1.273 885	2 466.150	483 982.0
736	1.358 696	2 312.212	425 447.0	786	1.272 265	2 469.292	485 215.8
737	1.356 852	2 315.354	426 603.9	787	1.270 648	2 472.433	486 451.3
738	1.355 014	2 318.495	427 762.4	788	1.269 036	2 475.575	487 688.3
739	1.353 180	2 321.637	428 922.4	789	1.267 427	2 478.717	488 926.9
740	1.351 351	2 324.779	430 084.0	790	1.265 823	2 481.858	490 167.0
741	1.349 528	2 327.920	431 247.2	791	1.264 223	2 485.000	491 408.7
742	1.347 709	2 331.062	432 412.0	792	1.262 626	2 488.141	492 652.0
743	1.345 895	2 334.203	433 578.3	793	1.261 034	2 491.283	493 896.8
744	1.344 086	2 337.345	434 746.2	794	1.259 446	2 494.425	495 143.3
745	1.342 282	2 340.487	435 915.6	795	1.257 862	2 497.566	496 391.3
746	1.340 483	2 343.628	437 086.6	796	1.256 281	2 500 708	497 640.8
747	1.338 688	2 346.770	438 259.2	797	1.254 705	2 503.849	498 892.0
748	1.336 898	2 349.911	439 433.4	798	1.253 133	2 506.991	500 144.7
749	1.335 113	2 353.053	440 609.2	799	1.251 564	2 510.133	501 399.0

n	$1000/n$	Circum. of circle πn	Area of circle $\frac{1}{4}\pi n^2$	n	$1000/n$	Circum. of circle πn	Area of circle $\frac{1}{4}\pi n^2$
800	1.250 000	2 513.274	502 654.8	850	1.176 471	2 670.354	567 450.2
801	1.248 439	2 516.416	503 912.2	851	1.175 088	2 673.495	568 786.1
802	1.246 883	2 519.557	505 171.2	852	1.173 709	2 676.637	570 123.7
803	1.245 330	2 522.699	506 431.8	853	1.172 333	2 679.779	571 462.8
804	1.243 781	2 525.840	507 693.9	854	1.170 960	2 682.920	572 803.4
805	1.242 236	2 528.982	508 957.6	855	1.169 591	2 686.062	574 145.7
806	1.240 695	2 532.124	510 222.9	856	1.168 224	2 689.203	575 489.5
807	1.239 157	2 535.265	511 489.8	857	1.166 861	2 692.345	576 834.9
808	1.237 624	2 538.407	512 758.2	858	1.165 501	2 695.486	578 181.9
809	1.236 094	2 541.548	514 028.2	859	1.164 144	2 698.628	579 530.4
810	1.234 568	2 544.690	515 299.7	860	1.162 791	2 701.770	580 880.5
811	1.233 046	2 547.832	516 572.9	861	1.161 440	2 704.911	582 232.2
812	1.231 527	2 550.973	517 847.6	862	1.160 093	2 708.053	583 585.4
813	1.230 012	2 554.115	519 123.8	863	1.158 749	2 711.194	584 940.2
814	1.228 501	2 557.256	520 401.7	864	1.157 407	2 714.336	586 296.6
815	1.226 994	2 560.398	521 681.1	865	1.156 069	2 717.478	587 654.5
816	1.225 490	2 563.540	522 962.1	866	1.154 734	2 720.619	589 014.1
817	1.223 990	2 566.681	524 244.6	867	1.153 403	2 723.761	590 375.2
818	1.222 494	2 569.823	525 528.8	868	1.152 074	2 726.902	591 737.8
819	1.221 001	2 572.964	526 814.5	869	1.150 748	2 730.044	593 102.1
820	1.219 512	2 576.106	528 101.7	870	1.149 425	2 733.186	594 467.9
821	1.218 027	2 579.248	529 390.6	871	1.148 106	2 736.327	595 835.2
822	1.216 545	2 582.389	530 681.0	872	1.146 789	2 739.469	597 204.2
823	1.215 067	2 585.531	531 973.0	873	1.145 475	2 742.610	598 574.7
824	1.213 592	2 588.672	533 266.5	874	1.144 165	2 745.752	599 946.8
825	1.212 121	2 591.814	534 561.6	875	1.142 857	2 748.894	601 320.5
826	1.210 654	2 594.956	535 858.3	876	1.141 553	2 752.035	602 695.7
827	1.209 190	2 598.097	537 156.6	877	1.140 251	2 755.177	604 072.5
828	1.207 729	2 601.239	538 456.4	878	1.138 952	2 758.318	605 450.9
829	1.206 273	2 604.380	539 757.8	879	1.137 656	2 761.460	606 830.8
830	1.204 819	2 607.522	541 060.8	880	1.136 364	2 764.602	608 212.3
831	1.203 369	2 610.663	542 365.3	881	1.135 074	2 767.743	609 595.4
832	1.201 923	2 613.805	543 671.5	882	1.133 787	2 770.885	610 980.1
833	1.200 480	2 616.947	544 979.1	883	1.132 503	2 774.026	612 366.3
834	1.199 041	2 620.088	546 288.4	884	1.131 222	2 777.168	613 754.1
835	1.197 605	2 623.230	547 599.2	885	1.129 944	2 780.309	615 143.5
836	1.196 172	2 626.371	548 911.6	886	1.128 668	2 783.451	616 534.4
837	1.194 743	2 629.513	550 225.6	887	1.127 396	2 786.593	617 926.9
838	1.193 317	2 632.655	551 541.1	888	1.126 126	2 789.734	619 321.0
839	1.191 895	2 635.796	552 858.3	889	1.124 859	2 792.876	620 716.7
840	1.190 476	2 638.938	554 176.9	890	1.123 596	2 796.017	622 113.9
841	1.189 061	2 642.079	555 497.2	891	1.122 334	2 799.159	623 512.7
842	1.187 648	2 645.221	556 819.0	892	1.121 076	2 802.301	624 913.0
843	1.186 240	2 648.363	558 142.4	893	1.119 821	2 805.442	626 315.0
844	1.184 834	2 651.504	559 467.4	894	1.118 568	2 808.584	627 718.5
845	1.183 432	2 654.646	560 793.9	895	1.117 318	2 811.725	629 123.6
846	1.182 033	2 657.787	562 122.0	896	1.116 071	2 814.867	630 530.2
847	1.180 638	2 660.929	563 451.7	897	1.114 827	2 818.009	631 938.4
848	1.179 245	2 664.071	564 783.0	898	1.113 586	2 821.150	633 348.2
849	1.177 856	2 667.212	566 115.8	899	1.112 347	2 824.292	634 759.6

n	1000/n	Circum. of circle πn	Area of circle $\frac{1}{4}\pi n^2$	n	1000/n	Circum. of circle πn	Area of circle $\frac{1}{4}\pi n^2$
900	1.111 111	2 827.433	636 172.5	950	1.052 632	2 984.513	708 821.8
901	1.109 878	2 830.575	637 587.0	951	1.051 525	2 987.655	710 314.9
902	1.108 647	2 833.717	639 003.1	952	1.050 420	2 990.796	711 809.5
903	1.107 420	2 836.858	640 420.7	953	1.049 318	2 993.938	713 305.7
904	1.106 195	2 840.000	641 839.9	954	1.048 218	2 997.079	714 803.4
905	1.104 972	2 843.141	643 260.7	955	1.047 120	3 000.221	716 302.8
906	1.103 753	2 846.283	644 683.1	956	1.046 025	3 003.363	717 803.7
907	1.102 536	2 849.425	646 107.0	957	1.044 932	3 006.504	719 306.1
908	1.101 322	2 852.566	647 532.5	958	1.043 841	3 009.646	720 810.2
909	1.100 110	2 855.708	648 959.6	959	1.042 753	3 012.787	722 315.8
910	1.098 901	2 858.849	650 388.2	960	1.041 667	3 015.929	723 822.9
911	1.097 695	2 861.991	651 818.4	961	1.040 583	3 019.071	725 331.7
912	1.996 491	2 865.133	653 250.2	962	1.039 501	3 022.212	726 842.0
913	1.095 290	2 868.274	654 683.6	963	1.038 422	3 025.354	728 353.9
914	1.094 092	2 871.416	656 118.5	964	1.037 344	3 028.495	729 867.4
915	1.092 896	2 874.557	657 555.0	965	1.036 269	3 031.637	731 382.4
916	1.091 703	2 877.699	658 993.0	966	1.035 197	3 034.779	732 899.0
917	1.090 513	2 880.840	660 432.7	967	1.034 126	3 037.920	734 417.2
918	1.089 325	2 883.982	661 873.9	968	1.033 058	3 041.062	735 936.9
919	1.088 139	2 887.124	663 316.7	969	1.031 992	3 044.203	737 458.2
920	1.086 957	2 890.265	664 761.0	970	1.030 928	3 047.345	738 981.1
921	1.085 776	2 893.407	666 206.9	971	1.029 866	3 050.486	740 505.6
922	1.084 599	2 896.548	667 654.4	972	1.028 807	3 053.628	742 031.6
923	1.083 424	2 899.690	669 103.5	973	1.027 749	3 056.770	743 559.2
924	1.082 251	2 902.832	670 554.1	974	1.026 694	3 059.911	745 088.4
925	1.081 081	2 905.973	672 006.3	975	1.025 641	3 063.053	746 619.1
926	1.079 914	2 909.115	673 460.1	976	1.024 590	3 066.194	748 151.4
927	1.078 749	2 912.256	674 915.4	977	1.023 541	3 069.336	749 685.3
928	1.077 586	2 915.398	676 372.3	978	1.022 495	3 072.478	751 220.8
929	1.076 426	2 918.540	677 830.8	979	1.021 450	3 075.619	752 757.8
930	1.075 269	2 921.681	679 290.9	980	1.020 408	3 078.761	754 296.4
931	1.074 114	2 924.823	680 752.5	981	1.019 368	3 081.902	755 836.6
932	1.072 961	2 927.964	682 215.7	982	1.018 330	3 085.044	757 378.3
933	1.071 811	2 931.106	683 680.5	983	1.017 294	3 088.186	758 921.6
934	1.070 664	2 934.248	685 146.8	984	1.016 260	3 091.327	760 466.5
935	1.069 519	2 937.389	686 614.7	985	1.015 228	3 094.469	762 012.9
936	1.068 376	2 940.531	688 084.2	986	1.014 199	3 097.610	763 561.0
937	1.067 236	2 943.672	689 555.2	987	1.013 171	3 100.752	765 110.5
938	1.066 098	2 946.814	691 027.9	988	1.012 146	3 103.894	766 661.7
939	1.064 963	2 949.956	692 502.1	989	1.011 122	3 107.035	768 214.4
940	1.063 830	2 953.097	693 977.8	990	1.010 101	3 110.177	769 768.7
941	1.062 699	2 956.239	695 455.2	991	1.009 082	3 113.318	771 324.6
942	1.061 571	2 959.380	696 934.1	992	1.008 065	3 116.460	772 882.1
943	1.060 445	2 962.522	698 414.5	993	1.007 049	3 119.602	774 441.1
944	1.059 322	2 965.663	699 896.6	994	1.006 036	3 122.743	776 001.7
945	1.058 201	2 968.805	701 380.2	995	1.005 025	3 125.885	777 563.8
946	1.057 082	2 971.947	702 865.4	996	1.004 016	3 129.026	779 127.5
947	1.055 966	2 975.088	704 352.1	997	1.003 009	3 132.168	780 692.8
948	1.054 852	2 978.230	705 840.5	998	1.002 004	3 135.309	782 259.7
940	1.053 741	2 981.371	707 330.4	999	1.001 001	3 138.451	783 828.2

CIRCUMFERENCES AND AREAS
OF CIRCLES[1]

[1] From *Machinery's Handbook*, 11th ed., The Industrial Press.

Diameter	Circumference	Area	Diameter	Circumference	Area	Diameter	Circumference	Area
1/64	0.0491	0.0002	2	6.2832	3.1416	5	15.7080	19.635
1/32	0.0982	0.0008	1/16	6.4795	3.3410	1/16	15.9043	20.129
1/16	0.1963	0.0031	1/8	6.6759	3.5466	1/8	16.1007	20.629
3/32	0.2945	0.0069	3/16	6.8722	3.7583	3/16	16.2970	21.135
1/8	0.3927	0.0123	1/4	7.0686	3.9761	1/4	16.4934	21.648
5/32	0.4909	0.0192	5/16	7.2649	4.2000	5/16	16.6897	22.166
3/16	0.5890	0.0276	3/8	7.4613	4.4301	3/8	16.8861	22.691
7/32	0.6872	0.0376	7/16	7.6576	4.6664	7/16	17.0824	23.221
1/4	0.7854	0.0491	1/2	7.8540	4.9087	1/2	17.2788	23.758
9/32	0.8836	0.0621	9/16	8.0503	5.1572	9/16	17.4751	24.301
5/16	0.9817	0.0767	5/8	8.2467	5.4119	5/8	17.6715	24.850
11/32	1.0799	0.0928	11/16	8.4430	5.6727	11/16	17.8678	25.406
3/8	1.1781	0.1104	3/4	8.6394	5.9396	3/4	18.0642	25.967
13/32	1.2763	0.1296	13/16	8.8357	6.2126	13/16	18.2605	26.535
7/16	1.3744	0.1503	7/8	9.0321	6.4918	7/8	18.4569	27.109
15/32	1.4726	0.1726	15/16	9.2284	6.7771	15/16	18.6532	27.688
1/2	1.5708	0.1963	3	9.4248	7.0686	6	18.8496	28.274
17/32	1.6690	0.2217	1/16	9.6211	7.3662	1/8	19.2423	29.465
9/16	1.7671	0.2485	1/8	9.8175	7.6699	1/4	19.6350	30.680
19/32	1.8653	0.2769	3/16	10.0138	7.9798	3/8	20.0277	31.919
5/8	1.9635	0.3068	1/4	10.2102	8.2958	1/2	20.4204	33.183
21/32	2.0617	0.3382	5/16	10.4065	8.6179	5/8	20.8131	34.472
11/16	2.1598	0.3712	3/8	10.6029	8.9462	3/4	21.2058	35.785
23/32	2.2580	0.4057	7/16	10.7992	9.2806	7/8	21.5984	37.122
3/4	2.3562	0.4418	1/2	10.9956	9.6211	7	21.9911	38.485
25/32	2.4544	0.4794	9/16	11.1919	9.9678	1/8	22.3838	39.871
13/16	2.5525	0.5185	5/8	11.3883	10.321	1/4	22.7765	41.282
27/32	2.6507	0.5591	11/16	11.5846	10.680	3/8	23.1692	42.718
7/8	2.7489	0.6013	3/4	11.7810	11.045	1/2	23.5619	44.179
29/32	2.8471	0.6450	13/16	11.9773	11.416	5/8	23.9546	45.664
15/16	2.9452	0.6903	7/8	12.1737	11.793	3/4	24.3473	47.173
31/32	3.0434	0.7371	15/16	12.3700	12.177	7/8	24.7400	48.707
1	3.1416	0.7854	4	12.5664	12.566	8	25.1327	50.265
1/16	3.3379	0.8866	1/16	12.7627	12.962	1/8	25.5254	51.849
1/8	3.5343	0.9940	1/8	12.9591	13.364	1/4	25.9181	53.456
3/16	3.7306	1.1075	3/16	13.1554	13.772	3/8	26.3108	55.088
1/4	3.9270	1.2272	1/4	13.3518	14.186	1/2	26.7035	56.745
5/16	4.1233	1.3530	5/16	13.5481	14.607	5/8	27.0962	58.426
3/8	4.3197	1.4849	3/8	13.7445	15.033	3/4	27.4889	60.132
7/16	4.5160	1.6230	7/16	13.9408	15.466	7/8	27.8816	61.862
1/2	4.7124	1.7671	1/2	14.1372	15.904	9	28.2743	63.617
9/16	4.9087	1.9175	9/16	14.3335	16.349	1/8	28.6670	65.397
5/8	5.1051	2.0739	5/8	14.5299	16.800	1/4	29.0597	67.201
11/16	5.3014	2.2365	11/16	14.7262	17.257	3/8	29.4524	69.029
3/4	5.4978	2.4053	3/4	14.9226	17.721	1/2	29.8451	70.882
13/16	5.6941	2.5802	13/16	15.1189	18.190	5/8	30.2378	72.760
7/8	5.8905	2.7612	7/8	15.3153	18.665	3/4	30.6305	74.662
15/16	6.0868	2.9483	15/16	15.5116	19.147	7/8	31.0232	76.589

SOME IMPORTANT CONSTANTS AND THEIR LOGARITHMS

$\pi = 3.14159265$

$2\pi = 6.28318531$

$\dfrac{\pi}{2} = 1.57079633$

$\dfrac{\pi}{4} = 0.78539816$

$\pi^2 = 9.86960440$

$\sqrt{\pi} = 1.77245385$

$\sqrt{2\pi} = 2.50662827$

$\dfrac{1}{\pi} = 0.318309886$

$e = 2.718281828$

$M = 0.434294482$

$\dfrac{1}{M} = 2.302585093$

$\log \quad \pi = 0.497149873$

$\log \quad 2\pi = 0.798179868$

$\log \quad \dfrac{\pi}{2} = 0.196119877$

$\log \quad \dfrac{\pi}{4} = 9.895089881 - 10$

$\log \quad \pi^2 = 0.994299745$

$\log \quad \sqrt{\pi} = 0.248574936$

$\log \sqrt{2\pi} = 0.399089934$

$\log \quad \dfrac{1}{\pi} = 9.502850127 - 10$

$\log \quad e = 0.434294482$

$\log \quad M = 9.637784311 - 10$

$\log \quad \dfrac{1}{M} = 0.362215699$

1 radian $= 57°.2957795$

1 radian $= 3437'.74677$

1 radian $= 206264''.8062$

1 degree $= 0.017453293$ radians

1 minute $= 0.000290888$ radians

1 second $= 0.000004848$ radians

$\log \qquad 57.2957795 \quad = 1.758122632$

$\log \qquad 3437.74677 \quad = 3.53627388$

$\log\ 206264.8062 \qquad = 5.314425133$

$\log \qquad 0.01745293 = 8.241877368 - 10$

$\log \qquad 0.000290888 = 6.463726117 - 10$

$\log \qquad 0.000004848 = 4.685562611 - 10$